D1580340

READER'S DIGEST
SELECT EDITIONS

READER'S DIGEST
SELECT EDITIONS

www.readersdigest.co.uk

The Reader's Digest Association Limited
11 Westferry Circus Canary Wharf London E14 4HE

For information as to ownership of
copyright in the material of this book,
and acknowledgments, see last page.

Printed in Germany
ISBN 0 276 42991 5

READER'S DIGEST
SELECT EDITIONS

READER'S DIGEST
SELECT EDITIONS

www.readersdigest.co.uk

The Reader's Digest Association Limited
11 Westferry Circus Canary Wharf London E14 4HE

For information as to ownership of
copyright in the material of this book,
and acknowledgments, see last page.

Printed in Germany
ISBN 0 276 42991 5

CONTENTS

It is the summer of 1540 and Henry VIII is on the throne, supported by his ruthless chief minister, Thomas Cromwell—a man whom lawyer Matthew Shardlake would prefer to avoid. But Shardlake's new case, defending a girl accused of killing her young cousin, draws him into Cromwell's dangerous political sphere.

Before long, the lawyer is manoeuvred into accepting a difficult assignment—to find the formula for Greek Fire, a legendary substance that could vanquish England's enemies. Together with his assistant, Jack Barak, he goes in search of it, knowing it is a secret that many would kill to possess. This is historical fiction at its very best and a wonderful depiction of a colourful period of British history.

Prepare yourself for action and underwater drama of the page-turning kind that only Clive Cussler can create. His latest exciting story has its basis in wartime history, but takes the notion 'what if' to a whole new level.

During the last days of World War II, the Japanese attempt a final desperate mission: they send two subs,

each with a deadly biological weapon on board, to attack America. Neither makes it to the target; both are sunk. Their deadly cargo, however, survives and, sixty years later, one man has recovered enough of it to inspire a radical new plan—one that will fulfil his political ambitions and bring America to its knees.

GWEILO
MARTIN BOOTH

329

When his father was posted to Hong Kong in the early 1950s, seven-year-old Martin Booth found himself with the whole colony to explore. Unrestricted by parental control and endowed with bright blond hair, which signified good luck, he had the freedom to venture into places normally closed to a 'Gweilo', and to befriend many Chinese—much to his father's displeasure.

Martin Booth's memoirs are a delight. Written with exceptional insight and humour, they paint a stunning portrait of a vibrant city rich in ancient tradition, as well as giving a rare and vivid glimpse of a now vanished colonial way of life.

John Madden may have retired from Scotland Yard, but his instincts are still those of the excellent copper he once was. So when a young girl is brutally murdered he is convinced that the local police have got it wrong. This isn't a spur-of-the-moment crime but a methodically planned attack by someone who will almost certainly strike again. Soon Madden finds himself helping his former colleagues in the hunt for the murderer—a cold-blooded psychopath who has been covering his tracks for years. Can they catch him before he goes to ground again?

This atmospheric murder mystery brilliantly evokes Britain in the thirties.

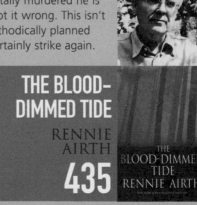

THE BLOOD-DIMMED TIDE
RENNIE AIRTH

435

Dark Fire

C. J. SANSOM

THE SECRET FORMULA FOR DARK FIRE,
A MYSTERIOUS SUBSTANCE USED BY
THE BYZANTINE EMPERORS TO TERRIFY
THEIR ENEMIES, HAS BEEN MISSING
FOR CENTURIES WHEN IT TURNS UP
IN THE DUSTY CRYPT OF A HALF-
DEMOLISHED MONASTERY.

IN THE WRONG HANDS DARK FIRE
COULD DO UNTOLD DAMAGE. AND WITH
ENGLAND UNDER THREAT FROM
ABROAD, HENRY VIII'S CHIEF MINISTER,
THOMAS CROMWELL, WILL GO TO ANY
LENGTHS TO SECURE IT.

CHAPTER ONE

I had left my house in Chancery Lane early, to go to the Guildhall to discuss a case in which I was acting for the City Council. Although the far more serious matter I would have to deal with on my return weighed on my mind, as I rode down Fleet Street I was able to take pleasure in the soft airs of early morning. The weather was very hot for late May, and I wore only a light doublet under my black lawyer's robe. As my old horse Chancery ambled along, I thought again of my ambition to retire from practice, to escape the noisome crowds of London. In two years I would be forty; in which year the old man's age begins; if business was good enough I might do it then.

At the Guildhall I met with Mayor Hollyes and the Common Council serjeant. The council had brought an action of nuisance against one of the land speculators buying up the dissolved monasteries, the last of which had gone down in this spring of 1540. This particular speculator was a fellow barrister of Lincoln's Inn, a greedy rogue named Bealknap. He had got hold of a small London friary and had converted it into a hotchpotch of unsavoury tenements. He had excavated a cesspit for his tenants, but it was a botched job and the tenants of the neighbouring houses, which the council owned, were suffering from the penetration of filth into their cellars.

The assize had ordered Bealknap to make proper remedy, but the wretch had served a writ of error in King's Bench, alleging that the friary's original charter excluded it from the City's jurisdiction and that he was not obliged to do anything. The matter was listed for hearing in a week's time. I advised the mayor that Bealknap's chances were slim, pointing out that he was one of those maddening rogues who take perverse pleasure in spending time and money on uncertain cases rather than admitting defeat.

I planned to return home the way I had come, via Cheapside, and made my way through the maze of narrow lanes. Although it was still early, the workshops were open and journeymen, street traders and water carriers crowded the lanes, slowing my passage.

I cursed as a rooting pig ran squealing across Chancery's path and made him jerk aside. A couple of apprentices glanced round at my oath and one of them gave me a contemptuous grin. I set my lips and spurred Chancery on. I saw myself as he must have: a whey-faced hunchback lawyer in black robe and cap, a pencase and dagger at my waist instead of a sword.

As I turned past the bulk of St Paul's, I heard the loud cry of a pamphlet seller. 'Child murderess of Walbrook taken to Newgate!' I leaned down to pass him a farthing. He peeled off a sheet and handed it up to me, then went on bawling. 'The most terrible crime of the year!' Beneath a woodcut of a woman's face I read:

Terrible Crime in Walbrook; Child Murdered by His Jealous Cousin

On the evening of May 16th last, a Sabbath Day, at the house of Sir Edwin Wentworth of Walbrook, a member of the Mercers' Company, his only son, *a boy of twelve*, was found at the bottom of the garden well with his *neck broken*. Sir Edwin's *fair daughters*, girls of fifteen and sixteen, told how the boy had been attacked by their cousin, *Elizabeth Wentworth*, an *orphan* whom Sir Edwin had taken into his house on the death of her father, and had been pushed by her into the well. She is taken to *Newgate*, where she is to go before the Justices the *29th May* next. She refuses to plead, so is likely to be *pressed*, or if she pleads to be found *guilty* and to go to *Tyburn* next *hanging day*.

I thrust it into my pocket and turned down Paternoster Row. So the case was public knowledge, another halfpenny sensation. Innocent or guilty, how could the girl get a fair trial from a London jury now?

IT WAS NEARLY noon when I reined Chancery in before my front door. Joan, my housekeeper, opened the door as I dismounted, a worried expression on her plump face.

'He is here,' she whispered, glancing behind her. 'That girl's uncle—'

'I know,' I said. 'What case is he in?'

'Sombre, sir. He is in the parlour. I gave him a glass of small beer.'

'Thank you.'

I passed the reins to Simon, the yellow-haired boy Joan had employed to help her about the house. He gave me a hasty bow and led the horse round to the stable. I took a deep breath and stepped inside.

Joseph Wentworth was a plump, ruddy-cheeked man in his early fifties. He was a working farmer, owner of some poor lands out in Essex, where he had remained when his two younger brothers had sought their fortunes in London. I had acted for Joseph two years before, defending his farm against a claim by a large landowner who wanted it to put to sheep. I liked him, but my heart had sunk when I received his letter a few days before and I doubted I could help him.

His face brightened as he saw me, and he came over and shook my hand eagerly. 'Master Shardlake! Good day, good day. You had my letter?'

'I did. You are staying in London?'

'At an inn down by Queenhithe,' he said. 'My brother has forbidden me his house for my championing of our niece.' There was a desperate look in his hazel eyes. 'You must help me, sir, please. You must help Elizabeth.'

I handed him the pamphlet. 'Have you seen this, Joseph?'

'Yes.' He ran a hand through his curly black hair. 'Are they allowed to say these things? Is she not innocent till proven guilty?'

'That's the technical position. It doesn't help much in practice.'

'I visited Elizabeth in Newgate this morning,' he said. 'God's mercy, it's a terrible place. But she still won't talk.'

'Come, Joseph, sit down. Let us start at the beginning. Now, one of your two brothers is the father of the boy who died—is that right?—and the other was father to Elizabeth?'

He took a chair and nodded. 'My brother Peter was Elizabeth's father. He was a dyer and did moderately well, but trade has gone right down these past few years. His wife died two years ago. When the bloody flux took Peter last autumn their house was sold and it barely covered Peter's debts.'

'Elizabeth was their only child?'

'Yes. She wanted to come and live with me, but I thought she'd be better off with Edwin. I've never married, after all. And he's the one with the fine house and the knighthood.' A note of bitterness entered his voice.

'And he is a mercer, as the pamphlet mentions?'

Joseph nodded. 'When Edwin followed Peter to London as a boy he went into the cloth trade. He has a good business head. Edwin offered to take Elizabeth in. He's already given a home to our mother—she moved from the farm when she lost her sight ten years ago.' He looked up with a wry smile. 'Since Edwin's wife died five years ago, Mother has run his house-hold with a rod of iron, though she's seventy-four and blind.'

'So Edwin is also a widower?'

'Yes. With three children. Sabine, Avice and . . . and Ralph.'

'The pamphlet said the girls are in their teens, older than the boy.'

Joseph nodded. 'Pretty and fair-haired like their mother.'

'And the boy? Ralph? What was he like?'

'He was the apple of his father's eye. Poor Edwin is grief-shot. Perhaps he spared the rod too much . . .' He paused.

'Why do you say that?'

'Ralph was an imp, it must be said. Always full of tricks.' Joseph bit his lip. 'Yet he had a merry laugh.'

'How did you hear of Ralph's death?' I asked quietly.

'A letter from Edwin, sent by fast rider the day after it happened. He asked me to come to London and attend the inquest. He had to view Ralph's body and couldn't bear doing it alone.'

'So you came to London, what, a week ago?'

'Yes. I made the formal identification with him. That was a terrible thing. Poor Ralph laid on that table in his little doublet. Poor Edwin wept on my shoulder, saying, "My boykin, my boykin. The evil witch," over and over.'

'Meaning Elizabeth.'

Joseph nodded. 'Then we went to the court and heard the evidence before the coroner. The hearing didn't take long.'

I nodded. 'Yes. Greenway rushes things. Who gave evidence?'

'Sabine and Avice first. They said that the afternoon it happened they had been doing tapestry work in the parlour. They could see Elizabeth through the window reading under a tree by the well. They saw Ralph go and talk to her. Then they heard a dreadful scream. They looked up from their work and saw that Ralph was gone. They ran outside. Elizabeth was standing by the well, an angry expression on her face. Sabine asked her what had happened. Elizabeth wouldn't reply, and she has not spoken since.'

'Is the well in use?'

'No, the ground water at Walbrook's been foul with sewage for years. Edwin got a founder to make a pipe to carry water underground from the conduit to the house. But they should have capped off that well.'

'What did the girls say happened next?'

'Avice ran for the steward, Needler. He got a rope and climbed down. Ralph was at the bottom with his neck broken. Needler brought him out.'

'Did the steward give evidence at the inquest?'

'Oh, yes. David Needler was there.' Joseph frowned. 'He's an impertinent fellow. Used to give me sneering looks when I visited.'

'So, according to their testimony, neither girl actually saw what happened?'

'No, they only looked up when they heard the shout. Elizabeth often sat out in the garden alone. Her relations with the rest of the family were . . . difficult. She seemed to have taken a particular dislike to Ralph.'

'I see.' I looked him in the eye. 'And what is Elizabeth like?'

He leaned back. 'Like Ralph in some ways. She was another that liked her own way. Her parents indulged her, being their only one. But she has a kind nature—she was always rescuing cats and dogs from the street.'

'I see. And things did not go well when she moved to Sir Edwin's?'

'No. Each time I visited them, Edwin and my mother said that Elizabeth was becoming more difficult. Refusing to talk to the family, keeping to her room, missing meals, not taking proper care of her clothes. If anyone tried to chide her she'd either say nothing or else fly into a screaming rage.'

'And she was on bad terms with all three of her cousins?'

'Sabine and Avice tried to interest her in womanly things but Elizabeth just told them to go away. She is eighteen, a little older than them, but they move in higher social circles; they could have taught Elizabeth much.' He bit his lip again. 'I had hoped for her advancement. And it has led to this.'

'And why do you think she disliked Ralph so much?'

'That I understood least of all. Edwin told me that if Ralph came near Elizabeth, she would give him such looks of hate it was frightening to see.'

'Elizabeth has no cause to hate the family that you know of?'

'No. Edwin is mystified.'

I wondered what had gone on at Sir Edwin's house, whether there were things Joseph knew but would not say.

'After they found the body,' he went on, 'Needler locked Elizabeth in her room and sent a message to Edwin at the Mercers' Hall. He rode home and when she wouldn't answer his questions he called the constable.'

'And at the inquest? Elizabeth said nothing then? Nothing at all?'

'No, she just gave the coroner a cold, blank look.' Joseph sighed. 'The jury found Ralph had been murdered by her and the coroner ordered her taken to Newgate to face a murder charge at the assize. He ordered her to be kept in the Hole for her impertinence in court. And then . . . then Elizabeth turned and looked at me. There was such misery in that look, sir.' Joseph bit his lip again. 'And when I visit her in that awful place she is now, she just lies there, filthy, as though waiting only for death. I beg her to speak, but she stares through me. And she is up for trial on Saturday, in only five days' time.' His voice fell to a whisper. 'Sometimes I fear she is possessed.'

'Come, Joseph, there is no point in thinking like that.'

He looked at me imploringly. 'Can you save her, Master Shardlake?'

I chose my words carefully. 'The evidence against her would be strong enough for a jury unless she has something to say in her defence.' I paused, then asked, 'You are sure she is not guilty?'

'Yes.' He banged a fist on his chest. 'I feel it here. She was always *kind* at heart. Even if she is ill in her mind, I cannot believe she could kill a little boy.'

I took a deep breath. 'When she is brought into court she will be asked to plead guilty or not guilty. If she refuses then she cannot be tried by a jury. But the alternative is worse. *Peine forte et dure.* Sharp and hard pains. She will be taken to a cell in Newgate and laid in chains on the floor. They will put a big, sharp stone under her back and a board on top of her. They will put weights on the board, adding more weights each day until she talks or dies of suffocation. When the weights are heavy enough, because of the pressure of the stone placed underneath her back, her spine will break.'

Joseph groaned and put his head in his hands. 'If only she would speak.'

'You know that criminal accused are not allowed representation in court?'

He nodded glumly.

'The reason the law gives is that the evidence needed to convict in a criminal trial must be so clear no counsel is needed. That is nonsense; the jury usually decides by preferring one man's word against another's. Her only hope is to agree to plead and tell me her story. If she *did* act in a fit of madness, I could plead insanity. It might save her life. She'd go to the Bedlam, but we could try for a royal pardon.'

He looked up and for the first time I saw hope in his eyes. I had said, 'I could plead,' without thinking. I had committed myself.

He leaned forward and clutched my hand between damp palms. 'Oh, thank you, Master Shardlake, thank you, I knew you'd save her—'

'I'm not at all sure I can,' I said sharply. 'But I'll try.'

'I'll pay, sir. I've little enough but I'll pay.'

'Five days—I need to go to Newgate and see her as soon as possible, but I have business at Lincoln's Inn this afternoon. I can meet you at the Pope's Head tavern next to Newgate tomorrow morning. Say at nine?'

'Yes, yes.' He stood up and grasped my hand. 'You are a good man, sir.'

A soft-headed man, more like, I thought.

'My mother and brother think her guilty,' he went on. 'They were furious when I said I might help her. But I must find the truth. And if this matter is not resolved and Elizabeth dies, the real murderer goes free, whoever he is.'

EARLY NEXT MORNING I rode into the City again. It was another hot day, the sunlight reflecting from the diamond panes of the Cheapside buildings. In the pillory by the Standard stood a middle-aged man, his head and arms pinioned and his neck bent forward, a painful position for one no longer young. I shuddered to think of the pain my back would have given me were I put in his place. And yet it gave me far less trouble these days, thanks to Guy.

Guy's was one of a row of apothecaries' shops in an alley just past the Old Barge, a huge, ancient house now let out as cheap apartments. As I dismounted and tied Chancery to the rail in front of Guy's shop, I had the uneasy sensation of being watched. The lane was quiet, most of the shops not yet open. I caught a movement at an upper storey of the Old Barge. I looked up, but had only the briefest glimpse of a shadowy figure at a window before the worm-eaten shutters were pulled closed. I stared for a moment, filled with uneasiness, then turned to Guy's shop.

It had only his name, *Guy Malton*, on the sign above the door. I knocked and went in. Apothecary Guy Malton, once Brother Guy of Malton, had fled Spain with his Moorish parents as a boy after the fall of Granada. He had trained as a physician at Louvain. He had become my friend three years before when I had investigated a murder at Scarnsea monastery for Lord Cromwell. When the monastery was dissolved I had hoped to set him up as a physician in London. But the College would not have him, with his brown face and papist past. With a little bribery, however, I had got him into the Apothecaries' Guild and he had built up a good trade.

He was seated at his table, and smiled when he saw me. 'And how have you been this last month, Matthew?'

'Still better. I do my exercises twice a day like a good patient. My back troubles me little unless I have to lift something heavy, like the great bundles of legal papers that mount in my room at Lincoln's Inn.'

He smiled. 'Well, I will have a look at it if I may.'

He rose, lit a candle, then closed the shutters as I removed my doublet and shirt. Guy was the only one I allowed to see my twisted back. He got me to move my shoulders and arms, then gently probed my back muscles.

'Good,' he said. 'There is little stiffness. You may get dressed. Keep on with your exercises. It is good to have a conscientious patient.'

'I would not like to go back to the old days, fearing ever-worsening pain.'

He gave me another of his keen looks. 'And you are still melancholy?'

'I have a melancholy nature, Guy. It is settled in me. I dream of a quiet life in the country somewhere, perhaps near my father's farm. London now—' I shook my head and pulled the crumpled pamphlet from my pocket, then laid it on the table. 'See there, the girl's uncle is an old client of mine. I am meeting him at Newgate at nine. He wants me to help her. Her trial is on Saturday.' I told him of my meeting with Joseph the day before.

'She refuses to speak at all?' he asked when I had finished.

'Not one word, not even when she learned she'd be pressed. It makes me think her wits must be affected.'

'People have many reasons for silence. Because there are things one is too ashamed or frightened to reveal. Or to protect someone else.'

'Whatever her reasons, I'll have to persuade the girl out of it if I'm to save her life.' I stood up. 'Well, I am due at Newgate.'

He extended a hand. 'I will say a prayer for you.'

'Beneath that big old Spanish cross of yours? You still have it?'

'It was my family's.'

'Beware the constable. Just because evangelicals are being arrested now it doesn't mean the government's any easier on Catholics.'

'The constable's a friend. Last month he drank some water he bought from a carrier and an hour later staggered into my shop clutching his stomach in agony. I made him swallow a spoonful of mustard to make him sick. It worked at once. He recovered and now he stumps merrily around the ward calling my praises.' His face became serious. 'Just as well: with all this talk of invasion foreigners are not popular these days. I get insults called after me in the streets more frequently.'

I shook my head. 'I am sorry. The times get no easier.'

'The City is full of rumours the king is unhappy with his new marriage,' he said. 'That Anne of Cleves may fall and Cromwell with her.'

'Are there not always new rumours, new fears?' I laid a hand on his shoulder. 'Keep courage. And don't forget that prayer.'

'I won't.'

I unhitched Chancery and rode up the lane. As I passed the Old Barge I looked up at the window where I had seen the figure. It was still shuttered. But as I turned into Bucklersbury I had the feeling of being watched again. I turned my head abruptly. The streets were getting busy, but I saw a man in a red doublet leaning against a wall, staring at me. He was in his late twenties, with a strong-featured face, comely but hard, under untidy brown hair. As he met my gaze his wide mouth twisted into a mocking grin. Then he turned away and walked towards the Barge, disappearing into the crowds.

THE POPE'S HEAD tavern was open all hours and did a good trade from visitors to Newgate gaol. Joseph was sitting at a table overlooking the rear garden, nursing a cup of small beer, the weak beer drunk to quench thirst. A posy of flowers lay beside him. He looked up as I eased myself into a chair.

'I've been to the gaol again,' he said gloomily. 'I told the gaoler I was bringing a lawyer. Another sixpence he charged, to allow the visit. And he had a copy of that filthy pamphlet. He told me he's been letting people in to look at Elizabeth for a penny. They call out through the spyhole and insult her. He laughed about it. It's cruel—surely they're not allowed to do that?'

'The gaolers are allowed anything for their own profit. He would have told you in hope of a bribe to keep her free of such pestering.'

'I have had to pay for food for her, water, everything. I can't afford more.'

I looked at him seriously. 'I went to Lincoln's Inn yesterday afternoon, Joseph. I learned the judge sitting at Saturday's assize is Forbizer. He's a strong Bible man and incorruptible, but hard as stone. I've appeared before him in civil matters. We *must* get Elizabeth to talk or she's as good as dead.'

He bit his lip. 'When I took her some food yesterday, she just lay there and looked at it. Not a word of thanks. She's hardly eaten for days. I've bought her these flowers but I don't know if she'll look at them.'

'Well, let us see what I can do.'

JOSEPH'S WHOLE BODY seemed to slump as we approached the gaol. I knocked loudly at the stout wooden door. A spy flap opened and a hard face looked out from under a greasy cap.

'Lawyer for Elizabeth Wentworth,' I said, 'with her uncle. He's paid for the visit.' The flap slammed shut and the door opened.

The gaoler looked at me curiously as we passed through. He called out, 'Williams!' and a fat turnkey in a leather jerkin appeared.

'Lawyer for the child murderess.' The gaoler nodded to the turnkey. 'Take 'em down to the Women's Hole.'

We were led down a wide corridor with wards on either side. Unlocking a heavy door, the turnkey led us down a flight of steps. At the bottom another door faced us. The turnkey pulled aside a flap and peered in before opening the door. As soon as we had passed through he locked it quickly.

The Hole, the deepest part of the prison, had a men's and a women's dungeon. The Women's Hole was a small, square chamber, lit dimly by a high barred window. It was as chill as the rest of the prison, with a miasma of damp that penetrated even the stink of ordure. The floor was covered with foul straw. Huddled in one corner was a fat old woman in a stained dress, fast asleep. At first I could see no one else, but then I saw that in the furthest corner the straw had been pulled into a pile around a human figure, hiding it save for a face begrimed with dirt and framed by tangled hair, as dark and curly as Joseph's. The face stared at us vacantly with large green eyes.

Joseph walked across to her. 'Lizzy,' he said chidingly, 'why have you piled the straw round yourself like that? It's filthy. Are you cold?'

The girl did not answer. Her eyes were unfocused; she could or would not look at us directly. I saw that under the dirt her face was pretty, delicate, with high cheekbones.

'I've brought you some flowers, Lizzy,' Joseph said. She glanced at the posy and then she did return Joseph's gaze and to my surprise her look was full of anger. I saw a plate of bread and stockfish lying on the straw with a flagon of beer. It must be the food Joseph had brought. It was untouched.

'Elizabeth'—there was a tremble in her uncle's voice—'this is Master Shardlake. He's a lawyer. He can help you. But you must talk to him.'

I squatted on my haunches so I could look into her face without sitting on that disgusting straw. 'Miss Wentworth,' I said gently, 'why will you not speak? Are you protecting a secret—yours, or perhaps another's?'

She looked right through me, not even stirring.

'You know what will happen if you refuse to plead?' I said. 'You will be pressed. They've told you what pressing means?' Still no response. 'A dreadful slow death that can last many days.'

At these words her eyes came to life and fixed mine, but only for a second. I shivered at the pit of misery I saw in them.

'If you speak, I may be able to save you. There are possible ways, whatever happened that day at the well.' I paused. 'What did happen, Elizabeth?'

But still she was silent. She began picking at the straw with one hand. As I got painfully to my feet, there was a rustle from the straw on the other side of the cell and I turned to see the old woman raising herself slowly on her elbows.

'She won't speak, gentlemen,' she croaked, shaking her head solemnly. 'I've been here three days and she's said nothing.'

'What are you here for?' I asked her.

'They say my son and I stole a horse. We're for trial on Saturday too.' She

looked over at Elizabeth. 'They say she has a demon inside her, that one.'
She laughed bitterly. 'But demon or no, it's all one to the hangman.'

I turned to Joseph. 'There is no more I can do here now. Come, let us go.'

I led him to the door and knocked. It opened at once: the turnkey must
have been outside listening. I glanced back; Elizabeth still lay unmoving.

A minute later, Joseph and I were outside again, blinking in the bright
sunlight. We returned to the tavern and I set a beer in front of him.

'Well, I confess I've never seen anything like it.' I tapped my fingers on
the table. 'But even if she were found guilty, there may just be ways to stop
her being hanged. The jury might be persuaded she was mad; she could
even claim she was pregnant, then she couldn't be hanged till the baby was
born. It would buy us time to investigate, find what really happened.'

Joseph leaned forward eagerly. 'Then you believe she is innocent?'

I gave him a direct look. 'You do.'

'I believe her because I know her. And because, when I see her there, I
see . . .' He struggled for words.

'A woman whose air is of one who has been done a great wrong, rather
than one who has committed a great crime?'

'Yes,' he said eagerly. 'Yes. That is it exactly. You feel it too?'

'Aye, I do.' I looked at him evenly. 'But what we feel is not evidence.'

'What can we do, sir?'

'You must go and see her every day between now and Saturday. If she
says anything, if her manner changes at all, tell me and I will come again.'

'I'll do it, sir,' he said.

'And if she still does not speak, I will appear in court on Saturday. If
Forbizer will hear me, I'll argue that her mind is disturbed, and that the
issue of her sanity should be remitted to a jury. I am sure there are prece-
dents. Again, that would buy us time.' I looked at him seriously. 'But I am
not optimistic. You must prepare your mind for the worst, Joseph.'

'No, sir,' he said. 'While you are working for us, I have hope.'

I RODE from Newgate to my chambers at Lincoln's Inn, just up the road
from my house in Chancery Lane. The Inn was semi-rural, with wide
orchards and the space of Lincoln's Inn Fields beyond. I left Chancery at
the stables and walked to my chambers across Gatehouse Court. Barristers
were striding purposefully around the precincts; the Trinity law term began
the following week and there were cases to set in order.

It was in no good temper that I entered the small set of ground-floor rooms I shared with my friend Godfrey Wheelwright. In the outer office my clerk, John Skelly, was studying a conveyance he had just drawn up. He was a small, thin fellow with rats' tails of brown hair. Though not yet twenty, he was married with a child and I had taken him on last winter partly from pity at his obvious poverty. He was an old pupil of St Paul's cathedral school and had good Latin, but he was a poor copier and forever losing papers.

He looked up at me guiltily. 'I have just finished the Beckman conveyance, sir,' he mumbled. 'I'm sorry it is late.'

'This should have been done two days ago. Is there any correspondence?'

'It is on your counting table, sir.'

I passed into my dim, stuffy room. I removed my robe and cap and sat at my table, breaking the seals on my letters with my dagger. I was surprised and disappointed to find I had lost another case. I had been acting on the purchase of a warehouse at Salt Wharf, but now my client wrote curtly to say the seller had withdrawn and he no longer required my services. This was the third case in two months where the client had suddenly withdrawn his instructions without reason.

There was a knock at the door and Godfrey came in. He was of an age with me. Twenty years before we had been scholars and ardent young reformers together, and unlike me he had retained his zeal. I saw that his narrow, delicate-featured face was troubled.

'Have you heard the rumours?' he asked.

'What now?'

'Yesterday evening the king rowed down the Thames to dinner at the Dowager Duchess of Norfolk's house with Catherine Howard beside him. In the royal barge, for all London to see. It's a sign the Cleves marriage is over. And a Howard marriage means a return to Rome.'

I shook my head. 'But Queen Anne was beside him at the May Day jousts. Just because he has his eye on a Howard wench doesn't mean he'll put the queen aside. He's had four wives in eight years. He can't want a fifth.'

'Can't he? Imagine the Duke of Norfolk in Lord Cromwell's place.'

'Cromwell can be cruel enough.'

'The duke would be far harsher.' He sat down heavily opposite me. 'He is a luncheon guest of the benchers here on Sunday, is he not?'

'Yes.' I made a face. 'I shall see him for myself for the first time. I do not greatly look forward to it. But, Godfrey, the king would never turn the clock back. We have the Bible in English and Cromwell's just got an earldom.'

He shook his head. 'I sense trouble coming.'

'When has there not been trouble these last ten years? Well, if London has a new topic that may take the heat from Elizabeth Wentworth. I've been to see her in Newgate. She won't say a word.'

He shook his head again. 'Then she'll be pressed, Matthew.'

'Listen, Godfrey, I need a precedent to say someone who won't speak because they're mad can't be pressed. There's a precedent somewhere in the yearbooks, I'm sure. I thought I might try the library.'

'When's gaol delivery—Saturday? You've little time. I'll help you look.'

'Thank you.' I smiled gratefully.

I walked with him to the library. We spent two hours among the great stacks of case law, where we found two or three cases that might be helpful.

'I'll send Skelly over to copy these,' I said.

He smiled. 'And now you can buy me luncheon as a reward for my help.'

'Gladly.'

We went outside into the hot afternoon. As we crossed the courtyard to the dining hall, I saw a fine litter with damask curtains standing outside a nearby set of chambers. Two attendant ladies stood at a respectful distance while a tall woman in a high-collared gown of blue velvet stood talking to Gabriel Marchamount, one of the serjeants.

I studied the woman, and as I did so she turned and met my eye. She murmured something to Marchamount and he raised his arm, bidding me to halt. He gave the woman his arm and led her across the courtyard to us.

Marchamount's companion was strikingly attractive, in her thirties, with a direct, open gaze. She wore a round French hood about her hair, which was blonde and very fine; little wisps slipped out, stirring in the breeze.

'Master Shardlake,' Marchamount said in his deep, booming voice, a smile on his rubicund face, 'may I introduce my client and good friend, Lady Honor Bryanston? Brother Matthew Shardlake.' She extended a hand.

I took the long white fingers gently and bowed. 'Delighted, madam.'

'Forgive my intrusion on your business,' she said. Her voice was a clear contralto with a husky undertone, the accent aristocratic. 'I have been in conference with Master Marchamount,' she continued, ignoring Godfrey. 'I recognised you from a description the Earl of Essex gave when we dined last. He was singing your praises as one of the best lawyers in London.'

The Earl of Essex. Cromwell. 'I am most grateful,' I said cautiously.

'I am ever on the lookout for fine minds to strike their wits against each other round my table,' Lady Honor continued. Her full-lipped mouth made girlish dimples in her cheeks as she smiled. 'Lord Cromwell suggested you.'

'You compliment me too highly. I am a mere jobbing lawyer.'

She smiled again. 'No, sir, I hear you are more than that. A bencher, who may be a serjeant one day. I shall send you an invitation to one of my sugar banquets. But now you must excuse me: I have an appointment at the Mercers' Hall.' She turned away, raising a hand. 'Expect to hear from me shortly, Master Shardlake.'

Marchamount bowed to us, then led Lady Honor back to her litter.

'I was going to introduce you, Godfrey,' I said, 'but she gave me no chance.'

'I would not have welcomed the introduction,' he said primly. 'Do you know who she is?'

I shook my head. London society did not interest me.

'Widow to Sir Harcourt Bryanston. He was the biggest mercer in London when he died three years ago. He was far older than she,' he added disapprovingly. 'She's a Vaughan, an aristocrat fallen on hard times. She married Bryanston for his money, and since his death she's set herself up as the greatest hostess in London. Trying to build up her family name again, which was trampled down in the wars between Lancaster and York.'

'One of the old families, eh?'

'Aye. She takes a perverse pleasure in setting reformers against papists over her dinner table.'

'So she's in with both factions then?'

'She has both Cromwell and Norfolk at her table, but she's no loyalty to either side. Don't go, Matthew.'

'I'll see,' I said. Being in the middle of such arguments would not be comfortable. And yet there was strength, a sophistication about Lady Honor that stirred something in me that had been quiet a long time.

chapter two

On Saturday morning I arrived in good time at the Old Bailey Court, a small, cramped building on the outer side of the City wall opposite Newgate.

Judge Forbizer sat on his dais working on papers, his scarlet robes a slash of colour among the dull clothes of the rabble crowding the benches—the Wentworth case had aroused much interest. I saw Joseph sitting at the end of a bench, biting his lip anxiously. He raised a hand in greeting and I smiled, trying to show a confidence I did not feel. I had met him the evening before and told him I would try for a plea of madness.

Some distance away I saw a man who looked so like Joseph it could only be his brother Edwin. He wore a fine green robe with a fur trim; his face was drawn. He met my look and glared. So he knew who I was.

And then, in the row in front of Edwin Wentworth, I saw the young man who had been watching me near Guy's shop. Today he wore a sober doublet of dark green. He stared at me speculatively, large dark eyes keen with interest. I frowned and he smiled briefly, settling himself more comfortably.

I hitched my gown and stepped away to the lawyers' bench. As I took my place, Forbizer stared at me coldly with hard coal-black eyes. A barrister appearing at a criminal trial meant troublesome legal interruptions.

'What do you want?' he asked.

I bowed. 'I am here to represent Mistress Wentworth, Your Honour.'

'Are you now? We'll see.' He lowered his head to his papers again.

There was a stir, and everyone turned as the jury, twelve well-fed London merchants, were escorted into the jury box. Then the door from the cells opened and the tipstaff led in a dozen ragged prisoners. The more serious cases were heard first: murder, burglary and thefts valued at more than a shilling. The accused were manacled together at the ankles and their chains made a clanking noise as they were led to the dock. Elizabeth was at the end of the line next to the fat woman, the alleged horse thief, who was grasping the hand of a ragged young man, her son no doubt.

The clerk stood and asked the prisoners, one by one, how they pleaded. Each replied, 'Not guilty.' Elizabeth was last.

'Elizabeth Wentworth,' the clerk said, 'you are charged with the foul murder of Ralph Wentworth on May 16th last. How say you—guilty or not guilty?'

I felt the courtroom tense. She bowed her head, the long, tangled hair falling forward and hiding her face.

Forbizer leaned across his desk. 'Mistress, you stand accused of one of the foulest crimes imaginable. Do you or do you not accept trial by a jury of your peers?'

She lifted her head and looked at him, her gaze blank.

'Very well, we shall address this at the end of the session.' Forbizer looked at her narrowly a moment more, then said, 'Bring on the first case.'

I took a deep breath. Elizabeth stood motionless as the clerk read the first indictment. She stood thus all through the next two hours.

I had not attended a criminal trial for years and was surprised anew at the speed of the proceedings. Five of the prisoners were found innocent and seven guilty, including the old woman and her son. She gripped his arm as he wept. The constable released those found innocent from their shackles and they scurried off. The condemned were led back to Newgate. Now Elizabeth alone remained in the dock.

'Well, Miss Wentworth,' Forbizer rasped, 'will you plead now?'

No reply. There was a murmuring in court: Forbizer silenced it with a look. I rose, but he waved me to sit down again.

'Wait, Brother. Now, Mistress. Guilty or not guilty, it takes little effort to say.' Still she stood like a stone. Forbizer set his lips. 'Very well, the law is clear in these cases. You will suffer *peine forte et dure.*'

I rose again. 'Your Honour—'

He turned to me coldly. 'This is a criminal trial, Brother Shardlake. Counsel may not be heard. Do you know so little law?' There was a titter along the benches; these people wanted Elizabeth dead.

I took a deep breath. 'Your Honour, I wish to address you regarding my client's capacity. I believe she does not plead because her wits are gone. She should not therefore suffer the press. I ask for her to be examined—'

'The jury can consider her mental state when she is tried,' Forbizer said shortly, '*if* she condescends to plead.'

'Your Honour,' I said determinedly, 'I would like to cite the precedent of *Anon* in the Court of King's Bench in 1505, when it was held that an accused who refuses to plead and whose sanity is put in question should be examined by a jury.' I produced a copy. 'I have the case—'

Forbizer shook his head. 'I know that case. The contrary case of *Beddloe*, King's Bench, 1498, says that only the trial jury may decide on sanity.'

'But in deciding between the cases, Your Honour, consideration must be given to my client's weaker sex, and the fact she is below the age of majority.'

Forbizer's lip curled. 'So a jury has to be empanelled now to determine her sanity, and you buy more time for your client. No, Brother Shardlake, no.'

'She may be pregnant,' I said desperately. 'We should wait to see if that may be so. The press would kill an unborn child!'

There was more muttering among the spectators. Elizabeth's expression had changed; she was looking at me with angry outrage now.

'Do you wish to plead your belly, madam?' Forbizer asked.

She shook her head, then lowered it, hiding her face in her hair once more.

'You understand English then,' Forbizer said to her. He turned back to me.

'I will not allow you to clutch at any excuse for delay, Brother Shardlake.' He addressed Elizabeth again. 'You may be below the age of majority, Mistress, but you are above that of responsibility. You know right from wrong, yet you stand accused of this hideous crime and refuse to plead. I order you to *peine forte et dure*, the weights to be pressed on you this very afternoon.'

I jumped up again. 'Your Honour—'

'God's death, man, be quiet!' Forbizer snapped. He waved at the constable. 'Take her down! Bring up the petty misdemeanours.'

The man stepped into the dock and led Elizabeth away. I sat with my head bowed. There was a babble of conversation and a rustling of clothes as the spectators who had come to see Elizabeth rose. Edwin Wentworth went out with the rest. Joseph remained alone on his bench, looking disconsolately after his brother. The sharp-faced young man had already gone.

I went over to Joseph. 'I am sorry,' I said.

He clutched my hand. 'Sir, come with me to Newgate. When they show her the weights, it may frighten her into speech. That could save her, could it not?'

'Yes, she'd be brought back for trial. But she won't do it, Joseph.'

'Try, sir, please—one last try. Come with me.'

I closed my eyes for a moment. 'Very well.'

As we walked out of the court, Joseph clutched his stomach. 'Agh, this worry has put my guts out of order,' he said. 'Is there a jakes here?'

'Round the back. I'll wait for you. Hurry.'

He shouldered a way through the departing crowd. Left alone in the hall, I sat down on a bench. Then I heard a rapid patter of footsteps from the court. The door was flung open and Forbizer's clerk, a round little man, ran up to me holding a paper, his face red, robes billowing around him.

'Brother Shardlake,' he puffed. 'Thank goodness. I thought you had gone. Judge Forbizer has reconsidered, sir. You are to have another two weeks to persuade Mistress Wentworth to plead.'

'What?' I stared at him uncomprehendingly. No one could have looked less like reconsidering than Forbizer.

'He asked me to give you this, sir. A copy has gone to Newgate already.' The clerk thrust the paper at me and vanished back into the courtroom.

I looked at it. A brief order above Forbizer's spiky signature, stating that Elizabeth Wentworth was to be detained in the Newgate Hole for another twelve days, until the 10th of June, to reconsider her plea. It was an extraordinary thing for any judge to do, let alone Forbizer.

There was a touch on my arm. I looked up to find the sharp-faced young man at my elbow. I frowned and he smiled again, showing white even teeth.

'Master Shardlake,' he said, 'I see you have the order.' His voice was as sharp as his face, with the burr of a London commoner.

'What do you mean? Who are you?'

He gave a nod. 'Jack Barak, sir, at your service. I persuaded Judge Forbizer to grant the order. You did not see me slip behind the bench?'

'No. But—what is this?'

His smile vanished. 'I serve Lord Cromwell. It was in his name I persuaded the judge to give you more time. He didn't want to, stiff-necked old arsehole, but my master is not refused. You know that.'

'Cromwell? Why?' My heart began pounding with apprehension.

'He would see you, sir. He asks me to take you to him at the Rolls House. He has a commission for you, sir.' Barak stared at me insolently. 'Two weeks' more life for the girl is your fee, paid in advance.'

BARAK LED ME at a brisk pace to the courthouse stables. I knew Lord Cromwell was not above bullying judges, but he would not have done this lightly. What in Christ's name did Cromwell want from me?

Barak's horse was a beautiful black mare, its coat shining with health. He cantered out while I was still saddling Chancery, pausing in the stable doorway to look back. 'Ready?' he asked impatiently.

I climbed on the vaulting block and eased myself onto Chancery's back. 'Wait a moment,' I said, seeing Joseph running across the yard to us, his plump face bright. When he had returned from the jakes I'd told him Forbizer had changed his mind; I said I did not know why. 'Your words moved his conscience, sir,' he had said. Joseph was ever a naive man.

'I have to go with this gentleman, Joseph,' I said now, as he beamed up at me. 'There is another urgent case I must attend to.'

'Some other poor wretch to save from injustice, eh? You'll be back soon?'

I glanced at Barak; he gave a brief nod.

'Soon, Joseph. Listen, there is something I would have you do for me. Go to your brother and ask if he will see me at his house. Say I am unsure of Elizabeth's guilt and wish to hear his side of things.'

He bit his lip, then nodded slowly. 'I will do what I can.'

I patted his arm. 'Good man. And now I must go.'

'I shall tell Elizabeth!' he called after me as we rode out into the road. 'I shall tell her, thanks to you, she is spared the press!'

Barak looked at me, raising an eyebrow cynically.

WE RODE DOWN Fleet Street. The Rolls House was not far, directly opposite Lincoln's Inn, in fact.

'I thought Lord Cromwell had given up the Mastership of the Rolls,' I said to Barak.

'He still keeps an office in the Rolls House. Works there sometimes.'

'Can you tell me what this is about? Am I in trouble?'

He shook his head. 'My master is to tell you himself.'

We turned up Chancery Lane, the horses troubled by the heat and flies. A guard in the yellow and blue quarters of Cromwell's livery stood outside the door of the Rolls House. At the centre of a complex of houses stood a large church. A guard in the yellow and blue quarters of Cromwell's livery stood outside the door. Barak nodded to him and the man bowed and snapped his fingers for a boy to lead our horses away. Barak pushed open the heavy door and we stepped inside.

'Through here,' he said. He led me towards a walled-off side chapel; another guard stood outside the door. Barak knocked and entered.

I took a deep breath as I followed him, my heart thumping against my ribs.

The side chapel had been converted into a large office, with cupboards against the walls and chairs drawn up before an imposing desk lit by a stained-glass window above. There was no one behind it. In a corner, behind a smaller desk, sat a short, black-robed figure I knew: Edwin Grey, Lord Cromwell's secretary. He had been at Cromwell's side for fifteen years. When I was in favour I had had much legal business through him. Grey rose and bowed to us. His round, pink face was anxious.

He nodded at Barak, then shook my hand. 'Master Shardlake. How do you fare, sir? It has been a long time.'

'Well enough, Master Grey. And you?'

'Well enough, given the times. The earl will be back in a moment.'

'How is he?' I ventured.

Grey hesitated. 'You will see.'

He turned abruptly as the door was thrown open and Thomas Cromwell strode into the room. At the sight of me he smiled broadly. I bowed low.

'Matthew, Matthew!' Cromwell said enthusiastically. He shook my hand with his powerful grip, then went and sat behind his desk. He was dressed soberly in a black gown, though the Order of the Garter awarded to him by the king swung from his dark blue doublet. I was shocked by the change in his appearance since I had last seen him three years before. His hair was far greyer, and his heavy features seemed pulled tight with strain and anxiety.

'Well, Matthew,' he said, 'how are you? Your practice prospers?'

I hesitated, thinking of my lost cases. 'Well enough, thank you, My Lord.'

Cromwell gave Barak a sharp look. 'Is it done?'

'Aye, My Lord. Forbizer gave no trouble.'

'I knew he wouldn't.' Cromwell turned back to me. 'I was interested to learn of your involvement in the Wentworth case, Matthew. It occurred to me then we might be of help to each other for old times' sake.' He smiled again.

'I am most grateful, My Lord,' I said carefully.

He fixed me with a serious look. 'I need your help, Matthew. It's an important matter, and secret. The bargain is I'll keep the girl alive for twelve days. We have only that for my task.' He nodded abruptly. 'Sit down.'

I did as bidden. Barak stood against the wall.

Cromwell nodded to Barak. 'Jack's a trusted servant. He's one of only eight who know this story, including myself and Grey here and his majesty the king. One of the other five is an old acquaintance of yours.' Cromwell smiled. 'I have always admired your mind, Matthew, your skills at teasing out the truth in men's affairs. Ever since the old days when we were young reformers.' A shadow crossed his face. 'Days with more hope and less care.'

'May I ask who this old acquaintance is, My Lord?' I ventured.

He nodded. 'You remember Michael Gristwood?'

'Gristwood the attorney, who used to work for Stephen Bealknap?'

'The same.'

I remembered a small, scurrying fellow, with bright sharp eyes. Gristwood had once been friendly with Bealknap and, like him, forever on the lookout for new moneymaking schemes. But he had none of Bealknap's calculating coldness and his schemes never came to anything.

'He had a falling out with Bealknap,' I said, 'and hasn't been around Lincoln's Inn. Didn't he go to work for the Court of Augmentations?'

'He did. To help Richard Rich pull in the proceeds of the dissolution.' Cromwell made a steeple of his fingers and looked at me over them. 'Last year, when St Bartholomew's priory in Smithfield surrendered to the king, Gristwood was sent to supervise the taking of the inventory of chattels. He took some Augmentations men with him to quantify the furniture, the plate, and so on. The Augmentations men are thorough and in the crypt under the church, in a cobwebby corner, they found something.' He leaned forward. 'Something that was lost to man centuries ago, something that became little more than a legend and a diversion for alchemists.'

I stared at him in astonishment. I had not expected this.

He laughed uneasily. 'Sounds like a mummers' tale, eh? Tell me, Matthew, have you ever heard of Greek Fire?'

'I'm not sure.' I frowned. 'The name is vaguely familiar.'

'Greek Fire was a liquid that the Byzantine emperors used in warfare eight hundred years ago. They fired it at enemy ships and it would set them ablaze from end to end. It could burn even on water. The formula for its creation was kept a close secret, passed down from one Byzantine emperor to another till in the end it was lost. The alchemists have been after it for hundreds of years. Here, Grey.' He snapped his fingers and the clerk rose from his desk and put a piece of parchment in his master's hands. 'Handle it carefully, Matthew,' Cromwell murmured. 'It is very old.'

I took the parchment from him and Grey returned to his desk. It was frayed at the edges and torn at the top. Above some words in Greek was a richly painted picture of two oared ships of ancient design facing each other across a stretch of water. At the front of one ship a golden pipe was belching red tongues of fire, engulfing the other.

Cromwell spoke again. 'One day last autumn, Michael Gristwood was called to the church by one of the Augmentations clerks. Among the lumber in the crypt they had found a large barrel. When they opened it, it proved to be full of a thick, dark liquid with a terrible smell. There was a plaque on the barrel, with a name, Alan St John. Gristwood set the librarian to search for the name St John in the library catalogue, which led them to an ancient box of manuscripts about Greek Fire, deposited there by one Captain St John, an old soldier who died in St Bartholomew's hospital a century ago. He was at Constantinople when it fell to the Turks. He left a memoir.' Cromwell raised his eyebrows. 'He told how a Byzantine librarian fleeing with him to the boats gave him the barrel, which he claimed contained the last of Greek Fire, and the formula to make the substance. The librarian gave it to St John so that at the last a Christian should have the secret, not the heathen Turks. You see the page is torn?'

'Yes.'

'Gristwood tore off the formula that was written in Greek above that picture, together with instructions for constructing the apparatus used to project it. Of course, he should have brought it to me—it was monastic property and it belongs to the king—but he didn't. Now, Michael Gristwood has an older brother, Samuel. Also known as Sepultus Gristwood the alchemist. When Sepultus heard Michael's story, he knew that the formula could be worth a fortune.'

I swallowed hard. 'If it's genuine,' I said.

'Oh, it's genuine,' he said. 'I've seen it used. The Gristwoods must have spent some time making more of the stuff, for it was March this year before Michael Gristwood came to me through intermediaries. One of them brought me that parchment and the other documents from the priory. Everything but the formula. With a message from the Gristwood brothers that they had made Greek Fire, they were offering a demonstration and if I decided I wanted the formula they'd give it to me. In return for a license on its development, so they'd have the exclusive right of manufacture. I decided to play along until I'd seen what they could do.' He set his thin lips. 'That was my mistake.'

Cromwell leaned back in his chair. 'England has lit a fire across Europe, Matthew, the first large state to break from the Church in Rome. The pope wants the French and Spanish to combine and overthrow us. They won't trade with us, there's undeclared war with the French in the Channel and we're having to plough half the revenues from the monasteries into defence.'

'I know, My Lord. Everyone is frightened of invasion.'

'Those who are loyal to reform, at least. So a new weapon, something that could make our ships invincible, you can see how important that could be.'

'Yes, but . . . sometimes, My Lord, in desperate times we clutch at desperate remedies. The alchemists have promised us wonders for hundreds of years, but precious few have actually appeared.'

'But remember, Matthew, I've seen it. I told the Gristwoods I'd arrange for an old crayer to be floated up to an abandoned jetty at Deptford and, if they could destroy it with Greek Fire in front of me, I'd make a deal with them. Jack arranged it, and only he and I and they were present early one March morning. And they did it.' He shook his head. 'They brought some strange device of steel they'd made with them, with a pipe on a pivot. They operated a pump on the device—and then a great sheet of liquid flame shot out and consumed the old boat in minutes. It wasn't an explosion, like gunpowder, just'—he shook his head again—'an inextinguishable fire, faster and more furious than any fire I've seen. Like a dragon's breath. And with no incantations, no magic words—this is no trick. I had a second demonstration a week later; they did it again. So now I've told the king.'

Cromwell took a deep breath. 'You should have seen his eyes light up. He clapped me on the shoulder and asked for a demonstration. There's an old warship, the *Grace of God*, in Deptford for breaking up. I've arranged for it to be there on the 10th of June, in twelve days' time.'

The 10th of June, I thought, the day Elizabeth's period of grace expires.

'I've been caught unawares,' he went on. 'I didn't think the king would jump at it so quickly. I can't fence with the Gristwoods any more. I must have that formula in my hands, and the Greek Fire they've made, before the king sees that demonstration. I want you to get it from them.'

I breathed heavily. 'I see.'

'Michael Gristwood knows and respects you, Matthew. If you remind him the formula is legally the king's and tell him the king is personally involved, I think you can make him give it to you. Jack has a hundred pounds in gold angels about him that Gristwood is to have as a reward. And you can warn him that if he doesn't cooperate I can call the Tower's rack to my aid.'

'Where does Gristwood live?'

'In a house in Wolf's Lane, Queenhithe, with his wife and Sepultus, who works from there. I want you to go there today. Jack will accompany you.'

'I beg this may be all. I live quietly these days, that is all I wish to do.'

Cromwell smiled wryly. 'Yes, Matthew, after this you may go back to your quiet.' He looked at me fixedly. 'Go now. And if the Gristwoods are not at Queenhithe, find them. Jack, I want you back here by the end of the day.'

'Yes, My Lord.' Barak moved to the door and opened it.

I rose and bowed. Before I followed Barak I turned back to my old master. 'May I ask, My Lord: why did you choose me for this?'

Cromwell inclined his head. 'Because Gristwood knows you for an honest man and will trust you. As I do because I know you are one of the few who would not seek to make advantage for themselves from this.'

'Thank you,' I said quietly.

His face hardened. 'And because you care too much for the fate of the Wentworth girl and, finally, you are too afraid of me to dare cross me.'

I STOOD on the steps of the Rolls House, looking out across Chancery Lane, while Barak fetched the horses. He reappeared, riding his black mare and leading Chancery. I mounted and we rode towards the City.

'So you were at the scene of this demonstration of Greek Fire, Barak?' I said in a haughty tone; I would not be cowed by this rude young fellow.

'Keep your voice down.' He frowned. 'We don't want that name bandied abroad. Yes, I was there. I wouldn't have believed it had I not seen it.'

'Many wonderful tricks may be performed with gunpowder. At the last mayor's procession there was a dragon that spat balls of exploding fire—'

'D'you think I don't know a gunpowder trick when I see one? What happened at Deptford was different.'

He turned away, steering his horse through the Ludgate. We rode along Thames Street, our progress slow through the crowds. At last we entered the maze of narrow streets leading down to the Thames. I glimpsed the river, its brown waters alive with wherries and white-sailed tilt boats, but the breeze that came from it was tainted.

Wolf's Lane was a long, narrow street full of old houses, cheap shops and lodging places. Outside one of the larger houses I saw a painted alchemist's sign showing Adam and Eve on either side of the philosopher's egg, the legendary sealed vase in which base metal could be turned to gold.

The front door was open. To my surprise I saw a woman in a servant's dress hanging on to the jamb with both hands, as though afraid of falling. I had a sudden feeling of dread.

Seeing us, she wailed, 'Help! For Jesu's sake, help me! Murder!'

Barak jumped down and ran towards her. I threw the horses' reins quickly over a rail, and ran over. Barak had the woman by the arms; she was staring wildly at him, sobbing loudly.

'Come on, girl,' he said with surprising gentleness. 'What ails you?'

She made an effort to calm herself. 'The master,' she said. 'Oh God—'

I saw that the wood of the door frame was splintered and broken. The door, which hung from one hinge, had been battered in. I looked past her and down a long dim corridor. Then I gripped Barak's arm. The rushes on the wooden floor were crisscrossed with footprints. They were dark red.

'What has happened here?' I whispered. Whoever smashed their way in could still be here. I gripped the dagger at my waist.

'We're here to help,' Barak told the girl. 'Come on, what's your name?'

'I'm Susan, sir, the servant,' the girl said tremulously. 'I'd been in Cheapside with my mistress, we—we came back and found the door like this. And upstairs my master and his brother—' She gulped. 'Oh God, sir—'

'Where is your mistress?'

'In the kitchen.' She took a deep, whooping breath. 'She went stiff as a board when she saw them. I sat her down and said I'd go for help, but when I got to the door I felt faint, I couldn't go another step.' She clung to Barak.

'You're a brave girl, Susan,' he said. 'Can you take us to your mistress?'

The girl let go of the door. She shuddered at the sight of the bloody footsteps inside, then, clutching Barak's hand, led the way down the corridor.

We followed Susan into a large kitchen with a view onto a stone-flagged yard. A woman sat rigidly at a worn table. She was small and thin, older than I would have expected. Straggles of grey hair were visible under her white coif.

'She's shocked out of her wits, poor soul,' I whispered.

'Madam,' Susan said hesitantly. 'Some men have come. To help us.'

The woman jerked and stared at us wildly.

I raised a soothing hand. 'Goodwife Gristwood?'

'Who are you?' she asked, something sharp and watchful in her face.

'We came on some business with your husband and his brother. Susan said you came home and found the place broken into—'

'They're upstairs,' Goodwife Gristwood whispered.

I took a deep breath. 'May we see?'

She closed her eyes. 'If you can bear it.'

'Susan, stay here and look after your mistress. Barak?'

He nodded. If he was feeling the same shock and fear as I, he gave no sign. We mounted a wooden staircase to the first floor. There were more bloody footsteps, wet and glinting—this blood had been shed very recently.

At the top of the stairs a number of doors gave off the hallway. They were closed except for the one straight ahead of us. Like the front door it hung off one hinge, the lock smashed in. I took a deep breath and stepped inside.

The chamber was large and well lit, running the whole length of the house. There was an odd, sulphurous smell in the air.

A man in a stained alchemist's robe lay sprawled on his back over an upturned bench amid a chaos of broken glass pipes, his face a hideous pulpy mess. I felt my stomach heave and turned away quickly.

The whole workshop was in chaos with broken glass everywhere. Next to the fireplace lay the remains of an iron-bound chest. It was little more than a heap of broken spars now, the metal bands smashed right through. Whoever had wielded the axe here—and everything pointed to an axe— must have had unusual strength.

Beside the chest Michael Gristwood lay on his back, his head almost severed from his neck, his mouth wide open in a last scream of terror. A great spray of blood had stained the floor and the walls. I blenched again.

'That the lawyer?' Barak asked.

'Aye.'

'Well, he won't be needing Lord Cromwell's bag of gold,' Barak said. I frowned. He shrugged. 'Well, he won't, will he? Let's go back downstairs.'

I followed him down to the kitchen. Susan seemed to have recovered somewhat and was boiling a pan of water on the range.

'Is there anyone that could come and sit with you?' I asked Goodwife Gristwood, who sat rigidly with her hands clenched. 'Any other relatives?'

Again a momentary sharpness came into her face, then she answered, 'No.'

'Right,' Barak said. 'I'm going to the earl. He must say what's to be done.' He pointed at the women. 'Stay here with them, make sure they don't leave. I'll be back soon.' He turned and left the kitchen.

Susan looked up anxiously. 'Does he mean Lord Cromwell, sir? But, sir—we've done nothing.' Her voice rose in fear.

'Do not worry, Susan,' I said gently. 'He must be told. He . . .' I hesitated.

Goodwife Gristwood spoke, her voice cold. 'My husband and Sepultus were working for him, Susan. I know that much, I told them they were fools, that he's dangerous. But Michael would never listen to me.'

Susan gave me a scared look: that was the effect Cromwell's name had on most people. I set my teeth. What in God's name had I got involved in? And who was Barak to give me orders?

I crossed to the window and looked out at the yard, surprised to see that both the flagstones and the high walls were stained black. 'Has there been a fire here?' I asked Susan.

'Master Sepultus did experiments out there sometimes, sir. Terrible bangs and hissings there were. I was glad he wouldn't let me see.'

Goodwife Gristwood spoke again. 'Yes, we were kept out of our own kitchen when he and my husband were at their foolery.'

My mind was racing. It struck me that the formula might still be in the workshop. Now was a chance to look for it before the room was disturbed further, though I shrank from returning there. I bade the women stay in the kitchen and mounted the stairs again.

The afternoon sun was shining into the room, illuminating Michael's dead face. I turned away from his look of terror and walked over to a wall lined with shelves. One shelf was full of books but the others were empty. From round marks in the dust I guessed jars and bottles had been stored there.

The contents of the chest lay scattered over the floor—letters and documents, one or two with bloody thumbprints on them. Something else caught my eye. I bent down and picked up a gold angel; it had fallen from a leather bag nearby that contained twenty more. Well, I thought, the brothers' money was not what the killers were after.

I drew the papers and the gold purse together. As I stood up I nearly slipped. I looked down, fearing that I had slithered in the blood, but saw a little pool of thick, clear liquid, which had spilt from a small glass bottle that lay on its side by the fireplace. I bent down and replaced the stopper that lay nearby. I dipped my fingers in the liquid and rubbed them together;

it had a slippery feel. I sniffed. The stuff was odourless, like water. Hesitantly, I touched the tip of my tongue to it, then jerked back as a stinging, bitter taste filled my mouth, making me cough.

I heard footsteps outside and crossed to the window. Barak was outside with half a dozen men in Cromwell's livery carrying swords. As I hurried downstairs I heard Susan give a little scream. The men had crowded into the kitchen; Goodwife Gristwood was frowning at them.

Barak saw the papers I carried. 'What are those?' he asked sharply.

'Family papers and some gold. They were in the chest upstairs. I fetched them for Goodwife Gristwood.'

'Let me see.' He grabbed the papers. At least, I thought, the churl can read. He opened the bag of gold and examined the contents. Satisfied, he laid the gold and papers before Goodwife Gristwood, who clutched them to her. Then Barak looked at me. 'Any sign of the formula up there?'

'Not that I can see. If it was in that chest they took it.'

He turned to Goodwife Gristwood. 'Do you know anything about a paper your husband and his brother had, a formula they were working on?'

She shook her head wearily. 'No. They told me nothing of what they did. Only that they were engaged on some work for Lord Cromwell.'

'These men will search your house from top to bottom,' he said. 'We have to find that paper. Afterwards two of them will stay here with you.'

She looked at him narrowly. 'Are we prisoners, then?'

'They are for your protection, madam. You may still not be safe.'

Barak turned to me. 'Lord Cromwell wants a meeting now. He's gone to his house in Stepney.' When I hesitated, Barak stepped closer. 'That's an order,' he said. 'I have told my master the news. He is not a happy man.'

CHAPTER THREE

Lord Cromwell's house at Stepney was a long ride, far beyond the City wall. Thankfully the afternoon shadows were lengthening, the over-hanging houses bringing a welcome shade to the streets. We rode in silence until at last we passed under the Bishopsgate, and the chimneys of Cromwell's house came into view. We rode through the main gate.

At the front door a servant met us. He asked us to wait in the hallway, then a few minutes later Lord Cromwell's steward appeared and led us to the door of Cromwell's study. He knocked and his master snapped, 'Enter.'

Cromwell sat hunched in his chair, head sunk between his shoulders, and gave us a baleful look. 'So,' he said coldly, 'you found them murdered.'

I took a deep breath. 'Yes, My Lord. Most brutally.'

'I've got men searching for the formula,' Barak said. 'The women know nothing. They're both scared out of their wits. I've told the men to ask round the neighbouring houses to see if anyone saw the attack, but Wolf's Lane looks like a place where people mind their own business.'

'Who betrayed me?' Cromwell whispered intently. 'Which of them?' He stared at me fixedly. 'Well, Matthew, what did you make of what you saw?'

'I think there were two men and that they broke in with axes. They killed the brothers at once in the workshop, then went to a chest that was kept there and smashed it in. There was gold inside, but they left it untouched.' I hesitated. 'My guess is that the formula was there and they knew it.'

'You can't be sure,' Barak interjected.

'I'm not sure of anything,' I replied. 'But the books on the shelves were undisturbed and they would have been an obvious place to look for a hidden paper. Also, I believe some bottles were taken from the shelves. I think the people who murdered those poor men knew what they were looking for.'

Cromwell nodded. 'See, Jack,' he said. 'Learn from a master of observation.' He turned bleak eyes on me again. 'Matthew, help me solve this.'

'But, My Lord—'

'I can't tell anyone else,' he said with sudden passion. 'I daren't. If it got to the king . . .' He sighed, a shuddering sound. 'You must solve this,' he repeated. 'You can have any authority, any resources.'

I stood on the fine carpet, my heart thudding. This was the first time I had seen Thomas Cromwell afraid.

Sudden anger flashed in his eyes. 'Christ's wounds, man,' he snapped. 'I've saved that girl's life for you. Or at least I'll save it if you help me; Forbizer can be made to change his mind again if need be.'

'I will help, My Lord,' I said quietly.

Cromwell gave a satisfied nod. He picked something up and turned it over in his hands: it was a miniature portrait. 'The reformist cause is tottering, Matthew.' He spoke quietly. 'The king grows more afraid every day as Norfolk and Bishop Gardiner tip their poison in his ear. Afraid of common people reading the Bible, fearing they'll overthrow the social order in bloody chaos. And afraid of invasion.'

He took the miniature and laid it on top of the Bible. 'Do you still paint, Matthew, for a pastime?'

I looked at him, puzzled. 'Not for some time, My Lord.'

'Give me your opinion of this portrait.'

I studied it. The woman was young, with attractive if vacuous features. From the jewels in her hood and dress she was someone of wealth.

'This is beautiful,' I said. 'It could almost be by Holbein.'

'It *is* by Holbein. It is the Lady Anne of Cleves, now our queen. I kept it when the king threw it in my face.' He shook his head. 'The king wanted to see the Lady Anne before agreeing to marry her, but the Germans took that as an affront. So I sent Holbein to make a picture. After all, his genius is to make exact representations, is it not?'

'No one in Europe does that better.' I hesitated. 'And yet—'

'Yet what is an *exact* representation, eh, Matthew? We all look different in different lights. I told Holbein to paint her in the best light. He did. That was another mistake. Can you see?'

I thought a moment. 'It is full face—'

'Not till you see her in profile do you notice her long nose.' His shoulders slumpcd. 'When she landed at Rochester in January the king disliked her on sight. And now the Duke of Norfolk's dangled his niece before the king. Catherine Howard is pretty, not yet seventeen, and he's caught. He blames me for saddling him with the Cleves mare. But if he marries Norfolk's niece, the Howards will have me dead and England back under Rome.' He got up and walked over to the window. 'I'm doing all I can to discredit them, to find papist plots. I've had Lord Lisle arrested, and Bishop Sampson's in the Tower; I had him shown the rack. But I can find nothing.'

He turned and faced me. 'Then I told the king about Greek Fire. He can't wait for the demonstration. He sees us making England's navy the greatest on the seas. He's my friend again.' He clenched his fists. 'A foreign power would pay much for that formula. Matthew, I must have it back before the demonstration. Today is the 29th of May. We have only twelve full days.'

He picked up the miniature and returned to his seat. 'Michael Gristwood had to use three intermediaries to get to me. They are the only others who know about Greek Fire. Two of them are lawyers, men of Lincoln's Inn that you know. The first was Stephen Bealknap—'

'Not Bealknap. Dear God, he's the last one any man should trust. And they'd had a falling-out.'

'They must have mended it. Talk to him; find out if he told anyone else.'

He paused for a moment. 'Bealknap went to Gabriel Marchamount.'

'Did he? They had some dealings in the past, I know, but Bealknap was too shady for Marchamount's liking.'

'Marchamount moves in semi-papist circles. That worries me. Question him too. Threaten him or flatter him or offer him gold. Loosen his tongue.'

'I'll try, My Lord. And the third?'

'Marchamount took the story to Lady Bryanston.'

'I met her only a few days ago. She invited me to dinner.'

'I dropped your name at her table last week. You must go. Talk to her too.'

'I shall, My Lord. But if I am to get to the root of this matter, I need to know more about Greek Fire. I could talk to the monastery librarian. Perhaps visit St Bartholomew's to see where the stuff was found.'

He smiled coldly. 'You don't believe in Greek Fire yet, do you? You will. As for Bernard Kytchyn, Brother Bernard the librarian as he used to be, I've been trying to find him to make sure he kept his mouth shut too. But he's disappeared without trace.'

'I could try the Court of Augmentations; he must have arrangements to collect his pension.'

Cromwell nodded. 'That's Richard Rich's territory. But you could say it was in connection with a case.' He looked at me sharply. 'I don't want Rich getting a whiff of this. I raised him to the king's council, but he will change sides in a moment to protect himself. If he went to the king and said I'd lost Greek Fire . . .' He raised his eyebrows.

'I would like to talk to Goodwife Gristwood again,' I said. 'I had a feeling she was keeping something back.'

Cromwell smiled suddenly. 'I see this matter intrigues you, Matthew.'

'I will bend my mind to it.'

He nodded. 'Come to me if you need anything. But time is all. You must move fast. You'll have Jack to help you. I'm setting him to work with you.'

What I felt must have shown in my face, for Barak smiled sarcastically.

'I work alone these days,' I said.

'You need help with this. Jack will lodge with you. You'll get used to him.' Perhaps Cromwell was setting Barak to keep an eye on me.

'My Lord,' I ventured, 'I must also give time to Mistress Wentworth's case.'

He shrugged. 'Very well. And Jack will help you with that. But this business comes first.' He fixed me with those hard brown eyes. 'If you fail, all those associated with me will be at risk. Your lives could be at stake too.'

He rang a little bell and Grey stepped in, looking worried.

'Grey's been told. Keep me informed of progress every day. Any news, anything you want, send it via Grey. No one else. I can't trust anyone now,' he growled. 'Not the people I raised to the council, not even my own staff, whom Norfolk pays to spy on me. But Grey's been with me since I was a nobody, the son of an alehouse keeper, haven't you, Edwin?'

'Aye, My Lord.' He hesitated. 'Is Master Barak to be involved in this too?'

'He is.' Cromwell looked at Grey, who pursed his lips. 'Matthew can do anything that requires diplomacy.'

'That . . . er . . . might be best.'

'Jack can deal with anything that requires a strong hand, eh?'

Barak was studying his master's face. I caught a look of concern, and realised that he feared deeply for Cromwell. And perhaps for his own fate too.

WHEN WE LEFT the room Barak told me he had things to collect. I went outside, fetched Chancery and led him into the front yard. My mind was in a whirl. Cromwell and reform about to fall? Though my faith had reached a low ebb, I felt a clutch of dread at the thought of the papists back in charge.

I turned to see Barak walking into the yard, a big leather satchel slung over his shoulder. He inclined his head to it. 'The papers from the abbey and some material my master has gathered about Greek Fire.'

He fetched the black mare and we rode out again. 'I'm starving hungry,' he said conversationally. 'Does your housekeeper keep a good table?'

'Good plain fare,' I replied shortly.

We rode on in silence for a while, up towards Ely Place. Then Barak drew his horse in close.

'Don't look round,' he said quietly, 'but we're being followed.'

I looked at him in surprise. 'Are you sure?'

'I think so. I've looked back once or twice and the same man's been there. Here, turn in by the church.' He led the way through the gate, behind the wall enclosing St Andrew's church, and jumped down from his horse.

I dismounted more slowly. 'Hurry now,' he said impatiently, leading the mare behind the wall. I joined him where he stood peering round the gateway.

'See,' he breathed, 'here he comes. Don't stick your head out too far.'

The only rider to be seen was a man on a white colt. He was about Barak's age, tall and thin, with a thatch of untidy brown hair. His pale face was pitted as an old cheese with the scars of smallpox. As we watched, the man halted, shading his eyes against the sun as he looked up the road.

Barak pulled me back. 'He's missed us. He'll be looking round in a moment. What a face, he looks as if he's just been dug up.' I frowned at his presumption in grabbing at me, but he smiled cheerily. 'Come on, we'll lead the horses round the church and go back by Shoe Lane.'

He took the mare's reins and I followed him through the churchyard.

'Who was that?' I asked as we halted on the far side of the church.

'Don't know. He must have been following us since we left His Lordship's house. There's not many would have the nerve to set watch there.'

He heaved himself deftly into the saddle, and I mounted Chancery more slowly; after my day of riding hither and thither my back was sore.

Barak looked at me curiously. 'You all right?'

'Yes,' I snapped, settling myself in the saddle.

He shrugged. 'Well, just ask, any time, if you want a hand. It's nothing to me you're a hunchback, I'm not superstitious.'

I stared after him, speechless, as he turned and led the way into Shoe Lane. At first I was too offended by his insolence to speak, but then I thought I should find out what I could about the wretched man.

'That's twice I've been watched this last week,' I said. 'By that man and before by you.'

'Aye,' he answered cheerfully. 'His Lordship set me to see whether you might stand up to this job. I told him you had a determined look about you.'

'Did you? And have you worked for the earl a long time?'

'Oh, aye. My father came from Putney, where the earl's father kept his tavern. When he died I was asked to enter Lord Cromwell's service'—he gave that cynical smile again—'and he's found me useful enough.'

'What did your father do?'

'He was a gong-screwer, cleaned out people's cesspits. Silly old arsehole, he fell into one of the pits he was digging out and drowned.' Despite the lightness of his tone a brief shadow passed across his face.

'I am sorry.'

'I've no family now,' Barak said lightly. 'Free of all ties. What about you?'

'My father is still alive. He has a farm in Lichfield, in the Midlands.'

'Son of carrot crunchers, eh? Where did you get your education? Do they have schools up there?'

'They do. I went to Lichfield cathedral school.'

'I've an education too,' Barak replied. 'I went to St Paul's school, got a scholarship for a clever lad, but I had to fend for myself after my father died.' He tapped his satchel. 'Those Latin papers my master gave me for you, I can read them, just about.'

As we turned in at my gate, Barak studied my house, with its mullioned windows and tall chimneys. He turned to me, raising an eyebrow. 'Fine place.'

'Now we are here,' I said, 'we had better have our story clear. I suggest we tell my servants you are the agent of a client and are helping me on a case.'

He nodded. 'All right. What servants have you?'

'My housekeeper, Joan Woode, and a boy.' I gave him a fixed stare. 'You should also look to how you address me. Given our respective stations, "sir" would be appropriate; "Master Shardlake" would at least be civil.'

'Right you are.' He grinned cheekily. 'Need a hand down, sir?'

'I can manage.'

As we dismounted, the boy Simon appeared from behind the house. He stared at Barak's mare in admiration.

'That's Sukey,' Barak told him. 'Look after her well and there'll be something for you.' He winked. 'She likes a carrot now and then.'

'Yes, sir.' Simon bowed and led the horses away.

Joan appeared in the doorway. She gave Barak a look of surprise. 'Good afternoon, sir. May I ask how it went at the court?'

'We've got twelve days' grace for Elizabeth,' I said. 'Joan, this is Master Jack. He will be staying with us a short while, to help me with a new matter on behalf of his master. Could you make a room ready for him?'

'Yes, sir.'

Barak bowed and gave her a charming smile. 'Master Shardlake did not tell me his housekeeper was so attractive.' Joan's plump face reddened and she pushed some greying hairs under her cap. 'Oh, please, sir—'

I stared, surprised my sensible housekeeper should fall for such nonsense. I supposed women would find him good-looking if they were susceptible to rough charm. She led him upstairs. 'The room hasn't been slept in for a while, sir,' she said, 'but it's clean.'

I remembered I must write to Joseph arranging to meet. I climbed the stairs to my study. As I passed Barak's room I heard my housekeeper clucking like an old hen about the state of the blankets.

JOAN PREPARED an early supper. We had trout and afterwards a bowl of strawberries. Barak joined me at table, and tucked happily into his fish, lifting his food to his mouth with his knife in an ill-bred way.

'I'll give you those books and papers later,' he said. 'By Jesu, they're strange reading.'

I nodded. 'And I should consider how to proceed. Let me get it right. The first person involved was the friar, the librarian.' I ticked names off on my fingers. 'The Gristwoods went to Bealknap and he went to Marchamount, who told Lady Honor, who told Cromwell. We can discount the friar as the force behind this. Someone hired two ruthless rogues to kill the Gristwoods, and it would cost much more than a pensioned-off friar could raise. I still want to talk to him. And I'll see Bealknap and Marchamount tomorrow at Lincoln's Inn; there's a luncheon for the Duke of Norfolk.'

Barak screwed up his face. 'That arsehole. How he hates my master.'

'I know. We can use tomorrow morning to go to Augmentations—they're so busy these days they keep open on Sundays. I'll try to see Joseph Wentworth then too. I can miss church for once.'

I took some strawberries and passed the bowl to Barak. He spooned half the dish onto his plate and added cream.

'Then there is Lady Honor,' I continued.

He nodded. 'She usually has these sugar banquets on a Tuesday. If you haven't heard by Monday morning, I'll ask His Lordship to give her a nudge.'

I looked at him levelly. 'Doing what you can do to assist, eh?'

'That's what his lordship asked me to do,' he replied briskly. 'I know what I'm about.' He changed the subject. 'That Wentworth case—there's more to it than meets the eye, if you ask me. But you're right to talk to the family; I'll warrant the answer's there.'

'I've sent Simon with a note asking Joseph to call here tomorrow at noon. And now I should look at those papers. Could you bring them to me?'

'Aye.' As he got up he nodded. 'You're getting to grips with the matter, I see. Planning everything out. My master said you were like that, didn't let go once you were started.'

THE SUN was beginning to set as I took Barak's satchel out into the garden. I sat on a bench, glad simply to be alone at last, and opened it.

I read for two hours as the sun sank and the first moths flickered towards the candles Simon lit in the house. I turned first to the papers Michael Gristwood had brought from the monastery. There were four illustrated manuscripts giving vivid descriptions of the use of Greek Fire. Sometimes they called it Flying Fire, sometimes the devil's tears, fire from the dragon's mouth, Dark Fire. I puzzled over that last name. How could fire be dark?

There was a page in Greek torn from the biography of the Byzantine emperor Alexios I who reigned four hundred years ago. It described an apparatus fitted in the prow of each of the Byzantine galleys: a flexible tube ending with the brass head of a lion, through the open mouth of which fire could be directed downwards or to either side.

I laid down the paper, wondering what had happened to the apparatus the Gristwoods had used. Had that been taken from Wolf's Lane too?

I turned to an account of a giant Arab fleet sent to invade Constantinople and destroyed by flying fire in AD 678, fire that burned on the very surface of the sea. Surely such things were impossible? I turned next to the only paper in the collection in English. It was written in a round, clumsy hand.

I, Alan St John, late soldier of the Emperor Constantine Palaiologos of Byzantium, do make this testament in the hospital of St Bartholomew's in Smithfield, this 11th day of March 1454.

I am told I am like to die and have confessed my sins. The friars of this blessed place have comforted me these last months since I returned from the fall of Constantinople sore wounded, which wounds grow infected again. To the friars I leave my papers, telling of the old secret of Greek Fire the Byzantines knew, which was passed down from emperor to emperor and lost at last, together with the last barrel of distilled Greek Fire itself, which I brought back from the East. The secret was found by a library-keeper of Constantinople as he rescued the books from the approaching Turks, and he gave the papers and the barrel into my care before we fled the city in the ships the Venetians sent. I do not understand the Greek and Latin and meant to consult with alchemists in England, but then my illness disabled me. May God forgive me: I meant to make a profit from this thing, but no money can aid me now. The friars say it is God's will, for this terrible secret could bring much bloodshed to unhappy humanity. It is no surprise they called its principal element Dark Fire. I leave it all to the friars to do with as they will, for they are close to the Grace of God.

So the friars had hidden the papers, and the barrel, knowing the potential for danger and destruction they had in their hands, not thinking that ninety years later King Henry and Cromwell would come and clear them all out.

I sniffed the paper. It had a faint scent, pleasant and musky. I turned to the remaining papers, the same odour lingered on them. I turned to the books, mostly Latin and Greek works that told stories of Greek Fire. There were also a couple of alchemical works, which I found incomprehensible.

I turned back finally to the old parchment Cromwell had shown me: the picture of the ship spouting Greek Fire, with the top part torn off. I ran my fingers along the torn edge. That act had cost Michael Gristwood his life.

I heard footsteps and looked up to see Barak approaching.

He nodded at the documents. 'Well, what d'you make of it all?'

'Not much. No one has a clue what Greek Fire really was. The alchemical works are obscure riddles, but I have a friend who may be able to make some sense of them. He is a learned man, an apothecary.'

'That old black monk of yours? He's well known round where I lodge. By God, he's a strange-looking one.'

'Guy's a very knowledgeable man.'

'Aye, so they say round the Old Barge.'

'That is where you live?' I remembered those shutters closing.

'Aye, it's not a fine place like this but it's in the middle of London—useful as my business takes me all over the City.' He sat beside me and gave me a sharp look. 'You're to say nothing to the monk about Greek Fire.'

'I'll ask him to elucidate these alchemy books, say it's something I've to look into for a client. He knows I have to keep clients' confidences.'

'Anything else those old papers reveal?'

'No. Except I think the monks hid the formula and the barrel for fear of the destruction Greek Fire could cause.' I looked at him. 'They were right. The devastation such a weapon could wreak would be terrible.'

'But if it could save England from invasion. Surely anything is worth that.'

I did not reply. 'Tell me what it was like. At the demonstration.'

'Back in March my master told me to buy an old crayer and have it brought down to an abandoned jetty out beyond Deptford. He asked me to be at the jetty at first light one morning and wait for him. As the sun came up I saw my master approaching on horseback. There were two men accompanying him, and one of their horses was pulling a cart with something hidden under a pile of sacking. They got to the wharf and dismounted.

'My master introduced me to the Gristwoods. They unloaded a pile of strange stuff from the cart: a long, thin brass pipe, a big metal handpump and an iron tank. I helped the earl look the boat over from end to end, to make sure there was no trickery, while the brothers set up their apparatus on the jetty. They heaved the metal tank onto a big iron tripod, and attached it to the pump at one end and to the pipe at the other, then lit a fire of sticks underneath it. The pipe was about twelve feet long, and under the other end they fixed a wick, a pot of string greased with candle wax. I caught a whiff of something from the tank. It was a harsh tang, like nothing I'd ever smelt before.

'It happened quickly then. Michael took a twig from the fire and lit the wick, then ran back, and he and Sepultus worked the pump up and down. I saw a movement at the front of the pipe and then a great spout of yellow flame, a dozen feet long, shot out with a roaring sound, flew through the air and hit the boat amidships. It seemed to twist in the air like a live thing. The wood caught light immediately, the flames seemed to stick to it and devour it. Some of the flames fell down on the water and I saw *the water burning*, saw it with my own eyes. Then the brothers turned the pipe round, pumped again, and another long spout of flame shot out and the old crayer was blazing from end to end. By Jesu, I was frightened. Moments later the boat had disappeared. A thirty-ton crayer had been burned to nothing.'

Barak took a deep breath. 'When the Gristwoods had left, my master told me that what I had seen was called Greek Fire and swore me to secrecy.'

I nodded thoughtfully. 'So to get Greek Fire to work you need that apparatus. Who built it for them, I wonder, and where did they keep it?'

Barak looked at me. 'You believe in it now that you've heard what I saw?'

'I believe you saw something very extraordinary.'

Barak stood up. 'I came to tell you I'm going out. I have to fetch some clothes from the Old Barge. And I am going to ask around the taverns, see if anyone knows of that pock-faced man. Then afterwards I've a girl to see, so I'll be back late. Got a key?'

I looked at him disapprovingly. 'Ask Joan for hers. We must start early tomorrow.'

He smiled. 'Don't worry, you won't find me wanting in diligence.'

'I hope not.'

'Nor will the girl.' He gave me a lubricious wink and turned away.

DESPITE HIS NIGHT of rousting, Barak seemed fresh as a new pin the next morning, eager to be off. He told me he had been unable to trace the man who had followed us, but had set enquiries in train among his acquaintances. After breakfast we rode to Westminster Hall, where the Court of Augmentations' offices were housed. We tied up the horses in New Palace Yard. Barak followed me up the steps to the north door. The guard, seeing my lawyer's robe, nodded and we entered the giant stone building.

From behind a door in a far corner, a murmur of voices was audible. 'Come on,' I said and led Barak to the Court of Augmentations' office.

It was no surprise that Augmentations had obtained a dispensation to open on a Sunday. Responsible for the sale of hundreds of monastic buildings and for the pensions of the former monks, there was no busier place in the land. I led Barak to a counter marked 'Pensions' and rang the bell.

'I'm looking for one Bernard Kytchyn,' I said, when an elderly clerk appeared. 'Former librarian at St Bartholomew's priory, Smithfield.'

The clerk began leafing through a massive ledger. After a minute he smiled and stabbed at an entry with an inky finger. 'There it is, sirs. Bernard Kytchyn. He's listed as chantry priest at St Andrew's church, Moorgate.'

I turned the ledger round to check the entry. 'Barak,' I said, 'when I go back to Chancery Lane, I suggest you go and find Kytchyn, tell him—' I broke off, as the door behind the clerk opened.

To my astonishment Stephen Bealknap stepped out, a frown on his thin face. 'Master clerk, we had not finished. Sir Richard Rich requires—' He broke off in turn as he saw me. He looked surprised, 'Brother Shardlake . . .'

'Bealknap, I did not know you had an interest in pensions.'

'I don't usually. But there . . . there is a corrodiary, a pensioner with right of residence, attached to my property at Moorgate. It seems I have taken on responsibility for him too. An interesting legal problem, is it not?'

'Yes.' I turned to the clerk. 'We are finished now. Well, Brother, I shall see you the day after tomorrow.' I bowed to Bealknap.

The clerk replaced his book and ushered Bealknap back to his room.

I frowned. 'Corrodies are attached to monasteries, not friaries. What's he really doing here?'

'He mentioned Rich.'

'Yes.' I hesitated. 'Could Cromwell have the clerk questioned?'

'That would be difficult; Sir Richard Rich would get to hear of it.'

I nodded. 'We must go,' I said. 'Joseph will be waiting for me.'

We returned to the yard, mounted the horses, and set off back to Chancery Lane. As we rode past Charing Cross, I noticed a well-dressed woman on a fine gelding, her face covered from the sun by a striped cloth vizard. She was attended by three mounted retainers, with two ladies walking behind. As we passed she lifted the vizard. I recognised Lady Honor.

She raised a hand in greeting. 'Master Shardlake! We are met again.'

I reined Chancery in. 'Lady Honor. Another hot day.'

'Is it not?' she replied feelingly. 'I am pleased to have met with you. Will you come and dine with me next Tuesday?'

'I should be delighted,' I said.

'The House of Glass in Blue Lion Street. Be there at five. It's a sugar banquet only, it won't go on late. There will be interesting company.'

'I shall look forward to it, Lady Honor.'

'Well, I must get on,' she said. 'I am visiting my late husband's relatives.'
She lowered her vizard and the party moved off.

'A fine-looking piece,' Barak said as we rode on.

I laughed. 'She is out of your league, Barak.'

'Out of yours too.'

'I would not be so impertinent as to think otherwise.'

'Come on,' he said abruptly. 'I've to find this Kytchyn fellow.'

'If you find him, ask him to meet me tomorrow. At St Bartholomew's.'

Barak turned in the saddle. 'At Barty's? But Sir Richard Rich lives there
now. My master wants him kept out of this.'

'I must see where the stuff was found, Barak.'

He raised his eyebrows. 'Very well. But we have to be careful.'

'God's death, d'you think I don't know that?'

At the bottom of Chancery Lane we parted. As I rode up the lane alone I
felt suddenly nervous, remembering how we had been followed yesterday. I
was relieved to reach my gate.

JOSEPH WAS WAITING for me in the parlour. He had taken a seat in my armchair and he jumped up, embarrassed.

I waved a hand. 'Don't worry, Joseph, it's a cursed hot day.' I took a chair
opposite him. Despite his tiredness I saw there was a gleam in his eyes.

'Sir,' he said, 'I have been successful. My brother will see you.'

'Well done. How did you manage it?'

'I told Edwin you were uncertain of Elizabeth's guilt and wanted to talk
to the family before deciding whether you could continue to represent her.
He was hostile at first, angry at my interference, but my mother persuaded
him. They'll see us tomorrow morning at ten. But I fear I let them believe
you have doubts about Lizzy's innocence.' He gave me an imploring look. 'I
don't like lying, but for her sake . . .' He shook his head sadly.

'Often the world does not allow us to be pure, I fear.' I looked at the
clock on the mantelpiece. I should have to hurry. 'I am sorry, Joseph, but I
must leave you again. I have an engagement at Lincoln's Inn. Meet me at
the Walbrook conduit tomorrow, just before ten.'

'I will, sir. You are good to give me your time when you are so busy.'

'Have you eaten? Stay here, my housekeeper will fetch you something.'

'Thank you, sir.'

I bowed and left him. I told Joan to fetch him some food, then hurriedly
donned my robe. I wanted to catch Marchamount before the luncheon.

I HAD EXPECTED my chambers to be empty but I found Godfrey in his room.

'I didn't think you'd be in, Godfrey. I came to leave you a note. You're not going to the luncheon with Norfolk, surely?'

He grunted. 'I thought I should see what the papist rogue looked like in the flesh.'

'Well, now that we are met, may I ask a favour? I have a . . . a new matter. Something urgent. Together with the Wentworth case it will take much of my time this next fortnight. Can you deal with some of my work?'

'I would be happy to. Including the Bealknap hearing?'

'No, I will keep that. But everything else. For a share of the fee, of course. Come to my room and I will show you what cases I have.'

'I am in your debt again,' I said when we had spent half an hour going through the papers. 'I will come into chambers when I can. I have another appointment now, but I will see you at the luncheon. Thank you, my friend.'

I went out again, crossing the courtyard to Marchamount's rooms. I knocked and entered his outer office. A clerk looked up enquiringly.

'Is the serjeant in?' I asked.

'He's very busy, sir. Has a big case starting in Common Pleas tomorrow.'

'Tell him it is Brother Shardlake, on Lord Cromwell's business.'

His eyes widened at that and he disappeared through a door. A moment later he was back and bowed me through.

Gabriel Marchamount, like many barristers, lived as well as worked in Lincoln's Inn. He sat in his opulent receiving room, in a high-backed chair behind a wide desk strewn with papers. A robe edged with fur lay on a cushion nearby together with his white serjeant's coif, the mark of his rank. Marchamount loved the status the law brought him. Since his admission to the Order of the Coif three years before, his patrician manner had become the subject of jokes. But I knew his intelligence was not to be underrated.

He rose and greeted me with a smile and a small bow, his dark eyes wary. 'Brother Shardlake. Are you here for my luncheon with the duke?'

'I might look in.'

He sat down again. 'I hear you are retained to advise in the Wentworth case. An unpleasant business. Not much *unguentum auri* there, I'd guess.'

I smiled tightly. 'No. A small fee. In fact, it is another killing I have called to see you about. Michael Gristwood and his brother have been murdered.'

He nodded sadly and said, 'Yes, I know. A dreadful business.'

'How did you know, sir?' I asked sharply. 'This has been kept quiet on Lord Cromwell's orders.'

He spread his arms. 'His widow came to see me yesterday. Asked for my help in getting the house transferred into her name.' His eyes narrowed. 'Is the Greek Fire formula gone?'

I paused; the words seemed to hang in the stuffy air for a moment. 'Yes, Serjeant. That is why Lord Cromwell wants the matter investigated quickly and secretly. I am instructed to talk to all who knew about Greek Fire. I have to ask you to tell me everything about your involvement, Serjeant.'

Marchamount settled himself in his chair, linking his hands together. A gold ring containing an enormous emerald glinted on one middle finger. 'I did not know Michael Gristwood well,' he said. 'He approached me to see if I needed a solicitor's assistance a couple of years ago. He had been working with Brother Bealknap, but they had quarrelled.'

'I had heard. What was that about? Do you know?'

He raised an eyebrow. 'Michael was not above a little sharp dealing, but he found the way Bealknap cheated everyone as a matter of daily routine hard to stomach. I farmed some work out to him, but it was not well done and I gave him no more.' Marchamount sighed. 'Then one day last March, Bealknap came to my office asking to see me. He told me what Michael had found at St Bartholomew's. He wanted an introduction to Lord Cromwell.'

I frowned. 'March, you said. But Michael Gristwood found those papers last autumn. What happened in the six months between?'

'Michael told me he and his brother had spent the winter building the apparatus to project the stuff, and experimenting to make more Greek Fire.'

'Had they succeeded?'

He shrugged. 'They said so.'

'So, you helped Michael Gristwood to a meeting with Lord Cromwell.'

'Of course, I could not approach the chief secretary myself.' He waved a hand self-deprecatingly. 'But I know Lady Honor, a fine and discreet woman, and she does know the earl. I asked her to take the papers to him.'

'But you could not give her the formula itself?'

'That was not in my gift. Michael told me they had torn it from that parchment, but not where it was kept. And the brothers wanted money for it.'

'But those papers belonged to the king. He should have taken them to Sir Richard Rich, Chancellor of Augmentations, to pass to Lord Cromwell.'

Marchamount spread his hands. 'Naturally, I told Gristwood that. But what else could I do? I couldn't *make* him give me the formula.'

'So you gave the papers to Lady Honor with a message?'

'I did. And a message came back through her, from the earl, for me to give to Gristwood. Afterwards two or three further messages passed through my hands—sealed, of course, so I knew nothing of what they said.' He spread his hands again. 'I am afraid that is all I know, Brother.'

OUTSIDE IN THE COURTYARD, I joined the crowd of black-robed barristers filing into hall. I saw Godfrey ahead of me and tapped him on the shoulder.

Lincoln's Inn Hall looked its very best. Beneath the vaulting hammer-beam roof the richly coloured tapestries glowed in the light of numerous candles. A throne-like chair had been set for the duke in the centre of the High Table at the north end of the hall, with other long tables set at right angles to High Table. A few students took places furthest from High Table; the serjeants sat nearest and the benchers and barristers in between. As benchers Godfrey and I were entitled to places next to the serjeants, and to my surprise Godfrey shouldered his way to a place close to where the duke would sit. As I sat down next to him, Bealknap took a place opposite me.

A servant banged his staff. Everyone rose as the officers of the Inn marched up the hall. Among the black robes was a man in rich scarlet, his collar trimmed with black fur: Thomas Howard, third Duke of Norfolk. I was surprised to see how small and old he was. The Inn's officers bowed as they bade the duke take his seat. I saw Marchamount take a place at High Table. I wondered how well he knew Cromwell's greatest enemy.

I studied the duke's lined face. The thin mouth under the prominent nose was pursed with severity. Small black eyes surveyed the crowd with lively calculation. The duke's gaze met mine for a second and I dropped my eyes.

The first course was brought in, steaming dishes of vegetables carved into the shapes of stars and half-moons, richly sauced with sugar and vine-gar and accompanied by cold meat. I turned appreciatively to Godfrey.

'This fare is almost worth the company,' I whispered.

'Nothing is worth this company.' Godfrey was staring at the duke, a bitter look on his normally amiable features. The duke was talking to the treasurer, Serjeant Cuffleigh, who was looking anxious. Cuffleigh was a reformer.

'Not just apprentices,' I heard the duke say. 'Even silly little women fancy they can read the Bible now and understand God's Word.' He laughed.

'It is permitted, Your Grace,' Cuffleigh replied weakly.

'Not for long. The king plans to restrict Bible-reading to heads of house-holds. I'd only permit it for the clergy. I've never read it and never will.'

All along the upper part of the tables, where the duke's words could be heard, men were looking at him, some approvingly and others with set faces.

He glanced over the assembly with bright, hard eyes and smiled cynically.

Then, before I could stop him, Godfrey rose in his place. All eyes turned to him as he faced the duke, and said loudly, 'God's Word is for all to read. It is the bringer of the sweetest light there is, the light of truth.'

His words echoed round the hall. All along the tables eyes widened. Norfolk stared at Godfrey with cold amusement.

'The Bible brings us from error to truth, to the presence of Jesus Christ,' he continued. 'Were I to be killed for my beliefs, I would rise from the grave to proclaim the truth once more,' he said and then sat down.

The duke rose in his place. 'No, sir, you would not,' he said evenly. 'You would be screaming in hell with all the other Lutheran heretics. Have a care, sir, that your tongue does not put you in the pit before your time.' He sat down again. Leaning over to Marchamount he began whispering in his ear.

'What were you thinking?' I asked Godfrey. 'You'll be disciplined for this.'

He looked at me, his eyes gleaming with self-righteous anger. 'I care not. Jesus Christ is my Saviour, through grace, and I will not have His Word made mock of.' I turned away. When his emotions were roused by his faith, Godfrey could change into a different person, a dangerous one.

CHAPTER FOUR

At last the meal ended. The duke and his retinue filed out and a buzz of conversation erupted. I stood up and hurried after Bealknap, who was heading for the door. I caught him as he stepped outside. 'Brother Bealknap,' I said crisply, 'I need to talk to you.'

'About the case?' He smiled. 'Your friend made a monkey of himself in there, by the way. He'll be disciplined—'

'It is not about the case, Bealknap. I have a commission, from Lord Cromwell. To investigate the murder yesterday of Michael Gristwood.'

His jaw dropped. If he was acting ignorance, it was a good performance. 'Your chambers, I think.'

Bealknap nodded and led the way across Gatehouse Court. He had a room on the first floor of a corner building. His chamber was plainly furnished, a poor-looking desk and a couple of battered tables heaped untidily with papers. In one corner stood a huge chest made of thick boards and secured by iron bands and padlocks. It was said that all the gold Bealknap earned went in there and that he passed his evenings counting it.

Bealknap took off his cap and ran a hand through his wiry blond hair. 'Will you take a seat, Brother?'

'Thank you.' I sat by his desk, casting an eye over the papers.

'In God's name, Brother,' he said. 'What is this about Michael Gristwood?'

'He was found dead yesterday morning at his home. His brother was murdered too. The formula is gone. You know what I am talking about.'

'My poor friend. This is very shocking.' His eyes avoided mine.

'Did you tell anyone apart from Serjeant Marchamount about the formula?'

He shook his head firmly. 'No, sir, I did not. When Michael brought me the papers he found at Barty's, I said he should get them to Lord Cromwell.'

'For payment, though they were the king's by right. Was that your idea?'

He hesitated, then looked at me directly. 'It was his. But I didn't quarrel with him about that, Brother. I thought the whole thing was nonsense. After I took Michael to Marchamount he paid me and I heard no more till now.'

'When did Michael first bring you the papers?'

'In March.'

'He waited six months after finding them?'

'He said he and his brother the alchemist had been experimenting with the formula, making more, building some sort of apparatus to fire the stuff.'

It was a similar tale to Marchamount's. 'Ah, yes,' I said, 'the apparatus. Did they build that themselves?'

Bealknap shrugged. 'I've no idea. Michael said only that it had been made.'

'They said nothing of where the apparatus, or the formula, were kept?'

'No. I didn't even study their papers. Michael showed them to me, but half of them were in Greek and what I could read sounded like nonsense.'

'Very well.' I rose. 'That will do for now. You will tell no one that Michael is dead, or that we have spoken, or you will answer to Lord Cromwell.'

'I've no wish to tell anyone; I don't want to be involved at all.'

'I am afraid you are, Bealknap.' I gave him a tight smile. 'I will see you at Westminster Hall on Tuesday for the case. By the way,' I added with apparent casualness, 'did you resolve the problem with your corrodiary?'

'Oh, yes.'

'Strange, I did not think friaries took on pensioners living in.'

'This one did,' he said. 'Ask Sir Richard Rich if you don't believe me.'

'Ah, yes, you mentioned his name at Augmentations. I did not know you had his patronage.'

'I don't,' he answered smoothly, 'but I knew the clerk had a meeting with Sir Richard Rich. That was why I urged him to hurry.'

I smiled and left him. Bealknap had been frightened, but had seemed suddenly confident when he mentioned Richard Rich. That worried me.

WHEN I GOT back to my house, Barak had returned and was sitting in the garden, his feet up on a shady bench and a pot of beer beside him.

'Joan is looking after you, then,' I said.

'Like a prince. What luck with the lawyers?' Barak asked.

I sat down and poured myself a mug of beer. 'They both say they just acted as middlemen. I'm not sure about Bealknap. He's involved with Richard Rich in some way, though I don't know whether it relates to Greek Fire. What about you? Did you find the librarian?'

'Aye. Funny little fellow. I found him saying Mass in a side chapel in his church.' He smiled wryly. 'He wasn't pleased to hear what I wanted, but he'll meet us outside Barty's gatehouse at eight tomorrow morning.'

I stood up wearily. 'Well, I suppose we had better be off to Wolf's Lane.'

We went round to the stables. Chancery was unhappy at being led into the sun again. He was old; it was time to think of putting him out to pasture.

As we rode, I went over what I should say to Goodwife Gristwood. I must find out if she knew anything of the apparatus for projecting Greek Fire.

As we passed down Cheapside I heard a high-pitched yell. A beggar girl, no more than ten and dressed in the filthiest rags, had just been thrown out of a baker's shop. People stopped to look as she turned and banged on the door of the shop. 'You took my little brother! You made him into pies!'

Passers-by laughed. Sobbing, the girl slid down the door and crouched weeping at its foot. Someone laid a penny at her feet before hurrying on.

'What in God's name is that about?' I asked.

Barak grimaced. 'She's mazed. She used to beg around Walbrook and the Stocks Market with her young brother. He disappeared a few weeks ago and now she runs up to people screaming they've killed him. That's not the only shopkeeper she's accused.' He frowned. 'Poor creature.'

I looked at the girl, her arms like sticks wrapped round her thin frame.

'Are you coming?' Barak asked.

I followed him down Friday Street, then down to Wolf's Lane. Under the alchemist's sign I saw that a crude repair had been made to the door with planks and nails. We dismounted and Barak knocked on the door.

It was opened by one of Cromwell's men. 'Good day, Master Barak.'

'Good day, Smith. All quiet?'

'Yes, sir. We've had the bodies taken away.'

The girl Susan appeared, looking composed now.

'Hello, Susan,' Barak said with a wink. 'How's your mistress?'

'Better, sir.'

'We would talk with her again,' I said.

She curtseyed and led us into a parlour with a view of the yard, then went to fetch her mistress.

Goodwife Gristwood came in. She curtseyed to us perfunctorily.

'I'm afraid I have some more questions for you, Goodwife,' I said gently. 'Please, sit down.' Reluctantly, she took a chair.

'Did your husband and brother-in-law seem as normal when you and Susan left the house for the markets?'

She looked at me wearily. 'Yes. Michael didn't go to Augmentations yesterday; he went up to help his brother with one of his experiments. When we got back at noon we saw the front door had been staved in and then those . . . those red footprints.' Her tightly held features seemed to sag a little. 'We went upstairs and found them.'

'And none of the neighbours saw or heard anything?'

'The goodwife next door told your man she heard a great banging and clattering, but that was nothing unusual when his brother was at his work.'

'I'd like to look at the workshop again. Do you feel able to come with me?'

She shrugged. 'If you wish. They've taken them away. After you've seen it, can I get it cleared? If I'm to keep myself fed, I'll have to let it.'

'Very well.'

She led us up the twisting staircase. The workshop door still hung off its one hinge. We stepped inside. The floor was still covered with blood, its faint tang mixed with the sulphurous stink. Goodwife Gristwood looked at the spray of blood on the walls and went pale.

Lifting a chair from the wreckage, I helped her sit. After a minute some colour returned to her face and she looked at the smashed chest.

'Michael and Samuel bought that last autumn. Heaved it up here. They'd never let me know what was in it.'

I nodded at the empty shelves. 'Do you know what was kept on those?'

'Samuel's powders and chemicals. Sulphur and lime and God knows what. Whoever killed them took Samuel's bottles as well, God knows why.'

'Did they ever mention the term Greek Fire?'

She hesitated before replying. 'Not to me. I tell you, I wasn't interested in what they did up here.' She shifted uneasily in her chair.

'You spoke of experiments, sometimes out in the yard. Did they have an apparatus, a large thing of tanks and pipes? Did you see anything like that?'

'No, sir. All they took out to the yard were flasks of liquid and powder.'

She was lying, I was sure. Her eyes had narrowed warily when I mentioned the apparatus. I nodded and stepped to the fireplace. The stoppered bottle lay where I had left it. I picked it up and saw it was still half-full.

'Might you have any idea what this liquid is, madam?'

'No, I haven't.' Her voice rose. 'I don't know what any of it means!'

I wrapped the bottle in my handkerchief, then slipped it into my pocket.

When she spoke again it was in a cold whisper. 'If you want to find who might have told the killers about my husband, you should go to *her*.'

'Who?'

'His whore.' Barak and I looked at each other in surprise as she continued. 'The woman that keeps the brewery told me in March she'd seen Michael in Southwark, going into one of the whorehouses. I asked him and he admitted it. He was besotted with that vile tart.' She stared at me, her eyes fierce. 'He said the tart was kind to him and he could talk to her. Well, *you* talk to her, sir. Bathsheba Green at the Bishop's Hat brothel at Bank End. Talk to *her*,' she repeated fiercely. Talk to *her*.'

BY THE TIME we arrived back at Chancery Lane the sun was low. I told Joan to fetch us some food. In my parlour I dropped gratefully into my armchair; Barak collected some cushions together and sprawled on the floor.

'We've had more new leads than answers so far,' I said. 'But that's what I'd expect at the start of a complicated investigation. We must visit that whore. And I think the goodwife is still holding something back. Something to do with the apparatus. Is your man Smith staying with her?'

'Till otherwise instructed.'

'I don't think they kept the apparatus at the house. But there was nothing about any other property among their papers.'

'You looked?'

'Yes.' I took the bottle from my pocket and handed it carefully to Barak. 'There was a pool of this stuff on the floor. It's almost colourless, has no smell, but if you taste it you get a kick like a mule.'

He unstoppered the bottle and sniffed the contents, then put a little on his fingers. He touched it to his tongue and made a grimace. 'Jesu, you're right!' he said. 'It's not Greek Fire, though. That had a fearsome stink.'

I took the bottle back, stoppered it and shook it gently, watching the colourless liquid swirl within. 'I want to take this to Guy.'

'I'll come with you.'

'As you will.'

'We've so little time,' Barak said. 'Are you sure we need to go to Barty's with that librarian tomorrow? Could you not see him at his chantry?'

'No. I need to go back to where it all started. We'll go to Barty's, then to see Guy and to the whorehouse in Southwark to see if that girl has anything to say. I've my interview with the Wentworths as well.' I sighed.

'Ten days.' He shook his head.

'Barak,' I said, 'you would rush at things too much if it was left to you.'

'We need this finished. And don't forget how we were followed yesterday,' he added gloomily. 'We might be in danger too.'

'I know that only too well.' I stood up. 'And now I am going to look at more of those old papers.'

NEXT MORNING, the 31st of May, was hotter than ever. Once more we left early on horseback. Barak had gone out again the evening before and I had been asleep when he returned. At breakfast he seemed in a surly mood; perhaps he had a hangover. I packed a couple of the alchemical books into a battered old leather satchel. I wanted Guy to look at them later.

The City was coming to life after the Sunday rest; shutters clattered as the shopkeepers made ready for the new week, shifting beggars from their doorways with curses.

'Did you manage to ferret any more out of those old papers last night?' Barak asked.

'There is reference to a liquid being used in Rome's wars in Babylonia. There are books on the Roman wars at Lincoln's Inn; I'll try to find them.'

'So long as it doesn't take too much time.'

Smithfield was quiet this morning, for it was not one of the cattle market days. To one side stood the hospital of St Bartholomew's, silent and empty, an Augmentations guard at the gate. The monastery stood at right angles to the hospital, dominating the square. Here too a guard stood outside the gatehouse. We rode across the open space, dismounted and tied the horses to a post, then went over to the fat watchman at the gatehouse.

'We have business here,' I said. 'We are due to meet a Master Kytchyn.'

'Lord Cromwell's business,' Barak added.

The man nodded. 'The fellow you want is here already, I allowed him into the church.' He studied us closely, eyes alert with curiosity.

I walked up to the gateway. The guard stepped aside and let us through.

The scene that met my eyes on the other side of the gatehouse made me stop dead. The nave of the great church and most of the neighbouring cloisters had been pulled down, leaving only a gigantic pile of rubble. I could see beyond to the prior's house, the fine dwelling Sir Richard Rich had bought. I had seen monastic houses brought down before—who had not in those days?—but not on this scale. A sinister silence hung over the wreckage.

Barak laughed and scratched his head. 'Not much left, is there?'

I followed Barak towards a door in the wooden barrier at the southern entrance of the church. I had a lifetime's contempt for these huge, rich monastic churches, yet as I stepped through the door I had to admit that what was left of the interior of St Bartholomew's church was magnificent. The walls soared in a series of pillared arches, richly painted in greens and ochres, up to a row of stained-glass windows. Near the top of the church stood a tall, grey-haired man of about fifty in a white clerical cassock.

'Master Kytchyn?' I called as we drew near.

'Aye. Master Shardlake?' He cast a nervous look at Barak, making me wonder if he had been rough with Kytchyn the day before.

'I want to see the place where a certain Master Gristwood discovered something last year.'

'Yes, sir.' He swallowed, still looking frightened. 'Master Gristwood said to say no word of what we found, on pain of death, and I haven't, I swear. Sir, is it true what this man told me? Master Gristwood has been murdered?'

'It is.' I looked around. 'I gather all this began when the Augmentations men found something in the church crypt last autumn?'

Kytchyn nodded. 'Yes. When the priory surrendered, they came to take an inventory. I was in the library when Master Gristwood came in. He asked if there was any record that might help with something they had found down in the crypt. I knew of nothing kept there apart from old lumber, though I'd been librarian twenty years. I asked Master Gristwood if he might show me what they had found and they brought me here to the church.'

'Which part of the church was the crypt in?'

'Over by yonder wall.'

I smiled reassuringly. 'Come, I would have a look.'

Kytchyn lit a candle then led us to an iron-studded door and down a flight of steps into a dark crypt running the length of the church. The candle illuminated pieces of lumber and broken statuary.

Kytchyn came to a halt by a wall. 'They brought me here, sir,' he said. 'There was a barrel standing by the wall. You can see the mark in the dust.'

He lowered the candle and I saw a circle in the dust on the stone flags.

I nodded and stood up again. 'Had it been opened?' I asked.

'Yes. One of the Augmentations men was there, holding a chisel he'd used to prise the lid off. He lifted the lid for me.'

'And what was inside?' I asked.

'Nothing but blackness,' he replied. 'And a dreadful smell, like nothing I'd ever known before. Sharp, with a strange sweetness, like something rotting yet lifeless too. It caught my throat and made me cough.'

'That's what I smelt,' Barak said. 'You've caught it well, fellow.'

Kytchyn swallowed. 'I lifted my candle over the barrel. The darkness inside reflected the light. It was so strange I nearly dropped the candle into it.'

Barak laughed. 'God's death, it's as well you didn't.'

'So it was dark, black,' I mused. 'That explains why one of the names the ancients had was Dark Fire.'

'I saw it was a liquid. I touched my finger to it.' Kytchyn shuddered. 'It had a horrible feel, thick and slimy. They pointed to the plaque with St John's name on, which showed it had been there a hundred years. I said there might be some record of it in the library. Master Gristwood ordered his man to seal the barrel up again, then came back to the library with me.'

'Let's go there too,' I said. 'I can see you would like to be out of here.'

We made our way back to the church, then out into the sunlight. Kytchyn led us across the back garden of the prior's house. We were halfway across when a door opened and a small man came out. I drew a sharp breath, for I recognised Sir Richard Rich at once. I had been introduced to him at a function at the Inn.

'Shit,' Barak murmured under his breath, then bowed low as Rich came over. I bowed too, as did Kytchyn, whose eyes had widened with fear.

'Brother Shardlake,' Rich said in a tone of amused surprise.

'You remember me, sir?'

'I never forget a hunchback.' He smiled coldly. 'Now then, what are you doing in my garden? Ah, the former Brother Bernard, is it not?'

'Sir . . . I . . . sir . . .' Poor Kytchyn was tongue-tied.

I spoke up, trying to make my tone as light as Sir Richard's. 'Master Kytchyn is showing us the library. Lord Cromwell said I might see it.'

Rich inclined his head. 'There are no books left, Brother, my Augmentations men have burned them all.' He smiled mockingly at poor Kytchyn.

'It was the design, My Lord,' I said. 'I am thinking of building a library.'

'By God's wounds, you must be doing well at Lincoln's Inn.' Rich's eyes narrowed. 'Well, if the earl says you may look at the library I suppose you may. But ask permission if you wish to walk though my garden again, Shardlake.' Without another word he went back indoors.

Kytchyn turned and led us rapidly away to a gate in the wall.

'I knew it was a bad idea to come here,' Barak said. 'My master said Rich was to know nothing.'

'We didn't tell him anything,' I said uncomfortably.

'He's curious. Don't look, but he's watching us through the window.'

Kytchyn led us through the gate onto a lawn surrounded on three sides by roofless buildings. He pointed. 'The library's there, next to the infirmary.'

We followed him into what must once have been a large, imposing library. Empty shelving covered the walls to a height of two storeys, and the floor was strewn with broken cupboards and torn manuscripts. I looked up to where a few roofbeams still stood. A flock of crows took off, cawing. They circled and settled again. Through a glassless window I caught a glimpse of a lawned close with houses beyond.

'So,' I asked, 'when you came here with Gristwood, what did you find?'

'Any papers left by those who died in the hospital were filed away. There were some under the name of that soldier St John, and Master Gristwood took them all. Then the next day he came back and spent a whole afternoon here, looking up any references to Byzantium and Greek Fire.'

'How did you know that was what he was after?'

'He got me to help him. He took more papers and some books. He never brought them back. Soon after the shelves were cleared, everything burned.'

There was a sudden clatter of wings as the crows took off again. They circled above, cawing noisily. 'What made them do that?' Barak muttered.

'Did you look at any of the papers you helped Master Gristwood find?'

'No, sir. I didn't want to know.' He looked at me seriously. 'I am not a bold man, sir. All I want is to be left to my prayers.'

'I understand. Do you know what happened to the barrel?'

'Master Gristwood had it taken away on a cart, I don't know where.' Kytchyn lifted his hand to open the collar of his surplice. 'Excuse me, sir, it's so hot . . .' As he spoke he took a sideways step. I heard a faint click.

Kytchyn's gesture saved my life. Suddenly he jerked forward with a scream, and to my horror I saw a crossbow bolt embedded in his upper arm, blood welling red over his white surplice.

Barak drew his sword and ran to the window. The pock-faced man who had followed us from Cromwell's house was standing outside it, fitting a new bolt to his crossbow. Seeing Barak almost on him, the man dropped the weapon and fled across the yard. Barak threw himself over the windowsill, but the man was already clambering up the abbey wall and disappeared over the top. Barak climbed up and looked at the street for a moment before letting himself down. He picked up his sword and sheathed it, walked back to the window and climbed through again. His face was like thunder.

I bent to comfort Kytchyn. He had crumpled to the floor, clutching his arm and sobbing as the blood welled between his fingers. 'I wish I'd never seen those papers,' he moaned. 'I know nothing, sir, nothing. I swear.'

Barak knelt down, lifting Kytchyn's hand from his wound. 'Come, let's see.' He studied the arm. 'It's all right, the head of the bolt's come out the other side. You need a surgeon to snap it off, that's all.' Barak took a hand-kerchief from his pocket and bound the arm tight above the wound.

'I think that bolt was aimed at me,' I said slowly. 'It would have hit me if Kytchyn had not moved when he did.'

'Aye, you're right,' Barak said grimly. 'How did he know we were here?'

'Perhaps we were followed from the house.'

'I'll take Kytchyn to the surgeon, then I'll have a little word with someone. Stand away from the window. I'll not be long.'

I was too shocked to do anything but nod obediently. I leaned against the wall as Barak lifted Kytchyn to his feet and helped him outside. My heart was thudding, my body cold with sweat.

A few minutes later the fat watchman was propelled through the doorway, protesting loudly. Large as the man was, Barak had his arm pinned behind him. He released him and sent him spinning across the room. The man fell with a crash among the debris.

'You've no right!' he shouted. 'When Augmentations hear about this—'

'Pox on Augmentations!' Barak shouted. He hauled the watchman to his feet again, then held his dagger to the fellow's flabby throat. 'Listen to me. I serve the Earl of Essex and I've authority to take what measures I like. Like slitting your weasand-pipe, see?' Barak jerked the man's head round to face me. 'That priest I brought out just now was struck by a crossbow bolt intended for my master there, Lord Cromwell's lawyer. And the only person who could have let him in was you, arsehole. So talk.'

The watchman gulped. 'Shortly after you arrived, sir, another man came up to me. A strange-looking fellow, he's had the smallpox. He held up a gold angel and asked what the two of you were doing here. I told him you were meeting someone. He offered me the angel to let him in.'

'Let's see it.'

The watchman fumbled in his belt and produced the big gold coin. Barak grabbed it. 'Right, I'll have that. It'll pay for our friend's surgeon. Now, this man. Was he carrying anything? A crossbow, for example?'

'I didn't see a crossbow,' the man whined. 'He had a big satchel, I didn't know what was in it.'

Barak stepped away from him. 'Get out, then, you great bag of guts. And don't say a word. Gabble about this and Lord Cromwell will be after you.'

He cringed at that. 'I'd not do anything against the earl, sir—'

'Get out!' Barak twirled him round and helped him through the doorway with a kick. He turned to me. 'I'm sorry I let Pock-face get so close,' he said. 'I dropped my guard. By Jesu, he's good. Are you all right?'

I took a deep breath and dusted down my robe. 'Yes.'

'I'll have to get word of this to the earl. He's at Whitehall. Come with me.'

I shook my head. 'I can't, Barak. I have my appointment with Joseph. I can't miss that; I'm still responsible for Elizabeth. Then I want to see Guy.'

'All right. I'll meet you outside the apothecary's in four hours, say at one o'clock, and we can go on to Southwark.'

'Very well,' I said. 'Come, we can ride together as far as Cheapside.'

At CHEAPSIDE, Barak turned south. I rode between the rows of stalls, keeping a careful eye out, then turned up Walbrook Road, where many merchants' houses stood. A little way up the street I saw Joseph pacing up and down. I dismounted and shook his hand. He looked strained and tired.

'I have been to see Elizabeth again this morning.' He shook his head. 'Still she says nothing, just lies there, paler and thinner each time.'

I took a deep breath. 'Well, shall we face your family?'

He set his jaw. 'I am ready, sir.'

Then so must I be, I thought. Taking Chancery's reins, I followed Joseph to an imposing new house. He knocked at the front door.

It was answered by a tall, dark-haired fellow of about thirty. He raised his eyebrows. 'You! Sir Edwin said you would be calling.'

Joseph reddened at the steward's insolent manner. 'Is he in, Needler?'

'Aye.'

'Can someone stable my horse?' I asked.

The steward called to a boy to take the animal, then led us through a wide hallway and up a carved staircase. We followed him into a richly appointed parlour where four people dressed in black sat on cushioned chairs, Sir Edwin Wentworth the only man among them. He stared at me, eyes hard with anger. His two daughters sat together: they were as pretty as Joseph had described, both with fair hair, milky complexions and startlingly large cornflower-blue eyes. Joseph's mother sat straight in her chair, white hair gathered under a black cap, veiny hands folded over a stick. Wrinkled eyelids were closed for ever over her decayed eyes. She should have been a pitiful figure, but somehow she dominated the room.

She was the first to speak. 'Is that the lawyer come with Joseph?' she asked in a clear voice with a trace of a country accent.

'Yes, Mother.' Edwin cast me a look of distaste.

She smiled crookedly. 'The seeker after truth.' She waved a hand at her son. 'Answer his questions, Edwin,' she said. 'Tell him everything.'

'Am I right,' Sir Edwin asked, 'that if you think Elizabeth is guilty you will cease to represent her? That those are the rules of your trade?'

'Not quite, sir,' I replied. 'If I *know* she is guilty, then I must and shall cease my representation.'

'Of course she is guilty!' Sir Edwin said fiercely. 'You didn't have her in your house nine months, sir, or see the viciousness she was capable of!'

'Can you tell me more about that?' I asked.

Sir Edwin sighed angrily. 'She was surly from the day she came, after my brother's funeral. We were prepared to make allowances as she'd lost everything. I was prepared to share all I had and I am not a poor man. I told the girls to make her welcome, teach her the lute and virginal, take her out visiting. Much thanks they got. Tell him, Sabine.'

The older girl turned her doll-like eyes on me. 'She was horrible to us, sir,' she said. 'She said she had more to do than tinkle on a music box.'

'We offered to take her to call on our friends,' Avice added. 'To banquets, to meet young gentlemen, but after one or two visits she said she didn't want to come again, called our friends mannered fools.'

'We did *try*, sir,' Sabine said earnestly.

'I know you did, girls,' their grandmother said. 'You did all you could.' She leaned forward. 'More and more she seemed to hate us. At meals you couldn't get a civil word from her. In the end she said she'd take her food in her room and we let her; her presence spoiled our meals.'

The old woman turned to Sir Edwin. 'Tell him how Elizabeth treated Ralph,' she said.

The mercer glared at Joseph, then at me. 'To begin with they seemed to get on well: she went for a couple of walks with him; they played chess together. But then she turned against him too. I remember one evening before dinner, about a month after she came, Ralph asked Elizabeth to play a game of chess. She agreed, though in a surly way. He was soon winning. He took her rook, and said, "There, I have him. That rook will peck out no more eyes from my men." And Elizabeth threw the board up in the air with a cry of anger and landed Ralph a great clout on the head. She left him sobbing and ran to her room.'

'They may say Elizabeth is mad,' the old woman said. 'But I say it was wicked jealousy, jealousy because her cousins were more accomplished than her.' She turned her face to me. 'Well, Master Shardlake, you have heard us. Do you still doubt Elizabeth threw Ralph down that well?'

I avoided a reply. 'You were here on that day, madam?'

'I was in my room. Needler ran up and told me what had happened. It was I ordered him to go down the well. I felt Ralph's poor dead face when he brought him up.' Her harsh features softened for a moment.

I turned to the girls. 'You agree with what your father and grandmother have said?'

'Yes, sir,' Avice said.

'I wish it were not so,' Sabine added. She rubbed her eyes. 'Grandam,' she said meekly, 'my vision is blurred. Do I have to use the nightshade?'

'Belladonna is good, child. By expanding your pupils, it makes you look more comely. But perhaps a smaller dose.'

I looked at the old woman with distaste. I had heard of drops of deadly nightshade being used for cosmetic purposes, but it was poisonous stuff.

I stood up. 'I wonder if I might see Elizabeth's room, and perhaps the garden, before I go? It will only take a few minutes.'

'This is too much—' Sir Edwin began.

His mother interrupted. 'Get Needler to take him, and Joseph too, then they can both leave. We will not have Joseph in our house again after today.'

'Mother . . .' Joseph had risen and taken a step towards the old woman, but she turned her head abruptly away.

Sir Edwin gave him an angry look, then rang a bell for the steward.

'Needler,' Sir Edwin said, when he entered, 'Master Shardlake wishes to visit the room that was Elizabeth's, and the garden. Show them, then show them out.'

'Yes, Sir Edwin.' Needler's manner was obsequious.

Neither Sir Edwin nor his mother made any move to say farewell, and the girls lowered their heads, though not before I saw Sabine glance at Needler and redden. I wondered if she could have a fancy for the boor.

The steward led us out, closing the door with a snap. He led us up a further flight of stairs, unlocked a door and we passed inside.

Whatever else had happened to her in that house, Elizabeth had had a fine room. There was a four-poster bed with a feather mattress, a dressing table with a looking glass, and chests for her clothes. Some books stood on a shelf above the dressing table: Tyndale's *Obedience of a Christian Man*, the Coverdale New Testament, and several devotional works.

'Is Elizabeth a religious girl?' I asked Joseph.

'A good Bible Christian like all the Wentworths. She liked to read.'

'Did Elizabeth have a maidservant?' I asked Needler.

'Wouldn't have one, sir. Said the servants mocked her.'

'What happened to Grizzy?' Joseph asked suddenly. He pointed at a basket in the corner, filled with straw. 'Elizabeth's old cat,' he explained.

'It ran away,' Needler said. 'Cats do when they come to a strange house.' Joseph nodded sadly. 'She was devoted to it.'

So she was deprived even of that company, I thought. I indicated I had seen enough and we left the chamber. Needler took us downstairs again, through a side door and into the garden. He led us across the lawn, then paused at the well and pointed to the bench, shaded by the large oak.

'She was sitting there when I came out after I heard the young mistresses screaming. They were standing by the well, wringing their hands. "Ralph's gone," Mistress Sabine screamed at me. "Elizabeth's put him in the well."'

'And Elizabeth said nothing?'

'Just sat there with her head bowed, a dark look on her face.'

I went over to the well. Joseph hung back. A round wooden board was fixed over it, secured by padlocks to metal rings driven into the brickwork.

'This looks newly done.'

'Yes, sir. The master had the cap put on last week. Bit late really.'

'I would like to see inside. Do you have keys to those locks?'

'Sir Edwin ordered them thrown away, sir. Nobody will be using that well again. The water's been poisoned for years. Not that there was any when I climbed down; we've had so little rain this spring.'

I bent down. There was a space of an inch or so between the wood and the rim on one side. I bent close and then pulled back at the smell that came from the gap; it was the stench of something dead, rotting. I turned to

Needler. 'There's a mighty stink coming from that well. How did it smell when you went down there?'

'Bad enough.' He shrugged. 'But I wasn't worrying about smells; I was feeling for poor Master Ralph's body.'

'Thank you, I have seen all I need. Now, Joseph, we should go.'

Joseph followed me back to the hall and into the street. The steward said he would have my horse brought round, then closed the door with a snap.

As we stood waiting on the step, Joseph gave me a direct look. 'Do you believe Elizabeth is guilty now, as my mother said?'

'No, Joseph, I think that she is innocent.' I frowned. 'There is something wrong in that house. It is interesting she only seems to have become hostile if a family member approached her. Otherwise she wished only to be left alone.' I saw from a church clock it was well past twelve and touched his arm. 'Once again I fear I must leave you, my friend. Another appointment I cannot miss. I will think what to do next. Can I reach you at your lodgings?'

'Aye, I'll be there until this matter is resolved,' he said firmly.

The boy appeared round the side of the house, leading Chancery. I gave him a farthing, straightened my satchel and mounted.

'I will be in touch, Joseph, very soon.'

Joseph shook my hand. I looked after him as he walked away down Walbrook Road, something oddly indomitable in his big, heavy figure.

ChAPTER FIVE

There was no sign of Barak's horse outside Guy's shop. Wondering whether he was still with Cromwell, I tied Chancery to the rail and went in. Guy was at his table, grinding herbs in a mortar, and looked up in surprise.

'Ho, Matthew. I did not expect to see you today.'

'Guy, I have a favour to ask, some information.' I slipped the satchel from my back, wincing a little at a stab of pain.

'You seem strung tight as a bowstring, Matthew.'

I sat down. 'Not surprising, as someone has just tried to kill me.'

'What?'

'I can't tell you all, but Lord Cromwell has spared Elizabeth Wentworth from the press for two weeks provided I undertake a mission for him—' I broke off, looking through the window. 'A young fellow named Barak, who I see tying his horse up outside, has been deputed by Cromwell to assist me.'

'Then the help you want is for Cromwell?' Guy looked at me seriously.

'To help to catch a brutal killer. I am not allowed to say more—I should not even have mentioned Cromwell's name. It is too dangerous.' I sighed. 'I will not press you if you feel you cannot in conscience help.'

The door opened and Barak came in. He looked at the bottles and jars lining the walls, then at Guy with his dark face and apothecary's robes.

Guy bowed. 'Master Barak, I pray you are well. Would you like a small beer?'

'Thank you, Master Apothecary,' Barak answered. 'It is a hot day.'

Guy went out to fetch it and Barak came over to me. 'The earl's worried. He's had Kytchyn taken to a place of safety till this is over. He says you're being too slow. There are only ten days till the demonstration.'

'Perhaps he should seek a miracle worker then.'

Barak stepped away as Guy returned, bearing two cups of small beer. I drank gratefully, for I was very thirsty.

'Well, then,' Guy said quietly. 'What help do you both wish from me?'

'We have to deal with alchemists,' I said. 'I know nothing of their trade, and would welcome your advice.' I carefully took the bottle from my pocket and held it out. 'Have you any idea what this strange stuff might be?'

He opened it carefully, then poured some on his finger and sniffed. 'Be careful, it burns like fire,' I warned as he bent and touched his tongue to it.

To my surprise, he laughed. 'There's no mystery here,' he said. 'This is aqua vitae, though distilled to a very high concentration.'

'Aqua vitae?' I laughed with astonishment. 'This new stuff that is distilled from bad wine and prescribed for sore eyes and melancholia?'

'The same. I think its value overrated; it just makes people drunk. A cupful, they say, will blind a horse.' He paused. 'The thickness and fiery taste suggest a very strong concentration. I may even be able to tell you where it came from. A few months ago we heard at the Apothecaries' Hall of a cargo that had been landed at Billingsgate from a ship that had ventured into the Baltic trade. They brought back a cargo of a colourless liquid they say men drink there. When people tried quaffing it here, as they would beer, it made them very sick. This sounds like the stuff.'

'What happened to the cargo?'

'One of my brethren went after it as a curiosity, but was told it had been sold. You would need to enquire among the sailors' taverns to find more.'

I nodded thoughtfully. 'What do you know of alchemy, Guy?' I asked. I took the alchemy books from my satchel and laid them on the table. 'These books are so full of mysteries and jargon I can scarce understand a word.'

He picked one up and leafed through it. 'Alchemy is part of natural science, the study of the world around us. God has left signs and clues in the world, that by struggling we might come to understand things: cure diseases, grow better crops—'

'Turn lead into gold?' I hesitated. 'Set water on fire?'

'Perhaps. And the task of alchemy is to read those clues. For each rogue who claims to have found the philosopher's stone that can turn base metal into gold there is another who makes real achievements by study of how the four elements of earth, air, fire and water interact to make the substances we know, and how they change. How heat can change one thing into another— wine into aqua vitae, for example. Or how to melt down ores in the furnace in such a way as to produce better iron, as they are doing in the Weald now.'

Something had stirred a memory. 'A furnace, you said. So alchemists must often work with founders, as they all have furnaces.'

'Of course,' Guy agreed. 'To melt ores and metals a furnace would be needed.' He frowned. 'What has this to do with this case of yours, Matthew?'

'I'm not sure.' I frowned in thought. 'A founder would also be needed to make, say, a large metal tank with a pump and pipes.'

'Yes. Alchemists often have arrangements with the Lothbury founders. It has to be someone they trust, of course, if they're to share their secrets.'

Guy looked at me wryly. 'Your eyes are alight, Matthew, alight with the prospect of progress in your chase. May I keep these books, by the way? I should be interested to look through them.'

'Please do.'

I turned to Barak excitedly. 'I am going to Wolf's Lane to ask Goodwife Gristwood if she knew whether Michael and Septimus were visiting the founders. You can go up to the Guildhall and ask for details of all the founders they employ on the conduits. I'll meet you at the Steelyard Steps in an hour and a half.'

THE GRISTWOODS' HOUSE was unchanged, the split and broken front door still in place. I knocked and Goodwife Gristwood herself opened the door.

She stared at me wearily. 'You again?'

'Yes, madam. May I come in?'

She shrugged and held the door open. 'Susan's gone,' she said.

'Where's the watchman?'

'Drinking and farting in the kitchen.' She led me into the dowdy parlour.

'I have a query, madam. I believe Sepultus may have worked with a founder in his recent experiments.'

The frightened look that came into her face told me I had hit the mark. Her voice rose. 'I've told you: I'd no interest in his mad doings beyond worrying he'd blow up the house. Why are you asking me these questions?'

'You are keeping something back, madam,' I said. 'I must know what it is.'

But she had stopped listening. She was staring out at the garden, her eyes wide. 'It's him again,' she whispered.

I whirled round. A gate in the wall was open and a man stood there, a stocky, dark-haired young fellow. Seeing us looking, he turned and fled. I turned back to Goodwife Gristwood. She had sat down at the table and was crying, her thin body wrenched with sobs. I waited until she calmed down.

'You know who that man was, madam?' I asked sternly.

She raised a piteous face to me. 'No! No! I saw him watching the house yesterday afternoon. He's one of the men who killed Michael, isn't he?'

'I don't know, madam. But you should tell your watchman.'

'This is punishment for my sin,' she whispered. 'God is punishing me.'

'What sin?' I asked sharply.

She took a deep breath, then looked me hard in the eye. 'When I was young, Master Shardlake, I was a plain girl. Plain, but full of base lusts and when I was fifteen I romped with an apprentice. I had a child.'

'Ah.'

'I had to give him away and confess my sin in church, Sunday after Sunday. I was thirty before I found anyone to marry me. Or rather, father did. Father was a carpenter and Michael advised him once over an unpaid debt. Michael had a few unpaid bills himself, and my dowry saved him from debtors' prison.' She sighed. 'But God does not forget a sin, does he? He goes on punishing, *punishing*.' She balled her rough hands into fists.

'The founder,' I said.

'They made me give my son away to the nuns at St Helen's. The nuns wouldn't let me near, but I bribed a washerwoman to give me news. When he was fourteen the nuns got him an apprenticeship as a founder. And then, when he was free of the nuns, I made myself known to David. I've visited him every week since then.' She smiled then, a triumphant little smile.

'And then Sepultus took house with you and was looking for a founder?'

She nodded. 'I didn't tell you because I didn't want David involved in this.'

'Madam, your son could be in danger if others know of his involvement.'

She half rose. 'Danger? David in danger?'

I nodded. 'But if you tell me where he is, Lord Cromwell will protect him.'

She spoke quickly. 'His name is David Harper. It was my maiden name. He is junior to another man, Peter Leighton of Lothbury. It was Leighton that Sepultus worked with.'

'I must see David and this man Leighton.'

She stood up. 'I'll go to David now. Warn him. Can I send word to you?'

I nodded and gave her my address.

'You will help us, sir?' she asked tremulously, all her harshness gone.

'I will do all I can, I promise. And I will see that watchman of yours, make sure he stays alert. Take him to Lothbury with you. Keep all your doors locked.' I remembered the crossbow. 'And shutter the windows.'

'But it's so hot—'

'It would be safer.' Pock-face and now the young man outside; I remembered the two sets of bloody footsteps. I had known there were two of them.

It was a relief to reach the river stairs. The tide was full, and a welcome breeze came off the river. There was no sign of Barak, so I left Chancery at the stables and hitched my satchel over my shoulder.

There was a touch at my shoulder; I turned to see Barak there.

'Did you find anything at the Guildhall?' I asked.

'Aye, I got a list of names of founders who work on the conduits.'

'And I got the information I needed from Goodwife Gristwood.' I told him all she had said. He passed me the list and I nodded. Peter Leighton's name was prominent. 'That's useful. It confirms we're on the right track.'

'I called in at the Old Barge, too,' Barak said. 'There's a note from Cromwell's clerk. Bealknap does a little work for some French merchants—routine stuff declaring imports at the Custom House. But the link is dangerous. Imagine French fire ships sailing up the Thames.'

'I'd rather not.' I studied him. 'You know I visited the Wentworths earlier?'

'Aye.'

'Are you any good at picking locks?'

He raised his eyebrows. 'Passing fair.'

'I thought you might be.' I told him what had passed at Sir Edwin's.

He whistled when I told him of the stink coming from the well.

'I want us to break into the garden at night and get those locks off. Then

I'd like you to climb down and take a look. We'll need a rope ladder.'

He laughed. 'God's death, you don't ask much, do you?'

'Less than the earl has asked of me. Well? It was part of the bargain, Barak, that you'd help me with the Wentworths.'

'All right, I'll do it.'

Just then a wherry with a canopy pulled up at the wharf, depositing a pair of Flemish merchants on the steps. Barak and I took their places and the wherryman pulled away.

'Is it tomorrow you've got your case against Bealknap?' Barak asked.

'Don't remind me. I'll have to spend tonight preparing.'

I jumped at the sudden, piercing sound of a trumpet. The boats in the middle of the river rowed frantically out of the way as an enormous canopied barge painted in gold appeared, a dozen oarsmen in the king's livery making rapid sweeps through the water in time to the beating of a drum. Our little wherry bobbed wildly in the royal barge's wake as, like everyone else in the boats, we doffed our caps and bowed our heads. The king's canopy was drawn shut as the barge swept upriver to Whitehall. I wondered if Cromwell was in there with him, or perhaps Catherine Howard.

The wherry dropped us at St Mary Overy Steps on the Southwark side. I followed Barak up to the wharf and Winchester Palace came into view as we mounted the slippery stairs. The Bishop of Winchester owned most of Southwark, including the brothels, and the palace was his London residence.

Barak made off confidently along the side of the high palace wall towards the warren of poor houses that lay to the east. I followed.

'The Winchester geese can be shy birds if they think you're anything official,' Barak told me. 'Take off your robe—it'll scare them. We'll pretend we're customers. I'm your servant that's brought you over for a bit of fun.'

I took off my robe and stuffed it in my satchel. It was a relief to be rid of it.

'When we're inside I'll ask for Bathsheba Green, say she's been recommended, then you get her alone and question her.'

We passed into a warren of small timber-framed houses, the unpaved lanes stinking with refuse. In accordance with Southwark regulations the brothels were painted white. Each had a sign outside with a lewd reference: a naked Adam and Eve or a bed or a nightshirt. We stopped before a house where the paint was flaking, a bishop's hat crudely painted on the sign. Shutters were drawn over the windows. Barak knocked on the door.

It was opened by a middle-aged woman. She was short and stocky, with a square ugly face and curly red wig. She had been branded as a whore in

London at some point, for a dark 'W' stood out on her white cheek.

'Good day, Mistress.' Barak smiled. 'I've brought my master over from the City; he's a taste for a quiet house.'

She looked me over, then nodded. 'Come in.'

We followed her into a hot, dark room, with a fug of unwashed bodies and cheap tallow candles. A thin boy in a greasy jerkin stood by a cupboard, holding a jar of beer. The madam nodded to the boy, who poured two mugs of beer and set them on the table. She smiled at us, showing decayed teeth.

'Make yourselves comfortable. I'll get a couple of the girls to join us.'

'Only a girl for my master,' Barak said. 'He's a shy fellow, wants a girl to treat him softly. We've heard of a girl called Bathsheba who works here.'

Her eyes narrowed at once. 'Who told you that?'

'Someone at one of the Guildhall lunches,' I replied. 'I like a gentle girl and he said Bathsheba was kindly. I'd pay more for a gentle girl.'

'I'll see.' She disappeared through an inner door, and soon I heard her call from within the house. 'Daniel, here!' The boy ran from the room. A minute later the madam returned. 'Bathsheba will see you in her room, sir.'

I rose from the table, trying to look enthusiastic. The madam led me down a corridor with several closed doors, then knocked at one of them.

'Here's Bathsheba,' she said, ushering me in. She closed the door behind her, but I heard no retreating footsteps, and knew she was outside, listening.

The room was small and mean, the only furniture a cheap trunk and a truckle bed. A girl lay on the bed in a stained old dress, her black hair disordered on the greyish pillow. I had expected Bathsheba to be pretty, but although young she had heavy features. Her best features were her large, intelligent brown eyes, though they stared at me, I saw, with fear. She had a large bruise and a half-healed cut on one cheekbone.

'Well, Bathsheba,' I said quietly, 'I am told you are a gentle girl.'

'Who told you that, sir?' Her voice was scared, faltering.

'Someone I met at the Guildhall.'

'I've only had one customer of your class,' she said. 'And he is dead.' To my surprise I saw tears in the corners of her eyes. I studied her face a moment, then laid my satchel on the edge of the bed and sat down carefully.

'I swear I mean you no harm,' I said soothingly, 'but I am here to enquire into the death of Master Gristwood. I am a lawyer. I only want to know what he talked about with you. Did he mention his work?'

I saw her glance at the door.

'I know nothing,' she said, her voice trembling. 'I told the others—'

'What others?' I asked quickly.

Bathsheba pointed to her bruised cheek. 'The ones who gave me this.'

I heard heavy footsteps outside, then the door was flung open. Two men stepped into the room. One was a bald, hulking fellow carrying a club and the other a stocky young man whose features were so like Bathsheba's he could only be her brother. He was the man I had seen in the Gristwoods' yard. As I jumped up from the bed he pointed a dagger at my throat. I caught a glimpse of the madam's worried face before the big man shut the door.

'He hasn't hurt you, Sheba?' the young man asked, never taking his eyes from my face.

'No, George, but I was afraid the boy wouldn't find you in time. I kept him talking. About Michael again.'

'We've got you this time,' George snarled. 'You won't get away with hitting a defenceless woman.'

'There's a mistake, I swear. I never met this girl before today.'

'No, but your pock-faced mate did last week. He'd have killed her if one of the girls hadn't run for me.' He turned to his sister. 'Is it him in the other room? Or that confederate of his, with the wens on his nose?'

'Madam Neller says no. She's keeping him occupied.'

'A pock-faced man?' I asked. 'Tall and pale? Asking about Gristwood?'

'Aye, your confederate.'

'Please listen. That man is after me as well—he tried to kill me yesterday. I mean no harm; I wished only to ask Bathsheba about Master Gristwood—'

'He was asking the same questions,' Bathsheba said. 'About Michael's work. He says he's a lawyer.'

The young man stepped closer and held the dagger to my neck. 'If you're a lawyer, you're working for somebody. Who is it?'

'Lord Cromwell,' I replied. 'My assistant has his seal.'

'Oh, George,' Bathsheba groaned, 'what have we done?'

The brother grabbed my arm and slammed me against the far wall, the knifepoint pressed against my throat. 'Why? How is he involved in this?'

There was a yell from the madam standing outside, then a loud crash. The man with the club staggered across the room as the door was flung open. He landed on the bed. Barak lunged in and brought his sword down on George Green's knife arm. Green yelled, dropping the dagger.

'You all right?' Barak asked me.

I gasped. 'Yes—'

'I heard these fellows in the hallway.' He turned to George, who was gripping his arm, blood running through his fingers. 'You'll be all right. I could've had your arm off, but I didn't. In return you can do some talking—'

'Look out!' I shouted.

The big man had jumped up from the bed and raised his club, ready to smash it down on Barak's head. I threw myself at him and he staggered against the wall. As Barak turned, George grabbed his sister by the hand, threw open the shutters and jumped from the window, Bathsheba screaming as she followed him. The big man fled through the open doorway.

Barak ran to the window. 'Stay here!' he shouted, as he jumped after Bathsheba and her brother, who were disappearing round a corner.

I walked back to the front room, trying to gather my wits. The girls and their customers had gone. The madam sat at the table, her head in her hands.

'Well, lady?' I said.

She looked up, her expression despairing. 'Is this the end of my house?'

I sat down. 'Not necessarily. I want to know about Bathsheba's doings with Michael Gristwood, and the attack on her.'

'There were things that man told Bathsheba that worried her. He was in trouble of some sort.'

'Did you learn what trouble?'

'No, Bathsheba turned close as an oyster. Then Gristwood stopped coming. Bathsheba went across to Queenhithe to make enquiries and came back crying that he was dead. I told her she should go back to Hertford where she came from. But she didn't want to leave her brother.'

'They're close?'

'Close as can be. Then two men came to the house. They barged in with drawn swords, told the girls to get out and demanded Bathsheba.'

'And one of them was a tall man with the marks of smallpox?'

'Aye, and another ugly ruffian with him. The girls ran. I sent the boy for George, same as I did today. By the time he arrived with a dozen of his mates, they had Bathsheba in her room and the pock-faced one was beating her. But the wherrymen were too many for them and they ran.'

The door opened and Barak came in, breathless. 'They've got away,' he said, then glared at Madam Neller. 'What's the old troll got to say?'

'I'll tell you outside.' I got to my feet. I took out my purse and laid a gold half-angel on the table. 'There's two more if you let me know if Bathsheba returns, or if you find where she is. You will find me at Chancery Lane.'

'Very well,' she said, and grabbed the coins.

Barak and I left the place and walked back to the river stairs. The Thames was still thronged and there were no boats waiting. Barak sat down on the top step and I followed. I told him what the madam had said.

'By the way,' I added, 'thank you for saving my life back there.'

Barak smiled ruefully. 'And to you for saving mine.' He looked over the river. The sun was low, turning the water silver. 'Tomorrow's the 1st of June. Nine days left then.' He smiled wryly. 'You do need me, you see?'

I sighed heavily and met his gaze. 'Aye.'

BARAK AND I supped early at Chancery Lane. We talked little, exhausted by our adventure, but ate in a feeling of better fellowship. Barak left the table early to walk back to the City and spend his evening making enquiries round the taverns. Meanwhile I had the Bealknap case to prepare.

I worked on it for two hours, then I gathered my papers into my satchel and went across to the library at Lincoln's Inn. I wanted to follow up what one of the papers from St Bartholomew's had said about something like Greek Fire being known to the Romans years before the Byzantines.

Most windows were dark now but there was a yellow glow from the library window. I went in. The light came from the librarian's desk, where Master Rowley, a scholarly old fellow, was working surrounded by a little ring of candles. He got up and bowed as I approached.

'May I take a candle, Rowley? I have some books to find.'

He smiled eagerly. 'Anything I can help you find, Master Shardlake?'

'Not tonight, thank you.' I lifted a candle from the rack and lit it from one of those on Rowley's desk. Then I crossed to the shelf where works on Roman history were kept. I had a list of works the papers had referred to.

Every single book I needed was gone. I frowned, and walked back to Rowley's desk. He looked up with an enquiring smile.

'All the books I need have been taken out, Rowley. Every one on this list.' I handed it to him. 'Can you tell me who has them?'

'I'll see, sir,' he said. He consulted a paper, then took a deep breath and looked up at me again. 'No, sir. These have not been taken out. The clerk must have misplaced them, I'll have a search done tomorrow.'

In the uneasiness of his smile I knew the old fellow was lying. Yet I saw too that he was frightened.

'This is a serious business, Master Rowley. I need those books and they are valuable. I shall raise this with the keeper of the library.'

'If you must, sir,' he said, swallowing. Whoever Rowley was scared of, he was more frightened of them than of the keeper.

I turned and left him. Outside I clenched my fists and swore. Every turn I took someone else had been there first. But I had learned that what was in those books had a bearing on the Greek Fire story. I had other sources; I would go to the Guildhall library.

OVER BREAKFAST I told Barak about the missing books at Lincoln's Inn. In return he related what he had discovered during his evening touring the taverns. He had heard that the strange Baltic drink had been offered for sale at a riverside tavern in Billingsgate.

'I did some more asking after Pock-face and the man with the wens on his face, too. Nothing. They must be out-of-town men.'

Joan entered with a note. I tore open the seal.

'From Goodwife Gristwood. She'll meet us at Lothbury at twelve. If the case is heard on time we can make it by then.'

'I'll come to Westminster with you first, if you like.'

'Thank you,' I said. 'I will feel safer. Have you something in sober black?'

'Aye, I can look respectable when I need.'

We walked down to catch a boat at Temple Stairs. Early as it was, a little crowd had gathered along Fleet Street. I wondered what they were waiting for, then heard the grate of iron wheels on cobbles and a cry of 'Courage, brothers!' It was hanging day. We halted to let a big cart pass by, on its way to the big gallows at Tyburn. There were a dozen prisoners within, hands bound behind them. I saw the old woman and her son, who had been convicted of horse stealing. The young man was staring ahead, his face twitching, while his mother leancd against him. The cart passed creaking by.

'We'd better get on,' Barak said, shouldering his way through the crowd. 'I've never liked that sight,' he said quietly.

INSIDE WESTMINSTER HALL a row of barristers stood waiting at the wooden bar, beyond which lay the great table where the court officials sat. Under the tapestry of the royal arms the judge sat on his high chair, listening with a bored expression to a barrister. I was disconcerted to see that the judge was Heslop, who I knew had bought a number of monastic properties himself.

'Master Shardlake.' I turned to find Vervey, one of the Common Council attorneys, at my elbow. He was a clerkly, serious man of my own age, a stalwart reformer. I bowed. Evidently he had been sent to keep an eye on the case; it was important to the council.

'Heslop is fair racing through the cases,' he said. 'We shall soon be on,

Master Shardlake. Bealknap is here.' He nodded to where my adversary stood leaning on the bar with the other advocates, sleek in his robes.

I forced a smile and lifted my satchel from my shoulders. 'I am ready. Wait here, Barak.' I went through the partition, bowed to the bench and took a place at the bar. Bealknap turned round and I bowed briefly. A few minutes later an usher called out, 'Common Council of London and Bealknap.'

I opened by saying the cesspit in dispute had been badly built and the sewage leaking into the tenement next door was making life miserable for the inhabitants. 'I have here half a dozen cases confirming the sovereignty of the Common Council over monastic properties in cases of nuisance, Your Honour.' I handed up copies and summarised their arguments.

Heslop nodded to my opponent. 'Brother Bealknap, what do you say?'

He rose with a confident smile. 'Your Honour,' he began, 'the going down of the monasteries has brought a glut of land to the market, and men of enterprise must make the best shift we can to turn our investments to a profit, or monastic sites will go to ruin and become the haunt of vagabonds.'

Heslop nodded. 'Aye, and the City will have to deal with them.'

'I have a case that I think will settle the matter to Your Honour's satisfaction.' Bealknap passed a paper up to the judge. '*Friars Preachers* versus *the Prior of Okeham*, Your Honour. A case of nuisance brought against the prior, remitted to the king's council as the monastery was under his jurisdiction. As all monastic houses are now. I submit therefore that when a question relating to the original charter arises, it must be submitted to the king.'

Heslop read slowly, nodding as he did so. I looked out over the crowd, then froze. Standing near the bar, a retainer on either side, was Sir Richard Rich, staring at me with grey eyes, cold as an icy sea.

Heslop looked up. 'Yes, Brother Bealknap. This case settles the matter.'

I rose. 'Your Honour, if I may answer. The cases I passed to you are both more numerous and later in time—'

Heslop shook his head. 'Brother Bealknap's case is the only one that deals directly with the issue of royal authority—'

'But Brother Bealknap *bought* this house; a contract intervenes—'

'I have a full list today, Brother. Judgment for the plaintiff, with costs.'

We left the court, Bealknap smiling. I glanced over to where Rich had stood, but he had disappeared. Why had he stared at me like that? I walked to where Vervey and Barak stood together.

'That was a monstrous decision,' Vervey said indignantly. 'It made a nonsense of the law.'

'Yes, it did. I am afraid my advice must be to take this matter to Chancery, expensive as that will be. Otherwise that judgment gives carte blanche to all purchasers of monastic properties in London to flout the City regulations. I am sorry, Master Vervey. I suspect the judge may have been bribed.'

'It would not surprise me,' Vervey replied. 'I know of Bealknap. Will you write to us with your recommendations as soon as may be?'

'Aye.'

Vervey bowed and disappeared into the throng. There was a stir in the crowd around us, and I turned to see Rich bearing down on me.

'Brother Shardlake and his ruffled-headed assistant.' He smiled at Barak. 'You should have a care to comb your hair, sir, before coming to court.'

Barak returned his stare evenly.

Rich turned to me. 'You need to teach that fellow manners, Brother Shardlake. And perhaps learn some yourself. You involve yourself in matters beyond your station. Stick to helping farmers with their land disputes.'

'What matters do you mean, Sir Richard?'

'You know,' he said. 'Don't play innocent with me. Take care or you'll suffer for it.' And with that he turned round and was gone.

There was a moment's silence. 'He knows,' Barak said, his voice low and intense. 'He knows about Greek Fire.'

'How? How could he?'

'I don't know, but he does. What else could he have meant?'

I frowned. 'But . . . if he threatens me, he threatens Cromwell.'

WE TOOK a wherry as far as Three Cranes Stairs, then walked north to Lothbury. Beside St Margaret's church, narrow lanes led off into a warren of little buildings from where a metallic clangour could be heard.

'Goodwife Gristwood will meet us at her son's foundry,' I said.

We turned into a narrow passageway between two-storey houses. Nearly all the houses had workshops attached; their doors were open and I could see men moving within, loading coal into glowing furnaces.

At length I halted in front of a small house. The workshop door was closed; Barak knocked twice. It was opened by a wiry young man wearing a heavy apron over a smock. He had Goodwife Gristwood's sharp features.

'Master Harper?' I asked.

'Aye.' He looked at us suspiciously.

'I am Master Shardlake.'

'Come in,' he replied in a less than friendly tone. 'Mother's here.'

I followed him into his little foundry. An unlit furnace dominated the room, a pile of charcoal beside it. A collection of pots was stacked by the door. On a stool in one corner Goodwife Gristwood sat.

She gave me a surly nod. 'Well, Master Lawyer,' she said. 'Here he is.'

Harper nodded at Barak. 'Who's that?' he asked me.

'My assistant. Your mother has told you we seek information about Michael and Sepultus's experiments?'

'Aye.' He sat down beside his mother. 'They told me they wanted to build something, a big watertight tank with a pump attached and a pipe leading off. That's beyond my capacity, but I do a lot of casting for Peter Leighton who works for the City repairing the conduits. I helped him cast the iron for the pipes and the tank.'

'When did the brothers first employ you?'

'November. It took till January to get the apparatus right.'

'The liquid that was to be put in the tank? Did you see anything of that?'

Harper shook his head. 'Michael said it was a secret. They did some tests in Master Leighton's yard. It has a high wall. They leased the whole yard from him and wouldn't let him near, though they paid him well for its use.'

'I would like to speak to Master Leighton,' I said. I looked at Harper. 'Can you take us to him?'

'And will that be the end of this business?' Goodwife Gristwood asked.

'You need be involved no further, madam.'

She nodded at her son. He rose and led the way outside. We walked up the lane, further into Lothbury. Harper stopped before a corner house, with a workshop next to it and a high wall beside that. He knocked at the door of the house. It was shuttered, as were the windows of the workshop. Harper tried the workshop doors, but they were locked.

'Master Leighton,' he called. 'It's David.' He turned to us apologetically. 'Many founders grow deaf in later years. But it's odd his furnace isn't lit.'

I had a sense of foreboding. 'When did you last see him?'

'Friday, sir. He told me he'd have some casting for me.'

Barak looked at the lock. 'I could have that open.'

'No,' Harper said. 'I know who has a key. Everyone has a neighbour's key in case of fire. Wait here.' He went off down the lane.

All around us the banging and clanging resounded in our ears. Goodwife Gristwood began twisting her hands together nervously.

Her son reappeared, a large key in his hands. He unlocked the door and we entered the yard. Blackened patches all over the walls caught my eye, larger than the ones I had seen in the Gristwoods' yard. Goodwife Gristwood and her son were standing nervously by the gate.

I gave David Harper a reassuring smile. 'Master Harper,' I said, 'tell me: does anything unusual strike you about this yard?'

He looked around. 'Only that it's been given a good clean recently.'

I nodded. 'That's what I thought. It's spotless. Come, I think we should have a look in the house.'

I led the way out of the yard. We knocked again at the house door, but still there was no sign of life. All around us the clanging continued.

'We can get in through the workshop,' Harper said. 'It's the same key.' He hesitated, then opened the workshop door and stepped inside calling, 'Master Leighton?' Barak followed him.

'I'll stay outside,' Goodwife Gristwood said nervously. 'Take care, David.'

I followed Barak in. David opened the shutters and I saw a cluttered workshop, some pipes and valves and pans and an empty furnace.

Set in one wall was a door to the house. Harper hesitated again, then inserted the key in the lock and opened it. Another darkened room.

I caught a slight, familiar tang and grabbed Barak's arm. 'Wait,' I said.

Harper opened the shutters and turned round. Then his mouth fell open. We were in a parlour, surprisingly well appointed, but it was in chaos. A cupboard lay on its side, silver plates scattered around.

'They got him too,' I whispered. 'They took the apparatus and killed him.'

'Then where's the body?' Barak asked.

'Somewhere in the house, maybe. I smell blood.'

Instructing Harper to stay where he was, Barak and I searched the rest of the founder's home. Everything was in order; only the parlour had been wrecked. We returned there to find David Harper had gone outside.

'They took the body with them,' I said. 'They didn't want a hue and cry about a murder in Lothbury.' I knelt and examined the floor. 'This part of the floor's been cleaned; there's no dust.' I saw a pair of flies buzzing round the overturned cupboard. 'Here, Barak, help me move this.'

Underneath the cupboard there was a patch of dried blood. Barak whistled.

'Where did they get the key?'

I looked over to the front door. 'They didn't break the door in. I guess they knocked, and when Leighton answered they shoved him inside and then killed him, and took the key from his body. Come, there's no more we can do here.' We rejoined Harper and Goodwife Gristwood in the street.

'Master Leighton is not there. I am afraid there are signs of violence . . .'

Goodwife Gristwood gave a little moan.

'Is the watchman still at your house, madam?' I asked.

'Aye, he brought me here, then I sent him back.'

I turned to Harper. 'I think your mother should stay with you for now. Tell no one where she is. I shall try to find somewhere safer for you both.'

The old woman gave me an appalled look. 'What did they do? For Jesu's sake, what did Michael and Sepultus *do* here?'

'Meddled with dangerous people.' I turned to David. 'Can you read?'

'Aye.'

I scribbled my address on a piece of paper. 'Ask around, would you, among the neighbours? Just say Leighton's missing. If you have any news, or require anything, you can reach me here.'

I INSISTED on stopping at a barber's for a shave in preparation for Lady Honor's banquet. Barak waited for me, then we caught a boat back to the Temple and walked home. I dozed for an hour and woke unrefreshed. I got up, feeling stiff, and for the first time in days did Guy's back exercises. I was trying to touch my toes, when there was a knock at the door.

Barak entered. 'That's a strange way to pray,' he said.

'I'm not praying. I'm trying to find some relief for my sore back. And haven't you the manners to be asked to enter a room before barging in?'

'Sorry.' Barak sat down cheerfully on the bed. 'I came to tell you I'm going out. An old acquaintance of mine has some information on Pock-face and his big mate. I'm going to meet him, then I'm going to see the earl.' His expression grew serious. 'Tell him about Rich. He may want to see you.'

I took a deep breath. 'Very well. You know where I'll be. And ask if he can find somewhere safe for the Gristwoods.'

Barak nodded. 'You'll have to ride to Lady Honor's house alone.'

'It is still light.'

'Do you want to have a crack at that well after the banquet?'

I shook my head. 'I'll be too tired. I have to pace myself, Barak,' I added irritably. 'I've more than ten years on you. Just how old are you, by the way?'

'Twenty-eight in August. Listen, make sure you question Lady Honor.'

'Of course I will,' I snapped.

Barak gave his sardonic smile. 'You're sweet on her; you're still a man of juice under all that learning.'

'You've a coarse tongue. Besides, as you pointed out yourself, she's out of my league.'

Barak got up. 'I must be gone,' he said briskly.

'And I should get ready. Good luck with the earl.'

As the door shut behind him, I turned to the window. The clouds were so heavy that although it was only late afternoon it was dim as dusk. Away over the Thames, a distant rumble of thunder sounded.

ChAPTER SIX

Lady Honor's house was in Blue Lion Street off Bishopsgate. It was a big old four-storey courtyard house, the front giving directly onto the street. I could see why it was known as the House of Glass: new diamond-paned windows had recently been put in along the whole frontage. The door was open, with liveried servants standing outside. I worried that I would appear an unsophisticated fellow, and pulled a little ruff of silk shirt above the collar of my best doublet to display the needlework.

A lad took Chancery's reins as I dismounted and another servant took me through the front door into a richly decorated hall that led to a large inner courtyard. Opposite, a large banqueting hall occupied the first floor, and candles flickered behind the open windows. The steward took me up a broad flight of stairs to a room where golden bowls of hot water were set out on a table with a pile of towels. Three men were already standing washing: a young fellow with the Mercers' Company badge on his doublet and an older man in a clerical robe. The third man was Gabriel Marchamount.

'Ah, Shardlake,' he said, a beaming smile on his broad face, 'I hope you have a sweet tooth. Lady Honor's banquets positively drip with sugar.'

'Not too sweet; I must watch my teeth.'

'Like me you still have a full set.' Marchamount shook his head. 'I cannot abide this fashion for women to blacken their teeth deliberately so people will think they live off nothing but fine sugar.'

'I agree. It is not pretty.'

'Women of Lady Honor's class, though, would disdain such effect.' He took a napkin from a pile and flung it over his shoulder; I followed his example and we went out to the banqueting chamber. Big tallow candles set in silver candleholders filled the room with a yellow glow. An enormous table dominated the room and serving men scurried to and fro, placing dishes and glasses on the broad buffet against one wall. As was the custom, I had brought my own dining knife, a silver one my father had given me.

The salt cellar, a foot high and particularly ornate, was set at the very top of the table, opposite a high chair thick with cushions. That meant nearly all the guests would be below the salt and therefore that a guest of the highest status was expected. I wondered if it might even be Cromwell.

Marchamount smiled and nodded round at the company. A dozen guests stood talking. Mayor Hollyes was there in his red robes of office. The other men mostly wore Mercers' Company livery, though there were a couple of clerics. And there were some wives in wide farthingales, wearing lead rouge to brighten their cheeks. Everyone was perspiring in the oppressive heat despite the open windows. A boy of about sixteen with long black hair and a thin, pale face was standing by himself in a corner, looking nervous.

'That's Henry Vaughan,' Marchamount said. 'Lady Honor's nephew. Heir to the Vaughan title and to their lands, such as they have left. She's brought him down from Lincolnshire to try to get him received at court.'

'He looks ill at ease.'

'Yes, he's a poor fellow, hardly cut out for the rumbustious company the king likes.' He paused, then asked, 'Have you resolved that unpleasant matter we discussed earlier?'

'I make progress. A strange thing happened in the course of my investigations.' I told him of the books that had gone missing from the library.

'Will your investigation be . . . ah . . . hindered, without the books?'

'Delayed a little only. There are other sources.' I watched his face closely, but he only nodded solemnly.

A serving man took up a horn and sounded a long note. The company fell silent as Lady Honor entered the room. She wore a wide farthingale in bright green velvet and a red French hood with loops of pearls hanging from it. But it was not to her that all eyes in the room turned; they fixed on the man who followed her, wearing a scarlet robe edged with fur despite the heat, and a thick gold chain. My heart sank—it was the Duke of Norfolk again. I bowed with everyone else as he strode to the head of the table.

Lady Honor smiled and clapped her hands. 'Ladies and gentlemen, please, take your places.'

To my surprise I was placed near the head of the table next to a plump middle-aged woman. On her other side Marchamount sat just below the duke. Lady Honor guided the nervous-looking boy to a chair next to Norfolk, who stared at him enquiringly.

'Your Grace,' Lady Honor said, 'may I present my cousin's son, Henry Vaughan. I told you he was coming from the country.'

The duke clapped him on the shoulder. 'Welcome to London, boy,' he said in his harsh voice. 'It's good to see the nobility sending their pups to court, to take their rightful place.' He looked the boy up and down. 'God's teeth, you're a skinny fellow; we'll have to build you up.'

'Thank you, Your Grace.'

Lady Honor guided Mayor Hollyes to a place next to the Vaughan boy, then sat herself almost opposite me. The boy's eyes followed her anxiously.

'Now,' Lady Honor said, 'the wine and our first confection.'

She clapped her hands and the servants bustled into action. Wine was set before the guests, in delicate Venetian glasses. Then the horn sounded again and a swan made of white sugar, nestling in a huge platter of sweet custard, was brought in. The assembly clapped and the duke barked with laughter.

'All the Thames swans belong to the king, Lady Honor! Had you permission to take this one?'

Everyone laughed sycophantically and reached out with their knives to cut into the magnificent confection.

'Are you a lawyer, like Serjeant Marchamount?' the woman next to me asked.

'I am. Master Matthew Shardlake, at your command.'

'I am Lady Mirfyn,' she replied grandly. 'My husband is treasurer of the Mercers' Guild this year.'

'I do some business with the Guildhall, though I have not had the honour of meeting Sir Michael.'

'They say at the guild, you have some other business now.' She eyed me severely. 'The disgraceful business of the Wentworth girl.'

'I am defending her, yes.'

'Sir Edwin is devastated by what happened to his son. He deplores that his wicked niece should be allowed to delay justice.'

'She is entitled to a defence.'

'She's entitled to hang!' Lady Mirfyn persisted. 'Edwin *doted* on that boy. He was a mischievous child, but that is to be expected in boys.'

'Was he indeed?' I asked.

'They said his misbehaviour helped drive his mother to her early grave.' She gave me a sharp look, suddenly aware that she had said too much. 'That doesn't excuse his vile murder, though.'

'No, indeed. It does not.' I was going to add that I believed the real murderer could still be at large, but Lady Mirfyn took my words for agreement, and nodded with satisfaction.

I heard a loud whisper from Norfolk to Marchamount. 'Damn it,' the duke hissed, 'she'll do as I command.'

'I fear she won't.' I heard Marchamount this time.

'God's death, I'll not be defied by a woman. Tell her I'll do nothing for the boy unless I get what I want.' The duke stared at Lady Honor, who was conversing with Mayor Hollyes. The duke was red-faced, and I remembered it was said he could turn brutal when drunk.

At last Lady Honor met his eyes. The duke smiled and raised his glass. She raised her glass in return, with a smile that I thought looked nervous, then she leaned towards me. 'The mayor says you have a knotty case for the council, Master Shardlake, involving the suppressed monasteries,' she said.

'Aye, Lady Honor. I fear we lost the first round, but we shall gain the second. It is a matter of the City's rights to regulate these buildings for the good of all the citizens.'

Mayor Hollyes nodded. 'I hope so, sir. The regulations on cleanliness need to be enforced to keep away the foul humours that bring plague. And so many houses are let out as poor tenements now. A house near the Joiners' Hall collapsed last month. Killed fourteen tenants—'

'Let them all fall!' All eyes turned to the duke. I saw that he was, indeed, drunk, and in a foul temper. 'The more houses fall on the diseased populace of this great cesspit the better. Perhaps that will scare some into going back to their parishes where they belong, to work on the land.'

A silence fell on the company. The Vaughan boy looked as though he wished to crawl under the table.

'Well, we may all agree much needs amending,' Lady Honor said, trying to make her voice light. 'Did not Bishop Gardiner preach a sermon last week, saying all must labour according to their station to keep the realm in proper order?' She looked round the table, hoping for someone to help defuse the topic. It seemed she did not wish for controversy tonight.

I stepped into the breach. 'So we must, Lady Honor.' She gave me a smile of gratitude. 'We must all aim to work for the common good.'

The duke snorted. 'Your *work*. Pen-pushing. I remember you, lawyer, you were with that churl who spouted Lutheran sentiments at me last Sunday.' I quailed under his hard stare. 'Are you a Lutheran, too, lawyer?'

Every eye turned to me. For a moment my voice caught, I was too frightened to answer. 'No, Your Grace,' I said. 'A follower of Erasmus only.'

'That Dutch pederast. I heard he lusted after another monk when he was a boy, and d'you know what his name was, eh?' He looked round the table, grinning now. 'Rogerus. Roger-us, hey?' He gave a sudden bark of laughter that broke the spell. The men up and down the table began laughing with him.

I sank back in my chair, my heart thudding, as the duke turned to young Henry Vaughan and began telling tales of his soldiering days.

Lady Honor clapped her hands. 'Some music, now.'

Two lute players appeared together with a gaudily dressed young man, who began singing popular songs. I looked down the table. The conversation had become desultory; between the heat, the drink and the sweet food most of the diners looked sticky and tired.

Lady Honor caught my eye and leaned forward. 'Thank you for trying to help me earlier,' she said. 'I am sorry it turned out ill.'

'I was warned your table talk could be controversial.' I leaned across to her. 'Lady Honor, I must talk with you—'

Her face was wary. 'In the courtyard,' she said quietly, 'afterwards.'

Everyone jumped as a crack of thunder sounded from outside. A draught of cool air swept through the room. Someone said, 'Is this the rain at last?'

Lady Honor took the words as her cue and stood up. 'It is a little early, but perhaps you should leave now, get on the road before the rain starts.'

People got up and bowed as the duke rose to his feet, stumbling slightly. He bowed curtly to his hostess and strode unsteadily from the room.

As the guests went to take their farewell of Lady Honor I hung back. I saw Marchamount bend close to her and speak intently. Her reply did not seem to satisfy him; he was frowning slightly as he turned away.

As he passed me he paused. 'Be careful, Shardlake,' he said. 'You seem to court the duke's disapproval. If the times change, that could have consequences.' He gave me a cold nod, then left the chamber.

I made my way downstairs and stood in the courtyard by the door. There was another rumble of thunder, closer now. I wondered what it was that Norfolk wanted from Lady Honor. Something Marchamount knew about.

There was a touch at my elbow. I jumped and turned round. Lady Honor stood beside me. She sighed heavily. 'That was a *disaster*. I have never seen the duke in such bad humour. I am sorry for the trouble he caused you.'

I hesitated. 'Lady Honor, there is something I must ask you—'

She raised a hand. 'I know. Serjeant Marchamount has told me that Michael Gristwood and his brother have been murdered. He said you would have some questions for me.'

'He is a friend, the serjeant?'

'A friend, aye,' she said quickly. 'I am afraid there is little I can tell you. I was only a messenger. I took a package to Lord Cromwell for the serjeant, passed a message that the contents would be of great interest to him. That was all; further messages went via Lincoln's Inn.'

Something about her speech was too pat. And now I was close to her, I realised with a shock that the scent she wore was the same musky odour the Greek Fire papers had had about them.

'Did you know what the package was?' I asked.

'Papers relating to the secret of Greek Fire. Gabriel told me. I suppose he shouldn't have done but he likes to impress me.' She laughed nervously.

'Did you look at the papers?'

She paused and took a deep breath, her bosom rising.

'I know you did,' I said gently. I did not want to hear her lie. 'That alluring scent you wear was on them. A faint trace—I could not place it till just now.'

She bit her lip. 'Yes, I read them. I resealed the package afterwards. It was wrong, I know. But I fear I have a woman's curiosity in full share.'

'This means that you are the only person who handled those papers to open them. Unless Marchamount did.'

'Gabriel is too careful to do that.'

But he knew this was about Greek Fire. Had he told Norfolk? Was Norfolk pressing Lady Honor to tell him more?

'Did you think the papers held the secret of Greek Fire?' I asked her.

She looked me in the eye. 'Perhaps they did. The old soldier's account was very clear. And the papers were old; they weren't some forgery.'

'One was torn.'

'I saw. I did not tear it.' For the first time I saw a look of fear in her eyes.

'I know. That was the formula. The Gristwoods kept it back.'

Lady Honor looked at me earnestly, her mouth tight with worry. 'Master Shardlake, will you have to tell Lord Cromwell I looked at the papers?'

'I must, Lady Honor. But if you told no one, no harm has been done.'

'I didn't, I swear.'

'Then I will tell him you admitted frankly that you read the papers.'

She let out a sigh of relief. 'Tell him I am sorry for what I did. I confess I have been worried I would be found out. I have been so foolish.'

'Foolishness may be forgiven,' I said. I hoped Cromwell would agree.

She looked at me curiously. 'You have a bloody trade, sir. Two murders to investigate.'

'Believe it or not, my specialism is property law.'

'Did that old shrew Lady Mirfyn tell you anything useful about the Wentworths? I saw you talking to her.'

Truly she missed little. 'Not much. All still depends on getting Elizabeth to talk. And I have been neglecting that matter.'

'You care about her.' She had recovered quickly; her tone was light again. 'She is my client.'

She nodded. 'Perhaps you are a man of too gentle feeling to deal with blood and death.' She smiled softly.

'As I told you last week, I am a mere jobbing lawyer.'

She shook her head, smiling. 'No, you are more than that. I thought so when I first saw you.' She shook her head. 'Forgive me, I say too much. If I were a common woman, I would be called a malapert.'

'You are certainly out of the common run, Lady Honor.'

She looked over the courtyard, sadness showing in her face. 'I miss my husband still, though it has been three years. People say I married him for his money, but I loved him. And we were friends.'

'That is a fine thing in a marriage.'

She inclined her head and smiled. 'But he left me the memories of our time together and also a widow's status. I am an independent woman, Master Shardlake; I have much to be grateful for.'

'I am sure you are worthy of that status, My Lady.'

'Not all men would agree. I was born a Vaughan, as you know. My early life was spent learning deportment, embroidery, just enough reading to make good conversation. The education of a woman of good birth is very dull.' She smiled. 'There, now, you *will* think me a malapert. But I could never help nosing into men's affairs.'

'Not at all. I agree with you. I too find conventionally accomplished girls dull.' As soon as I had said the words, I wished I had not, for they could be taken as flirtatious. I found Lady Honor fascinating, but did not wish her to know that. She was, after all, still a suspect.

'Lady Honor,' I ventured, 'I have Lord Cromwell's commission. If . . . if anyone is putting pressure on you to give information about those papers, he will afford you his protection.'

She gave me a direct look. 'Some say he will soon have no protection to afford anyone, if he cannot resolve the king's marriage problems.'

'Those are rumours. The protection he can give now is real.'

I saw her hesitate, then she smiled tightly. 'Thank you for your care, but I have no need of protection.' She turned away a moment, then looked back at me, her smile warm again. 'Why are you unmarried, Master Shardlake?'

'Perhaps because I am not an attractive proposition.'

'In some dull eyes, perhaps. But some women prize intelligence and sensitivity. That is why I try to bring good company round my table.' She was looking at me keenly.

'Though sometimes the mixture turns explosive,' I said, turning the conversation into a jest. 'And perhaps the arguments are entertaining to watch?'

She laughed and raised a finger. 'You have found me out. But usually it does no harm. The duke can be good company when he is sober.'

'You would like your nephew to regain your family's old fortunes? A place at court beside the king?'

She inclined her head. 'I would like my family to regain what it lost. But perhaps Henry is not the one to do it; he is not the brightest boy, nor the most robust. I cannot see him at the king's side.'

A tremendous crash of thunder sounded right above us. The heavens opened and a great torrent of rain fell down, soaking us in an instant.

Lady Honor looked up. 'Oh God, at last!' she said.

I blinked the rain out of my eyes. The cold water was indeed marvellous after the broiling heat of the last days. I gasped with the relief of it.

'I must go in,' Lady Honor said. 'But we should talk more, Master Shardlake. We must meet again. Though I have no more to tell about Greek Fire.' And then she came close and quickly kissed my cheek, a sudden warmth amidst the cold rainwater. Without looking back, she ran through the door to the stairs and closed it. As the rain pelted down on me I stood there with my hand on my cheek, overcome with astonishment.

I RODE AWAY from the House of Glass through rain that fell straight and hard, bouncing off my cap like a million tiny pebbles. But the storm was quickly over; by the time I reached Cheapside the last fading rumbles of thunder were sounding.

The extraordinary conversation with Lady Honor went round and round in my head. Her kiss, while chaste, was a daring thing from a woman of rank. But it was only after I had got her to admit she had read the papers that her tone had become intimate. I shook my head sadly. This was no time to allow my mind to be cloyed by affection for a woman.

When I reached home, Barak had not yet returned and Joan was abed. I had to rouse Simon to take the horse to the stables. I took a mug of beer and a candle and went up to my room. I turned to the papers on the Bealknap case I had brought back from court, for I had to prepare my recommendations for the council about an application to the Court of Chancery.

It was late when I heard Barak come in. I went to his room and found him in his shirt, hanging his doublet out of the window to dry.

'You were caught in the storm, then?'

'Aye.' He gave me a serious look. 'I've seen the earl. He's not pleased. He wants progress, not a stream of refugees. He has to go to Hampton Court to see the king tomorrow, but he wants to see us the day after.'

I sat down on the bed. 'Was he angry?'

Barak shook his head. 'Anxious. He didn't like the idea Rich may be involved in this.' I saw again Barak's fear for his master—and for himself if Cromwell fell. 'What happened at the banquet?' he asked.

'The Duke of Norfolk was there, in a foul mood and drunk.' I told him all that had passed. I even told him about Lady Honor's kiss. I half expected some mocking remark, but he only looked thoughtful.

'You think she was making up to you because you found out she'd read those papers?'

'Perhaps.' I told him of the conversation I had overheard. 'Norfolk wants something from her, something that Marchamount knows about.'

'Shit! Norfolk may be in the know too. That would be worse than Rich. Do you think Norfolk's trying to get what was in those papers out of her?'

I nodded. 'There's not much in them, but he doesn't know that.'

Barak shrugged and said, 'At least I've found who Pock-face is.'

I sat up. 'Who?'

'He's called Bernard Toky. He's from out Deptford way. He had a bad dose of smallpox a few years back. Spent some of his youth soldiering against the Turks and developed a taste for killing, apparently. The big man is called Wright. He's an old mate of Toky's. They've both been involved in various bits of dirty business, though they've never been caught.'

'Dirty business for whom?'

'Rich merchants with scores to settle, mostly. Toky left London a few years ago; things were getting too hot for him. Now he's back, although he seems to be avoiding old friends. But I've got people looking for him.'

'Let's hope he doesn't get to us first.'

'And I went to the tavern where the sailors hang out. Offered money for information about that Baltic cargo. The tavern keeper remembers someone trying to sell the stuff there, a man called Miller. He's at sea now, but he should be back the day after tomorrow. We can go to the tavern then.'

We both jumped at a knock on the front door. Barak reached for his sword as we hurried downstairs. Joan, roused from her bed, was already at the door. I motioned her back. 'Who is it?' I called.

'A message,' a childish voice called. 'Urgent, for Master Shardlake.'

I opened the door. An urchin stood there, holding a letter. I gave him a penny and took it.

'Is it from Grey?' Barak asked.

I studied the superscription. 'No. This is Joseph's writing.' I broke the seal and opened the letter. It was brief, and asked me to meet him first thing tomorrow at Newgate, where a terrible thing had happened.

NEXT MORNING we rode out early again. Any hope that the storm might have heralded a change in the weather was gone; it was hotter than ever, and a malodorous steam rose from heaps of rubbish washed down from the alleyways.

We rode up to Newgate again and left our horses at the nearby inn. I ignored the hands at the begging grate, and banged on the door.

The gaoler opened it. 'The lawyer again,' he said. 'Your client's given us a peck of trouble today.'

'Is Joseph Wentworth here? He asked me to meet him.'

'Aye.' He stood in the doorway, barring our entrance. 'He won't give me a sixpence he owes me for shaving the witch's head when she went mad yesterday. We've had to chain her and I got a barber to come and shave her head to cool her wild brain. That's what you're supposed to do, isn't it?'

Wordlessly, I passed him a sixpence. He nodded and stepped aside, letting us into the dark entrance hall, where Joseph sat on a bench.

'What's happened?' I asked him. 'The gaoler said Elizabeth's run mad.'

'Thank you for coming, sir. I don't know what to do. When they took that old horse-thief woman away yesterday they say Lizzy started screaming. They put her in chains, sir.' He looked up at me in anguish. 'They cut off all her hair, her lovely curly black hair, and tried to make me pay for the barber. I wouldn't—I hadn't asked for such a cruel thing.'

'Joseph, if you don't pay them what they ask they'll only treat her worse.'

He bowed his head and nodded reluctantly.

I sat beside him. 'How is she now?'

'Quiet again. But she's cut and bruised herself . . .'

'Let's go and see.' Joseph looked enquiringly at Barak. 'A colleague,' I said. 'Do you mind if he comes too?'

He shrugged. 'No. Anyone who can help.'

'Come on then,' I said with a cheerfulness I did not feel. 'Let's see her.'

Once again the fat turnkey led us down to the Hole. He opened the door and we passed through into a stink even more overpowering than before. My jaw dropped open when I saw Elizabeth, for she scarcely looked human now. She lay crouched in the straw, her face covered with grazes and streaks of blood, and her head had been shaved quite bald.

I went over to her. 'Elizabeth,' I said calmly, 'what has happened to you?' I saw her lip was split; someone had hit her when they were restraining her.

She stared back at me with those vivid green eyes. There was more life in them today, angry life. Her gaze flickered past me to Barak.

'That's Master Barak, a colleague,' I said. 'Did they hurt you?' I reached out a hand and she shrank back. There was a clanking, and I saw she was manacled to the wall by long chains, heavy gyves on her wrists and ankles.

'Did it make you angry when they took the old woman away?' I asked.

She did not reply, only continued fixing me with that ferocious stare.

Barak knelt close and whispered to me. 'May I ask her something?'

I looked at him dubiously. But what more harm could he do? I nodded.

He knelt before her. 'I don't know what your sorrow is, Mistress.' His tone was gentle. 'But if you won't talk, no one will ever know. You'll die and people will forget. In time they'll just give it up as a puzzle and forget it.'

She stared back at him for a long moment. Barak nodded. 'Was that why the old woman being taken made you angry? The thought you might be ripped out of the world unheard, like her?'

Elizabeth sat back against the wall, her eyes darting between us.

I thought a moment, then bent closer to her. 'I have been to your uncle Edwin's house, Elizabeth. I have spoken to your uncle, your grandmother, your cousins and the steward. They all say you must be guilty.'

At that a bitter smile played round the corner of her mouth.

I leaned in close, so only she would hear, and said, 'I think there is something down the well in the garden that they are trying to hide.'

She shrank back, her eyes full of horror.

'I propose to investigate it,' I said softly. 'I will find the truth, Elizabeth.'

Then she spoke for the first time, her voice cracked from disuse. 'If you go there, you will do naught but destroy your faith in Christ Jesus,' she whispered, then sat forward, burying her head in her knees.

'Lizzy!' Joseph's voice was trembling. 'What did you mean? Tell us, please!' But she would not lift her head. 'Lizzy, please tell us more!'

Barak gave him an exasperated look, and I put a hand on the farmer's trembling shoulder. 'Come, Joseph, come. Let us leave her for now.'

I knocked at the door and the turnkey led us away, back to the main door. This time it was even more of a relief to be outside again.

Joseph was still agitated. 'We can't just leave her there, now she's started to talk. We've only got eight days, Master Shardlake!'

I raised my hands. 'I have an idea, Joseph. I can't tell you what it is now, but I hope to find the key to this riddle soon. Give me a little more time. Trust me. And if you visit Elizabeth again, please, in Jesu's name, do not harangue her. That will only make things worse.'

Joseph looked at me. 'I haven't any choice but to do as you say, have I? Though it's driving me mad, sir, mad.'

I SAID FAREWELL to Joseph and Barak at the inn where we had left the horses, and rode down Cheapside to the Guildhall. There I left Chancery in the stables and went to find Vervey in his office. He welcomed me warmly and I gave him the opinion I had written out the previous evening. He read it, nodding occasionally, then looked up at me.

'You are hopeful, then, of a victory in Chancery?'

'Aye, though it may be a year before we get there. I am going to look at Bealknap's property this morning, by the way. The Chancery judge will want to know all the circumstances of the nuisance.'

'Good, good. Some of these tenements in the old monastic properties are shocking. Insanitary and a fire risk too, with everywhere as dry as tinder. If a fire breaks out people may not be able to get enough water from the conduits to quench it. Then the Common Council will be blamed. We're trying to stop leaks in the pipes, but some of them run miles from the streams.'

'I know of a man who repairs the conduits. Master Leighton.'

'Yes. I have a note to chase him; he was supposed to bring our contractors some new pipes but he hasn't appeared. He's a very skilled fellow.'

Probably a dead fellow, but I could not tell him. I changed the subject. 'I wonder if I might have a look at your library. Perhaps borrow a book or two?'

He laughed. 'I can't see we would have anything Lincoln's Inn does not.'

'It's not legal works I'm after. Roman history. Livy, Plutarch, Pliny.'

'Let me prepare a note for the librarian.'

I had a niggling fear the books might be gone from the Guildhall library too, but they were all there, on the shelf. With the aid of Vervey's note I was able to get past the librarian. He watched sourly as I put the volumes in my satchel. As I walked down the Guildhall Steps and away to the stables I felt a little pleased with myself, for the first time in days.

When I reached Chancery's stall he nuzzled my hand, hoping for food. I slung my bag of books over my shoulder, mounted and rode north towards the City wall, where the former Franciscan priory of St Michael's lay. The wide doors of the church stood open and, curious, I dismounted and looked inside. Both sides of the nave had been blocked off with tall, flimsy-looking wooden partitions. There was a series of doors at ground level and rickety steps led up to more dwellings, making a dozen apartments in all.

Beside the door frame a couple of iron rings had been hammered into an ancient font. From the piles of dung on the floor I could see this was where horses were tethered. I slung Chancery's reins round a ring and walked down the central passage. So this was Bealknap's conversion. It was so rickety it looked as though the construction could come down at any moment.

One of the doors on the upper floor opened. An old woman stepped out and stood at the head of the staircase; it wobbled slightly under her weight.

She gave my robe a hostile look. 'Have you come from the landlord, lawyer?' she asked in a sharp northern accent.

I doffed my cap. 'No, madam, I represent the City Council. I have come to look at the cesspit; there have been complaints.'

The old woman folded her arms. 'That pit's a disgrace. Thirty of us share it, and the vapours off it would stun a bull. I'm sorry for them living next door to the church, but what can we do? We have to go somewhere!'

'No one blames you, madam. Your conditions are clearly bad,' I agreed. 'How do I get to the cesspit?'

She pointed up the passage. 'There's a little door by where the altar was. The pit's in the cloisters. Hold your nose, though.'

I bowed and walked to the door she had indicated, which hung from loose hinges. The former cloister yard had been converted too, the roofed walkway filled with more wooden partitions between the pillars to make a quadrangle of tiny ramshackle dwellings: hovels for the poorest of the poor. The smallest of the dwellings had an open door, from which a horrible stink issued. Holding my nose, I looked inside. A hole had been dug in the earth, with a plank set on bricks thrown across. The cesspit should have been twenty feet deep, but from the cloud of flies buzzing round I guessed it was no more than ten feet deep. I looked down and saw that the hole had not even been lined with wood, let alone the mandatory stone: no wonder it leaked.

I stepped outside with relief. I had to visit the house next door, the one the council owned, then get back to Chancery Lane. I paused and rubbed my sleeve across my brow, easing the uncomfortable weight of my satchel.

Then I saw them. They stood one on each side of the door to the church: a tall thin man with a pale face pitted with pox marks, and an enormous, hulking fellow hefting an axe, the shaft cut short, in his big hand. Toky, and his mate Wright. I swallowed, feeling my legs tremble. Other than the door to the church there was no way out of the cloister yard. I felt for my dagger.

Toky smiled as he lifted his own dagger. 'Didn't see us following you, did you?' he asked. He nodded at the cesspit. 'Fancy going down there? They wouldn't find you till they cleaned it out.' He grinned.

'Whatever you are being paid,' I said, trying to keep my voice steady, 'Lord Cromwell will double it in return for the name of your employer.'

Toky laughed, then spat on the ground. 'That for the tavern-keeper's son.' He moved towards me as the big man stepped to the side, raising his axe.

'Help!' I called out. My heart thudded and I almost gave in. Then in my mind's eye I saw Sepultus Gristwood's shattered face and resolved that if it was to end like that, I would go down fighting.

Their eyes were concentrated on my dagger arm. I let my shoulder drop so the strap of my satchel slid down my other arm, then I grabbed it and swung at Wright with all my strength. The heavy books caught him on the side of the head and he stumbled with a cry. I ran for the doorway.

I heard Toky close behind me and winced in anticipation of a blade thrust into my back. I grabbed at the door. It came right off the hinges. I turned and thrust it at Toky; he stumbled against it with a cry, giving me time to run into the nave. The old woman was still on her staircase, talking to a younger woman. I ran down the passage and turned.

Toky was standing in the doorway, blood running from his nose. To my surprise, he laughed. 'We'll put you down the pit *alive* for this, matey.'

Wright charged through the door and headed straight for me, axe raised. Then he howled as a flood of liquid landed on him from above, followed by an earthenware pot that banged on his shoulder. I stared upwards. The old woman had thrown a full pisspot at him. Her neighbour ran from her door, carrying another. She hurled it too at the big man. This time it caught him on the forehead and he stumbled against the wall, dropping his axe.

'Run!' the old woman yelled.

Toky was running down the aisle, fury in his eyes. I sped for the main doors, jerking Chancery's reins free. I leapt clumsily into the saddle and they were seized from below, jerking Chancery's head aside. To my horror I saw Toky directly underneath me, the sunlight flashing off his dagger. I fumbled frantically for my own, which I had slipped up my sleeve as I mounted, but I was too late. Toky thrust upwards at my groin.

Chancery reared up, neighing in terror and kicking out. As Toky jumped back, I saw that his dagger was bloody, but it was Chancery's blood that stained it, welling from a great gash in his side. Toky struck at me again but Chancery, screaming, shied away, almost unseating me. Along the street, shutters were banging open; a group of men had appeared in the doorway of an inn. I pulled at the reins and Chancery stumbled towards them, his blood dripping on the road. I looked over my shoulder. Wright had joined Toky now, sunlight glinting on his axe, but half the street lay between us.

'Hey, what's going on?' someone called. 'Constable!'

The men from the inn spilled into the road; doors were opened along the street, people peering fearfully out. Toky gave me a savage look, then turned and ran off up the street, Wright running after him. The men from the inn came over to where Chancery stood trembling from head to foot.

The innkeeper approached me. 'You all right, lawyer?'

'Yes. Thank you, yes.'

'God's death, what happened? Your horse is hurt.'

At that moment Chancery slipped forward to his knees. I had barely time to jump off before he fell on his side. My old horse was dead.

ChAPTER SEVEN

Some hours later, as the heat of the day began to fade, I sat under the shade of a trellis in my garden. I had told the crowd in the street that I had been the victim of a robbery. The innkeeper had insisted a cart be sent for to remove the horse, which was blocking the narrow street, and that I pay for it. As they loaded Chancery onto the cart to take him to the Shambles, I walked down to the river to catch a boat, blinking back tears.

Young Simon wept when I told him Chancery was dead. I had not realised the boy was so fond of the poor old horse, with his quiet gentle ways. Tears formed at the corners of my eyes again. I wiped them away.

There was a cough at my elbow and I turned to find Barak, looking hot and dusty. 'What's happened? The boy tells me your horse has died.'

I told Barak of the attack. He frowned as he sat beside me.

'Shit, that's more bad news for the earl tomorrow. How did they know you were going there?'

'I think Toky was following me again. I was careless.'

He eyed my face. 'Have you been weeping?'

'For Chancery,' I said, my voice gruff with embarrassment.

'God's death, it was only a horse.'

'I am hungry,' I said quickly. 'I'll get Joan to make us an early supper.'

'And then—the well?' Barak looked at me.

'No.' I glanced at the satchel, which I had retrieved from the cloister of St Michael's before returning home. 'Then, I must have a look at those books.'

I RETURNED to my study after supper. I read for hours, lighting candles as the summer sun dropped to the horizon. I read about Roman experiments with fire weaponry that seemed to come to naught. The name Medea came up again and again: the name of the ancient Greek sorceress who presented her enemy with a shirt that burst into fire when it was put on. Placing 'the Shirt of Medea' on victims in the arena was a sport in Nero's time, mentioned in Plutarch and Lucullus. But what was it that made the shirt burn, and why had the Romans not developed this 'infernal fire' for military use?

I read on, finding references to military experiments with a mysterious substance called 'naphtha' that was found in Mesopotamia, on the eastern frontier of the empire. Pliny said it bubbled to the surface from underground and could be set on fire even if it spilled into a river.

I laid down my book and rubbed my eyes. There was something in these books, some clue, I was sure. Or why had the Lincoln's Inn copies been stolen? Who had stolen those books? Who was the librarian afraid of? I sighed. Every step I took seemed only to throw up more puzzles.

THAT NIGHT I slept deeply, exhausted. I woke knowing that I would have to face Cromwell that afternoon. The 3rd of June. The demonstration was due in exactly a week's time. I lay there, wondering how much longer I could keep up this pace.

Barak was already at breakfast when I went downstairs. Joan was serving and kept giving us worried glances. I had told her that Chancery had collapsed and died of heat stroke, but I suspected she did not believe me.

'Well, what now?' Barak asked after she had left.

'I'll go to Lady Honor's first, question her again.'

'I see you've put a new doublet and robe on for her.'

'Might as well look my best.'

He took a deep breath and made a grimace. 'We've to see the earl at one. He wants us at Whitehall. Shall I come with you to see Lady Honor?'

'No. I thought you might visit Madam Neller again, see if there is any news of Bathsheba. I'll meet you here at twelve.'

'Yes. I suppose it'd do no harm to see old Neller,' Barak said. 'But are you sure you'll be safe on your own?'

'Aye. I'll be going by public ways, and I'll be keeping a careful eye out.'

We were interrupted by Joan's knock at the door. 'There's a messenger from Lord Cromwell's office,' she said. 'He has a new horse for you, sir.'

Barak got up. 'I sent a message to Grey yesterday afternoon, saying your horse was killed and asking for a new one to be sent. You've no time to go to the market and you need a horse; we can't go everywhere by water.'

'Oh,' I said. I was suddenly filled with anger. Did Barak think Chancery's loss could be repaired so casually? Yet from a practical point of view he was right. I went outside. Simon had brought both horses round. Barak's sleek mare was accompanied by a big brown gelding. I patted it. It seemed placid enough. 'What's his name?' I asked the boy.

'Genesis, sir,' Simon replied.

I gave him a note to take to Joseph's lodgings then heaved myself into the saddle. Barak had come to the door. I gave him a brief wave and rode off.

THE HOUSE OF GLASS lay quiet and still in the morning heat. A servant in the Vaughan livery answered the door. I asked if I might see Lady Honor on an urgent matter and he admitted me, asking me to wait in the hall.

The servant reappeared and led me up to a first-floor parlour. Lady Honor sat in an armchair, dressed in a light blue dress with a square bodice and a square hood, for once free of attendants. 'Will you sit down?' she asked, gesturing to some cushions on the floor. I lowered myself to them and unhitched my satchel.

'Well,' she said softly, 'what do you want from me today?'

I hesitated. 'Lady Honor,' I said, choosing my words carefully, 'I have to make a report to Lord Cromwell this afternoon. I have not got as far as I would like in my enquiries, not least because the founder who aided the Gristwoods in their work has disappeared and has probably been killed. Attempts have also been made on my life.'

She gasped. 'Am I in danger too?' A nerve flickered under her eye.

'I do not believe so. So long as you have truly told nobody but me that you looked in those papers about Greek Fire.'

'Nobody.' She took a deep breath. 'If you tell the earl I looked in those papers, he may seek to try my testimony with rougher methods than yours.'

'That is partly why I came this morning so I can make the fullest report to him. Lady Honor, the night of the banquet I saw you talking to Serjeant Marchamount. You looked as though you were discussing something serious.'

I braced myself for anger, but she only sighed and lowered her head. 'Jesu,' she said, 'where have I brought myself with my foolish curiosity?'

'Tell me everything,' I said. 'I would help you with the earl if I could.'

She smiled sadly. 'Yes, I believe so, for all that you are sent after me like a hunter. I see it in your face. You do not like this work, do you?'

'What I like is neither here nor there, Lady Honor. I must ask what you and the serjeant were talking about.'

'Gabriel Marchamount advises me on the many legal matters I have to deal with.' She took another deep breath. 'Gabriel has been, shall we say, attentive. He has indicated that he would like to take my husband's place.'

'Ah.' I felt myself redden. 'I see. He loves you.'

She surprised me with a mocking laugh. 'Loves me? Gabriel wants more than anything to have a son who can say he is of noble birth. His attempts to persuade the College of Heralds to provide him with a coat of arms, though his father was a fishmonger, have failed. So now he would like to marry into a noble family.'

'I see.'

'But, truly, Master Shardlake, there are some who are not fit to rise above their station and Marchamount is one.' Her voice trembled. 'He is an ambitious boor. I have refused him, yet he will not give up his designs.' She lowered her head a moment, then returned her gaze to me. 'But I have never mentioned looking at the Greek Fire papers to him. I would not be such a fool. And he has never mentioned them to me.' She turned to the window.

I rose, then sat down again. I was ashamed of humiliating her, but there remained another question I must ask. 'I overheard something else at the banquet, Lady Honor. The Duke of Norfolk muttered to Marchamount that there was something he would have you do, but that you would not.'

She did not turn round. 'The Duke of Norfolk covets land. He would be the greatest landowner in the realm. My family still has some left and the duke would have part of it in return for advancing my cousin at court. But Henry is not cut out for the role of saviour of our family.'

'I am truly sorry to expose these private sorrows,' I said.

She turned round then and to my relief she was smiling. 'Yes, I believe you are. You have done your work well, Master Shardlake.' She crossed to the little table and picked up a Bible. 'Here, take this.'

Puzzled, I took the heavy book. She laid her hand on it, the long fingers pressed flat against the leather cover, and looked me in the face.

'I swear by Almighty God,' she said, 'that I have never discussed the contents of the papers relating to Greek Fire with any living soul other than you. Will you tell the earl that I made this oath freely and of my own will?'

'I will,' I said.

'And though you must tell him everything, I ask you to keep these— these difficulties with Gabriel and the duke secret.'

'I promise to tell no one but the earl, My Lady.'

She smiled, her old warm smile. 'Then we may be friends again?'

'I would like nothing better, My Lady.'

'Good.' She paused. 'Gabriel sent me an invitation to the bear-baiting tomorrow. He is making a party of it and I feel obliged to go. He said to bring whoever I chose. Would you care to come as well? To prove there is no ill feeling?' Her look had something flirtatious in it again.

'I will come, Lady Honor, with pleasure.'

'Good. We meet at noon, at Three Cranes.'

I rose, conscious time was passing. 'I must go, My Lady.'

'I will see you out.'

Lady Honor led me downstairs. In the hall I turned to her. 'I am sorry for your troubles,' I said again. 'And for raking them up.'

She laid a hand on my arm. 'You were doing your duty even though it was uncomfortable. I admire that.' She studied me. 'But you are meant for finer things than work like this. You demean yourself, Matthew.'

'I have no choice.'

'For now, perhaps.' She took my hand. 'Until tomorrow. Remember, Three Cranes Wharf at noon.'

BARAK WAS WAITING for me in Chancery Lane, a gloomy look on his face.

'Any news?' I asked.

'I told Madam Neller what to expect from Lord Cromwell if Bathsheba turns up and she doesn't tell us. But she knows nothing. And I found where Toky and Wright have been staying: a cheap lodging house by the river. They left there yesterday, though. What did Lady Honor have to say?'

'She told me Marchamount is after her hand and she has refused him. And the Duke of Norfolk is trying to get some lands from her in exchange for introducing her nephew at court. She swore on the Great Bible she's told no one else she opened those papers.' I sighed. 'She's invited me to the bear-baiting tomorrow. I thought I'd go. Marchamount will be there as well. It will be a chance to check her story.'

'Looks like that lead's closed off. You'll be glad to see her in the clear, eh?'

'I admit I like her, but I would not let that cloud my judgment.'

'Never knew it not to.'

I gave him a look; he was worried by the coming interview with Cromwell, I could tell, and diverting himself at my expense.

I got up. 'We had better go. We'll take the wherry.'

'How's the new horse?'

'Quiet enough,' I said, then added, 'but he's no personality.'

Barak laughed. 'I'm sorry, I should have asked at the royal stables if they'd a horse that could talk.'

'When you are in a bad humour you become oafish,' I said sternly. 'But we'll do no good sniping at each other and I am too tired for it. Come on.'

We said little on the journey. I felt a growing nervousness as the wherry drew in at Westminster Stairs. We disembarked and walked past Westminster Hall, heading for Whitehall Palace just beyond. We turned into the new Privy Gallery building, where Lord Cromwell had offices. Barak seemed to know his way through the echoing corridors. He stopped outside a door guarded by a halberdier, and we were admitted to an outer office where Grey, ubiquitous as ever, sat behind a desk.

He rose and greeted us. 'Master Shardlake, is there any more news? I have seen Barak's messages. There is so little time left—'

'Our news is for the earl,' Barak told him sharply.

Grey looked at him and inclined his head. 'I warn you he's in no good frame of mind. And he has the Duke of Norfolk with him.'

Grey broke off as the inner door burst open. The duke strode out. He flung the door casually shut behind him, then turned to us with a wolfish smile on his long face. I bowed deeply.

Norfolk laughed harshly. 'You again! You seem determined to impress yourself on my mind.' His penetrating eyes were full of malice. 'The friend of the heretic. Don't worry, Master Shardlake, I have you well marked.' He turned to Barak. 'You as well, my young friend.' He turned to Grey. 'You too, I have you all marked.' He gave us a triumphant nod then walked out.

Barak blew out his cheeks. 'Shit.'

Grey swallowed. 'He's crowing like he's cock of the roost already.' He stared at the closed inner door a moment, then got up, knocked nervously and went in. A few moments later he reappeared. 'Lord Cromwell will see you.'

In his large office, behind a desk cluttered with papers, Cromwell sat very still, his square, heavy face strangely expressionless, eyes fixed thoughtfully on us as we bowed low. 'Well, Matthew,' he said. 'Jack.'

'My Lord.'

He smiled bleakly. 'The duke came to demand I release Bishop Sampson from the Tower. I shall have to; he wouldn't confess to any plots even when they showed him the rack. The papists keep their conspiracies so close I've nothing that would turn the king against Norfolk's party.' He shook his head, and when he spoke again his eyes were full of anger. 'The one thing I have to keep me in the king's favour, Greek Fire, remains lost and the thieves slaughter all those who know of it under your very noses.'

'We've been working hard, My Lord,' Barak ventured.

Cromwell ignored him. He leaned forward, staring at me. 'The king's insisting on a divorce from Queen Anne now and I'm the one who must find the way. Then he'll marry Catherine Howard and Norfolk will never be out of his presence, telling him he should have my head for tying him to that German drab. If I can give him Greek Fire he'll keep me in his service. Perhaps then I can turn the tide before the Howards have us under Rome again.' He leaned back. 'Perhaps, then, I will be allowed to *live*.' His heavy frame seemed to quiver slightly as he uttered the last word.

He blinked, then stared at me again. 'Is there any more news? Have you achieved anything apart from landing me with a menagerie of scared fools?'

'I needed to discover what they knew, My Lord.'

'So what of the suspects, the people who matter?'

'They all say they know nothing. Lady Honor I have questioned closely.' I repeated all she had told me.

He grunted. 'She's a fine woman. Pretty.' I remembered Cromwell was a widower now. I wondered if Barak had told him I liked her.

'I intend to check her story with Marchamount.'

'Another one who maintains he knows nothing. Bealknap makes a third.'

'He has questions to answer about his involvement with Richard Rich.'

Cromwell's face clouded at that name. 'Yes, you have added him to our list of suspects, Barak tells me. Him and Norfolk.'

'Bealknap and Marchamount are under their respective patronage.'

'All my protégés are falling away, becoming spies and enemies, making shift to protect themselves if the tide turns against me.' He looked at me. 'Solve this, Matthew,' he said with sudden passion. 'Solve this.'

WE TOOK a wherry back to Temple Stairs, then walked up to Lincoln's Inn. We climbed the narrow steps to Bealknap's door only to find it closed, a heavy padlock through the handle. From the barrister who occupied the chambers below we learned only that Brother Bealknap had gone out early that morning. Frustrated, we went across to my own chambers.

Godfrey was in the outer office, going over some papers with Skelly. He looked up in surprise as we came in. I left Barak in the office and went with Godfrey to his room.

'No problems with your work,' he told me, 'but I'm afraid you've another case gone. The house conveyance down by Coldharbour.' Godfrey looked at me seriously. 'You ought to look into this, Matthew. It seems that someone is putting out bad words about you.'

'You're right, but I haven't time now. I won't have before next Thursday.'

'You'll be free then?'

I smiled wryly. 'Yes. One way or another.' I noticed that he looked tired and felt a twinge of conscience. 'Are my matters taking up much time?'

'No, but I had some news this morning. I'm to be fined ten pounds for my insolence to the duke.'

'That is a heavy load. I'm sorry, Godfrey. If it places you in difficulty, you can always come to me. Let me know what you need.'

He looked relieved. 'Thank you. I must work out how much I can raise myself. How goes it with the Wentworth case?'

'Slowly. Everything goes slowly. Listen, Godfrey, I need to speak to Bealknap, but he's out. Can you watch for him, tell him I wish to speak to him urgently?'

'Aye, all right.'

I went back to the outer office. Barak was standing at Skelly's desk, listening with interest as the clerk explained how copying was done.

'Come,' I said, 'Godfrey will let us know when Bealknap arrives.'

Barak and I walked back to my house where I asked Joan to bring us an early supper. Afterwards I walked back up to Lincoln's Inn, but the padlock was still on Bealknap's door. I returned home and told Barak we might as well ride down to the tavern where he had arranged to meet the sailor from the Baltic; there was no point in waiting any longer for Bealknap.

THE BARBARY TURK was a gloomy, cavernous place, smelling of stale beer. In the middle of the room a huge thigh bone, thrice the size of a man's, hung in chains from the rafters. When we arrived, Barak went to fetch some beer and I looked at the plaque fixed to it: *The leg of a giant of old times, dug from the Thames silt, anno 1518.* The year I came to London. I touched it lightly, causing it to swing gently in its chains. It felt cold, like stone.

Barak reappeared and pointed me to a gloomy corner, setting two mugs of beer before us. 'The landlord says Master Miller and his friends don't usually come in before eight.' He took a long draught of beer. 'God's wounds, I've never seen the earl in such a parlous state.'

I leaned close, lowering my voice to a whisper. 'But Cromwell can't fall. Half the king's council are tied to him and London's a reformist city—'

He shook his head sadly. 'Londoners are fickle as seed. No one will help the earl if the Howards turn the king against him. Who would defy the king?'

The door opened and half a dozen big heavy fellows tramped in, their hands and smocks black with coal dust. The landlord signalled to them and Barak joined them at the hatch where beer was served, talking fast. Nods from the men indicated the conversation had come to a satisfactory conclusion, and Barak walked back to me, laying two more mugs of beer on the table.

'That's Hal Miller and his mates. They've been unloading coal all afternoon. They didn't want to talk to me at first, but I promised them money and showed them the earl's seal.'

The men took their drinks to a large table in the centre of the room. I followed Barak over to them. He introduced me as one of Lord Cromwell's officials and we sat down. The smell of coal dust made me want to sneeze.

'Been working hard, bullies?' Barak asked.

'All day,' one said. 'Coal for the king's bakeries.'

'Hard work in this heat,' I ventured.

'Aye, and not well rewarded,' another said, with a meaningful look at Barak, who nodded and slapped the purse at his belt, making the coins jingle.

'Which one of you is Hal Miller?' I asked, bringing matters to the point.

'I'm Hal.' A burly man in his forties spoke up.

'I wanted to talk to you about a new drink that was brought from the Baltic some months ago. I understand you had a part in trying to sell it.'

'I might have done,' he said. 'Why is Lord Cromwell interested?'

'Mere curiosity,' I said. 'He is interested in how it was made.'

'There were others who were interested. Others who threatened me.'

'Who?' I asked sharply.

'A man who called himself Toky.' Miller spat on the floor. 'He wanted to buy it from us.' Miller sat silent a moment, then said, 'Last autumn I was on a ship one of the merchant adventurers was running up to the Baltic Sea. We made landfall at a place called Libau. The Polacks there were keen to trade with us. We took on a cargo of furs, and a barrel of this stuff called wodky the Poles drink. We crewmen tried a little, but the stuff burned like fire. Captain Fenchurch brought half a barrel back with him.'

'What happened to it?'

'Captain Fenchurch paid us off in London. He'd no plans then for another voyage. So I went back to the colliers. But he gave me a bottle of the Polish stuff as a keepsake and I brought it here. Remember that night, Robin?'

'I'll not forget it.' One of the others, a young fellow, took up the tale. 'Hal came in and told us all about the Poles, then he brought out this bottle of pale stuff and passed it round, saying it was what they drank. Well, I took a long swig and thought my head was going to burst. I spat the stuff straight out across the table. It was winter and dark, and it hit the candle on the table and knocked it over and then, by Jesu, the whole table-top burst into a strange blue flame. Everyone jumped up and shouted out. But the fire died as quickly as it started, leaving hardly a mark on the table.'

'It was like witchcraft,' Miller said. 'After that I threw the stuff away.'

I frowned. 'You said this was in the winter.'

'Aye, January.'

'When did the man Toky approach you?'

Miller's eyes were watchful. 'Later that month, when we got back from Newcastle. The story had got around, see. He came here one night with another, a big man carrying an axe. Said he'd been asked to get some of this stuff, and his master would pay good money.'

'Did he say who his master was?'

'No, and we didn't ask. He didn't believe me at first when I said I'd chucked the bottle off Queenhithe dock. Started to get threatening, but he went away when I gave him Captain Fenchurch's address. I enquired after Fenchurch later, from one of his servants. Fenchurch had told the servant he'd sold the barrel on and made a handsome profit.'

'Who to?'

'The servant knew no more. The pock-faced man, I assumed.'

'Where does Captain Fenchurch live?'

'On the Bishopsgate Road, but he's abroad again. He's taken a ship to Sweden. He won't be back till the autumn.'

Then at least he had not been killed too. 'Thank you, anyway.' I nodded to Barak, who took out his purse and passed some coins to Miller.

I led the way outside, halting a little way from the inn.

'Stumped again,' Barak said. 'If only that captain hadn't gone abroad.'

I raised a hand. 'Think of the dates, Barak,' I said excitedly. 'Master Miller causes a great stir in the tavern in January. That's three months after the Greek Fire was found at Barty's, but two months *before* the Gristwoods contacted Bealknap. What were they doing in those months?'

'Building the apparatus and trying to produce more Greek Fire, using the formula! The Polish stuff must be part of it.' Barak looked excited.

'Or perhaps they heard the story of the fiery liquid, and sent Toky down here to try to get some to see if it could be of use.'

'But they must have known what they needed. They had the formula.'

'You'd think so, wouldn't you? So Toky's paymaster, whoever it was, was involved at a very early stage. Working *with* the Gristwoods.'

'But then why have Toky kill them?' He stared at me. 'Perhaps they went to Cromwell behind their first sponsor's back, looking for a better offer.'

'Then why wait until two months after the approach to Cromwell to kill them? And if the paymaster is one of our suspects, the Gristwoods wouldn't have used them as an intermediary to Cromwell.' I raised my eyebrows. 'I must talk to Bealknap, Barak. We need to lay hold of him.'

He gave me a serious look. 'What if Toky's got to him already?'

'I'd rather not think of that. Come on, we can check at Lincoln's Inn before we go home.'

At Lincoln's Inn there was only a note from Godfrey to say Bealknap had not returned. When we went to his chambers, his door was padlocked.

CHAPTER EIGHT

The next morning, after going to Lincoln's Inn to find no trace of Bealknap again, I rode over to meet Lady Honor.

I left Genesis at an inn stables near the river bank and walked down a crowded lane to Three Cranes Wharf where Marchamount's party was to meet. I had left off my robe for the occasion, donning a bright green doublet and my best hose.

The Thames was alive with wherries, barges and tilt boats. All London seemed to have come to the river to savour the breeze. A raucous crowd was waiting at the wharf for boats to take them across to the bear-baiting, and I saw Lady Honor standing with Marchamount by the river steps. Today she wore a black hood and a wide yellow farthingale. Her two attendant ladies and a pair of servants stood with her, together with young Henry Vaughan.

Lady Honor saw me and called out, 'Master Shardlake! The boat is here!'

I hurried across and bowed. 'I am sorry, I hope I've not kept you waiting.'

'Only a few minutes.' Her smile was warm.

Marchamount bowed briefly to me, then began ushering people officiously towards the river steps. 'Come along, everyone, before the tide turns.'

A tilt boat with four oarsmen was waiting, its bright blue sail flapping gently in the breeze. The party chattered merrily as they all stepped aboard.

I glanced at the head of the boat, where Lady Honor sat looking out over the river. Ahead, on the Southwark side, the high, circular bear-baiting arena loomed up. I sighed inwardly, for I had ever disliked watching the huge, terrified animals torn apart.

I felt a touch on my arm. Marchamount beckoned me to lean down so he could whisper to me. 'Are you closer to finding the missing papers?'

'My investigations continue—'

'I hope you will not be troubling Lady Honor further about them. She is a woman of great delicacy. I like to think she looks on me as a counsellor now that her poor husband is dead.' He smiled complacently.

I leaned in to Marchamount's ear. 'I've had my eye on you, Serjeant, by Lord Cromwell's authority. I know you have had conversations with Lady Honor involving matters of interest to yourself and to the Duke of Norfolk.'

'You have no right . . .' he blustered.

'I have every right, Serjeant, so don't pretend an authority you do not have in this matter. Your interest is of a romantic nature, I believe.'

His face reddened. 'Please say nothing about that. For her sake as well as mine. It is . . . it is embarrassing.'

'Be assured, I will say nothing. Nor about the duke being after her lands.'

His eyes widened briefly for a moment in surprise. 'Ah, yes, the lands,' he said a little too quickly. 'A privy matter.'

The boat hit the Bankside Steps, making us all jerk slightly. Looking at Marchamount clambering out ahead of me, I thought: He was surprised when I spoke of the duke being after Lady Honor's lands. Was it something different that Norfolk really wanted of her?

The bank was crowded with people, mostly of the common sort, heading for the baiting. Lady Honor sighed. 'Really, one wonders if coming here is worth it with all this crush and noise.'

'It will be, Lady Honor,' Marchamount said. 'There is a fine bear from Germany called Magnus being baited today. He's over six feet tall, killed five dogs yesterday and ended the day alive, though much bloodied.'

Lady Honor looked over at the high wooden amphitheatre. A great crowd was waiting by the gates, and cheering could already be heard from within: the old blind bears were already in the ring, the dogs loosed on them.

She sighed again. 'When is the great Magnus to be brought on?'

Marchamount did not appear to notice the ironic emphasis in her voice. 'Not for an hour or so.'

'I will join you then. I cannot stand that dreadful hurly-burly right now. If you will forgive me, I shall take a walk along the bank with my ladies.'

Marchamount looked crestfallen. 'As you wish, Lady Honor.'

'I'll join you, My Lady,' I said.

She smiled. 'Excellent. Company would be pleasant. Lettice, Dorothy, come along.' She turned and began walking upriver.

I stepped to her side. Her two women walked a few paces behind, with the pair of sword-carrying servants. A loud roar came from the stadium.

She made a moue of distaste. 'I can't stand the noise. And I was afraid I might faint; it would be so hot in there today, and smelling of blood. Ah, this is better.' A cloud had passed across the sun, easing the heat.

When we had walked some distance up the bank Lady Honor stopped and looked across the river at the bulk of Bridewell Palace. Her ladies and servants halted at the same moment, ten paces behind.

She looked at me seriously. 'Matthew, I do hope I am not in trouble with Lord Cromwell. It preys on my mind. Did you talk with him?'

'I repeated what you said. He spoke of you admiringly.'

She looked relieved. 'Yes, they all like coming to my banquets, Lord Cromwell and the duke and all the courtiers. But I know each side wonders if my sympathies lie with the other. When in truth'—she gave a little laugh—'I am with neither. I only ever wanted good conversation round my table.'

I hesitated. 'I spoke with Serjeant Marchamount in the boat coming over.'

'I saw your heads together. Were you checking what I had told you?'

'Yes, I had to. You must understand that. Marchamount appeared surprised when I said the Duke of Norfolk was after your lands.' I paused. 'My impression was that that was not the subject the two of them were discussing at the banquet, when he spoke of getting Marchamount to press you.'

'Am I to have no peace?' she asked softly. 'Matthew, I swore on the Bible that Norfolk has asked me no questions about Greek Fire and I swore truly. And it is true that he is after my lands. That is how it started.'

'How what started?'

'Something that became more complicated. A family matter that is none of your business.' She sighed wearily. 'I am going to say no more, Matthew. If you want you can tell Cromwell and he can have me brought before him. He will get the same answer. Some matters are private.'

'The days of private matters among aristocratic families are gone, My Lady. Such matters led to the wars of Lancaster and York.'

'Yes, all power is with the House of Tudor now. Yet is it not hard to take seriously, the king as head of the Church deciding how his people should relate to God, when his policy is ruled by his fickle passions?'

'That is dangerous talk, Lady Honor.'

'It's the talk of the streets. But you are right, these days we have to be careful what we say. We all have our responsibilities. Mine is to my family.'

'I am sorry I pressed you again, but—'

'No more, Matthew, I am weary. Walk with me a little further, to the next river stairs. I will send a servant back to say I have been taken faint.'

She screwed up her eyes as the hot sun appeared again, bringing sparkling waves of silver to the brown Thames water. We walked on slowly.

'Perhaps you think my devotion to family foolish,' Lady Honor said.

'Not foolish. Single-minded, perhaps.'

'Were not things better when the aristocracy owned the lands rather than it being turned over to these new men who put it to pasture and throw the peasantry on the road? Sheep eat men, they say.'

'Aye, and it is a great abuse. But it is better that people should have the chance to rise if they have the merit.'

'But so few have, Matthew, so few.' Her use of my Christian name gave me an unexpected frisson. 'I think you do, but you are not ordinary. There is such a thing as natural nobility.'

'You compliment me, Lady Honor,' I said, blushing, then added hastily, 'The king's government is full of new men. Cromwell, Richard Rich.'

She laughed. 'Rich. A cruel brute in a velvet doublet. His wife is a mere grocer's daughter. Besides, for every man who comes to town and manages to rise from the common herd, a thousand starve in the gutters.'

'Then measures should be taken for their welfare.'

'The lawyers and merchants in parliament will never allow that. Have they not put down all the reforms Cromwell had brought before them?'

I hesitated. 'Yes.'

'So much for your new man.'

I shook my head. 'Lady Honor, I think you are the cleverest woman I have met for a long time.'

'You are not used to bright converse from women, that is all.' She smiled at me. 'But I am glad you have known other women who were not content to drop their eyes and talk of cooking and embroidery.'

'I knew one.' I paused. 'I wished to marry her, but she would not have me.'

'Because of your . . . your condition?' Even Lady Honor struggled for a moment to find the appropriate word.

'Aye.' I looked away, across the river.

'You are a fool to worry about that. You will waste your opportunities. Perhaps you think all women seek in a man is a tall carriage and a fine calf.'

'Those do not harm a man's prospects.'

'They are no help if he has coarse features or a poor wit.'

I saw we had reached Barge House Stairs. A wherry stood there, waiting for business. 'Shall we cross here?' I asked. 'My horse is down by Three Cranes Wharf; we could return there.'

'Very well. A moment—I must send Paul back with a message or Gabriel Marchamount will think I have been robbed.' She walked over to where her servants and ladies stood, and spoke to the men. Then she picked up her skirts and began descending the steps.

In the boat the attendant ladies, one on either side of Lady Honor, cast curious glances at me from under lowered eyelids. I avoided their gaze.

When the boat bumped into the mud at Three Cranes Wharf, Lady Honor raised her eyebrows and smiled wryly. 'Well, here we are. I think I shall take the boat on to Queenhithe, then go home.' She paused. 'Visit me again soon. Give me news of how the converse with Lord Cromwell goes.'

'I will, Lady Honor.' I stood up and bowed. Planks had been set across the mud. I stepped on them gingerly, and by the time I had crossed to the steps, the boat was sculling down the river. I shouldered my way through the crowds to the stables and rode home with a mind sorely unsettled.

At last I reached Chancery Lane. As I let myself into my hall, Barak was walking downstairs. 'You're back early,' he said. 'Thank God. I wasn't sure I could keep her much longer.'

'Who?'

He did not answer, but walked back into my parlour. I followed him. There, sitting uneasily on a hard chair, was Madam Neller.

'She's back,' Barak said. 'Bathsheba Green.'

Madam Neller nodded. 'Came back last night with her brother, looking for shelter. Pock-face almost got them two days ago and they had to run from the friends they were with.' She looked at me fixedly. 'You promised me two more half-angels if I brought you the news.'

'You shall have them,' I said.

'I've persuaded them to talk to you. They'll meet you at the house of Michael Gristwood at Wolf's Lane. It's empty with his wife gone.'

'How do you know that?'

'George Green broke in a few days ago. Bathsheba kept pestering him to do it. There's something in the house she believes Michael was killed for.'

'What was it?' I hesitated. 'A piece of paper?'

She shrugged. 'I don't know. George got in through a window, twice, and the house was deserted. I don't think he found what he was after.' Madam Neller straightened her red wig. 'They'll meet you there tonight, after dark.' She looked at me again. I passed her two half-angels. She bit the coins and slipped them into her dress.

'Tell them we'll be there,' I said.

She heaved herself out of the chair and left without another word.

IT WAS after curfew and the streets of Queenhithe were quiet. The air was hot and still. In Wolf's Lane, candlelight shone from a few windows, but the Gristwood house was dark, sinister-looking in the moonlight.

I looked up uneasily at the shuttered windows. 'Where's the watchman?'

'I don't know. I've been looking out for him. Let's go.'

Barak knocked gently at the front door, jumping back in surprise as it swung open. The new lock had been smashed in.

Barak whistled. 'Insolent arseholes, they've broken it.'

'Madam Neller said George Green got in through a window.'

'You're right,' Barak said, kicking the door wide open. 'Hello!' he called. There was no reply. 'I don't like this,' he said. 'Something feels wrong.'

Barak stepped into the hall, sword raised. I followed him. He took out a tinderbox and handed me a pair of candles. 'Here, let's get these alight.'

He struck a spark and the tinder caught. I lit the candles. A dim yellow light flickered over the crooked walls and stairs.

'Let's try the kitchen,' Barak said. He opened the door and I followed him inside. 'Look there,' he whispered. I lowered my candle and saw the dusty floor was marked by footprints, several pairs.

'There's at least three sets there,' I whispered. 'This could be a trap.'

'Here!' Barak called, an urgency in his tone. He had drawn the shutters back and was looking out at the yard. The gate was wide open and something was lying against the wall beside it, a heap of deeper blackness.

'It's a man,' I said.

'It's the watchman! Come on!'

The door to the yard, like the front door, had been broken open. I looked up briefly at the shuttered windows, then joined Barak as he held his candle over the slumped figure by the gate. For a moment I hoped that the man was asleep in some drunken stupor, but then I saw the great wound in his head.

Barak stood up. 'You were right. It's a trap. Let's get out of here.'

Then we heard the sound. It came from inside the house, starting as a moan and rising to a keening wail, filled with sorrow and pain.

'It must be Bathsheba,' I said. 'We have to go to her.'

He took a deep breath, then raised his sword once more. I followed him back through the kitchen, into the hall. The house was silent again except for a slow drip-drip of water from somewhere.

Then the moaning began again, and broke into choking sobs. I looked up the dark staircase. 'That came from Sepultus's workshop.'

Barak held his sword ready, and mounted the stairs holding the candle. I followed slowly. The workshop door was open. Barak stepped inside. I followed him, nearly gagging at the awful stench.

'Oh Jesus,' Barak whispered. 'Oh, our Saviour.'

The room was still bare except for Sepultus's large table. Young George Green was lying sprawled across it. His throat had been cut; the table was covered with dark blood that dripped slowly to the floor. Sprawled over him, weeping, was Bathsheba, her dress torn and soaked with blood.

Barak was the first to move. He crossed to Bathsheba and leaned over her. 'It's all right,' he said. 'We won't harm you. Who did this?'

I stood beside him as Bathsheba tried to speak. To my horror, when she opened her mouth a foamy trickle of blood spilled out; she too was badly hurt. She managed only to moan again. I tried to see where she was injured, but it was too dark and she would not let go of her brother's body.

'It's all right,' I whispered. 'Don't speak. We'll help you.'

She lifted wild eyes to me. 'Get . . . out . . . while you can.'

Barak turned to the doorway, but there was nothing there. The house was silent. Then we heard a door open downstairs, the parlour, I was sure. A sudden harsh smell stung my nostrils, making me cough.

Barak caught it too. His eyes widened. 'Shit,' he shouted. 'No—'

An extraordinary noise came from downstairs, a loud *whump*. It was followed by a crash as someone threw shutters open. Barak and I dashed to the window. I made out the shapes of two men, running down the street. Toky and Wright.

'Oh Jesu.' I turned at Barak's voice. He was standing in the doorway, looking out. I could see the staircase was lit with a red, dancing light.

I ran to the door and stood beside him, hardly able to believe what I saw. The door to the parlour was wide open and the room was alive with fire. A heavy, evil-smelling black smoke began rolling across the hall.

'Jesu,' Barak breathed. 'It's Greek Fire. They mean to kill us with it!' He turned to Bathsheba. 'We've got to get out of here. Help me with her!'

I helped him lift the girl from her brother's body. Weak as she was, she tried to resist; she looked at me and I caught a throaty bubbling, 'No.'

'Your brother is dead,' I said gently. 'You can't help him.'

As Barak and I lifted her up I saw fresh blood run down her dress from a wound in her stomach. The poor creature had been stabbed.

'Hold her,' Barak said. He ran back to the door. The flames were almost at the bottom of the staircase. I caught a whiff of the smoke and gagged.

Barak paused a second, then grasped the workshop door and, with a tremendous heave, pulled it free of its remaining hinge. 'Follow me! Quick, before the staircase goes! Come on!'

Holding the door in front of him like a shield, Barak stepped across to the staircase and began descending. Flames were licking at the banisters, smoke curling upwards from the ground floor. This was the thing I had always feared: death by fire. I stood, paralysed. I had a terror that the staircase would collapse and bury us in burning wood.

Barak turned round and screamed at me. 'Come on, you arsehole! We've only seconds! See, there's the front door!'

His words brought me to my senses. Across the burning hallway I could just make out the half-open door to the street. It spurred me to follow him, dragging the girl with me. From outside I heard a cry of 'Fire! Dear God, fire!' The smoke stung my eyes and Barak and I were both coughing now.

Suddenly I was at the foot of the steps, red flames all around me. I heard Barak scream, 'Run!' I thought I was about to fall, but then a flame licked at my arm and from somewhere I found the energy to leap forward. In a moment I was outside in the street, the searing heat and the smoke gone. Someone grasped me and I fell into their arms. Someone else took Bathsheba's weight and she slid away from me. I was lowered to the street and lay gasping, every intake of air burning my throat.

At length my breath returned and I sat up groggily. Ahead of me the Gristwoods' house was ablaze and the fire had already spread to the neighbouring house. People were running to and fro with terrified faces, calling for water, desperate to save their homes. I saw Barak sitting beside me, retching and coughing. Next to him lay Bathsheba, still as death. Barak turned to me, his face black and all the hair on one side of his head gone.

'You all right?' he gasped.

'I think so.'

A man in a watchman's jerkin bustled over to us, his face alive with fury. 'What have you done to set the house on fire like that?' he shouted.

'We didn't do it,' Barak croaked. 'Fetch a physician; a woman's hurt here.'

The man looked at Bathsheba, his eyes widening as he saw the blood covering her. I shook my head, the tumult of shouts and running feet seemed to have taken on a strangely distant, echoing sound. Then the noise of the fire and the shouting faded away, and I blacked out.

I CAME TO SLOWLY, as though swimming up from a dark lake. I could not remember what had happened or where I was. I tried to sit up but lay down again with a groan. My back was agony, I had a smarting pain in my left forearm and I was thirsty, a terrible dry thirst—when I swallowed it was like gulping down thorns. I tried to call out but could only croak. I leaned over, wincing at a sharp pain from my left arm, and banged on the floor.

I heard movement downstairs, then footsteps. Guy came in, carrying a large flagon and a cup. His face was drawn with anxiety and lack of sleep.

'Wa—water,' I croaked.

He sat on the bed and lifted my head to the cup. 'Do not gulp it,' he said. 'You will want to, but you must take small sips or you will be sick.'

I nodded, letting him trickle water slowly into my mouth. At length I lay back, noticing that my arm was bandaged. 'What happened?' I whispered.

'You were brought here insensible last night, on a cart with Barak and the girl Bathsheba. You are suffering from the effects of smoke and you have a burn on your arm.' He looked at me seriously. 'The fire has caused much damage. Two streets at Queenhithe were burned down. Thank the Lord they were so close to the river—they were able to draw water from there.'

'Is anyone hurt?'

'I do not know. Your friend Barak has gone to rouse Lord Cromwell; he says he will need to deal with this. Barak was affected by the smoke too. I told him he should not go out but he insisted.'

'Bathsheba,' I said. 'The girl, how is she?'

Guy's face darkened. 'She has been stabbed in the stomach; there is little I can do. I have given her some drugs to ease her pain and she is sleeping. But it is only a matter of time. Who did that to her, Matthew?'

'The same villain who set fire to the house and left me and Barak to burn to death. There were two more bodies: the girl's brother and the watchman.'

'Dear Christ.' Guy crossed himself. 'I went out while you were sleeping to buy some things I needed. There are rumours abroad that the fire was started by supernatural means. Apparently, it roared up suddenly and consumed the ground floor of the house in a moment.'

'It did,' I said. 'I was there. But there is no magic, Guy, I swear. An ancient way of making fire rediscovered, that is all. It is what I have been working on for Cromwell. I could not tell you.'

He looked at me questioningly. 'I see. Your friend distrusts me. Perhaps you did too, if this matter affects Cromwell whom, yes, I see as an enemy. I wondered why you would not tell me more.'

'I don't distrust you, Guy. God's wounds, you're the only one left I do trust.'

WHEN BARAK returned an hour later, Guy brought him to my room and left us together. Barak's eyes were red and smarting and his voice was a strangled croak. The hair on the right side of his head was singed away. The contrast with the untidy brown locks on the other side was so bizarre I could not help letting out a bark of nervous laughter.

He grunted. 'You should see your own face: it's black as soot. And Lord Cromwell's not laughing. He'll have to put pressure on the mayor and coroner to keep this quiet. It's lucky there was no wind or the fire could have spread across the City.'

'Was anyone else hurt?'

'A few have burns and plenty more are homeless. The Gristwoods' house is a pile of ashes. Goodwife Gristwood will have no home to come back to.'

'No. Poor old creature.' I paused. 'Well, now I've seen it. That was Greek Fire, wasn't it?'

'Yes, I recognised the smell as the fire started. Those bastards must have been waiting in the parlour till we were trapped upstairs. They must have coated the walls with the stuff, set light to it, then got out the window.' He sat down on the bed. 'But why try to kill us in that way?'

'To show Lord Cromwell they had Greek Fire.'

'That they could make and use it at will.'

'Yes. That was what they wanted him to think.' I looked at him again. 'Thank you, Barak. I would not have got out of that house without you. For a moment there I could not move from fear. How did you get us here?'

'I grabbed a horse and cart that had been used to bring water and got you and the girl on it. I was afraid we'd be arrested or slain on the spot. I couldn't think where to go, then I remembered your apothecary lived nearby.'

I nodded. His quick thinking had saved us.

'How is the girl?' he asked.

'Like to die, Guy said. Are you all right?'

He winced. 'I got burned on the shoulder as I went through the door.'

There was a knock and Guy entered. 'The girl is awake,' he said quietly. 'She wants to speak to you. I don't think she can last long.'

He led us into a room where Bathsheba lay on a bed, her eyes closed. Gently, he touched Bathsheba on the shoulder and her eyes flickered open. 'Mistress Green, I have brought them as you asked.'

Bathsheba stared at us. She said something, her voice so faint I could not hear. I took a stool and sat beside her. She turned and looked at me.

'They were waiting for George and me. They rushed in at us with their swords. That man with the scarred face struck me in the stomach.' She shuddered. 'They left us for dead, said they would give the hunchback lawyer a spectacular death when he arrived.' She closed her eyes, exhausted.

'How did they know you were there?' I asked gently.

'Madam Neller must have told them. She'd do anything for gold.' She winced with pain, then opened her eyes again and spoke rapidly. 'I want to tell you what Michael said to me. If it will help you find them.'

I tried to smile. 'Go on. You are safe now.'

'Those last weeks before he was killed Michael was afraid. He said he and his brother were involved in a scheme that could make them rich. It involved some papers he had at his house. He feared for their safety.'

'Madam Neller said your brother had been searching there.'

'Yes. He thought if he could find them, perhaps Lord Cromwell would help us. But they'll all be burned to cinders now.'

'I already have the papers, Bathsheba. Except for one that is missing. A formula. Did Michael say anything about that?'

'No. Only that he feared the people they were working with. He feared they would be killed. They were working to bring down Lord Cromwell.'

'But . . . but I thought he was working *with* Cromwell. He had something the earl wanted badly.'

'No. No, the scheme was *against* the earl.'

I stared at her. It made no sense. She coughed and winced, then looked at me again. 'We were going to have a child. Michael talked of us escaping the country, going to Scotland or France and starting afresh. But then he was killed. That man last night killed my baby when he stabbed me.'

I took her hand. It was as light and thin as a bird's foot. 'I am sorry.'

'What do our lives matter?' she asked bitterly. 'What are any of us but pawns in the schemes of the great?' She closed her eyes.

Barak leaned forward, put a finger to the pulse in the girl's neck. 'She's gone,' he said quietly.

Guy knelt by the bed and began praying softly in Latin.

'What good's that going to do?' Barak asked harshly.

I rose and took his arm, leading him from the room. We returned to my chamber and I sat back on the bed, exhausted.

'Poor bitch,' Barak said. 'I'm sorry, I didn't mean any disrespect to the Moor.' He ran a hand through what was left of his hair. 'What in heaven's name did she mean, Michael was involved in a plot *against* Lord Cromwell?'

'I don't know. But there are things that don't add up. Toky's involvement from the beginning, investigating that Polish stuff months before the Gristwoods went to Cromwell. Why the delay? And there are other things—'

I broke off as Guy entered, carrying a bowl of water and some cloths. There was an awkward silence. 'I must dress your arm, Matthew,' he said.

'I've a burn on my shoulder,' Barak said. 'Could you look at that too?'

Guy nodded. Barak took off his shirt, revealing a muscular torso boasting a number of scars from old knife thrusts. One shoulder was red and raw, the skin peeling. Guy coated the burn with a harsh-smelling oil, then sent him back to his room while he dressed my arm. I winced as he applied some of his oil to the livid red mark, the puckered skin.

'What is that stuff?'

'Oil of lavender. It draws the heat from the fire that has stung your flesh.'

I looked at him seriously. 'There is a fire I think no amount of lavender could quench. Guy, I was going to talk to you anyway about the matter that has caused all this death and ruin. It involves alchemy, as I told you, and there are aspects that have me puzzled. I would tell you all, if you will listen.'

'Cromwell would not be pleased, I think,' he said as he bound my arm with a strip of cloth. 'I note you have waited till friend Barak was gone.'

'I'll take the risk if you will.'

'Very well.'

I told him all I knew of Greek Fire, from Cromwell's first summons to the fire last night. As he listened his face grew more troubled.

'Have you considered the havoc Greek Fire may wreak? It could burn whole navies. It could be used to fire a city, as we saw last night.'

'I know,' I said quietly. 'But, Guy, if Cromwell does not get it, others will, foreign powers who would use it against England.'

'And take her back to Rome?' He raised his eyebrows, and I remembered he was neither English nor Protestant.

'I know that there was a barrel of Greek Fire kept at Barty's for a hundred years,' I continued. 'And there was a formula. The Gristwoods used the period between their discovery last October and their approach to Cromwell in March to build their apparatus and to try to make some more. With two ships destroyed, most of the barrel is probably used up. That they could set that fire last night may indicate they have made more. But *how*, Guy?'

'Without the formula, it is impossible to tell.'

I sat up. 'I have been reading about the history of fire weapons in the east. The Byzantines had no problem creating the liquid that is set on fire. Similar substances are mentioned by the Romans, but they were not developed as weapons. I think perhaps a crucial ingredient of Greek Fire is hard to get. The Gristwoods may have been looking for a substitute for it. This could have led them to the Polish drink that burned the table at the tavern.'

He stroked his chin. 'So they used that to make Greek Fire?'

'I don't know. Perhaps.'

'And, from what you say, they were already working with the rogues who were to become their killers in a plot *against* Cromwell?'

'Yes. I don't know how that came about.'

Guy looked serious. 'This thing of ruin and destruction is a monstrosity. If you find that formula, you should destroy it and the world will be safer.'

I sighed. 'I am bound to Cromwell. And to help my country.'

'And how do you think Cromwell, and King Henry, would use Greek Fire, ruthless men of blood that they are? For murder and mayhem, that is how.' He was angry. 'Cromwell has used you to aid him in a cruel blasphemy.'

I bit my lip. 'You do well to upbraid me,' I said. 'I have worried about what Greek Fire may do, but I have been driven on by a passion to catch these murderers, recover what was stolen. And to save Elizabeth Wentworth. At any cost.'

'That cost may be too high. You must decide when the time comes, Matthew. It will be between you and God.'

IT WAS LATE morning by the time we arrived home. I opened the front door quietly, hoping we might get upstairs without Joan seeing our sorry condition, but paused at the sight of a note in Godfrey's hand on the table.

I broke the seal. 'Bealknap's back!' I said. 'He's in his chambers. Thank God, I feared he might be . . .' I did not finish the sentence.

'Let's go to Lincoln's Inn, then,' Barak said.

Just then Joan appeared from the kitchen, alerted by our voices. Her eyes widened at the state we were in. 'Sir, what's happened now?' There was a quaver in her voice. 'When you didn't come back last night I was worried.'

'There's been a bad fire over at Queenhithe,' I said gently. 'We were caught up in it, but we're all right, Joan.'

'You look worn out, sir. What happened to your hair, Master Barak?'

'It got singed. I look monstrous, hey?' He gave her his most charming smile. 'I need someone to cut the other side, so I don't frighten the children.'

'I could have a try.'

'You are a pearl among women, Mistress Woode.'

While Joan fetched some scissors, I went up to my bedroom. I shut my door and leaned on it wearily. Guy's words returned to me. I had been too tired, too frightened to think much further than uncovering the conspirators. But what if I were to succeed? What would I do if the Greek Fire formula were in *my* hands? I shook my head. For now there was nothing to do but go on. It was the 5th of June—only five days left.

AT LINCOLN'S INN I left Barak in my rooms, then crossed the courtyard to Marchamount's chambers. His clerk said he was out at Hertford and would not be back until the morrow. Cursing inwardly, I told the clerk I would return on the morrow also, and went back to where Barak waited, watching Skelly copying out the application for the Chancery writ for Bealknap's case.

I knocked at Godfrey's door and went in. He was standing at the window, a troubled expression on his thin face. He gave me a watery smile.

'Are you all right, Godfrey?'

He fingered the hem of his robe. 'It seems the Duke of Norfolk is not satisfied with my fine. He wants a public apology in hall.'

I sighed. 'Well, Godfrey, you did break all the rules of courtesy—'

'You know it is not about that!' he snapped out. 'However it is worded, it will be taken as an apology for my religious beliefs.'

I closed my eyes for a moment, then looked at him. 'You won't apologise, will you?'

He smiled gently, a fierce holy light in his eyes. 'No, Matthew, I will not.'

WE MOUNTED the narrow stairs to Bealknap's rooms. The padlock had been taken away. I knocked on the door and Bealknap himself opened it.

'Brother,' I said, 'I have been trying to find you. Where have you been?'

He frowned. 'On business.' He eyed Barak's shorn head as we stepped inside. 'Who's this? And what do you want?'

Bealknap's chamber was as untidy as ever, the chest prominent in its corner. The door to his living quarters was open.

I turned back to Bealknap and saw his face was red with outrage. 'You remember I have a commission from Lord Cromwell?'

'I told you all I knew about that matter. Which was next to nothing.'

'I want to know the nature of your connection with Sir Richard Rich.'

'That is none of your damned business,' he said stoutly. 'Yes, I have a commission from Sir Richard, I work for him. It is his business I have been on these last few days. And I will not be questioned about that.'

'If you do not answer my questions I shall go to Lord Cromwell.'

'Then he can speak to Sir Richard.' Bealknap nodded. 'I shall go to him now. You are out of your depth, sir; you have been dabbling in matters that are beyond you. Now, out of my chambers.' He threw open the door.

Barak clenched his fists. 'Lord Cromwell can have you on the rack, you great bony arsehole.'

Bealknap laughed. 'I think not, though he might make your arses smart after my master and he have spoken. Now leave!' He waved at the door.

There was nothing left but to go. As soon as we were outside, the door was slammed behind us. We stood on the landing.

'Well, that went well,' Barak said sarcastically.

'What can Rich have to say to Cromwell that will turn his anger onto us?' I shook my head. 'Cromwell is the chief secretary; Rich is a big fish but nowhere near that big.'

'And what does he know about Greek Fire? I'm going to have to get word to the earl about this.' He began descending the stairs.

I followed him. 'Do you know where Cromwell is today?'

'Whitehall again. I'll ride there now. You go home and rest. You look like you need it. Do nothing till I return.'

I wondered if he and Cromwell might have things to say he did not want me to hear. But if he did, there was nothing I could do about that.

IT WAS two hours before Barak returned. I was waiting for him in my parlour, looking out over the garden as the afternoon shadows lengthened. As he stepped inside, he blew out his cheeks.

'The earl was fierce with me,' he said bluntly. 'He was furious to hear your efforts to make Bealknap talk had sent him off to Rich.'

'I wasn't to know Rich could be a shield against Cromwell.'

'He can't. The earl was outraged at the very idea. He thinks Rich has been exaggerating his powers to Bealknap and Bealknap believed him. He's sending men out now to find Rich.'

I frowned. 'Bealknap's every sort of rogue, but he's no fool. He wouldn't have said what he did unless he knew he was safe.'

'Cromwell was prowling around his office at Whitehall like a bear in a pit, ready to lash out. And he's scared,' Barak said. He slumped down on the cushions. His face had a grey tinge; the events of last night were catching up with even his powerful constitution. He sighed. 'We must see what the earl gets out of Rich. He'll send a message once he's talked to him.'

'And Marchamount is back tomorrow. I'll go into chambers and see him.'

Barak nodded, then looked up at me. 'Are you up to trying the well tonight? There won't be a message from the earl for hours.'

I was far from up to it; I ached with tiredness from head to toe and my arm hurt. But I had promised, and after all it was for Elizabeth that I had agreed to do everything else in the first place. I nodded wearily. 'Let us both get some rest, and some food, then we will go.'

THE SUN had set by the time we came downstairs. Joan had prepared a pottage for us, which she brought to the parlour.

Barak scratched at his near-bald pate. 'This itches, damn it. I'll have to wear a cap when I go out from now on. I hate the way people stare at me—' He was interrupted by a loud knock at the front door. 'That'll be the message,' he said, rising. 'That was quick.'

But it was Joseph Wentworth that Joan showed into the parlour.

'Joseph,' I said. 'What has happened?'

'I've come from Newgate,' he said. 'She's dying, sir. Elizabeth is dying.'

And then the big man burst into tears, covering his face with his hands.

I made him sit down and tried to calm him. 'What has happened?' I asked again gently.

'These last two days Elizabeth has had another cellmate: a mad beggar girl who has been accusing all she meets of abducting her little brother.'

'We saw her the other day—'

'She made trouble at a baker's shop in Cheapside. She was picked up by the constable and taken to the Hole. When I went to visit Lizzy this morning the turnkey told me the child had been removed to the Bedlam. But when he went to take them food last night, he heard Lizzy and the girl talking. He remarked it; it was the first time he had heard Elizabeth speak.'

'What was the girl's name?'

'Sarah, I believe.' He sighed. 'When I went to see Lizzy this evening, she was lying insensible, her face burning hot to the touch. She has gaol fever.'

Barak and I exchanged glances. Outbreaks of fever were common in gaols and if Elizabeth had it, her chances were slim.

I rose wearily. 'I'll come to the gaol. They have good rooms for those who can pay. And I know an apothecary who can cure her if anyone can. He is a physician, though as a foreigner he is not allowed to practise here.'

'I'll come if you like,' Barak said.

'You will?' Joseph stared at him a little as he noticed his shaven head.

'Thank you, Barak. Then come, I will get Simon to run to Guy with a note, ask him to come to Newgate.' I stood up. From somewhere I had found a last reserve of energy. If Elizabeth died now, after all my decision to act for her had led me into, the irony would be so dark as to be beyond bearing.

CHAPTER NINE

The gaoler was angry at being woken until I pressed a shilling into his hand. He summoned the turnkey, who led us to the Hole. Quickly unlocking the door, he retreated and stood against the opposite wall. Elizabeth lay insensible on the straw, her limbs askew, her colour high. I put my hand to her brow. Joseph was right—she was burning.

I motioned the others to go back outside and went over to the turnkey. 'Listen,' I said, 'I know you have comfortable rooms upstairs.'

'Only for those that can pay.'

'We'll pay,' I said. 'Take me back to the gaoler.'

The turnkey locked the door again and, motioning the others to remain behind, I followed him back up to the gaoler's chamber. The gaoler was sitting at his table, a worried look on his hard features.

'We want to get her out of these foul airs,' I said. 'I'll pay for a good room.'

The gaoler shook his head. 'Moving her will spread the humours of her fever round the gaol. And the judge's order was she was to stay in the Hole.'

'I'll answer to Forbizer. I have an apothecary who may be able to help her. He might be able to cure her fever. Then it won't spread, eh?'

He pursed his lips. 'Two shillings a night's the price. I'll show you where to take her.' Even in his terror of gaol fever, greed glinted in his sharp eyes.

'Agreed,' I said. I reached for my purse and held up a gold half-angel. 'For five nights. That'll cover her till she goes before Forbizer.'

That seemed to decide the wretch. He held out his hand for the coin.

THE TOWER room my half-angel had bought was four floors up from the Hole. The gaoler walked well ahead with a candle while Barak and Joseph carried Elizabeth up the stone steps. As I clambered up behind them, I knew my strength was ebbing—I could not possibly make it to the well that night.

We were shown into a light, airy room with a good bed with a blanket, a ewer of water on a table and a large window, which though barred was at least open. Joseph and Barak laid Elizabeth on the bed.

She seemed unaware of her removal, only stirring slightly and moaning.

'My apothecary should be here soon,' I said.

'You are generous, sir,' Joseph said. 'How much—?'

I raised a hand. 'No, Joseph, we can discuss that later. Barak, you look exhausted. You should go home. I need you fit.'

He nodded reluctantly and went out. Joseph and I stood in silence, listening to Elizabeth's fevered breathing.

GUY ARRIVED an hour later. The gaoler himself fetched him up, goggling at his brown face till I bade him to be gone. I introduced Guy to Joseph, who likewise stared at him in surprise, although Guy affected not to notice.

'So this is the poor girl whose travails have worried you so,' he said to me.

'Yes.' I told him of the onset of her fever.

He looked at her for a long moment. 'I don't think it's gaol fever,' he said at length. 'The fever would be higher. I'm not sure what it is. But I shall give her something to stop her burning up, and it would be good if she were to be washed and that filthy dress taken off her.'

Joseph blushed. 'It would hardly be proper for me to see her unclothed—'

'I will do it, if you like. In my trade a naked body is hardly a new sight. Could you buy her a shift tomorrow and bring it here?'

'Yes. Yes, I will, sir.' Joseph paused. 'Is there any hope?' he asked.

'I do not know,' Guy said frankly. 'This may be one of those cases where much depends on the sufferer's will to live. And now, if you will leave me, I will wash her.'

Joseph and I waited outside while Guy carried out his task. 'I cannot help being angered, sir,' he said. 'But I love her; for all she has put me through, I still love her.'

I touched his shoulder. 'That is very plain, Joseph.'

At length Guy called us back. He had laid Elizabeth under the blanket and lit some sort of sweet-smelling oil in a lamp. A cloth, black with dirt, floated in the ewer. Elizabeth's face was clean, the first time I had seen it so.

'What is that smell?' Joseph asked.

'An infusion of lemons to lift her spirit.' Guy looked at us. 'You both look exhausted. You should sleep. I will stay with her till morning, if you wish.'

'I could not ask that—' Joseph protested.

'Please, I would be happy to.'

'I would stay a little,' I said.

Joseph left, with fulsome thanks, his footsteps clattering down the stairs.

'There are only five days now till the demonstration before the king.' I sighed, watching the motionless girl. 'The day Elizabeth goes back to court.'

As though in response to her name Elizabeth stirred, her legs moving beneath the blanket. 'Sarah,' she muttered again, then, 'That evil boy.' And then her eyes fluttered open and she looked at us uncomprehendingly.

'Miss Wentworth,' Guy said softly, 'you are in a clean room in the prison. You have a fever. I am Guy Malton, an apothecary. Your good uncle and Master Shardlake had you brought here.'

I leaned over her. Her eyes were heavy with fever but she seemed fully sensible. Knowing this was a chance that might never come again, I said slowly, 'We are still trying to find the truth, Elizabeth. We are trying to save you. I know there is something in the well at your uncle's house—'

She shrank back. 'The death of God,' she whispered. 'The death of God.'

'What?' I asked, but her eyes closed again.

I made to shake her but Guy held my arm. 'Do not distress her further.

The death of God is despair. When I was a monk sometimes one of my brethren would lose his faith, succumb to despair. Usually they came back to faith, but until they did it felt as though God was dead.'

WHEN I ARRIVED home, Barak had already gone to his room. I hauled myself upstairs and fell fully clothed onto the bed, falling asleep at once. I jolted awake to the bright light of morning, the bells of London's hundred churches clamouring in the distance. It was Sunday, the 6th of June.

I dressed then stumbled downstairs to find Barak sitting at the parlour table, staring gloomily at a letter.

'From Cromwell?' I asked, taking a seat.

'Aye. It's from Hampton Court; he must be there on business for the king.' He tossed the paper over to me. It was in Cromwell's own hand.

I have spoken to Rich. You have both been worrying at the wrong hare; his schemes with that churl Bealknap have nothing to do with Greek Fire. Continue your investigations, for what they are worth, and I will see you at Whitehall tomorrow, when I return to London.

I laid the letter on the table. 'He's not pleased with us.'

'No. What in God's name were Bealknap and Rich up to?'

'We shall find out tomorrow. Today there is Marchamount to deal with.'

I ate a hasty breakfast, then we walked along the dusty lane to the Inn.

'Elizabeth had a moment of consciousness last night,' I said. 'I mentioned the well again and she said, "The death of God". Guy said it means she's in despair. And she said something about the girl and "that evil boy".'

'Her young cousin or the mad girl's brother?'

'I don't know.' I looked at him. 'But we must go to the well tonight.'

He nodded. 'I want to see the truth of this too.'

I hoped Marchamount would be in. As we entered the courtyard I saw the service had ended in the chapel and the lawyers were filing out. I picked out Marchamount among the throng, his robe billowing around his portly form. We caught up with him at the door to his chambers.

He looked round in surprise. 'Brother Shardlake, this is an unexpected meeting.' He stared at Barak. 'Who is this?'

'An agent of Lord Cromwell's. He is helping me on the Greek Fire matter.'

Barak took off his cap and made a little bow.

Marchamount frowned, but permitted us to follow him to his private room. There he sat in his throne-like chair and gave us a haughty stare.

I leaned forward. 'On Friday, in the boat to Southwark, Serjeant, we spoke of a certain pressure the Duke of Norfolk was putting on you, to obtain something from Lady Honor. You confirmed he wanted to obtain some of the Vaughan lands in return for furthering young Henry Vaughan to a place at the king's court.'

Marchamount sat very still. I knew at once I had struck a nerve.

'I thought you seemed evasive in the boat, so while you attended the bear-baiting, I asked Lady Honor about the matter on our walk—'

'Sir, you had no right. For a gentleman to ask—'

'Lady Honor told me the matter began with pressure from the duke over the land, but then it developed into something else. She refused to say more, but I need to know what it was. No evasions, Marchamount, the whole story.'

He sat back in his chair. 'It is nothing to do with Greek Fire.'

'Then why is it so secret?'

'Because it is shameful.' He frowned, reddening. 'You know I had a romantic interest in Lady Honor.' He took a deep breath. 'She would not have me and I would not press a lady who rejected me.' He fingered his emerald ring, then looked me in the eye. 'But the duke would.'

'The *duke*?'

He frowned. 'He does not just want her family lands in return for helping that boy. He wants Lady Honor as his mistress.'

'Dear God, poor Lady Honor.'

'He would not approach her directly'—he laughed bitterly—'he made me act as intermediary. It was a job I disliked but I could not gainsay the Duke of Norfolk. He said the Vaughan boy's a fool and a weakling, which is true enough, and he'd have to exert a mighty effort to get him accepted at court. He wanted a high price in return. Lady Honor has refused him time and again.' He shifted uneasily. 'But I have had to try to persuade her.'

'What has he promised you in return? Help towards a knighthood?'

'To advance one's family is not dishonourable.'

'Thirty pieces of silver would be the right reward for you,' I said.

Barak laughed harshly and Marchamount gave him a furious look. He glared at me, his face reddening further. 'How dare you talk to me like that! And you—you are no impartial witness. You lust after her yourself.'

'Come, Serjeant, you are losing control of yourself. So that is the whole story, is it?' I asked. 'No connection at all to Greek Fire?'

The merest hesitation. 'I have told you before, I know nothing of that.' He began to bluster. 'You have troubled me enough with this. No gentleman—'

I stood. 'Come, Barak. I think I have an apology to make to Lady Honor.'

Barak got up and made another bow to Marchamount, a mocking one.

The serjeant glared at me. 'You have embarrassed me, Shardlake, in front of this churl,' he said. 'I will not forget it.'

IN THE COURTYARD, I turned to Barak. 'He's still keeping something back— I'd swear he is. But what? I'll have to talk to Lady Honor again.'

'She won't be pleased you know this story.'

'There's no help for it. I must go there after visiting my chambers.'

We crossed the courtyard and I entered the office to find Godfrey working quietly at his desk. 'Here on the Sabbath?' I asked.

He looked at me seriously. 'God will forgive me. I want to get my cases in order. Word is I am to be disbarred if I don't apologise to the duke.'

'What will you do if you leave chambers?'

'Become a preacher. I believe that is what God is calling me to do.'

'Dangerous times may be coming.' The hideous tangle of loyalties I was caught in made me feel faint and I clutched at the edge of a chair.

'Are you all right, Matthew?'

I nodded. 'I have been working hard.'

'At least no more of your cases have gone,' he said.

'Good. I may not be in for a few days now, Godfrey.'

I stepped back into the office, where Barak was waiting.

'I'm going to Lady Honor's now,' I told him.

'I'll ride with you,' he said. 'Then I can call in at the Old Barge.'

We fetched the horses and rode down to the City, where we parted company at the Walbrook. Barak went off to send a message to Cromwell, saying that he would call to collect me in an hour at Lady Honor's.

At the House of Glass I passed Genesis to a stableboy and was ushered through the house to the inner courtyard where Lady Honor was sitting on a bench. She wore a blue dress and her blonde hair was uncovered today.

She smiled in welcome. 'Matthew. This is an unexpected visit.'

I bowed. 'I apologise for coming unannounced. But—'

'Official business?'

'I fear so.'

She took a deep breath. 'Come then, sit with me.'

'Lady Honor,' I said. 'I have spoken to Marchamount. I needed to follow up the question you left me with on the river bank. I know about the Duke of Norfolk's pursuit of you.'

I half expected anger but she only turned away and stared ahead for a moment. When she turned back to me her face wore a tired smile. 'After we spoke on the river I feared you would report me to Cromwell. Did you ask Marchamount first to save me from the earl's rough ways?'

'Perhaps. I am sorry I could not save you from my knowing.'

'At least you will not gossip like most would.' She laid a hand on mine for a second, then lifted it. 'You are a natural gentleman.' She sighed. 'I have sent Henry back to the country and so I am able to reject that old brute's crude advances with a clear conscience.'

'I did not realise you disliked the duke so.'

'He is unfit for the position he occupies. He may be the senior peer of the realm, but his lineage is not old.' She smiled. 'Unlike the Vaughans'.'

I took a deep breath. 'Lady Honor, I must ask—for the last time, I promise—is there anything you have not told me that could possibly be of relevance to my search for the Gristwoods' murderers?'

She looked at me impatiently. 'Matthew, I swore on the Bible that the duke had put no pressure on me about Greek Fire. And I swore true.'

I looked into her eyes. 'I felt when Marchamount spoke about the duke and you this morning he was still keeping something back.'

'If he did, it is nothing to do with me, I swear. Shall I fetch the Bible again?'

I shook my head. 'No. That is not necessary. Forgive me.'

She looked at me indulgently. 'You are a courteous inquisitor.'

'Marchamount would not agree.'

'That puffed-up creature is a rogue.' She shuddered. 'I am thinking of escaping to my Lincolnshire estates. I have had enough of Marchamount and the duke and everyone.' She smiled quickly. 'Almost everyone.'

'I would miss you. Though I have also been thinking of the country.'

She looked at me in surprise. 'Would not the country bore you?'

'I come from Lichfield—my father has the freehold of a farm there. He is old now and his steward is not getting any younger. I do not visit enough.'

She laid her hand on mine again and inclined her head towards me. Then she jerked away as footsteps sounded in the yard. I turned to see Barak standing there with the steward, cap in hand.

Barak was grinning broadly. 'Come at a bad time, have I?' he asked.

Lady Honor stood, her face dark with anger. 'Matthew, do you know this fellow?'

I rose too. 'This is Jack Barak,' I said hastily. 'He is assisting me. He works for Lord Cromwell.'

'Then the earl should teach him some manners.' She rounded on him. 'How dare you burst in on us like this?'

Barak reddened, his eyes angry. 'I have a message for Master Shardlake from Lord Cromwell.'

'What is the matter with your head? Do you have nits? You had better not spread them in my house.' She spoke with a harshness I had never heard from her, but Barak had been extremely discourteous.

'I am sorry, Lady Honor,' I said quickly. 'Perhaps we should withdraw.' I took a step away, then gasped as my head swam. My legs seemed suddenly heavy and I half fell, half sat on the bench again.

Lady Honor's face was at once full of concern. 'Matthew, what is it?'

I struggled up, though my head still swam. 'I am sorry . . . the heat . . .'

'Come inside,' she said. 'You,' she snapped at Barak, 'help your master.'

Barak put my arm round his shoulder and helped me into the parlour, then sat me on a pile of cushions. Lady Honor waved him away. He gave her a hard look, but left the room.

'I am sorry. A moment's weakness.' I struggled to get up. What a fool I must look. Damn Barak, if he had not come then—

Lady Honor stepped to a cabinet. I heard her pour some liquid into a glass. She crossed and knelt beside me, smiling gently. 'I have some aqua vitae here; my apothecary prescribes it for faintness.'

'Aqua vitae?' I laughed as I took the delicate little glass she gave me.

'You have heard of it?'

'Oh, yes.' I took a cautious sip of the colourless liquid. It burned, but far less than the Polish stuff. It seemed to reawaken me. 'Thank you,' I said.

She looked at me thoughtfully. 'I think you have had much to try you.'

I stood up, ashamed at my weakness. 'Lady Honor, I must go. If Barak has a message from the earl I must attend to it.'

'Come again soon,' she said, 'to dinner. Just the two of us.' She smiled.

'I should like that, Lady Honor.'

'Honor will do.'

We stood facing each other. I was tempted to lean forward and kiss her, but I merely bowed and left the room. Outside I cursed myself for my cowardice.

Barak was standing glowering in the hall. I led the way out and we stood waiting while the horses were brought round.

'What was the message?' I asked curtly.

'He's brought the meeting forward, to eleven o'clock.'

'Was that all? It could have waited.'

'A message from the earl could have waited? I think not. What did Lady Honor tell you, by the way?'

'She confirmed the Duke of Norfolk has sought her for his mistress. She didn't want to talk about it. It was fealty to her family. But she knows nothing more than what she has told me before. I am convinced of that now.'

'Rude woman,' he said.

'God's death,' I snapped, 'you *are* a churl. You enjoy mocking your betters, don't you? Refinement seems a crime in your eyes.'

'She's got haughty ways and a vile tongue,' Barak said, 'like all her class. People like her grow rich on the sweat of those who toil on their lands.' He smiled bitterly. 'They use honeyed words when it suits them, but see how they address their inferiors and you divine their true natures.'

'Oh, you are a bitter man, Jack Barak,' I said. 'She has more care for the people around her than you do.'

'And you?' he asked unexpectedly. 'Do you have a care for your servants?'

'You are hardly a servant. If you were I should have put you out long ago.'

Barak jammed his cap back on his head as a boy appeared with the horses.

WHEN WE REACHED home I felt faint again as I dismounted and almost fell down in the yard. I leaned against the horse, taking deep breaths.

Barak looked at me. 'You all right?'

'Yes,' I replied curtly. 'But I think I'll lie down for a while.'

'What about Marchamount? Shall I send word to the earl, get him brought in for questioning?'

'Yes, but to Cromwell's house, not the Tower. It will keep the matter privy.'

He nodded. 'I'll ride on to Whitehall, then. I'll be back later.'

I nodded and went indoors to ask Joan to get me some bread and cheese and a jug of beer. I took them up to my room. Sitting on the edge of the bed, I put my hand on my brow and was relieved to find no sign of fever. My faintness must have been due to the strain of the last two weeks, and this endless heat. Four more days and everything would be settled one way or another.

My arm was stinging. I removed the bandage and applied some of Guy's oil to the reddened skin, then bound my arm up again, lay on the bed and slept.

I woke some hours later, to find the air mercifully cooler and long shadows stealing across the sky. I heaved myself up and descended the stairs.

I found Barak in the kitchen. He gave me a sharp look as I sat down opposite him.

'Come, Jack, let's not quarrel.'

He grunted. 'Yes, you want me to go down that well tonight, don't you?'

'If you will.'

'I said I would.'

'Did you get the message to Cromwell?'

'I left it with Grey. He made a tart comment about how I kept asking the earl to do things when it ought to be the other way round.'

I smiled. 'He's a sober old fellow. You probably rub him up the wrong way.'

'Like Lady Honor.' He gave me a direct look. 'But are you sure the lady is all she seems? Can you see her clearly?'

'I try to.' I frowned. 'Yes, I believe so. I think we can clear both her and the duke from our calculations: that was another wrong trail.'

'So, it seems, were Bealknap and Rich.'

'Not necessarily. We should wait and see what Cromwell says about them. I hope he can make Marchamount talk.'

'He can make anyone talk. He'll show him the rack if he won't cooperate.'

We stopped talking as footsteps sounded on the stairs. Joan appeared and we went through to the parlour while she prepared supper.

'Are you fit to go to the well after we have eaten?' Barak asked.

'Aye,' I said. 'I don't know what came over me earlier.' I looked at him. 'But let us go tonight, then perhaps at least we shall have one thing solved.'

WE WALKED DOWN to Temple Stairs to catch a boat. Barak carried a heavy knapsack that he told me contained tools, candles, a tinderbox and a rope ladder. The moonlit river was quiet, only a few boats carrying officials between the City and Westminster.

The wherry bumped into Dowgate Steps with a thud. Barak stepped out, offering me a hand, and we set off to Walbrook. When we reached Sir Edwin's house, Barak turned into Budge Row and down a narrow alley.

'There's an orchard on the other side of that wall,' Barak whispered, 'and beyond it is the Wentworths' garden. I had a look round earlier.' He stopped beside a door in the wall, then stepped back and put his shoulder to it. It fell open with a crack. We slipped through an orchard towards a ten-foot wall, where Barak made a stirrup of his hands and I climbed up, grasping the top of the wall, until I lay spreadeagled on the top.

The lights were out all over the house, the garden silent, the well a dim shape in the moonlight.

'Everything quiet?' Barak whispered from below.

'Seems to be. All the lights are out.' I whispered back.

Barak hauled himself up beside me then leapt down onto the lawn and I followed, wincing at the jarring my spine took as I landed. Then Barak loped quickly across the grass to the well, with me behind him. He dropped his knapsack on the ground and pulled out a couple of tools, then quickly removed the padlocks from the well. I helped him off with the lid.

The smell still made my stomach clench. Barak unfurled his rope ladder and climbed down. I kept glancing over at the house. For a moment I thought I saw a movement, a deeper blackness at one of the upper windows, but when I looked again I saw nothing.

Barak managed to light his candle the first time he tried. I turned from the house as a faint white glow lit the well, and leaned over the side. It was shallower than I had expected, no more than twenty feet. Barak was crouching at the bottom, looking at a huddle of dark shapes. This time he was quite silent.

'What is it?' I whispered.

He looked up at me. 'Animals. There's a cat here, a couple of dogs. Horrible things done to them: the cat's had its eyes put out. And the neighbour's dog—Jesu, it's been hanged.' He turned and examined a larger shape. This time he did cry out, an abrupt shout that echoed off the bricks.

'What? What is it?'

'I'm coming up,' he said abruptly. 'Keep watch on the house.'

He snuffed out the candle and clambered up again. I peered at the house, my heart beating fast. All remained dark and silent.

Barak clambered over the top of the well. His eyes were wide. 'Help me get the well cap back on,' he breathed. 'We have to get out of here.'

We slid the cap back and Barak replaced the locks. With a last look at the silent house we ran back to the wall and clambered over. Back in the orchard, Barak leaned against a tree. He stared at me, then gulped.

'Someone in that house has been torturing animals. But not just animals. There's a little boy down there, a ragged boy of about seven. He's been . . .' He broke off. 'You don't want to know, but he's dead and he didn't die quick.'

'The mad girl's brother,' I breathed. 'The girl in Elizabeth's cell.'

'Perhaps. Whoever took him probably thought a beggar boy wouldn't be missed.' He blew out his cheeks. 'It scared me, I'll admit. I had to get out.'

'I don't blame you.' I thought a moment. 'Joseph said Elizabeth had a cat she was devoted to. Needler said it ran away, but I think it's her cat down there. I think young Ralph did this. First the animals, then the child.'

'But then . . .' Barak stared at me aghast. 'This gives Elizabeth a motive to put the boy down the well! Perhaps she found out what he was doing—'

'But when Needler pulled Ralph from the well, why did he say nothing about the animals or the child?' I shook my head. 'He must have seen what was down there. I have to see Elizabeth again—I have to get her to talk.'

'If she's still alive.'

'I'll go early tomorrow. Thank you for what you did,' I added awkwardly.

Barak gave me a sombre look. 'You think me hard, but I'd never hurt a defenceless creature.'

'I believe you,' I said. 'Come, let's get back to Chancery Lane.'

He nodded. 'All right. Jesu, I'll be having nightmares tonight.'

THE MORNING was hot again but a wind had risen, sending little white clouds racing across the sky. As Barak and I rode down Fleet Street I saw that his face was still marked with the shock of what he had found down the well. I was surprised how deeply it had affected him.

Joseph was waiting outside the gaol. He looked tired and unshaven.

The gaoler answered our knock. He called for the turnkey, who led us away to the winding stone staircase.

I turned to Joseph as he followed me up the steps. 'I have some fresh evidence,' I said. A desperate hope lit Joseph's features. 'I must tax her with some hard things, sir. Things about Sir Edwin's family.'

He took a deep breath, then nodded. 'Very well.'

Elizabeth was lying on her back. I took a stool and sat down, bending forward so my face was close to hers. Joseph and Barak stood behind me. She must have been awake for as I leaned close she opened her eyes.

I took a deep breath. 'Elizabeth,' I said, 'Jack Barak here has been down your uncle Edwin's well.'

Her eyes widened slightly, but she did not speak.

'We broke into the garden last night, and took off the cap that had been put over the well. Barak climbed down and saw what was there.'

Joseph's mouth fell open.

'We placed ourselves in danger, Elizabeth, to find the truth. For your sake.' I paused. 'We saw them. All the poor animals. Your cat. And the boy.'

'What boy?' Joseph's voice was sharp with fear.

'There is the corpse of a little boy down the well.'

'Oh, Jesu.' Joseph sat down heavily on the bed.

I saw tears well up in Elizabeth's eyes.

'I am sure you did not do those terrible things, Elizabeth. Was it Ralph?'

She coughed, and then spoke, in a low voice. 'Yes, it was.'

Joseph brought his hands up to his mouth, his expression horrified.

'I told you what was down there would shake your faith,' she told me. She paused, then let out a long, groaning breath. 'I knew that Grandam and Uncle Edwin did not want me. They thought with my rough ways I might spoil their turning their children into gentlefolk. But they did not know how cruel they were. They did not know how Ralph would torture any animal he could lay hands on. Sabine and Avice brought him my poor Grizzy.'

'*Sabine and Avice!*' Joseph's voice was incredulous.

'Ralph got them to bring him animals—they thought what he did amusing, though they didn't like getting blood or fur on their clean clothes. They were glad to have me to tease and torment, to relieve their boredom.'

I passed a hand across my brow. 'It sounds like madness, a madness the three of them infected each other with.'

'I did not know about Ralph at first. In the beginning he was friendly in a rough boy's way. Then he took me for a walk and showed me a fox he had caught in a trap. He had come with a needle to put its eyes out. I freed it and told him it was a wicked thing he did. That turned him against me. After that he joined with his sisters in finding ways to torment me.'

'You should have told Edwin,' Joseph said, 'or your grandmother.'

'Uncle Edwin would have believed nothing against Ralph or the girls. And Grandam knew, but she turned her blind eyes from it.'

'What about the other servants?' I asked. 'How much do they know? There must have been . . . been terrible cries from the animals.'

'Ralph did his vile deeds down the well. He had a little ladder. It was his torture cell as well as his hiding place. I think the servants heard things, but they said nothing. Ralph had talked of finding some beggar child to toy with, but the girls said he must be careful not to be caught. There was a little crippled boy and his sister who begged around our street.'

'And the girl was Sarah?'

'Yes. When poor Sarah was put in the Hole I remembered her. Ralph must have enticed her brother away.'

'Dear Jesu,' Joseph said. 'Ralph must have been possessed by a demon.'

'Yes.' Elizabeth spoke to her uncle directly for the first time. 'By the devil, or perhaps by God, who is one and the same.'

He looked aghast. 'Elizabeth. That is blasphemy!'

She lifted herself on her elbows, coughing painfully. 'Once I believed that God took care of all His creatures. I have asked Him to tell me how He can do such evil, but He does not reply. Does not Luther say God chooses who will be damned and who saved, before one is even born? He has chosen me to be damned and for my damnation to start in this life!'

'Rubbish!' I turned with surprise to Barak. 'You should listen to your self-pity. That'll do no good.' He shouldered past Joseph and leaned over Elizabeth. 'Listen, I've seen that little boy. His death should be avenged. Ralph may be gone, but others covered up his killing that child as though it was a thing that mattered not at all. And his sister, Sarah, maybe they'll release her from Bedlam when they find her brother *was* taken and killed.'

'Release her to what?' Elizabeth asked. 'To beg, or go for a whore?'

I put my head in my hands, full of the horror of it all. Was there not an awful logic in her belief that God had deserted her? Surely He had.

'Elizabeth.' She looked up at me again. 'Whatever you think God has done, surely Barak is right. It is your uncle Edwin's family you should be blaming, for they did the evil. If one of them killed Ralph, you should tell. They should be brought to justice.'

'They will not be. I am damned, I tell you.' Her voice rose again. 'Let God have His way, let me be killed. Let His work be done!'

'Very well,' I said. 'Then I shall have to confront the family myself.' I rose from the stool and turned to the others. 'Come,' I said.

I opened the door and called for the turnkey, who had retreated to the bottom of the steps. We left the cell, Joseph stumbling and almost falling.

Outside the gaol he shivered, despite the heat. 'I thought it could get no worse,' he said quietly. He looked at me and I saw stark terror in his face. 'My brother has spawned a family of devils.'

'I will find who did this,' I said. 'I will have an answer from your family, Joseph, I promise.'

THE THAMES was busy and we had difficulty finding a wherry at the river stairs. Barak cursed roundly, fearing we would be late. At length a boat arrived and a strong southerly wind drove the craft briskly to Westminster Stairs. We scrambled up the stairs, half running to the Privy Gallery. Then, stopping to catch our breath, we walked through to Cromwell's office.

Grey was waiting for us. 'Master Shardlake, I was beginning to fear you would be late. The earl is . . . is not in a patient mood today.'

'I am sorry, the river was busy—'

'I'll take you in.' He knocked on Cromwell's door, and ushered us inside.

The earl was standing by the window, looking out at Whitehall. He turned a frowning face towards us. He was dressed magnificently today in a robe of red silk edged with sable. The star of the Order of the Garter hung from a ribbon round his neck.

'Well,' he said grimly, 'you've come.' He strode to his desk, which was heaped high with papers, and sat down heavily in his chair and stared at us.

'So, Matthew, it seems you have sent me on a fool's errand.'

'My Lord?'

'Sir Richard Rich,' he snapped. 'I called him in here on Saturday night. The reason Rich has been making threatening remarks to you and the reason Bealknap thought he was safe have nothing to do with Greek Fire.'

'Then what?'

'You have been acting for the Common Council on a case involving whether a monastic property may be exempt from the City statutes.'

'Indeed. It is going up to Chancery.'

'No,' he said heavily. 'It is not.' He took a long breath. 'Many influential people have bought monastic properties, Matthew. When the case over Bealknap's cesspit arose, Rich came to me and said it was important Bealknap won. Otherwise the council would use the case as a precedent and make it difficult for the new owners to turn a profit. Do you see now?' He raised his eyebrows. 'Many of these are men whose loyalty I am trying to keep, in these days when all are ready to turn against me.'

'Oh.'

'Rich did not tell me you were the lawyer acting for the council, or I would have guessed what all this was about long ago. I agreed to his bribing Judge Heslop to get the right judgment. Rich tells me he put pressure on some men who are his clients to take cases they had with you to other lawyers as a warning. A Chancery judgment against Bealknap could upset the whole applecart—do you see?' He spoke coldly, distinctly, as though to a foolish man. 'That's what his threats were about. Weren't you worried, Matthew, that cases were being taken from you? Didn't you investigate?'

'I have been too busy, My Lord,' I said. 'I have thought of nothing but Greek Fire and the Wentworth case.'

'It seems clear to me, from their reactions, that neither Bealknap nor Rich is holding anything back about Greek Fire. Rich didn't even know about it. I managed to elicit that without alerting him to its existence. Just.'

'I see. I am sorry, My Lord.' I felt a fool, a dolt.

'That leaves Lady Honor and Marchamount.' He stood up and began pacing the room. 'I gather you and Lady Honor have been having a merry time together.'

I glanced at Barak, who gave a shrug.

'There was something she was holding back,' I said. 'Something between her and Marchamount and the Duke of Norfolk. It has taken some digging, but that too was nothing to do with Greek Fire.'

'What was it?' he asked sharply.

I hesitated a moment. But when Cromwell raised his head and gave me a look of great fierceness, I told him.

He grunted. 'Well, let Norfolk chase her all over London instead of plotting against me. So, there is no evidence to link her with Greek Fire either?'

'No, My Lord. None.'

He turned and paced the other way. 'And Marchamount?'

'Just a feeling he's not telling all, My Lord. Barak said you'd summon him.'

'I did.' He stopped and looked at me. His face was not angry, only filled with a desperate weariness now. 'Marchamount has disappeared. I sent a couple of men to his chambers. They found his clerk in a state because he had not turned up for a case. Did you threaten him with my wrath?'

'Not directly.'

'But he may have guessed he was not out of the woods and fled. Or has he gone the way of the Gristwoods?'

I shivered. 'If he is not safe, Bealknap and Lady Honor may not be either.'

Cromwell sat down again, shaking his head. 'They've been one step ahead of you all the time, haven't they? Whoever is behind this is the most cunning, clever rogue I've ever encountered and I've met many.' He shrugged his heavy shoulders. 'There are only three days till the demonstration and we're no further forward in finding the formula, or the apparatus.' He turned to Barak. 'Jack, try once again to trace Toky and Wright. Tell your contacts I'll pay the pair anything if they'll come over to me.'

'I will, My Lord. But I doubt they'd risk changing sides at this stage.'

'Well, try. I think I must tell the king tomorrow, Wednesday at the latest. Matthew, Barak reported the prostitute who died said the whole thing was a plot against me from the beginning.'

'Yes, My Lord.'

'Well, there have been enough of those. Don't give up yet. Put your *mind* to it.' There was desperation in his voice. 'And go to Lincoln's Inn. They'll maybe tell you things they won't tell my men. Search Marchamount's rooms.'

'Give me until Wednesday, My Lord. I will do what I can. I will think, as you ask. Do not tell the king till then.'

He looked at me hard for another long moment, then turned back to his desk. 'Go then,' he said. 'God's death, Grey will bury me in papers.'

I stood there a moment, surprised by his resigned manner. Barak motioned to the door, and I heard footsteps scurrying away as he opened it. We stepped out to see Grey sitting down at his desk, his face flustered.

Barak grinned. 'Been eavesdropping, Master Secretary?'

He did not reply, but reddened.

'Leave him, Barak,' I said. I thought: Grey is terrified of what may be about to happen. He is right to be.

BARAK AND I sat on the steps of Westminster Hall, each deep in thought.

'I expected he'd be furious,' I said, 'but he seems—almost resigned.'

'He knows what will happen if he has to tell the king Greek Fire is lost,' he said. 'I'll try again for news of Toky and Wright, but I fear I'll find nothing. I think some of my contacts are being paid to keep their mouths shut.'

'Isn't it strange how, every time we approach the truth, the person we seek is killed? As though someone was telling the enemy of our movements.'

He frowned. 'I don't see that. It was Madam Neller that betrayed Bathsheba and her brother. The founder disappeared long before we got there. And Marchamount may have fled of his own accord.'

'That would mean he was the one behind it all. It starts to look that way.'

'It does. But we need more evidence.'

'We could go through his rooms.'

'I must look for Toky first. I'll come with you later.'

I stood up. 'Very well.' I looked at him. 'Be careful.'

'I can look after myself.' He stood and dusted himself down. 'It's letting my master down, that's what's hard.'

CHAPTER TEN

I walked down to the river and stood on the bank watching the ships unload their cargo. I wondered whether, one day, a ship might bring something else as terrible and dangerous as Greek Fire here.

A little way off I saw the tavern where we had met the sailors, the Barbary Turk. I went in. At this hour the place was empty and my footsteps echoed. I went over to the serving hatch and ordered a mug of beer.

The landlord looked curiously at me. 'We don't often see gentlemen. Weren't you in here a few nights ago, talking to Hal Miller and his friends?'

'Aye. They told me of the time they set their table alight.'

He laughed, resting his arms on the edge of the hatch. 'That was a night. I wish they'd given me some of that stuff—I like novelties.'

'Like the giant's bone?' I nodded to where it hung.

'Aye, it was washed up just by the wharf here, twenty years ago. My father took the bone and hung it up here. Imagine what size the man must have been. Better to have had the whole skeleton, but that one bone's enough to bring people here to look, and that's good for trade.'

He would have talked on, but I wanted to be alone and took my beer over to the dark corner where I had sat with Barak that night.

His words, though, kept coming back to me. *That one bone's enough to bring people here to look, and that's good for trade.* I thought of the Gristwoods, working with Toky and Wright and whoever their master was for six months before going to Cromwell, trying to make Greek Fire, hunting out the Polish drink. What a profit they must have anticipated. Profit from what had been, from the start, a plot against Cromwell.

And then, all at once, I saw what had happened. What and how, though not who. My heart began to beat excitedly. I turned the theory over in my mind half a dozen times. It fitted the facts better than anything else. Abruptly I got up and left the inn, so preoccupied I stumbled into the giant's bone on the way out, setting it swinging once more in its chains.

BARAK WAS not at home when I returned. I waited impatiently for two hours as the sun set, hoping he had not met with danger. It was a great relief when I heard him come in and throw off his boots. I called him into the parlour.

'Not more bad news?' he asked, looking at my flushed face.

'No.' I closed the door. 'Barak,' I said excitedly, 'I think I have worked out what happened. This afternoon I went back to the tavern where we met the sailors. There was a giant's bone hanging from the ceiling, remember?'

He raised a hand. 'What's the giant's bone to do with anything?'

'It was something the landlord said. "Better to have had the whole skeleton, but that one bone's enough to bring people here to look, and that's good for trade." That set me thinking. We've wondered all this while why the Gristwoods waited six months between finding Greek Fire and going to Cromwell. Especially if they were plotting against him from the start.'

'Aye.'

'The Gristwoods knew, when they stumbled on Greek Fire at Barty's, that this was something big. And very profitable. Michael Gristwood would have known that the anti-Cromwell faction was growing.'

'Everyone knew that.'

'So I think they decided to offer it to someone in the anti-reformist faction as something *they* could take to the king and use to advance themselves. The Gristwoods probably thought it was safer to be in with the coming faction. They took the barrel and the formula to someone—call them Cromwell's enemy for now—and promised to make more Greek Fire for them. Toky and Wright were set to work to help them and to keep an eye on them too.'

'Yes, that fits.'

'So for six months they try to make more Greek Fire. But the stuff is like nothing they've ever seen and the formula, perhaps, referred to an ingredient they didn't have. I wondered earlier why the Romans, who knew of something like Greek Fire, didn't develop it as a weapon. There were sources, pools of strange flammable liquid in the ground, which the Byzantines had access to but the Romans didn't. Far beyond Jerusalem. And we don't have access, either, to whatever it was.'

'Something essential to make Greek Fire?'

I nodded. 'I see Michael and Sepultus following all sorts of trails, like the Polish drink, trying different experiments, increasingly desperate.'

'Because they couldn't make Greek Fire, despite having the formula.'

'Exactly. They had reconstructed the apparatus used to project Greek Fire with the aid of Leighton the founder, and practised in his yard using the stuff in the barrel. They knew it worked but the two demonstrations used up nearly all the stuff from the barrel. By March I think Cromwell's enemy was losing patience with the Gristwoods. So they devised another plan—'

Barak raised a hand, frowning. 'They went to the earl and said they *had* got Greek Fire, said they *had* made some, and he told the king.'

'Exactly. And they used Bealknap, Marchamount and Lady Honor to reach him—that would make the story sound more plausible.'

'Then none of those three need have been involved?'

'None, or some, or all.'

'And then they staged the demonstrations, using what was in the barrel, to trick the earl into making a promise to the king he could never keep.'

I nodded. 'But the Gristwoods weren't told about the final part of the plan—to kill them and make it appear as though the formula had been stolen and might be given to a foreign power. *After* Cromwell had promised the king a demonstration on Thursday. The unfortunate founder was killed because he knew too much, I'd guess.'

Barak nodded. 'And poor Bathsheba was killed lest Michael Gristwood might have told her something between the sheets. As he had.'

'I suspect they fired Goodwife Gristwood's house with what little of the stuff they had left to show Cromwell it still existed.'

Barak gave me a look of horror. 'But if you're right, there can never be another demonstration. The earl will have to tell the king.'

'Yes, yes. But he can tell him the whole thing was a plot by his enemies, that the king was deceived as well. Cromwell could still turn it to his advantage. If we can find who's behind it, if he can give the king a name.'

Barak looked at me eagerly. 'If we can uncover who the earl's enemy is, they may have kept back some Greek Fire. If that were given to the king, he could set a troop of alchemists to make it and he might have it after all.'

I took a deep breath. 'Why does nobody think of the death and destruction this thing could wreak? You most of all, Barak—you've seen it, you were nearly killed by it! How can you be so disturbed by what was down that well, yet face the death of thousands by fire without a second thought?'

'They would be soldiers. Soldiers expect to fight and die for their country.' He looked at me fixedly. 'If it will save my master, he shall have it.'

I said nothing. He was too excited to notice the depth of my concern.

'You should write a letter to the earl at once,' he urged. 'I'll take it to Grey. He should know about this.'

I hesitated. 'Very well. It's too late to go to Lincoln's Inn now, but we'll go tomorrow and see what we can find in Marchamount's rooms.'

'If it turns out he's behind it, and we can bring proof, the earl is safe.'

I nodded. But if we find more Greek Fire, I said to myself, Cromwell shall not have it. If I have to, I will prevent Barak from giving it to him.

DESPITE EVERYTHING, I slept peacefully and woke at six feeling refreshed. I did Guy's exercises, then changed the bandage on my arm. I was pleased to see it had almost healed. It was the 8th of June; we had two days left.

After breakfast Barak and I walked up to Lincoln's Inn. We passed my rooms and headed for Marchamount's chambers.

The two clerks in his outer office were agitated. One of them was leafing frantically through a pile of papers; he gave a groan and sped across to the open door of Marchamount's room. We followed him in. He glanced up from another pile of papers and gave us a harassed look. 'This room is private. If you're here about one of Serjeant Marchamount's cases, please wait. We have to find the papers for this morning.'

'We're here on Lord Cromwell's orders,' I said. 'To investigate his disappearance. And make a search.' Barak produced his seal.

The clerk shook his head in despair. 'The serjeant will be angry; he has private things in here.' He found the paper he was looking for, and hurried out.

Barak shut the door behind him. 'What are we looking for?' he asked.

'I don't know. Anything. Look in those drawers, I'll search the desk.'

A locked drawer raised our hopes, but when Barak prised it open we found nothing inside but a genealogical chart. There was nothing in his living quarters either; just clothes, more legal papers and some money. All the clerks could tell us was that they had come into work the day before to find Marchamount gone. Defeated, we crossed the courtyard to my chambers.

'I'd hoped there would be something,' Barak said.

I shook my head. 'The people involved in this wouldn't leave evidence of Greek Fire in their homes.'

'The Gristwoods kept the formula at home.'

'And look what happened to them. No, everything's hidden somewhere.'

'But where, if not in a house?'

I stopped dead. 'What about a warehouse?'

'That's possible. But there are dozens along the river bank.'

'There was a warehouse conveyancing among the cases I lost. Near Salt Wharf. The transaction was conducted in the name of nominees. I wondered who'd want to keep ownership of a warehouse secret.'

'But it was Rich who took those cases away from you.'

I paused a moment, then hastened into chambers. Skelly was sharpening a quill into a nib; he squinted up at me.

'John,' I asked. 'Will you do something for me? You know a number of cases have been taken away from me recently—half a dozen or so. Would you make a list for me now? The names, what they were about and the parties.'

'Yes, sir.' He scurried away.

'Do you think that warehouse could really be where they are storing the Dark Fire and the apparatus?' Barak asked.

'It was the last of my cases to go—just after I took Cromwell's assignment. It seems a long shot, I know. But it's a possibility; we have to follow it up.' I looked into his sceptical face. 'Unless you have a better suggestion.'

Barak nodded. 'All right, then. Anything's worth a try.' Barak had crossed to the window. 'What's going on out there?' he asked suddenly.

I joined him. A small crowd of people had gathered round one of the students, a stocky young fellow with fair hair. He stood gesticulating wildly, his eyes wide with shock. 'It's murder,' I heard him say.

Exchanging a look, Barak and I hurried outside. We shouldered our way through the crowd and I grasped the young fellow by the arm.

'What's going on?' I asked. 'Who's murdered?'

'I don't know, sir. I was going rabbit hunting, up by Coney Garth, and in the orchard I found . . . a foot. A foot in a shoe, cut off. And blood everywhere.'

'Take us there,' I said.

He hesitated a moment, then turned and led us towards the gate to the orchard on the north side of Gatehouse Court. Part of the crowd followed us.

'Stay back,' I said. 'This is official.'

People grumbled, but they remained outside as we passed through to the orchard. The student led the way through the trees.

'What's your name, fellow?' I asked.

'Francis Gregory, sir. I wanted some rabbits for the pot. I came out early, but I ran back when I saw that—thing.' He seemed very frightened.

'All right, Francis. There's nothing to fear, but a man is missing and we have been ordered to find him.'

Reluctantly young Gregory led us on into the trees. In the middle of the orchard, a wide patch of ground was covered with blood, black and sticky-looking. One tree had had a branch hacked off and a great gouge cut in its side. The mark of an axe, Wright's weapon of choice. And lying at the bottom of the tree was a shoe, with an inch of white leg visible above.

I stepped onto the bloody ground to look at the severed foot, my stomach churning at the sight. Then I saw something else on the ground. I jerked upright in disgust. Three fingers from a man's hand lay there, sliced off like the foot. And on one of them a large emerald ring.

'What is it?' Barak called. He stepped to my side and picked up the finger.

'That is Marchamount's ring,' I said, in a low voice so the student could not hear. He had not ventured onto the patch of bloody ground.

'Shit,' Barak breathed.

'He must have come to meet somebody by arrangement and they went for him with an axe.' I took a deep breath.

'Toky and Wright.'

'Aye. He must have struggled, tried to escape. They probably swung at his foot to bring him down. Then he tried to defend himself with his hands.'

'Why did they take the body away and leave these remains?'

'If it was dark, they may not have noticed the fingers or the ring.'

His back to the student, Barak pulled the ring from the severed finger and slipped it in his pocket, letting the finger drop. We walked over to the boy.

'There's no saying who this is, lad,' I said. 'Best report to the authorities.'

He was happy to run from the place. Barak and I followed more slowly.

'So Marchamount *was* involved with Toky and Wright,' Barak said.

'So it appears. Perhaps he was worried I was going to have him before Cromwell and told his master. Who decided to stop his mouth.'

'Perhaps he was the master,' Barak said. 'Perhaps he had been running the whole thing with Toky and Wright, told them things were getting hot, and they killed him and made off with the Greek Fire, to sell to the highest bidder.'

'You could be right,' I said. 'But where are they? Where have they taken Marchamount's body? Where are the apparatus and the formula? Come, let's see if Skelly has done that list.'

By the time we reached the courtyard, young Gregory was back at the centre of a crowd, declaiming about what we had found. I saw Bealknap on the fringe of the crowd, his eyes wide.

Back in chambers Skelly was waiting for us, a paper in his hand.

'It's all done, sir.'

'Thank you.' I laid it on the table and Barak and I looked over his untidy scrawl. Four pieces of litigation over land, one over a will, and the warehouse conveyancing. Pelican Warehouse, off Salt Wharf.

'Ask Bealknap to step in here, would you? Tell him, quietly, that we believe the dead man is Marchamount.' A thought occurred to me. 'John, would you add a couple of cases to the bottom of this list. Any cases of mine, choose them at random. Then bring it to me.'

Skelly, who had been standing open-mouthed, nodded and went into my office. A minute later Barak returned, Bealknap beside him.

The rogue's eyes were full of fear. 'Is this true? Serjeant Marchamount is murdered? I feared it when I heard—'

'It is, though I order you to say nothing, by Lord Cromwell's authority. No one who has any association with Greek Fire is safe any more.'

He waved his hands angrily. 'I've told you a dozen times, Shardlake, I've had nothing to do with the pestilential stuff beyond being a messenger!'

I handed him the list. 'Here, these are the cases I've lost recently. Can you confirm these are the ones Rich took from me?'

Bealknap ran his eye down the paper. 'I don't know. Sir Richard only told me he was going to damage your trade as a warning; he didn't say which cases he'd take!' He paused. 'If I'm in danger I need protection.'

'Bealknap,' I said quietly, 'I need to see Sir Richard Rich with this list. I need to know which cases he took away. Do you know where he is?'

'He should be at St Paul's to hear Archbishop Cranmer preach. The archbishop is giving the midday sermons this week, as Bishop Sampson's in the Tower. Half the king's council will be there.'

'I'd forgotten. Barak, we'd better go there. I need to show him this list.' I turned to Bealknap. 'Thank you. As for protection, perhaps you should lock yourself in your chambers the next few days with your chest of gold.'

ST PAUL'S WALK, the huge central nave of the cathedral, with its vaulted stone ceilings, was the greatest marvel in London and normally visitors from the country would have been walking to and fro, gazing up in wonder. But today the nave was almost empty. Further up the cathedral, though, a crowd of several hundred people stood around the pulpit. There, under a painting of the Last Judgment, a man in a white cleric's robe and black stole stood preaching. Barak took a chair and stood on it, peering over the heads of the crowd and drawing disapproving glances from those nearest him.

'Can you see Rich?' I asked.

'No, there's too many folk. He's likely near the front. Come on.' He jostled his way through the crowd, and I followed in his wake.

We reached the front, where robed merchants and courtiers stood with their heads lifted to the speaker. Barak stood on tiptoe, looking out for Rich. I studied Cranmer, the great archbishop who together with Cromwell had supervised all the religious changes since the break with Rome. He was surprisingly unimpressive, short and stocky with a long oval face and large brown eyes that seemed fuller of sadness than authority.

'There he is,' Barak whispered in my ear. He began weaving through the crowd again and I followed him.

At the very front, a small group of retainers round them, stood two richly robed figures: Richard Rich and Thomas Audley, the lord chancellor.

Barak took the earl's seal from his pocket and handed it to me. 'Here, you take this. It'll get you past those retainers.'

I nodded. My heart was beating fast. One of the retainers turned as I approached, his hand going to his sword hilt. I showed him the seal.

'I need to speak to Sir Richard urgently. On Lord Cromwell's business.'

Rich had seen me. A frown crossed his face, then he smiled sardonically and stepped towards me. 'Well, Brother Shardlake, you follow me every-where. I thought I had settled our business when I spoke to the earl.'

'This is another matter, Sir Richard. Another matter of the earl's I need to discuss with you. May we go somewhere a little quieter?'

With a sign to his retainers to stay where they were, he waved an arm to indicate I should lead the way through the crowd. I led him across to the far wall, out of earshot of the preaching. Barak followed, keeping at a distance.

'Well?' Rich asked.

I took the list from my robe. 'I need to know, Sir Richard, which of these cases are the ones you persuaded my clients to take away from me.'

He eyed me sharply. 'What has that to do with the earl?'

'I can tell you only that he has an interest in one of the matters.'

He tightened his hard mouth. 'One day, Shardlake . . .' he said quietly. He snatched the list and ran his eyes down it. 'The first, second, fourth and fifth,' he said. 'Not the third, sixth or seventh.'

The third was the warehouse. I studied his face, but could read nothing. He thrust the list back at me. 'Well, is that all?'

'It is. Thank you, Sir Richard.'

'God's death,' he said with a mocking laugh, 'how you stare at one. And now, if I may, I shall return to the archbishop's sermon.' He turned away without a bow, shoving his way back through the crowd.

Barak appeared at my side. 'What did he say?'

'He said the warehouse wasn't one of the ones he'd had taken.'

'D'you believe him?'

'He didn't pause for a second as he read the list. But he's so clever.' I was seized by uncertainty. 'I don't know. I don't know.'

But Barak did not reply. He was looking down the hall. Then he turned slowly and said to me quietly, 'Wright's here, I saw him. He's dodged behind that pillar. I don't think he saw me looking. He's watching us.'

Instinctively I backed against the wall. 'What's he doing here?'

'I don't know. Maybe he's after us again.'

'Maybe he's here with Rich. Can you see Toky?'

'No.' Barak's face set. 'This is our chance. Will you help me catch him?'

I nodded, though my heart raced at the thought of facing that monstrous creature again. I tried not to look at the pillars. 'Is he armed?'

'He's a sword at his belt. We'll walk down the nave as though nothing is the matter. When we reach that pillar I'll rush round to one side. You go the other way and cut him off.' He looked at me intently. 'Can you do it?'

I nodded again. Barak began to stroll down St Paul's Walk. On the far side of the cathedral Cranmer's voice could be heard still rising and falling.

We reached the pillar, then Barak unsheathed his sword and leapt round the side. I heard a sharp ring of metal on metal. I ran round the other side to see Wright and Barak with swords raised against each other, circling. People stopped and flattened themselves against the wall. A woman screamed. I drew my dagger and stepped forward.

Wright heard me and turned, even as he parried a thrust from Barak. He bounded to one side and ran down the nave.

'Shit!' Barak said. 'Come on.'

He ran after Wright and I followed, as fast as I could, down St Paul's Walk. Wright ran for the door to the roof. An elderly woman had just reached the bottom of the stairs; Wright thrust her aside and began running up, Barak at his heels. I ran after them, my robe billowing around me. By the time I neared the top of the staircase I could scarcely breathe. I saw the open door to the roof ahead, a rectangle of sky, and raced up the last few steps.

The breeze, colder and stronger here, struck my burning face. Ahead of me was the broad flat roof, the great wooden spire thrusting five hundred feet into the sky. Over the low parapet I saw all London laid out before me. Frightened strollers stood crouched against the parapet, staring at Barak. He had Wright at bay, his back against the steeple, sword held up as Barak circled. I ran over to join him, standing between Wright and the door to the stairs. Behind me, people began running for the door.

A mocking smile appeared on Barak's face. 'Come on, bully, it's all up now. You shouldn't have left your mate Toky at home. Drop the sword and come quietly. We've got some questions Lord Cromwell wants answered. Answer him nicely and he'll make you rich.'

'No, he won't.' Wright's voice was deep and heavy. 'He'll make me dead.'

His eyes darted between Barak and me. My stomach clenched with fear, but I would not let him escape, not now, no matter what the cost. I took a firm stance. Wright saw my resolution and he knew he was trapped.

'Come on,' Barak said. 'If you tell Lord Cromwell all, you may be spared the rack, eh?'

Then Wright jumped away from the steeple, not at me but further out on the roof. The move took us by surprise. Barak jumped after him and I followed, helping him edge the big man towards the parapet to trap him again.

Wright looked over his shoulder at the dizzying drop. 'I always vowed I'd never hang!' he said, his voice high-pitched with fear.

'What?' Barak paused, his sword held in midair.

I guessed what Wright meant before Barak and made a grab for his arm but he had already leapt onto the parapet. He vanished into the great void without even a cry. We ran to the parapet, but by then Wright had already hit the ground. He lay there a hundred feet below, blood from his smashed body spreading slowly out across the yard.

Barak pulled me from the roof and hustled me down the stairs. As we neared the door a woman ran in screaming that a man was fallen from the roof. We slipped out unnoticed.

Barak led me at a half-run into the maze of alleys round Foster Lane. He stopped at last near the Goldsmiths' Hall. I collapsed against the wall of a candlemaker's shop, gasping for breath.

'Take off your robe,' he said. 'They'll be looking for a man in lawyer's garb.'

I pulled it off, bundling it under my arm.

'Come on,' Barak said. 'There'll be a hue and cry out soon.'

'It'll be a murder hunt. And I'll be identified—a hunchback lawyer will be easily remembered. They'll be looking for a bald young man too. Here.' I gave him my cap—his own had fallen off during the struggle.

He put it on. 'Thanks. I have the earl's seal, but we haven't time to argue with thick-headed constables.'

I wiped my brow. 'What now?' I asked wearily. 'The warehouse?'

'Aye, we should do it now. We'll go by the back ways. Come on.'

SALT WHARF was a wide triangular inlet that had been carved into the river bank to allow small boats to unload. A street of warehouses ran along one side of Queenhithe dock. Pelican Warehouse was the last of the buildings, hard by the river and constructed of brick, four storeys high. A faded sign showing a bird with a huge beak hung outside. The windows were shuttered and barred and the door was secured with a padlock. Although people were working in the adjacent buildings, Pelican Warehouse seemed deserted.

We walked to the south end of the building, which dropped directly into the river. Peering up, I saw an open hatchway at the first-storey level, with a winch to draw goods from boats below projecting from it.

'No sign of life,' Barak said at my elbow. 'I've knocked but there's no reply. There's a hollow sound, like nothing's stored here. Shall I break in?'

I nodded and he produced his little metal tool and bent to pick the lock as he had at the Wentworths' well. There was a click and the padlock fell open. The door opened smoothly on well-greased hinges. A dark interior was revealed, lit only by one glassed window high up. The warehouse was as wide as the nave of a church, and quite empty.

Drawing his sword, Barak stepped in. I followed. At the end of the warehouse, a flight of wooden steps led up to an upper floor, which was merely a wooden platform running round the wall, except for a room next to the stairs, its door closed.

'That must be the office,' I said.

'Shall we go up?' Barak asked.

I nodded, my heart beating fast. We climbed the rickety staircase carefully. As we reached the platform, I saw that the office door was also secured by a padlock. It seemed darker now, and I heard a rumble of thunder.

Barak bent to the padlock, grunting with satisfaction when it fell open. He stepped back and kicked the door open. The room was empty, nothing there but the big open hatchway giving a view of the lowering sky, the end of the winch secured to the floor with bolts. Then I saw a door to a second room. I nudged Barak and he threw it open, then whistled at what was inside.

A table stood in the middle of the room. There was a beer jug and three plates, an unlit tallow candle and a hunk of bread. A bale of cloth by the table served as a seat. We stepped inside.

'Someone's been here very recently,' I said.

Then Barak stopped as he saw what was stacked against the far wall. A long metal pipe with a wick at one end, a complicated-looking pumping machine, and a metal tripod, all bundled together beside a large metal tank.

'The Greek Fire apparatus,' he breathed. 'And look at this.'

Beside the ugly tangle of metal was a porcelain vase about two feet high. I approached and, very carefully, lifted the little lid. Inside I saw a dark viscous liquid. The familiar stench of Greek Fire set the hairs at the back of my neck prickling.

Barak stood beside me, peering into the vase. He dipped a finger into the stuff and lifted it to his nose. 'We've got it,' he breathed. 'God's blood, we've got it!' He stepped back, his face alight.

'It's probably all they have left,' I said. 'It would barely cover the bottom of that tank. Nowhere near enough to burn a ship.'

'I know.' Barak sniffed his finger again. 'But there's enough to show the king, enough for him to give to his alchemists. This could save the earl—'

There was a laugh behind us, loud and triumphant. We froze, then turned slowly. Toky stood there, sword raised, a broad grin on his ravaged face. Two others were with him: a short stocky fellow with a straggly beard and a younger, less rough-looking man whom I had seen somewhere before.

'Drop the weapon, baldy,' Toky said. 'You're outnumbered.'

Barak hesitated, then let his sword fall to the floor with a clatter.

Toky grinned again. 'Well, my beauties, we've been waiting for you.' He nodded at his younger confederate. 'Master Jackson here saw you walking down Potter's Lane and ran here to warn us. We padlocked the door, hid round the corner, then came back once you'd broken in. You were so intent on the Dark Fire you never heard us creep across the boards.'

'Dark Fire,' I repeated. 'So you know that old name?'

'Aye, it's a better one than Greek Fire, for this is English Fire now and it will bring a mighty darkness to our enemies. And gold to us.' He laughed, then nodded at his confederates. 'Kill them both,' he said.

Barak set his jaw. I stepped back, pointing to the jar. 'This is all you have left, isn't it?' I said hurriedly. 'You don't know how to make more. The barrel from Barty's was nearly used up in the demonstrations. It was all a trick to disgrace Cromwell. We know that and so does the earl.'

'Then why are you here?' Toky asked. 'Why not a troop of soldiers?'

'It was only a guess brought us. We didn't know where the stuff was. But others will follow soon. You'd best turn yourself over to the earl's mercy.'

Toky frowned. 'Do you know who our masters are?' he asked.

I hesitated. 'Richard Rich,' I said.

Toky smiled slowly. 'Rich. My arse. You don't know—this is bluff.'

'Kill them,' young Jackson said nervously, 'while there's still time.'

'Not yet,' Toky rasped. 'Our masters will need to hear how much they know. Fetch them here; they will have to decide what's to be done.'

'Both?' The young man's accent had some effort at cultivation; the accent of someone who served a rich master. Where had I seen him before?

'Aye. Tie them up first.' He nodded at some coils of rope in the corner.

Our hands were grasped roughly and tied behind us. We were manhandled into a corner and shoved down roughly onto the boards.

'Hurry, Jackson,' Toky urged.

The young man left the room. I heard his footsteps descending the stairs. Toky sat on the bale of cloth, looking at us thoughtfully. The bearded fellow sat on the table, bit off a hunk of bread and washed it down with a swig of beer. He smiled at us, yellow teeth like a rat's dimly visible in the gloom.

'You're a scarecrow-looking pair to have caused so much trouble. Ain't they, Toky?'

Toky grunted. His ebullience had evaporated.

'Who are you anyway?' Barak asked.

'Jed Fletcher, out of Essex. Old friend of Toky's.' He gave a mocking bow.

'And who are they, then,' I asked, 'these masters of yours?'

Toky smiled. 'You'll know them. You that's dined with the aristocracy.'

I felt suddenly cold. The only aristocrat I knew was Lady Honor. And now I remembered where I had seen the young man. He had been serving at Lady Honor's banquet. I stared at Toky. 'The House of Glass,' I whispered.

'You'll see,' Toky said. 'Have patience.' He reached for the bread.

There was silence for a minute. Then I heard the loud hiss of rain. Thunder sounded again, a mighty crack right overhead.

'It's come, then,' Fletcher said.

'Aye,' Toky agreed. 'God's bones, it is dark. We'll have a candle lit, but keep it on the far side of the table, away from that vase.'

Fletcher set the candle on a plate, there was a struggle with a tinderbox and a yellow glow spread over the room. Our captors sat back, waiting.

'Listen,' Barak said. 'You know we work for Lord Cromwell. If we're killed you'll be hunted down. If you let us go you'll be richly rewarded.'

'Too late for that, matey.' Toky sat looking at Barak, his eyes glinting points in the candlelight. 'I don't like the way you've led me such a dance.'

'More of a dance than you think,' Barak said. 'Your mate Wright was killed this morning. Took a dive off the roof of St Paul's.'

'What?' Toky leaned forward.

'Join us, bully, before you join him.'

'You've killed Sam?' Toky's voice was a croak. 'You've killed Sam?'

Fletcher looked at him uneasily. Barak had made a bad mistake.

Toky half rose, then sat down again. 'By God,' he said, 'I'll see you two die slowly for this. You'll learn the tricks I know with my knife . . .'

Barak leaned back, towards me. He still stared at Toky, but I felt fingers brushing against my belt: he was trying to reach my dagger with his bound hands. They had not thought I might be carrying a weapon. Taking care not to look at Barak, I edged towards him. I felt the dagger withdrawn. Toky had put his head in his hands. Fletcher was still watching him anxiously.

Barak began sawing at my bonds, carefully so as not to attract attention. I bit back a cry as the dagger sliced into my skin, then felt the rope fall away. I flexed my fingers gently, then palmed the dagger from Barak and began sawing at his ropes in turn, all the while watching our captors. Toky was absorbed in his thoughts, and Fletcher passed us only an occasional glance.

Then I heard feet on the stairs. Fletcher got up. I stopped sawing at

Barak's bonds—surely I was almost through now? I risked a glance at him, but Barak kept his face impassive as Fletcher opened the door.

Serjeant Marchamount came in, shaking the water from a heavy coat. He looked down at us with a cold brutality I had never seen before in his face.

'You did get out of your depth, didn't you?'

We stared at him open-mouthed. 'You're supposed to be dead,' Barak said.

Marchamount smiled. 'You were getting too close, so I decided I'd better disappear. Just as well we'd kept that founder alive here. Toky and Wright took him to Lincoln's Inn orchard and hacked the life out of the fool. Then they put my ring on his finger and brought the body here on a cart. That hatch is useful for throwing things into the Thames. You'll be leaving that way.'

'Wright's dead,' Toky said with a grim look at me. 'They threw him off the roof of St Paul's. I want my revenge with them.'

'So it's him they're talking about all over the City,' Marchamount said, taking his coat off. He looked at Toky. 'All right,' he said. 'Do what you like with them later. We'll have to wait a little for a full house.' He sat on the edge of the table, looking thoughtful. 'So. Cromwell knows we haven't been able to make any more Dark Fire. But not our names?'

'No,' I said. There was no point in denying that now.

'Was the alchemy too hard for you?' Barak asked scoffingly.

For answer Marchamount struck him savagely across the face. 'I'm a serjeant, churl, you'll take a respectful tone when you talk to me.'

Barak stared boldly back at him. 'That didn't stop you conjuring up a common fraud. That's all this is.'

'No, it is not,' an aristocratic voice said from the doorway.

Marchamount and the two villains bowed deeply as the Duke of Norfolk entered, rain falling from his fur-lined coat. Young Jackson followed him; he was evidently at the banquet as Norfolk's servant, not Lady Honor's, and I felt relief as well as horror as I understood just how high the plot reached.

Norfolk threw his coat to Fletcher, then stared at me with that cold, haughty look of his. There would be no mercy from him, I knew.

'Well, Master Shardlake,' he said, 'I've had a wet trip across the river in the rain thanks to you.' He smiled coldly. 'Yet you did well, considering the forces against you. I wouldn't have minded a man like you on my side. But you've different loyalties, eh? Now, what does Cromwell know?'

'He knows that the Gristwoods were unable to make Greek Fire,' I lied.

'And how did you discover that?' His tone was conversational.

'I delved into the old books and sources. I concluded that there was a missing ingredient, something that cannot be found in England.'

Marchamount nodded. 'Aye, it seems we have been following the same path, Shardlake. I have driven my mind to aching with those books. But I know we shall never be able to make Greek Fire in England.'

Norfolk nodded. 'But you didn't know I was behind the plot, or that Marchamount here was my man?'

'No.'

Norfolk nodded slowly. 'Did you guess what our first plan was?'

'I think you planned to give Greek Fire to the king yourself, but when Sepultus Gristwood failed to make it you decided to turn it into a fraud to get Cromwell into worse odour with the king.'

Norfolk gave a bark of laughter. 'Why's the crookback not a serjeant, eh, Gabriel? He could outwit you in court any day.'

Marchamount scowled.

'By God,' the duke continued, 'the Gristwoods angered me. Promising they could make Greek Fire, then every week saying it would take a little longer—it was months before they finally confessed they'd failed. It was Gabriel's idea to turn it against Cromwell; he's a clever fellow after all. He'll have his knighthood when Cromwell's gone, eh?' He clapped the serjeant on the shoulder; Marchamount reddened with embarrassment.

'So, no Greek Fire for the king. You should see him when he is in a rage. It is—spectacular!' Norfolk threw back his head and gave a bark of laughter.

Marchamount and Fletcher joined in sycophantically, though Toky sat glaring at us, fingering the knife he had pulled from his belt.

'This failure will bring Cromwell down,' the duke said quietly. 'Then, a few months after I step into his shoes, this vase will be mysteriously found, and I shall be celebrated as the one who rediscovered Greek Fire.'

'You can't make more,' I said.

'No? You have the formula safe, Marchamount?'

'Yes, Your Grace,' the serjeant said. 'It never leaves my person.'

The duke turned back to me. 'We shall find the stuff the formula calls naphtha. We shall make a voyage to where some can be found.'

'All those places are under the Turks.'

'Are they? Well, I am not short of gold.' Norfolk narrowed his eyes. 'This will be my triumph. The king tires of reform; he sees the chaos it brings. In the end he will be persuaded back to Rome, and perhaps Catherine will give him another son. A Howard heir, in case anything should happen to the little Seymour prince.' He smiled and raised his eyebrows, then stood up and nodded at Toky. 'Have what sport you wish, but before the lawyer's dead I want all the details of what he found in those old books. Marchamount, stay and help question him. Note what he says.'

Marchamount sighed. 'Very well.'

'And now I am going back to Bishop Gardiner's house to dine with Catherine. Inform me when it's done.'

The duke snapped his fingers at young Jackson and the boy helped him back into his coat, then opened the door to the outer room. Fletcher and Toky bowed as the duke swept through the doorway, followed by Jackson.

Toky pulled out a long, sharp dagger. He smiled. 'Each cut will be for Sam Wright.' He stood up. 'Here we go, crookback, we'll start with your ears—'

I felt Barak tense beside me. His hands, untied, shot down to the floor. Balancing on them, he launched a high kick at Fletcher. It caught him in the stomach and sent him crashing against the wall, hitting his head with a bang that shook the room, and he slid down the wall, senseless.

Barak leapt to his feet and lunged for the corner where his sword had been thrown. I hauled myself up, almost screaming at the pain from my back and my cut wrist, as Toky dropped his knife and pulled out his sword. Barak reached his weapon, but stumbled as he turned. Toky would have stuck him had I not grabbed my dagger and stabbed him in the thigh. As he let out a bellow of pain and fury Barak slashed at his hand, half severing it. Toky's sword clanged to the floor.

Marchamount reached to his belt and produced a dagger of his own. He lunged at me, but Barak kicked out again and knocked the big man's legs from under him. He landed on the floor with a thump. I winced as Barak lunged with his sword, burying it in Toky's heart. Toky stared round at us, unbelieving, then crumpled slowly to the floor.

There was a moan from the corner as Fletcher came to. Marchamount hauled himself up with the aid of the table, dusty and red in the face.

Barak turned and held the sword at his throat. 'Now, you big old toad, you're going to come with us and croak to the earl.'

Marchamount swayed. 'Please,' he said. 'Listen. The duke will pay—'

Barak laughed. 'Not us, he won't. You'll have to do better than that.'

Fletcher struggled to his feet. He stood groggily against the wall, taking in Toky's body and Marchamount pinned against the table. Then he jumped to the door, threw it open and ran. I made to follow but Barak held me back.

'Let him go. We've got our prize.'

'Please,' Marchamount groaned, 'let me sit. I feel faint.'

Barak gestured to the bale of wool. 'Go on, then, you great bag of guts.' He watched contemptuously as Marchamount half fell onto it, then turned to me. 'Get that vase. We're taking that to the earl as well.'

I picked up the vase. It was very heavy, almost full. 'I am not sure about this, Barak,' I said. 'We have Marchamount, we know about the duke. That's enough to save Cromwell and damn the Howards.'

He looked at me seriously. 'I must have that vase,' he said quietly.

'But, Jack, you know what it can do—'

'I must have it. I—'

Barak broke off with a yell. Marchamount grabbed Toky's sword, then jumped up and thrust at Barak's neck. Barak twisted just in time to deflect the blow, but it caught his sword arm. He grabbed at his bicep, blood welling between his fingers. He dropped the sword, his arm useless. Marchamount hefted Barak's sword and glanced at me standing with the vase. He drew back his sword arm to give Barak a killing blow.

I threw the contents of the vase at him. A great spout of thick black liquid shot out, its stink filling the room as it drenched Marchamount. He howled, staggered back, and slipped in some of the stuff that had fallen to the floor. He overbalanced, falling back against the table. The candle overturned. The flame touched his sleeve, and before my unbelieving eyes Marchamount's whole body erupted into a pillar of fire. I jumped back in horror as he screamed and beat his hands against his side, frantically, uselessly. I saw the table was burning too, and the floor where some of the stuff had fallen.

Marchamount ran for the open door, his legs swirling with flames, and staggered into the other room. I followed as he stumbled across to the hatchway, pieces of burning clothing falling from his body. He leapt through the hatchway, howling as he fell into the river and disappeared.

I heard Barak shout and turned back. The other room was an inferno, the vase that had held Greek Fire lying smashed in the centre of the flames.

I grasped Barak's shoulder. 'It's too late. Come, or we'll burn with it.'

He gave me an anguished look, but followed me to the stairs. We ran down into the body of the warehouse; looking up, we saw flames licking round the walls of the office. Barak paused, blinked, collected himself.

'We must get to the earl,' he said. 'We must leave the fire to burn.'

I nodded. We ran outside into the rain. I gasped at the cold water lashing into my face. I looked down at the water and thought I saw something black surface before it was swept upriver on the tide; it might have been a log of wood, or the remains of Marchamount, Greek Fire's last victim.

ChApTeR eLeVeN

We walked back along Cheapside then down to the river, through lanes that had already turned into trails of mud. There can be something pitiless about rain when it pounds, hard, on exhausted heads, as though cast from heaven by an angry hand.

Barak paused and leaned against a wall. He clasped his wounded arm and I saw a trickle of blood welling between his fingers.

'You need that seen to,' I said. 'We can walk to Guy's, it's not far.'

He shook his head. 'We must get to Whitehall. I'll be all right.' He looked at my wrist. 'How's your hand?'

'It's fine, it wasn't a deep cut. Here, let me bind your arm up.' I pulled a handkerchief from my pocket and tied it round his arm, pulling it tight.

'Thank you.' Barak took a deep breath. 'Come, let's get a wherry.' He heaved himself away from the wall. 'We've won,' he said as we struggled on to the river stairs. 'It will be Norfolk who suffers, not Cromwell. Norfolk tried to gull the king and that won't ever be forgiven.'

'If the earl is believed. We've no proof now Marchamount is dead and everything destroyed in that fire.'

'Norfolk will be interrogated. We'll get Fletcher picked up.' He gave me a searching look. 'You saved my life by throwing the vase at Marchamount. If he hadn't attacked us, would I have had to take it from you by force?'

I met his gaze. 'It's all one now,' I said. 'Past mattering.'

Barak said no more. A wherry was waiting at the stairs, and soon a surging tide was carrying us upriver to Whitehall. I saw from a church clock that it was almost three. I remembered I should have gone to the Wentworths' today; I had only tomorrow left now. Joseph would be worrying.

The boat bumped into Whitehall Steps. While I paid the boatman, Barak showed his seal to one of the guards and we were waved on into the palace. Once again we made our way to the Privy Gallery and on to Cromwell's quarters. The guard admitted us to the outer office, where Grey sat over his papers. He looked up in surprise at our drenched, muddy forms.

'Master Grey,' I said, 'we have an urgent message for Lord Cromwell.'

'What has happened, Master Shardlake? Barak, your arm—'

'We have the answer to Greek Fire,' I said. 'It was all a fraud, planned by

Norfolk to discredit Cromwell.' I quickly told him what had happened at the warehouse. 'Please,' I concluded urgently, 'we must tell the earl at once.'

He glanced at Cromwell's closed door. 'He's not here. He had a message to go to Hampton Court; Queen Anne sent for him. He left an hour ago.'

'Then we'll go to Hampton Court.' Barak stepped away from the table, then groaned. He staggered and would have fallen had I not caught him.

Grey's eyes widened. 'What ails him? Look, his arm is bleeding.'

I sat him on a chair and saw the tourniquet had loosened and Barak was bleeding again. He was deathly pale and there was sweat on his face.

'You're in no state to go to Hampton Court, Barak,' I said. I turned to Grey. 'Is the king's physician here?'

Grey shook his head. 'The king ordered Dr Butts away yesterday with a volley of oaths, when he wanted to open the ulcer on the king's leg again.'

'Then you should see Guy, Barak,' I said. 'I'll take you.'

'No. You must go to Hampton Court. Leave me here.'

'I'm half fainting myself. Master Grey, can you have a message taken to Hampton Court at once? By someone you can trust?'

He nodded. 'If you think that best. Young Hanfold is here.'

'I remember him. Yes, send him.' I took a quill and scribbled a note to Cromwell. Grey impressed Cromwell's seal on the letter and bustled from the room with it, calling for Hanfold. I looked out over the sodden garden.

'What will Norfolk do now?' I asked pensively.

'He still thinks he's safe. It'll be hours before he starts to worry because no message has come from the warehouse.'

I studied him. 'Can you make it to Guy's?'

'All right.' He got up slowly. 'Maybe I'd better, before I bleed to death over Master Grey's fine chair.'

The secretary returned to say the message was on its way and a boat was waiting to take us back downriver. I gave him the address of Guy's shop, should Lord Cromwell send for us, and we hurried away.

Another half-hour in the rain and we disembarked. I helped Barak through the lanes to Guy's shop. Guy answered the door and let us in with little more than raised eyebrows. Barak removed his shirt and Guy examined his arm. It was a horrible gash, very deep.

'I should sew your arm, Master Barak,' Guy said. 'Can you bear the pain?'

Barak screwed up his face. 'Have I any choice?'

'Not much, I fear, unless you would bleed to death.'

I waited in the shop while Guy took Barak through to his workshop, after coating my wrist with some stinging oil. He brought dry clothes and I changed in the shop, transferring my belt and purse to my borrowed hose, wincing at a stifled cry from Barak in the other room. I went across to the window and looked out; the rain seemed to be lessening. I leaned my head on the cool glass, shutting my eyes. Then the door opened behind me and Guy entered, flecks of blood on his robe.

'There,' he said quietly, 'that's done. I've told him to rest. He's a brave young fellow.'

'Aye, he's hard as nails.' I smiled tiredly. 'We've won, Guy. There will be no Greek Fire.' I told him what had happened at the warehouse.

He sat down on a stool. 'Praise God.'

THERE HAD BEEN no message from Cromwell by the time we left Guy's an hour later. Nor was there any news at home. I sent Simon to retrieve our horses from an inn near St Paul's, where we had tethered them before entering the cathedral earlier in the day. Then Barak and I ate luncheon and waited in my parlour as afternoon turned slowly to evening.

'I must go to bed,' Barak said at length.

'Aye, I need rest too.' I frowned. 'Why hasn't Cromwell contacted us?'

'He's probably waiting for a chance to see the king,' Barak said. 'Likely he will do that first, then fetch us later. We'll hear something in the morning.'

I heaved myself upright. 'Barak, do you think you are fit enough to come to the Wentworths' tomorrow? It will be our last chance.'

He nodded, getting to his feet. 'Aye. It takes more than a sword thrust to lay me low. And what's to fear from a greasy steward, a fat old merchant and a brood of women? I'll come. The business started there after all, didn't it?'

'Aye, and it must end there, before Elizabeth comes back before Forbizer.'

NORMALLY JOAN would have woken us for breakfast, but after seeing the state in which Barak and I had returned home the good woman had decided to let us sleep. Neither of us woke until nearly midday. I felt much better, though my wrist still hurt, and Barak seemed almost restored to his usual self. To my surprise there was still no word from Cromwell.

'He must have seen the king by now,' I said. 'Maybe we should send another message?'

'Demanding news? That would be a mighty insolence.'

'At least we can send a message saying if we're not here we'll be at the Wentworths'.' I looked at him. 'Are you fit to go to Walbrook?'

'Fit as a fly. You look better too.' He laughed. 'You're not as weakly as you pretend.'

'It's all right for you to say that at your age. I'm going to write a note, then we ought to go. I'll send Simon, get him to put it into Master Grey's hands. I'll borrow your seal, if I may, so I can stamp it in the wax.' I hesitated. 'I ought to go myself, but there's no time. We should not have slept so long; it is less than twenty-four hours before Elizabeth returns to court.'

WE TOOK a boat into the City, then walked up to Walbrook. I had dressed in my robe and my best doublet and urged Barak to borrow my second-best robe to conceal his bandaged arm. A maid answered the Wentworths' door.

'Is Sir Edwin in?' I asked. 'I am Master Shardlake.'

Her eyes widened a little. 'He's at the Mercers' Hall, sir.'

'Goodwife Wentworth, then?' The girl hesitated. 'Come,' I said, 'we have business with Lord Cromwell at Whitehall today. Is your mistress in?'

Her eyes widened further at Cromwell's name. 'I'll see, sir. Please wait.' She left us at the door and scurried off into the house. Minutes passed.

'What's keeping her?' Barak asked irritably.

The girl reappeared, looking flustered. She took us upstairs, and once again we were led into the parlour, with its view of the garden and the well. This time the old woman was the only member of the family present. The young steward Needler stood behind her, his eyes watchful. The old woman had evidently just eaten, for a tray stood on a table at her elbow, with the remains of a dish of vegetables and cold beef. I saw that the empty plate, the mustard pot and the little salt cellar were all of silver.

Goodwife Wentworth did not get up. 'You will forgive me if my steward stays, Master Shardlake. There are no other members of the family at home just now.' She smiled. 'He can be my eyes. Tell me, David, who is it that accompanies him? He has the steps of a young man.'

'A bald young fellow,' Needler said. 'Though he dresses well enough.'

'He is my assistant,' I told her.

'Then we each have a chaperon,' Goodwife Wentworth said. 'Now, what may I do for you? Elizabeth returns to court tomorrow, does she not?'

'She does indeed, madam, unless fresh evidence can be brought. Evidence, for example, of what lies at the bottom of yonder well.'

'Our well?' she asked calmly. 'Whatever can you mean, sir?'

'The bodies of the animals your grandson Ralph tortured and killed for sport are there. Including Elizabeth's cat, which Sabine and Avice brought to him. And a tortured child, a little beggar boy. Whom Needler must have seen, but of which you said nothing at the inquest.' I looked from one to the other of them. They were silent, their faces expressionless.

'What the boy had done to him would make a hangman sick,' Barak added.

The old woman laughed then, a shrill cackle. 'Are they mad, David? Are they frothing at the mouth, plucking straws from their hair?'

I spoke evenly. 'It must have been hard, these last weeks, for your grand-daughters to keep such a secret.'

She was silent for a long moment. Then her lips set hard. 'I see you have learned much.' She sighed. 'It seems I must tell you all. David, I would like a glass of wine. Master Shardlake, you and your assistant will have one?'

I did not answer, surprised by the speed of her capitulation.

'Get some wine, David,' the old woman said quietly.

Needler went over to the buffet, then turned to his mistress. 'The family had the last of it yesterday, madam. Shall I fetch a bottle from the cellar?'

'Aye, do that. I will be safe enough, I think.'

'Quite safe,' I replied grimly as Needler left the room.

'Elizabeth has spoken, then?'

'Reluctantly, yes. To us and to your son Joseph.'

She pursed her lips again. 'My family has come far,' she said quietly. 'Edwin has brought us advancement, wealth, the chance for his children to mix with the highest in London. Now that Ralph is gone our hopes rest on good marriages for Sabine and Avice. It is all we have left.'

'Are they safe for a young man to marry? After what they have done?'

She shrugged. 'They only need strong lusty fellows to take them in hand.'

Needler returned with a bottle of red wine and three silver goblets on a tray. He laid the tray on a table and gave a goblet to the old woman, then passed the others to Barak and me. His face was expressionless as he returned to his place behind his mistress's chair. Why were they both so calm? I wondered. I took a sip of the wine. It was sweet and sickly. Barak took a large draught.

'The truth, then,' Goodwife Wentworth said decisively.

'Yes, madam, the truth. If not here, then in court tomorrow morning.'

She nodded then paused, gathering her thoughts. 'David saw it all, from this window,' she said. 'Elizabeth was in the garden alone that afternoon, sulking as usual. She would have done better to stand up for herself; the way she used to cower in corners only encouraged the children to be cruel.' She gave a snort of contempt. 'That day, Ralph had gone down to the garden. He sat on the edge of the well and spoke to Elizabeth. You could not hear what he said, could you, David?'

'No, madam.' He looked at us and shrugged. 'He was probably tormenting her. She just sat under the tree and took it as usual, her head bowed.'

'Did you know your grandson had killed a little boy, madam?' I asked.

'We heard the boy had disappeared. I wondered. I knew the things Ralph did and I was waiting for a chance to speak to him about it—I feared he was placing himself in danger. My son Edwin knows nothing,' she added.

'You did not fear Ralph was growing into a monster?' I coughed. My throat was suddenly dry.

She shrugged. 'Ralph would have learned to conceal his cruelties. People do.' She sighed. 'You go on, David, this is tiring me.'

The steward looked at us intently. 'After a while Sabine and Avice came outside and sat with Ralph on the edge of the well. Then Ralph said something to Sabine. Something she did not like.' The steward reddened.

'He referred perhaps to her feelings for you?' I asked.

The old woman raised a hand. 'Sabine developed a girlish fancy for David. He did not encourage her; he is loyal. Tell them what you saw next, David.'

'Sabine grabbed at Ralph. He twisted away from her, fell down the well.'

Goodwife Wentworth sighed. 'Of course, if Elizabeth had not been there, Sabine and Avice could have said Ralph merely slipped, but Elizabeth saw everything. And she has no love for us.' She spread her hands and smiled. 'You see, that was our problem.'

'So she had to be silenced. By being accused.' My voice came out as a croak and hurt my throat. I wondered if I was sickening for something.

'When I saw Ralph go down the well,' Needler went on, 'I ran downstairs to the garden. Sabine and Avice were screaming, howling. I looked down the well. I could just make out Ralph's body. Elizabeth just sat there under the tree, gawping. Then, not knowing I had been looking from the window, Sabine pointed at Elizabeth and said, "She's killed Ralph. She put him in the well! We saw her!" Elizabeth sat like a stone, saying nothing. Then Avice joined in, pointing at Elizabeth, accusing her.'

Goodwife Wentworth nodded. 'Then I came down; I had heard the screaming. I found Sabine and Avice howling that Elizabeth had killed Ralph. Elizabeth would not answer when I spoke to her. I ordered Edwin fetched and he had the constable take Elizabeth away. It was only afterwards that David told me the truth. I questioned the girls and they admitted all. They knew about the beggar boy. They have been very frightened,

Master Shardlake, but they will make fine gentlewomen one day.'

'They'll make devilish monsters, like their brother,' Barak said.

The old woman ignored him. 'We waited two days, to see if Elizabeth would tell her story, but she kept her silence. Joseph came and told us she was refusing to plead. So we decided, if Elizabeth was prepared to go to her death, let her.' She spoke calmly, as though of a business arrangement.

I coughed drily. 'Well, madam, what do you expect to happen now?'

She said nothing, only smiled. I was aware that my heart was pounding fast. I heard voices from the hall, then the closing of the front door.

'Shit,' Barak said. 'My eyes. I'm seeing double.'

I looked at him. The pupils of his eyes were enormous.

'They've poisoned us,' I breathed.

'The nightshade's working quickly,' the old woman said quietly.

Needler crossed quickly to the door and locked it, then stood against it.

'The servants have all gone?' Goodwife Wentworth asked.

'I told them there's nothing more to do this morning, to go out and enjoy the air while it's fresh after the storm.' He turned to me. 'You thought you were unseen that night you went down the well, but my mistress heard someone in the orchard. She told me to wait at a window and see what happened. I saw the pair of you sneak in, saw baldy there go down the well.'

The old woman cackled. 'The blind have wondrous hearing, Master Shardlake. After that we feared the constable would come for us. When nothing happened we knew that Elizabeth must still be refusing to plead.'

Barak tried to get to his feet but fell back, his eyes staring wildly. 'I can't see,' he said. His head began to shake. He had drunk more of the stuff than me.

I tried to say something, but my voice would not come. I remembered Guy telling me once that the way to counteract nightshade, if taken quickly enough, was an emetic.

Needler returned to his place behind the beldam. 'We knew you would come here.' She smiled evilly as I took deep breaths. 'The well is empty now, by the way, the carcasses in the river. It's ready for you.' Her voice was low, a whisper. 'They are weakening, David. Kill them now.'

The steward drew a dagger and came round the chair, his face grim.

And then I remembered the mustard, what Guy had said about its emetic properties. I hauled myself upright, shaking from head to foot. Barak managed to rise unsteadily and fumble for his sword. Needler appeared suddenly uncertain. I reached out and grasped the mustard pot and, before Needler's astonished eyes, thrust a big spoonful into my mouth.

Barak made an uncertain lunge with his sword. He cut only air, but Needler retreated quickly behind the chair.

I felt my stomach turn, then leaned over and vomited its contents onto the floor with a horrible retching sound. 'Jack!' I cried. 'Here, take this!'

He grabbed the pot and swallowed what was left. He gasped and leaned back against his chair, sword still raised at Needler. I put a hand on the back of my chair, took long, deep breaths, and felt my heartbeat steadying. I pulled out my dagger.

The old woman stood too, trembling, hands stretched out before her. 'David!' she called in a shrill howl. 'David! What is happening?'

Needler's nerve broke and he ran to the door. Barak started to follow, but staggered. The old woman turned to the sound of Needler's footsteps, her hands waving helplessly. 'David! Where are you? What's happening?'

Needler unlocked the door and threw it open. He ran down the steps and out of the house just as Barak leaned forward and vomited as spectacularly as I had. He sank to his knees, gasping.

The old woman turned, panicky now. 'David!' she shouted. 'David!' Then she stumbled, lost her balance and her head struck the wall as she fell.

I staggered to the door of the parlour, down the stairs and through the open front door. I called 'Help!' in a cracked voice, making heads turn along the crowded street. 'Murder! Call the constable! Help!' Then my legs seemed to disappear beneath me and I fell into blackness.

I CAME TO with a start, jerking away from a vile smell under my nose. I gasped and looked round in confusion.

I was back in the Wentworths' parlour, but sitting in a chair now. A thick-set man in a constable's jerkin stood watching me. Beside me stood Guy, holding the bottle he had just thrust under my nose. Barak sat sprawled in another chair, looking pale—but alive. 'The old woman—' I croaked.

'It's all right,' Guy said. 'She and her granddaughters have been taken away. You've been senseless nearly an hour.' He lifted a cloth from a bowl on the table, and a sharp smell filled the room. 'I want you to drink this.'

I suffered him to tip the stuff gently into my mouth. It was bitter.

'There,' he said, 'sit back now.' I did so, gasping.

The door opened and Joseph came in, his face ashen. But he smiled when he saw I had come to. 'Ah, sir, you are recovered. Thank God.'

I clasped Guy's arm. 'Did Needler get away?' I asked.

'Yes. There's a hue and cry out for him.'

'How did you get here?'

'You called for the constable. He found you, Barak and the old woman all unconscious. But you came round for a moment and asked for me.'

'I don't remember.'

The constable spoke up. 'David Needler's been taken, sir, that's what I came to tell you. He's in Newgate now.'

Barak looked at me. 'Sabine and Avice have been taken there already with the old woman, though she hurt her head badly in the fall. The girls were hiding upstairs in their room; the constables had to pull them screaming from under the beds. I told the magistrate everything when I came round. He is with Sir Edwin now.'

I took a deep breath. 'Does Elizabeth know?'

'Yes,' said Joseph. 'She set to weeping when I told her.' A ghost of a smile crossed his face. 'But she held my hand when I left. I will look after her now, sir. But I had to come here,' he added simply. 'My brother needs me.'

I looked at him. I saw clearly the reason I took the horrible case on at all: it was for his goodness, such natural goodness and charity as few men have.

Things kept floating into my mind. 'Cromwell!' I exclaimed. 'It's been hours, is there word from Grey?'

Barak nodded. 'This arrived here a short while ago.' He took a note with the earl's seal from his pocket and handed it to me. I read, in Grey's precise hand: *Lord Cromwell has your message. He is seeing the king today and will contact you should you be needed. He thanks you mightily.*

'Then it's done.' I leaned back. He looked in my mouth and eyes, then did the same to Barak. 'You're both all right,' he said. 'But you should go home, sleep. You will be very tired and shaky for some days.'

'I'll not argue with you, sir,' Barak said.

'And now I ought to return to my shop. I have patients.' He bowed to us and turned for the door, exotic-looking as ever in his long hooded robe.

'Thank you, old friend,' I said quietly.

He raised a hand and smiled, then went out. The door opened again immediately and a tall, thin man I recognised as Magistrate Parsloe entered, looking sombre. He bowed, then turned to Joseph. 'Master Wentworth, I think perhaps you should go to your brother.'

Joseph stood eagerly. 'Has he asked for me?'

Parsloe hesitated. 'No, but he needs someone with him, I think.' He looked at me. 'Master Shardlake, I am glad to see you are recovered. It was quite a scene that met my eyes when the constable called me here.'

'I can imagine. You have questioned Sir Edwin?'

'Yes. He says he knew nothing of his family's doings. I believe him; he is a stricken man.' Parsloe shook his head. 'We found this in the wine cellar.' Parsloe passed a little glass phial to me. 'Your apothecary friend says it is a very strong concentration of belladonna.'

I handed it back to him, suppressing a shudder.

'Can you come to the Old Bailey tomorrow, sir, to give evidence?' he asked. 'Elizabeth Wentworth is up before Judge Forbizer.'

'I will.' I turned to Joseph. 'Can you be at court at ten tomorrow as well? Then Elizabeth can be discharged into your care.'

He nodded. 'Yes. And thank you, sir, thank you for everything.'

WE WENT HOME. Though I felt light-headed and kept having to pause, I prepared a statement for Forbizer and had Barak, who was in little better case, do the same. Reading his statement over, I was surprised at how neatly and fluently he wrote; the monks' school had taught him well. Afterwards we ate and then, for a second night, went wearily up to bed to sleep like stones.

Next morning there was no further word from Cromwell. It was the 10th of June. The demonstration before the king would have been today.

At the Old Bailey everything was ready. Parsloe was waiting in the outer hall with a collection of statements for me to look over. Joseph stood next to him, still pale though more composed than yesterday.

I took his arm. 'Are you ready, Joseph?'

'Aye. Edwin was unable to come, he is in a bad state. I stayed with him last night. I think he will forgive me. I am all he has now.'

I nodded. 'He could have no greater support.'

'I may see if I can get him to come to the farm with me and Elizabeth. It will be a familiar place for both of them, with happy associations at least.'

'Yes. And it may be better to leave London. The pamphleteers will be busy again once this news is out, pox on their jeering cruelty.' I turned to Parsloe. 'Are we in open court with the rest of the cases?'

He shook his head. 'No. The judge will see us in his chambers.'

I took a deep breath. 'Then let's get it over. There's his clerk.' I looked over to where Forbizer's plump assistant was bustling about.

Parsloe, Joseph and Barak accompanied me to the judge's chambers, where Forbizer sat, swathed in his red robe, behind a desk stacked with papers. He looked at us coldly then snapped his fingers. 'The statements.'

I handed them to him. Forbizer read them through, occasionally pausing to frown and check something. At length he laid down the statements.

'So she was innocent after all,' he said.

'Yes,' I replied.

'She should still have been pressed,' he said coldly. 'That was the correct sentence for a refusal to plead.' He stroked his grey beard reflectively. 'I have been considering whether to sentence her to some more time in the Hole for her contempt of court.' I saw Joseph pale. Forbizer shrugged. 'But I have a busy morning. I will let her go. At least until the rest of her family are tried—she will need to be a witness then.'

'Thank you, Your Honour,' I said quietly.

Forbizer signed the order of release, then flicked it across the table to me. 'There you are, Brother Shardlake.' I reached to take it but he placed two fingers on the edge. I looked into his eyes. They were cold and angry. 'Do not cross me again, Brother,' he said, 'or, whatever political connections you might have, I shall make your life a very hell.' He lifted his fingers and I took the order, rose and bowed. We filed silently out of the room.

Outside, Joseph turned to me. 'What did the judge mean?'

I hesitated. But Joseph had a right to know, if anyone did. 'Barak and I have been involved in a . . . a case for Lord Cromwell. It was very important; that was why I had so little time to give Elizabeth. It was his influence made Forbizer grant Elizabeth that stay. But, please, you must tell no one.'

He nodded. 'I will not, sir.' He shook his head. 'The earl. God bless him.'

I handed him the order. 'There, take that to Newgate and Elizabeth will be released. Would you like us to come with you?'

He smiled. 'This is something I would rather do alone, if you do not mind.'

'I understand.'

Barak and I watched as he left the Bailey with the precious document.

'Well,' I said, 'it's all over. What do you want to do now? I must go to Lincoln's Inn, to catch up on business.' Now that the parting of our ways was near, I knew I would miss him.

'Might I come with you to Chancery Lane?' he asked diffidently. 'I won't be able to sleep again, or settle to anything, until I hear from the earl.'

'Very well. I feel the same. Maybe there is a letter at Lincoln's Inn.'

AT CHANCERY LANE there was no message from Cromwell. Skelly was at his copying, peering painfully at his papers. Godfrey, though, was gone. I went into his office to find a note addressed to me on top of a pile of papers.

Please take custody of my cases, I know you will serve my clients well. I will send to you telling where to remit such fees as are due to me. Some friends and I are going to preach the Word of God in the towns; I had better not say where for now.
Your brother, in the law and in Christ,
Godfrey Wheelwright

I sighed. 'So that's that,' I said. I looked through the cases. Everything was meticulously in order. Then I went through to the outer office again.

Barak was sitting looking out of the window, his face gloomy. 'That arsehole's here,' he said, nodding to where Stephen Bealknap was crossing the quadrangle. He looked tense, casting fearful glances around him.

I laughed. 'Let us put him out of his misery.'

We went into the courtyard. Seeing us, Bealknap hastened over.

'Brother Shardlake, is there any news?' he asked.

'You need fear no more, Bealknap,' I said with a smile. 'The issue of Greek Fire is settled. You are quite safe.'

He sighed with relief. 'What happened?' he asked, his eyes eager with curiosity. 'Who was behind it? Does Lord Cromwell have Greek Fire?'

I raised a hand. 'Those matters remain confidential, Brother. All I can say is that you may resume your normal life in safety.'

His eyes narrowed. 'And the case about my houses? You'll be dropping that, now you know of Sir Richard's interest?'

'Why, no,' I replied. 'I shall still be going to Chancery.' And Cromwell, I gambled, would not stand in my way.

Bealknap drew himself up, frowning. 'You would take a fellow barrister to court! That is dishonourable—I shall make sure it is known.'

I thought of those hovels, the people made to use that stinking cesspit, the neighbouring houses spoiled. 'You are a son of sin and death, Bealknap,' I said. 'And I shall fight you every way I can.'

I turned as Barak nudged my arm. Joseph was running towards us from the gate. He reached us and stopped, taking deep whooping breaths.

I felt a terrible apprehension. 'Elizabeth?' I asked.

He shook his head. 'She is safe at my lodgings. But in the City, I heard . . .'
'What?'

He took a shuddering breath. 'Lord Cromwell has fallen! It has just been announced. He was arrested at the council table this morning, for treason, and taken to the Tower. His goods have been seized.'

'Attainder,' I said. 'He'll be condemned unheard.'

'They say the Duke of Norfolk himself ripped the seal of office from his neck. All his associates are being arrested too!'

I took Joseph's shoulder and led him away. Bealknap stood goggle-eyed for a moment, then turned and hastened to the hall to spread the news.

'I thought you should know at once, sir,' Joseph said. 'After what you told me this morning, I thought . . . you may be in danger.'

I turned to Barak. 'But our message! Grey said he had it. It should be Norfolk that's arrested—'

'Master Grey?' Joseph asked. 'The earl's secretary?'

'Yes. What of him?'

'They're saying he's turned his coat, given evidence against the earl. Half his people have.' He clenched his fists. 'The rogues.'

'Grey!' Barak said. 'It was him feeding news of our doings to our enemies.'

'I've known Grey years.' I laughed bitterly. 'I thought it couldn't possibly be him who was working against us. So we've failed after all. And Norfolk's won.' I turned to Joseph. 'Are you quite sure of this?' I asked.

'Yes. It was the talk of the streets when I left Newgate.'

'Any word of the Duke of Norfolk?'

'No, none.'

I looked at Barak. 'So he hasn't been given Cromwell's place, or not yet.'

'Treason,' Joseph said incredulously. 'What could that mean, treason? No one could have served the king more faithfully—'

'It's just an excuse,' I said bitterly. 'An excuse to get him out of the way.'

'He's fallen off the tightrope of the king's pleasure at last,' Barak said slowly. 'He always feared he would.' He looked at me. 'We have to get out of here,' he said. 'If they're arresting the earl's associates, it would be the ideal opportunity for Norfolk to put us out of the way before we tell any tales.'

'Tales?' Joseph asked. 'What tales?'

'Better you don't know,' I replied. I turned back to Barak. 'You're right, Jack, it's not safe for us in London. Grey. By God—he started as a lawyer.'

'And learned to dissemble.' Barak frowned. 'Why didn't he kill Kytchyn and Goodwife Gristwood? He knew where they were.'

'He was almost the only one who did. If they'd been killed the trail would have led back to him. I hope they will be safe now, given what they know.'

Barak shook his head. 'We can't hang around to find out.'

'But where will you both go?' Joseph asked.

'I've got people who'll keep me safe over in Essex,' Barak replied. He turned to me. 'You could go to your father's place—at Lichfield, isn't it?'

I nodded. 'Yes, that's safest. Joseph, you should leave. Better you are not seen with us.'

Joseph was looking at the gate, where a messenger in the king's livery was dismounting. He ran across the courtyard to the hall.

'They're bringing the news to the lawyers,' I said.

'I'm off,' Barak said. He stared at me with those keen dark eyes, then reached out and shook my hand. To my surprise his eyes were moist. 'We gave them a good run, eh?' he said. 'We did all we could?'

I returned his grip. 'Yes. We did. Thank you, Barak, for everything.'

He nodded, then turned and walked rapidly away across the yard, pulling his cap down low. I felt alone, unprotected.

'Are you truly in danger, Master Shardlake?' Joseph asked quietly.

'I could be. I shall leave now, go home and pack some things, then ride out. There is just one visit I have to make before I go.' I shook his hand. 'Go, Joseph, now. Take Elizabeth and your brother to Essex.'

He shook my hand firmly. 'Thank you, sir. I shall never forget what you have done. If anyone asks, I'll say I don't know where you've gone.'

'That would be best. Thank you, Joseph.'

A bell began ringing through the misty morning, calling the members of the Inn to hear the news. A puzzled throng of lawyers appeared, crossing to the chapel. I stood a moment, gathering all the reserves of strength I had left, then went back to my chambers.

I LEFT SKELLY some money and instructions to refer Godfrey's and my cases to barristers I trusted. I told him I did not know how long I would be away. Then I slipped out while everyone was in the chapel and walked quickly home. Joan was out; she had taken Simon with her on some errand.

I took some money from the store in my room, leaving the rest for her with a note. Then I went out to the stable. Barak's mare Sukey was already gone, but Genesis was in his stall. I patted him. 'Well, I think we may be stuck with each other. Lord Cromwell will not be wanting you back.'

And then, quite suddenly, it all overwhelmed me. I thought of that great man of power, now locked in the Tower, where he had sent so many of his foes. I had failed to save him. Perhaps no one could have saved him after the Cleves debacle, but I laid my head against the horse's flank and wept for him.

'I am sorry,' I said aloud. 'I am sorry.'

I must leave, I told myself, I must pull myself together. I dried my face on my sleeve, then rode out into the City. I had one more thing to do.

A BLACK CARRIAGE with four horses in the shafts was pulled up at the door of the House of Glass, and servants were piling it high with trunks. I dismounted and asked one of them whether Lady Honor was indoors.

'Who should I say—? Hey, you can't just go in!' But I had, tying Genesis to the rail and stepping inside, dodging a lady attendant struggling with an armful of voluminous silk dresses. I ran upstairs to the parlour.

Lady Honor stood before the fireplace, checking items from a long list. She wore a light dress such as might be used for travelling in summer.

'Lady Honor,' I said quietly. 'You are leaving?'

She looked taken aback. 'Yes, for the country. Have you not heard—?'

'I know. Lord Cromwell has fallen.'

'One of my friends at court has sent word the duke is displeased about my part in helping him over the Greek Fire business. And helping *you*,' she added with sudden asperity.

'You have done nothing—'

She laughed bitterly. 'When did anyone need to *do* something to be in danger? My friend says it might be good for me to go to my estates until the new dispensation is clearer.'

'So Norfolk's in the saddle.'

'The Cleves divorce and the Howard marriage are likely to be announced in the next few days.'

'My God.'

'I wish I'd never let you involve me in that matter!' she said with anger. 'Now I am going to have to live in Lincolnshire, for good for all I know.'

I must have looked as stricken as I felt, for her face softened. 'I am sorry, I hate all this hurry. There is so much to do.' She looked at my bandaged wrist. 'What happened there?'

'It is nothing. I am leaving too. For the Midlands.'

She studied my face, then nodded. 'I see. Yes, you must go too. What happened with the Wentworth girl?'

'She is free.' I sighed. 'And I found the answer to Greek Fire, but too late to save Cromwell.'

She raised a hand. 'No, Matthew, you must not tell me any more.'

'Of course, I am sorry. Honor—'

She gave that wry smile of hers. 'Am I not a lady any more?'

'Always. But . . .' Although I had not planned the words, they came tumbling out. 'We are both going to the Midlands. Perhaps we could ride together as far as Northampton. And we will not be so very far apart. It is summer, the roads will not be too bad. Perhaps we could meet . . .'

Her face flushed. She was standing three paces away, and I stepped towards her. I should not want for courage now. But she raised her hand.

'No, Matthew,' she said gently. 'No. I am sorry.'

I gave a long, sad sigh. 'My appearance—'

Then she did close the distance between us and took my arm. 'Is most pleasing to me. And always has been. Your features are as fine as any lord's. But . . .' She paused, choosing her words carefully. 'I am a Vaughan. Once I would have been happy to know you; you are one of those fit to be raised up, as my husband was. But not now, given your past loyalties and who the new powers are in the land. And I will not be lowered to your status, Matthew.'

'Then you did not love me,' I said.

Her smile was sad. 'Love is a child's romantic dream. I admired you, I liked you, yes. But my family's place is what matters. If you came from noble lineage, you would understand.' She gave me a last, affectionate look. 'Goodbye, Matthew, keep safe.' And then, with a rustle of skirts, she was gone.

I RODE OUT of Cripplegate an hour later. A throng of people was waiting to pass through, some looking fearful. A group of the king's guard was posted there and I was afraid I might be stopped, but I was allowed through. I rode away through the dull afternoon, and did not pause till I reached Hampstead Heath. There I rode off the track into the long grass and looked back at the City. I could make out the bulk of the Tower, where Thomas Cromwell lay now, the river flowing past. London looked strangely peaceful from up there, a tableau rather than a city on the edge of panic. I patted Genesis. 'We've far to go, good horse,' I said, then turned and rode away fast, to the north.

EPILOGUE
30TH JULY 1540

I walked down from Chancery Lane to the Temple Stairs, looking about me to see what changes might have occurred, for I had been away nearly two months. In truth people were going about their business much as ever, though there were fewer than usual for there were rumours of plague in the eastern suburbs and many lawyers had left the City. The letter from Barak had come a few days before, brief and to the point.

Master Shardlake,

I am back in London: I still have friends in the king's service and have had word that you and I may safely return to the City. Lord Cromwell is to die, but none of his supporters are to suffer unless they misbehave. If you wish to return to London and meet me, I shall be pleased to tell you more.

JB

His words tied in with other news that had reached the Midlands. The expected persecution of reformers had been milder than feared, though three Protestant preachers were to be burned that day at Smithfield. But three papists were to be hanged, drawn and quartered at Tyburn at the same time: a message from the king that neither side had the upper hand now and there would, after all, be no return to Rome. Archbishop Cranmer, to everyone's surprise, had kept his place. And though a speedy divorce from Anne of Cleves had been approved by the Church, and everyone awaited the announcement of the king's betrothal to Catherine Howard, neither Norfolk nor anyone else had been appointed to Cromwell's place. The word was that for the first time in nearly thirty years Henry intended to govern himself, without a chief minister. What a disappointment that must be to the duke.

I had arrived that morning and, to my relief, found everything quiet and normal at home. Joan had not been happy at my prolonged absence, and I promised her that my life would now resume its quiet course.

As I reached the river, I took off my cap and rubbed sweat from my brow. The blazing heat had returned in the days after Cromwell's fall and given no respite since. I scanned the stairs. Barak was waiting at the spot where I had asked him to meet me in my reply. His hair had grown again and he looked well set up in his best green doublet, his sword at his belt as usual. He was leaning over the parapet, staring pensively at the busy river. I tapped his shoulder and he turned, his sober look replaced by a broad grin.

He extended a hand. 'You are well?' he asked.

'Quite recovered, Barak. I have been having a quiet time. You?'

'Aye, I'm back at the Old Barge and glad to be. Essex is too quiet for me.'

'I know what you mean.' And indeed my sojourn at Lichfield had cured me of the desire for a country life. Walking around the parched countryside, listening as my father and his steward endlessly bemoaned the weather, had begun to grate on my nerves.

'Our old master died two days ago. Did you know?'

'Aye.' I lowered my voice. 'I heard the execution was bungled.'

'It was. I saw it.' His face darkened. 'His head's boiled and on a spike on London Bridge now, pointed away from the City so he cannot look on the king any more. But he died bravely, refusing to admit any fault.'

I shook my head. 'Those charges were ridiculous. Conspiring to make war on the king? If there was one thing Thomas Cromwell did faithfully all his life it was serve Henry Tudor.'

'When they arrested him at the council table he cried out, "I am no traitor." Then Norfolk tore the Order of the Garter from his chest.'

'And what of Norfolk?' I asked. 'Are you sure we are safe?'

'Aye. I have friends in some of the less public parts of the king's service. I've had word from Norfolk himself we won't be touched. He's terrified of a single word getting out about Greek Fire. I've dropped a hint that if anything happened to either of us there might be others who knew the tale.'

'Did you hear anything of Kytchyn? Or Madam Gristwood and her son?'

'They are safe. They fled with the man who guarded their house as soon as they heard of Cromwell's fall. I don't know where they are.'

I nodded. 'So I may resume practice?'

He nodded. 'If that's what you wish.'

I stepped forward and leaned on the parapet, for my back hurt after my long ride. Together we looked over the river.

Barak turned to me with sudden intensity. 'Could we have saved Lord Cromwell, do you think? If we'd guessed Grey was a traitor?'

I sighed deeply. 'That question has tormented me night and day. I think he was so deep in trouble over the Cleves marriage he would have fallen in the end. Unless he'd agreed to abandon Queen Anne and reform, and he wouldn't have done that.' I smiled sadly. 'At least that's what I tell myself.'

'I think you're right,' Barak said.

We leaned there in silence for a moment. Then I saw a boat turning in to the stairs, two faces I recognised. I nudged Barak. 'I've arranged for some others to meet us here. They wished to see you.'

'Who?' Puzzled, he followed my gaze to the wherry.

It pulled up and Joseph Wentworth stepped out. He gave his hand to a young woman in a dark dress and hood to help her out of the boat.

'Is that—?'

I nodded. 'Elizabeth.'

She walked a little unsteadily, her head bowed low, and Joseph had to help her up the steps. I went to the head of the stairs and Barak followed.

Joseph took my hand warmly and bowed to Barak. 'Master Barak, I am ec.

glad you are here. My niece wished to thank you both.'

Barak shuffled awkwardly. 'I did nothing, really.'

Elizabeth raised her head. Her hair had grown again too, a few curly strands escaping from her hood. For the first time I saw her face properly. It was pretty but full of character too, though her eyes were infinitely sad.

'Yes, sir, you did.' Her voice trembled and she clung tightly to her uncle's hand. 'You went down into that terrible well, you nearly died at my grandmother's hands.' She looked at Barak. 'And when you spoke to me that day in the gaol, sir, you showed me how my silent suffering did no good, for me or my poor uncle. You made me begin to see things I had not seen before.'

Barak inclined his head. 'If I helped save you, I count it a great honour.'

'I owe you both so much. You and Uncle Joseph, you never wavered in your support, however wickedly I treated you.' Her lip trembled and she lowered her head again.

Joseph patted her hand. 'Elizabeth is still sore tired and troubled,' he said. 'The peace of the countryside is a balm to her, she finds London a trial. But she insisted on coming up with me today to thank you.'

'And we are grateful.' I hesitated. 'How is your brother?'

'Sore afflicted since Sabine was found guilty of manslaughter and she and Avice imprisoned. Though he has paid for good lodgings for them. He is selling his house to try and buy a royal pardon. I come up each week. He needs me.' He hesitated. 'My mother died in Newgate, a week after her arrest.'

'I had not heard. Was it the fall?'

'No.' He sighed. 'It was as though, with the family in total disgrace, she did not want to live any more.'

I nodded sadly.

Joseph smiled at Elizabeth. 'We should go on now. But thank you again.'

He and Elizabeth shook our hands, then Joseph guided her away, up to Temple Walk.

'Will she recover, do you think?' Barak asked.

'I don't know. At least now she will have a chance.'

'Have you seen Lady Honor? I heard she's left London.'

I laughed. 'You hear everything. No, I shall not see Lady Honor again.'

'I am sorry.'

'It was a matter of status,' I said heavily. 'That means everything to her, you know.' I frowned. 'No, that was bitterness talking. But all those formal banquets and receptions would have bored me; I am better off as a mere jobbing lawyer.' I sighed. 'I shall go back to the Inn and pick up my cases;

burrow into my books again.' I shrugged. 'Get Bealknap into Chancery.'

'Watch out for Richard Rich. You've made an enemy there.'

'I can deal with that. In fact, I rather enjoy using the law to right wrongs.'

I looked at Barak. There was an idea I had been turning over in my mind for several days. I was not at all sure it was a good one.

'I have Godfrey's cases now as well as my own. I have a great deal of work to catch up on and more will come in. I need more help than Skelly can give; I need an assistant, someone to exchange ideas with, do some of the investigative work. I suppose you are unemployed now?'

He looked at me in feigned surprise; I was not taken in. 'I'll not get work with the government again. I'm known too well as Lord Cromwell's man.'

'Do you think you could work for me? Is that dog Latin of yours up to it?'

'I should think so.'

'The work will be boring sometimes. You will have to get used to legal language, learn to understand it rather than mock it. You'll have to knock off some of your rough edges, learn to address barristers and judges with respect. And you'll have to call me sir.'

Barak bit his lip and wrinkled his nose, as though in an agony of indecision. It was all pretence, of course; I had come to know his ways too well to be taken in. I had to prevent myself from laughing.

'I will be happy to serve you, sir,' he said at last. And then he did something he had never done before. He bowed.

'Very well,' I said. 'Come, then, let's go to Chancery Lane. See if we can bring a little order into this wicked world. A tiny bit.'

We walked through Temple Gardens. Ahead lay Chancery Lane. Beyond that Smithfield, where the fires would be lit now. Behind us the river, flowing to London Bridge where Cromwell's head stood fixed on its stake. Between Smithfield and the river the roiling city, ever in need of justice and absolution.

C. J. SANSOM

Place of residence: Hove, Sussex
Likes: Fish and chips, Dr Who, Spain and Anne Tyler novels
Dislikes: Jane Austen, bagpipes, Japanese food and political correctness

'Ideas for historical novels set in Tudor times have been buzzing around my head for years,' says C. J. Sansom, who has long been fascinated by the period. 'The dissolution of the monasteries was a major event in English history. As such it had tremendous dramatic potential and I was surprised that this had never been exploited, so I decided to have a go.'

Sansom had always enjoyed writing, but his career as a solicitor had prevented him from making it anything other than a hobby. Finally he realised that if he was going to have a proper crack at a novel he would have to take a year off. He resigned from his job and sat down to write *Dissolution*, which has been hailed as a great success, garnering praise from critics and the public alike. There is even the possibility of a film in the offing—Kenneth Branagh's production company, Contagious Films, has already optioned the rights.

Dissolution is a hard act to follow but Sansom's second book, *Dark Fire,* seems certain to emulate its success. It is set three years after the end of *Dissolution* and also features the hunchback lawyer, Matthew Shardlake. 'He came riding into my mind fully formed—hunchback and all,' Sansom explains. 'But I don't know where from. The fact that he is a hunchback is useful in that I always wanted my detective to be "different" and to view society as an outsider.'

'I'm doing what I always wanted to do, which is to combine writing and historical research to tell a story—that's the best thing.'

Sansom is now hard at work on another Shardlake story, but he has also written a spy thriller set in Madrid just after the Spanish Civil War—a period which he studied for his doctorate at Birmingham University. The book, tentatively called *Winter in Madrid*, is due to be published after the third Shardlake novel.

Sansom (who prefers not to be photographed), says that although he enjoyed the eleven years he spent working as a lawyer, he loves his new life as a full-time novelist. 'I'm doing what I always wanted to do, which is to combine writing and historical research to tell a story—that's the best thing.'

CLIVE
CUSSLER

AND DIRK CUSSLER

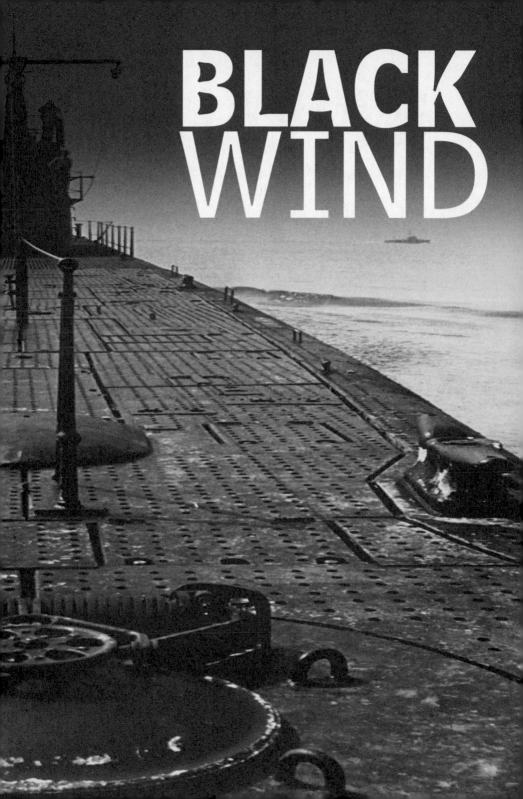

Deep beneath the cold waters of the Pacific, the wreck of a Japanese submarine has lain undisturbed and undetected for decades. Inside is a weapon that was designed to wreak havoc on the American mainland and bring a speedy conclusion to World War II.

Sub *I–403* was written off as lost, but its deadly cargo is perfectly preserved—ready to be used again in pursuit of the ambitions of a powerful and ruthless billionaire.

PROLOGUE

Lieutenant Commander Takeo Ogawa glanced at his watch and shook his head in irritation. 'Half past midnight already,' he muttered anxiously. 'Three hours late and still we wait.'

A young ensign nodded but said nothing. Waiting atop the conning tower of the Japanese Imperial Navy submarine *I-403*, the two men gazed across the naval yard searching for signs of a pending arrival. A light drizzle fell, lending an eerie tranquillity to the late hour, which was broken only by the distant sounds of hammers, cranes and welding torches, as round-the-clock repairs were made in a futile rush to aid the increasingly bleak war effort.

At last the whine of a diesel engine echoed across the water, and a slate-coloured Isuzu cargo truck rumbled into view and inched its way towards the submarine's pen. It ground to a halt and six heavily armed soldiers sprang from the truck bed. As Ogawa made his way down to the dock, two uniformed men exited the cab of the truck and approached him. Recognising a superior officer, Ogawa stood at attention and saluted smartly.

Captain Miyoshi Horinouchi, staff operations officer for the Sixth Fleet, returned the salute. 'Commander, this is Dr Tanaka of the Army Medical School. He will be accompanying you on your mission.'

'Sir, I am not accustomed to carrying passengers while on patrol,' Ogawa replied, ignoring the small, bespectacled man at Horinouchi's side.

'Your patrol orders to the Philippines have been rescinded,' Horinouchi stated, handing Ogawa a brown folder. 'You have new orders. You are to take Dr Tanaka and his cargo aboard and proceed immediately to launch an attack on the American mainland.'

'This is most unusual, Captain,' Ogawa asserted.

Horinouchi tilted his head to the side, then took a few steps to his right. Ogawa followed, leaving Tanaka out of earshot. 'Our surface fleet was annihilated by the Americans at Leyte Gulf,' Horinouchi said softly. 'It's a matter of time before all our remaining resources are assigned in defence of the homeland.' He didn't add that the Japanese submarine fleet, too, was being decimated in the Pacific and that the navy had no answer to the anti-submarine warfare technologies being deployed by the American forces.

'The army has approached us for assistance in a valiant operation against the enemy,' Horinouchi continued. Succeed in this, Ogawa, and the Americans will bow to a truce and our homeland will be preserved.'

Ogawa was stunned by the words. He would have ridiculed the idea that he could launch an attack that would end the war, had it not been a fleet staff officer dictating the order to him. 'I am honoured by your confidence, Captain Horinouchi,' he said. 'Rest assured my crew and officers will uphold the honour to the emperor. May I ask, sir, what *is* Dr Tanaka's cargo?'

'*Makaze*,' Horinouchi muttered quietly. 'An evil wind.'

HALF A DOZEN wooden crates were carefully loaded into the forward torpedo room of the *I-403* and tightly secured. At 2.30 a.m., the iron sub nosed into the inky harbour and inched past several other I-boats docked in the yard.

Gradually the lights of Kure fell away and the submarine snaked round several large, mountainous islands, then entered the Seto Inland Sea. Ogawa ordered increased speed, and patches of predawn light tinted the eastern sky. As he marked their route in the conning tower with the *I-403*'s navigator, Ogawa was approached by the executive officer, Lieutenant Motoshita.

'Hot tea, sir,' Motoshita said, thrusting a cup towards the commander.

'Yes, thanks,' Ogawa replied crisply before gulping the tea. The hot liquid was a welcome tonic against the chill December air.

'The sea is unusually calm this morning,' Motoshita noted.

Ogawa nodded thoughtfully. 'Yoshi, we'll initiate a zigzag running pattern when we reach the strait, then submerge before we leave the mainland. We can take no chances with enemy submarines patrolling off our coasts.'

'I'll alert the crew, sir.'

As a crimson sun crept up over the eastern horizon, the *I-403* veered south from the Inland Sea into the Pacific Ocean. Several officers crowded the conning tower to take a final glimpse of their green island nation, uncertain whether they would ever return home again.

Ogawa issued the command to dive.

THE *I-403* was no ordinary submarine. Stretching over 390 feet long, it was one of a handful of massive iron subs equipped to carry three Seiran float-planes, small converted dive-bombers that could be launched from a cata-pult on the centre bow. While at sea, the disassembled planes were stored in a watertight hangar that stretched along the sub's deck. A shortage of air-craft had forced Ogawa to give up one of his seaplanes for coastal recon-naissance, so his vessel now carried just two of them.

Once the *I-403* had safely entered the Pacific, he retired to his cabin and reread the orders that Horinouchi had given him. They called for him to sail north across the Pacific, with a refuelling stop in the Aleutians. He was to proceed to the northwest coast of America, where his two planes were to launch air attacks on the cities of Tacoma, Seattle, Victoria and Vancouver.

It appeared a futile gesture, Ogawa thought. But there was the question of his unwanted passenger, Dr Tanaka, and his unidentified cargo . . .

Summoned to Ogawa's cabin, Tanaka bowed gracefully and seated him-self at a small wooden table. The slightly built scientist had a shrewish and unsmiling face, and his vacant eyes were magnified by thick glasses.

'Dr Tanaka,' Ogawa began, 'there is no mention in my orders of your duties or the nature of your cargo. I must ask what your role in the mission is.'

'Commander Ogawa, I am with the Army Medical School's Epidemic Disease Prevention Group. We have received materials from a research facility in China that have enabled us to develop an effective new weapon. Your submarine has been chosen as the means to launch the weapon and I am responsible for its security and deployment.'

'This weapon will be dropped from my aircraft?'

'Yes, in special canisters. I have already made the necessary arrange-ments with your ordnance crew.'

'And my men. Are they in any danger with this weapon aboard?'

'None whatsoever.'

Ogawa didn't believe him, but figured that the US navy's antisubmarine forces were a greater risk to his sub than anything carried on board. As Tanaka volunteered little additional information, Ogawa dismissed him, and silently cursed the Fleet Command for selecting his vessel for the assignment. It was a mission he didn't want.

FOR THE NEXT twelve days and nights, the sub nosed northeast. On the thir-teenth night, the *I-403* surfaced near the Aleutian island of Amchitka and found a supply ship anchored in a small cove. The refuelling operation was completed in less than three hours, then the *I-403* cast off yet again on an eastward tack towards North America.

'Captain, I have plotted a route to the coast,' the *I-403*'s navigator stated as he unrolled a chart in front of Ogawa.

'What is our present position?' Ogawa enquired.

'Approximately two hundred kilometres west of Vancouver Island.'

Ogawa studied the chart intently. 'We're too far north. I wish to launch the attack from a point central to the four targets, to minimise flight time. Bring us south and we'll approach the coastline here.' He stabbed his finger at Cape Flattery on the northwest tip of Washington State, an angular peak of land that jutted into the Pacific Ocean like the snout of a hungry dog.

With a little luck, Ogawa thought, they might be on their way home in just over twenty-four hours.

A BUZZ of activity overtook the *I-403* after it surfaced that evening as preparations were made to launch the aerial strike. Mechanics began piecing the aircraft parts together, seamen rigged the hydraulic catapult and tested the device. The pilots studied topographic maps, plotting their course to the drop zones. And the ordnance men, under Dr Tanaka's direction, configured the bomb racks of the Seiran bombers to hold the twelve silver canisters.

At 4 a.m., a squat man in a grease-stained jumpsuit approached Ogawa. 'Sir, sorry to report we are having troubles with the aircraft.'

'What is the problem?' Ogawa asked, clearly annoyed.

'Aircraft number one has been found to have a faulty magneto, and aircraft number two has a damaged elevator.'

'And how long will it take to complete the repairs?'

The mechanic paused, contemplating his response. 'Approximately one hour for the repairs, sir, plus another twenty minutes to load the ordnance.'

Ogawa nodded grimly. 'Proceed with all haste.'

One hour turned into two and still the planes were not ready. Ogawa's impatience grew as he noticed grey streaks in the eastern sky, signalling the approaching dawn. Then the stillness of the morning air was shattered by a cry from the sound detection operator below decks.

'Captain, I have an echo! Vessel approaching ahead . . . sound intensity one,' he reported.

Few Japanese submarines were equipped with radar in 1941, unlike their American counterparts, so they had to reply on sound-detection equipment to reveal the enemy.

On deck, both of the aircraft had been moved out of their hangars while repairs continued. With neither plane ready for flight, they would have to be sacrificed should the submarine have to make an emergency dive.

'Deck gun at the ready,' Ogawa ordered.

'Sound intensity two and increasing,' the sound operator relayed calmly.

'Secure all aircraft and clear the aviation deck,' Ogawa instructed.

An ensign sprinted down the deck, shouting at the mechanics and pilots.

'Sound intensity three, off our bow. May be a destroyer,' the operator reported, identifying the churning sound of twin propellers.

As if on cue, a grey ship materialised out of the fog half a mile away, white foam bursting off its bow in angry torrents as it drove straight at the sub.

In an instant, the *I-403*'s deck gun boomed in an attempt to halt the oncoming dervish. The slim, head-on profile of the destroyer made for a difficult target, however, and the shell passed harmlessly to one side. Hurriedly, the gun crew took aim and fired again.

Recognising the futility of a surface duel with a superior vessel, Ogawa ordered a crash dive. The mission would have to be sacrificed for the safety of the ship and crew, he reasoned, if it wasn't already too late.

As the dive alarm sounded, the gun crew fired off a last desperate shot before scrambling below deck. They had overcompensated for the speed of the destroyer and the shell splashed harmlessly into the water fifty feet ahead of the ship's bow.

On the bridge of the *I-403,* Ogawa hesitated momentarily before dropping down the hatch. As he waited for the huge hull of the *I-403* to make its descent, he played one more card. 'Prepare to fire torpedoes!' he commanded.

'Tubes loaded,' the torpedo officer reported.

The sub's nose dipped beneath the waves and a wash of sea water flooded over the forward deck.

'Fire one!' Ogawa shouted. He counted off three seconds silently, then ordered, 'Fire two!'

With a blast of compressed air, the two twenty-three-foot-long torpedoes burst out of the sub's forward tubes on a deadly course towards the advancing destroyer, each packing an 890-pound lethal warhead.

AN ENSIGN standing on the bridge wing of the US destroyer, *Theodore Knight,* noticed two white trails burrowing towards the ship under the surface of the water. 'Torpedoes off the port and starboard bow!' he shouted, frozen in rapt fascination as he watched the speeding explosives approach.

Either by miscalculation, divine intervention, or just plain luck, the two deadly fish somehow missed their target.

'She's diving, sir,' noted the destroyer's helmsman as he watched the waves slosh over the bow of the sub.

'Steer for the conning tower,' Lieutenant Commander Roy Baxter commanded. 'Let's go right down her throat.'

The destroyer went in like a charging ram, intent on crushing the submersing vessel. The two floatplanes were hit first by its sharp prow, and were dissected into large sections of mangled metal, fabric and debris. Then the ship's surging bow tore into the conning tower with a crunch. Ogawa and his operations officers were killed instantly as the structure was ripped away.

Aboard the *Theodore Knight*, the crew and officers cheered as they watched a slick of black oil pool on the surface above the sunken boat.

None of the men on the destroyer suspected the horror that would have befallen their countrymen had the *I-403* succeeded in its 'mission. Nor could they know that the horror still lingered in the wreckage of the sub.

CHAPTER 1

THE ALEUTIAN ISLANDS, ALASKA: MAY 22, 2007

The winds swirled lightly about the faded yellow tin hut that housed the Coast Guard weather station on Yunaska Island. One of dozens of volcanic islands that curved off the Alaskan mainland, Yunaska rose like an emerald from the frigid ocean. Barely seventeen miles across, it was distinguished by two dormant volcano peaks, one at at each end, separated by rolling grass hills. Lying central to the North Pacific currents, the island was an ideal location for tracking sea and atmospheric conditions that would brew into fully fledged weather fronts as they moved towards North America.

The nearest village was ninety miles away across open water, while Anchorage was more than 1,000 miles distant. But, despite the seclusion, meteorologist Ed Stimson and technician Mike Barnes considered their three-week stint manning the station to be a plum assignment. Stimson enjoyed being out in the field while Barnes relished the time off he would accrue, which he would spend prospecting in the Alaskan back country.

'I'm telling you, Ed, you'll have to find a new partner after our next R&R. I found a fissure of quartz in the Chugach Mountains that would knock your socks off. There's got to be a thick, juicy gold vein lying right beneath it.'

'Sure, just like that strike you made wild claims about in the McKinley River,' Stimson chided, amused as always at Barnes's naive optimism.

'Just wait till you see me driving around Anchorage in my new Hummer; then you'll believe,' replied Barnes.

'Fair enough,' Stimson replied. 'In the meantime, can you check the anemometer mounting? The wind readings have stopped recording again.'

Barnes pulled on a heavy coat, then stepped out of the hut. Stimson peered at the weather radar monitor. He was watching a storm front some 200 miles to the southwest that would douse their island for several days. His concentration was interrupted by a rapping sound overhead. Barnes was now up on the tin roof fooling with the anemometer.

Static-filled chatter suddenly blared from a radio set mounted on a wall—the captains of nearby fishing boats yakking about the weather. Then the radio fell silent and Stimson could hear an odd whooshing sound, similar to a jet aircraft. For several long seconds, the noise continued, seeming to diminish slightly in intensity before ending in a loud crack. Thinking it might be thunder, the meteorologist adjusted the scale view on his radar to a twenty-mile range. The monitor showed only a light scattering of cloud. Must be the air force up to some tricks, he figured.

His thoughts were broken by a wail outside the door to the hut. It was their pet husky, Max.

'What is it, Max?' Stimson called out, opening the door.

The Siberian husky let out a howl as it turned, shaking, towards its master in the doorway. Stimson was shocked to see the dog's eyes glazed in a vacant stare while thick white foam oozed from its mouth. The dog teetered back and forth for a moment, then keeled over.

'Jesus! Mike, get down here quick,' Stimson yelled to his partner.

Barnes was already climbing down the ladder from the roof but was having a hard time catching the rungs with his feet. Nearing the ground, he missed the last rung with his left foot altogether and lurched to the ground.

'Mike, the dog just . . . Are you OK?' Stimson asked, realising something was not right. Running to his partner's side, he found Barnes fighting for breath, his eyes nearly as glassy as Max's. Throwing his arm round Barnes's shoulder, Stimson half carried, half dragged him into the shack.

Gasping, Barnes whispered, 'There's something in the air.'

No sooner had the words left his mouth than his eyes rolled up into the back of his head and he fell down dead.

Stimson straightened up, only to find that the room was spinning like a top before his eyes. A throbbing pain wracked his head while he felt a vice-like grip squeeze the air out of his lungs. Choking and losing all vision, he staggered and fell, and was dead before he hit the ground.

TWO MILES to the east, Sarah Matson eased herself slowly into a prime vantage point beside a rock. Barely thirty feet away a noisy colony of Steller's sea lions basked at the water's edge. A dozen or so of the fat-whiskered mammals sat huddled together, while four or five could be seen swimming in the surf. Two young males barked loudly at each other. Several pups slept, blissfully oblivious to the racket.

Pulling a small notepad from her jacket pocket, Sarah began jotting down particulars about each animal, estimating its age and health. After nearly an hour, she replaced the notepad in her pocket, and slowly retraced her steps across the boulder-strewn gully.

Sarah relished working outdoors. The flaxen-haired thirty-year-old had a slender frame and delicate features, but she had grown up in rural Wyoming and had spent all her summers hiking and horse riding in the Teton Mountains. Now, in her role as field epidemiologist for the Center for Disease Control, she was able to combine her passion for the outdoors with her love of wildlife by helping to track the spread of animal diseases that were communicable to humans.

A number of mysterious sea lion deaths had been reported along the western Alaskan Peninsula, and Sarah and two CDC associates had been sent to the Aleutian Islands from Seattle to determine the extent and range of the die-off. This was her second day on Yunaska, and so far she had failed to find any indications of an ailment in the local sea lion population.

Sarah hiked the two miles back to camp, easily spotting the trio of bright red tents some distance away. A squat, bearded man wearing a baseball cap was rummaging through a large cooler when she approached the campsite.

'Sarah, there you are. Sandy and I were just making plans for lunch,' Irv Fowler said with a smile. An easygoing man on the wrong side of fifty, Fowler looked, and acted, like someone ten years his junior.

A petite, red-haired woman crawled out of one of the tents clutching a pot and ladle. 'Irv's always making plans for lunch,' Sandy Johnson remarked with a grin, rolling her eyes.

'How did you two do this morning?' Sarah enquired as she grabbed a camp stool and sat down.

'We checked a large colony of Steller's on the eastern beach and they all looked fat and healthy.'

'That's consistent with what I observed,' Sarah replied.

'We can check the colony on the west coast this afternoon, since our pilot won't be back to pick us up until morning. In the meantime,' Fowler announced, placing a large pot on the portable stove, 'it's time for the speciality of the house.'

'Not that fire-belching—' Sandy began, before being cut off.

'Yes, indeed. Cajun chilli du jour,' Fowler grinned, and he scraped the contents of a large tin can into the heated pot.

THE THREE scientists were just finishing their lunch when Sarah saw a pair of birds flying overhead suddenly stop in midflight as if they had struck an invisible wall and fall to the ground. Then Sandy clutched her stomach and doubled over in agony.

'Come now, my chilli wasn't that bad,' Fowler joked before he, too, became light-headed and nauseous.

As Sarah stood and took a few steps towards the cooler to retrieve some bottled water, fire shot through her thigh muscles.

'What's happening?' Fowler gasped as he staggered to the ground.

For Sarah, time seemed to slow as her senses dulled and her muscles refused to obey her brain's commands. Each breath was a stab of agony. She fell on her back and stared blurry-eyed at the grey sky as a fog enveloped her mind. Then everything turned to black.

'HELLO, Sleeping Beauty.' The words came from a warm deep voice.

Sarah opened her eyes to a grey canopy, only this one was flat and without clouds. As her eyes regained focus, she could see that it was not the sky above her but a ceiling. She was lying in a bed with a soft pillow under her head. The room she was in was small and simply decorated, with a writing desk in one corner and a painting of an old ocean liner above it.

A movement caught her eye and she turned to find a tall man standing in the doorway, looking at her with a slight grin. He was in his late twenties, broad-shouldered, fit and wiry. Wavy black hair set off a rugged face that was more intriguing than classically handsome. But it was the eyes that radiated a special aura. They were a deep shade of iridescent green and revealed a sense of intelligence, adventure and integrity all rolled into one.

'My apologies for not introducing myself on the island, Sarah,' he said, stepping towards her. 'My name is Dirk Pitt.' He neglected to add 'Junior', which distinguished him from his father, who shared the same name.

'You know who I am?' she asked, still confused.

'Well, a brainy scientist named Irv told me a little about your project on Yunaska. He seemed to think he poisoned everyone with his chilli.'

'Irv and Sandy! Are they all right?'

'Yes. They took a little nap, like you, but are fine now. They're resting just down the hall.' Seeing the bewilderment in her eyes, Dirk gave her shoulder a reassuring squeeze. 'Don't worry, you're in good hands. You're aboard the National Underwater and Marine Agency research ship *Deep Endeavor*. We were returning from an underwater survey of the Aleutian Basin when we picked up a distress call from the Coast Guard weather station on Yunaska. I flew to the station in our helicopter and happened to see your camp while flying back to the ship. I gave you and your friends an all-expenses-paid aerial tour, but you slept through the whole thing.'

'I'm sorry,' Sarah murmured. 'I guess I owe you a big thanks, Mr Pitt.'

'Please, call me Dirk.'

'OK, Dirk,' she replied with a smile. 'How are the weather station people?'

A look of sorrow crossed Dirk's face. 'I'm afraid we didn't make it in time. We found two men and a dog—all dead.'

A shiver went up Sarah's spine. 'What on earth happened?' she asked.

'We don't know for sure. It could have been some sort of airborne fumes or toxin. We flew in with gas masks but, whatever it was, it had dissipated by the time we landed at the weather station. You and your team were apparently far enough away from the source to be impacted less severely.'

Sarah fell quiet as the horror of the whole ordeal came back to her.

'I'll let you sleep some more. Perhaps later I can buy you a plate of king crab legs for dinner?' Dirk asked with a smile.

'I'd like that,' Sarah murmured, then fell fast asleep.

THE CAPTAIN of *Deep Endeavor*, Kermit Burch, was standing at the helm reading a fax when Dirk stepped onto the bridge. Burch turned to Dirk with an annoyed look on his face. 'We've notified the Department of Homeland Security, but nobody intends to do anything until the public safety officer from Atka has filed his report, and he can't get here until tomorrow morning. Two men dead and they treat it as an accident.'

'We don't have much to go on,' Dirk replied. 'The CDC scientists don't remember much, other than that it struck pretty rapidly.'

'I'll rest easier when we get them to a proper medical facility,' Burch said. 'We can make Unalaska, the nearest airfield, in under fourteen hours. I'll radio ahead for a medical flight to transfer them to Anchorage.'

'Captain, I'd like to take the helicopter back out and reconnoitre the island. Maybe there's something we missed. Any objections?'

'No . . . just so long as you take that Texas joker with you,' Burch replied with a pained grin.

AS DIRK RAN through a preflight checklist from the pilot's seat of the NUMA Sikorsky S-76C offshore helicopter, a sandy-haired man ambled across the small landing platform mounted amidships. With scuffed cowboy boots, muscled arms and a bushy moustache, Jack Dahlgren looked like a bull rider who had got lost on the way to the rodeo. A notorious practical joker, he had annoyed Burch by spiking the galley coffee urn with cheap rum on their first night at sea. However, the Texan was an engineering whiz who knew his way round every type of mechanical equipment.

'Is this the scenic island tour my travel agent recommended?' he asked Dirk as he climbed into the copilot's seat.

'Step right up, sonny boy, you won't be disappointed. All the water, rocks and sea lions your eyes can absorb.'

'Sounds swell.'

The two men had become fast friends years before, while studying ocean engineering together at Florida University. After graduating, Jack completed his college Reserve Officer Training Corps commitment in the navy while Dirk obtained a master's degree from New York Maritime College and trained at a commercial dive school. They had been reunited when Dirk joined his father, Dirk Pitt Senior, at the prestigious research agency NUMA, and convinced his old friend to do so too.

The rotor blade of the Sikorsky wound to a high pitch as Dirk gently eased the helicopter up and off the landing platform and headed northeast.

'Back to Yunaska?' asked Dahlgren.

Dirk nodded. 'I want to check out the source of whatever killed the men and the dog. Did you bring Basil?' he asked, glancing about the cockpit.

'He's right here,' Dahlgren replied, grabbing a small cage from beneath his seat and holding it up. Inside, a white mouse peered at him, whiskers twitching. 'Breathe deep, little friend, and don't go to sleep on us,' Dahlgren begged. Then he strung the cage from an overhead lanyard, like a canary in a coal mine, so they could see if the mouse succumbed to any toxins in the air.

The grassy island of Yunaska rose out of the slate-green water ahead of them, a sprinkling of light clouds dancing about the larger of its two extinct volcanoes. Bringing the helicopter to hover above the yellow weather station, Dirk examined the surrounding area. The husky was still lying outside the hut's door and brought to mind the pain and horror he had seen in the dead men's faces when he and Dahlgren had landed at the station earlier that day.

'The prevailing winds are from the west,' Dirk said, 'so the source would likely have come from farther up the coast. Or possibly from offshore.'

'Makes sense. The CDC team was camped to the east of here and they obviously caught a less lethal dose of the mystery gas,' Dahlgren replied, peering at the ground through low-power binoculars.

For the next hour, Pitt traced wide semicircular arcs north and south across the island, and the two men searched for signs of a natural or man-made origin for the toxin. Eventually they returned to the weather station.

'Nothing but grass and rocks,' Dahlgren grumbled. 'The seals can keep it, as far as I'm concerned.'

'Speaking of which, take a look down there,' Dirk replied, pointing to a small gravel beach ahead of them, where half a dozen brown sea lions lay stretched out on the ground.

'Jeez, they're not moving,' Dahlgren exclaimed. 'They bought it, too.'

'The toxin must have come from the sea, or the next island over.'

'Amukta is the next rock pile to the west,' Dahlgren replied, running his finger across a chart of the region.

Eyeing the fuel gauge, Dirk said, 'I think we've got time for a quick gander before our fuel runs low. I'll let Burch know where we're headed.'

As Dirk radioed the survey ship, he guided the helicopter towards the island of Amukta, skimming low over the open water. After they'd been cruising steadily for ten minutes, Dahlgren pointed out of the cockpit window to a white speck on the horizon. It was growing larger by the second, and slowly revealed itself to be a large, steel-hulled trawler.

'Now, there's a tub calling out for a little spit and polish,' Pitt remarked as he eased off the throttle to match speed with the boat.

Though the rusty fishing vessel showed obvious signs of hard use, her twin diesel engines pushed her hard through the waves with barely a wisp of black smoke from the funnel. Dirk also noted with interest that no flag flew from the mast. The bow sides and the stern both lacked a name for the ship or its home port. As he perused the stern deck, two East-Asian-looking men in blue jumpsuits stepped into view and peered up at the helicopter.

'Don't look overly friendly now, do they?' Dahlgren remarked, waving towards the boat. The two jumpsuits simply scowled in return.

'Anything strike you as odd?' Dirk asked, eyeing the stern deck.

'You mean the fact that there's no fishing equipment to be seen?'

'Precisely,' Dirk replied.

As the helicopter crept closer, the two men in jumpsuits began jabbering animatedly to each other, then they ducked down a stairwell. At the head of the stairwell, five sea lion carcasses were stretched out side by side.

'I don't think Nanook of the North would be too happy about these guys stealing his dinner,' Dahlgren observed.

Then came the flash of fire. Dirk detected it out of the corner of his eye and instinctively pressed hard on the left pedal, throwing the Sikorsky into a half-spin. As the helicopter began to turn, a spray of bullets hit the machine and ripped into the instrument panel, shattering the console and radio.

'Guess they didn't like the Nanook comment,' Dahlgren muttered as the two men reappeared and fired into the helicopter with automatic rifles.

Dirk pushed the throttle to maximum thrust and wheeled round in a wide arc to the starboard side of the trawler, putting the ship's bridge between him and the gunmen. Temporarily free from attack, he aimed the aircraft towards the island of Amukta.

But the damage had been done. The cockpit filled with smoke as Dirk fought the bucking controls. The rain of lead had smashed into the electronics, pierced hydraulic lines and riddled the control gauges. Dahlgren detected a warm trickle on his ankle and felt down to find a neat hole shot through his calf. Several rounds had found the turbine, but still it chugged on.

'I'll try for the island, but be prepared to ditch,' Dirk shouted over the racket of the disintegrating engine. In his hands, the control stick shook like a jackhammer and he had to use all his strength to hold the craft steady.

Just short of the island's shoreline, the shot-up turbine could take no more, and it ground to a halt with a loud pop. The Sikorsky hung suspended for a moment before gravity caught up with it and the craft dropped to the water, slapping the surface with a smack. Remarkably, it held together, and bobbed on the surface for a second before being sucked under the waves.

IMMEDIATELY after he lost radio contact with Dirk and Dahlgren, Captain Burch launched a search-and-rescue mission. He brought *Deep Endeavor* to Dirk's last reported position, then began a visual search for the two men, sailing west in a zigzag pattern from Yunaska to Amukta.

After three hours, no trace had been found of the helicopter and a feeling of dread fell over the crew as dusk approached.

Executive Officer Leo Delgado was studying the steep shape of Amukta's lone volcanic core when a faint blur caught his eye. 'Captain, there's smoke on the shoreline,' he reported.

Burch held a pair of binoculars to his eyes.

'Burning debris, sir?' Delgado asked, fearful of the answer.

'Perhaps. Or it could be a signal fire. Can't tell from here. Delgado, take two men in the Zodiac and see what you can find on shore.'

'Yes, sir,' Delgado responded.

By the time the Zodiac was lowered into the water, a gusty breeze had kicked up, making the evening seas choppy. Delgado and two crewmen got doused repeatedly with cold sea spray as the twelve-foot rubber boat bounced over the swell towards the island's rocky shoreline. Delgado caught a glimpse of the fire. He steered the boat towards it through a channel between the rocks, and ground to a stop on a pebble-strewn beach.

He jumped out of the inflatable and ran towards the smoky fire, where two shadowy figures were hunched, their backs turned to him.

'Pitt? Dahlgren? Are you guys OK?' Delgado shouted out.

The two soggy-looking derelicts turned slowly. Dahlgren was holding a half-eaten crab claw in one hand, while the head of a white mouse peeked out of his chest pocket, sniffing the night air. Dirk was holding a sharp stick, the end of which pierced the shell of a huge Alaskan king crab.

'Well,' Dirk said, tearing a steaming leg off the big crustacean, 'we could use some lemon and butter.'

BACK ON BOARD *Deep Endeavor*, Dirk and Dahlgren briefed Captain Burch on their encounter with the trawler. While the captain reported the incident to the Coast Guard and the Atka village public safety officer, the two men limped to the ship's medical station for treatment.

The bullet that had pierced Dahlgren's left calf had fortunately missed damaging any tendons. The ship's doctor inserted sutures, handed him a pair of crutches and told him to stay off his leg for three days.

Dirk, who had caught a face full of shattered glass when the helicopter hit the surf, had his bloodied cheek and forehead cleaned and bandaged. Then, after donning a black turtleneck sweater and jeans, he made his way to the wheelhouse, where Burch was plotting a course at the chart table.

'Aren't we heading back to Yunaska to retrieve the bodies?' Dirk asked.

Burch shook his head. 'Not our job. Better to allow the proper authorities to handle the investigation. I'm laying a course for Unalaska to disembark the CDC scientists.'

'I'd rather make for that trawler,' Dirk said.

'We've lost our helicopter and they have an eight-hour lead on us. We'd be lucky to find them. The navy and Coast Guard have been alerted to your description. They have a better chance of finding that trawler than we do.'

Dirk nodded. 'You're right, of course.' He turned and headed down the ladder to the galley for a cup of coffee. Dinner had long since been served and a cleanup crew was working over the kitchen before shutting down. Dirk filled his mug from an urn, then turned and spotted Sarah at the end of the dining hall. She sat alone at a table, peering out of a porthole at the moonlit water outside. As Dirk approached, she looked up and her eyes twinkled.

'Too late for dinner?' he asked apologetically.

'Afraid so. You missed the chef's excellent Halibut Oscar.'

'Just my luck,' Dirk replied, drawing up a chair.

'What happened to you?' Sarah asked with concern in her voice as she eyed the bandages on Dirk's face.

'Just a little accident with the helicopter. My boss isn't going to like the news,' he said with a grimace, thinking about the expensive aircraft sitting on the seabed. He described the events of the flight all the while gazing intently into Sarah's hazel eyes.

'Do you think the fishing boat had something to do with the death of the men at the weather station and us getting sick?' she asked.

'It figures. They obviously weren't too keen on us seeing them poaching sea lions, or whatever else they were up to.'

'Did you see any dead sea lions on the island when you flew over?'

'Yes, Jack spotted several near the weather station.'

'Do you think *Deep Endeavor* could obtain one of the cadavers? I could have it sent to our lab in Washington. We could perform an autopsy and determine the cause of death relatively quickly.'

'I'm sure I can convince Captain Burch to retrieve one for scientific purposes,' Dirk said. 'Do you think there might be a link with the dead sea lions that were found on the other Aleutian islands?'

'I don't know. The cadavers found near the mainland were infected by a canine distemper virus, but the outbreak didn't appear to have reached this far west. Which will make an examination of one of the dead sea lions you saw from the helicopter that much more intriguing.'

There was a pause, and Sarah could see a faraway look in Dirk's eyes. After a moment, she broke the silence. 'The men on the fishing boat. Who do you think they were?'

'I don't know,' Dirk replied quietly, 'but I intend to find out.'

SIX DAYS LATER, *Deep Endeavor* inched up to a private dock on Lake Union, Seattle, outside a small modern-looking glass building that housed the NUMA northwest field office. A gathering of the crew's wives and children waved enthusiastically as the ship approached.

'Looks like you've got your own welcoming committee, Dirk,' Burch remarked.

Dirk looked out of the bridge window as the ship docked and recognised Sarah and Sandy among the happy throng. Sarah looked radiant in a pair of blue capri pants and a maize satin blouse.

'You two look like the model of health,' Dirk said after he'd disembarked and warmly greeted the pair.

'No small part in thanks to you,' Sandy gushed. 'Just one night in Alaska Regional Hospital and we were all on our way good as new.'

'How's Irv?'

'He's fine,' Sarah replied. 'He's staying in Anchorage for a few more weeks.'

'I'm glad. So what was the diagnosis?' Dirk asked.

Sarah shrugged and shook her head. 'They didn't find anything. It's something of a mystery. We all showed signs of an inflamed respiratory tract, but that was about it. If we did inhale a toxin, it was purged from our systems by the time we reached Anchorage.'

'That's why we're here to pick up the sea lion. Hopefully, there will be some indicators still evident in the animal's tissue,' Sandy said.

'So, you're not here to see me?' Dirk intoned sadly.

'Sorry, Dirk,' Sarah said, laughing. 'Why don't you come meet us at the lab later after we do our analysis? We can go grab a late lunch.'

'I would like to know the results,' he agreed.

Dirk led the two on board to collect the sea lion, which had been retrieved from Yunaska and frozen on board *Deep Endeavor*. Once the mammal was hauled away, he helped secure the ship. Then he borrowed the keys to a turquoise NUMA Cherokee Jeep and drove a short distance to his rented town house overlooking Lake Washington. Although his home was in Washington, DC, Dirk was enjoying the assignment in the Northwest. The lush woods and cold, clear waters made for a refreshing environment.

Dirk showered, threw on a pair of dark slacks and a pullover, then downed a peanut butter sandwich while listening to a litany of messages on his answering machine. Satisfied that the earth had not come to a stop in his absence, he hopped into the Jeep and headed north on interstate I-5 towards the Washington State Public Health Laboratories.

When he reached the labs, the receptionist phoned up to the CDC office and a few moments later Sarah and Sandy appeared in the lobby.

'Dirk, it's good of you to come. There's a quiet Italian restaurant down the street where we can talk,' Sarah suggested.

'Sure thing,' Dirk replied, holding the front door open for the two scientists.

After the threesome had shoehorned themselves into a red vinyl booth at the nearby restaurant, Sarah explained their findings.

'An initial examination of the sea lion revealed the classic signs of respiratory seizure as the cause of death, with no concentrated levels of toxicity.'

'Similar to the test results for you three in Anchorage,' Dirk added between bites of bread.

'Exactly. So then we re-examined the animal's tissue and finally detected trace elements of a toxin,' Sarah continued. 'We are now fairly confident the sea lion was killed by cyanide poisoning.'

Dirk arched an eyebrow. 'Cyanide?'

'Yes,' Sandy replied. 'Cyanide is expelled rapidly from the human body. So in the case of Sarah, Irv and me, our bodies had naturally purged most of the toxins before we arrived in Anchorage.'

'I thought cyanide had to be ingested in order to be lethal,' Dirk remarked.

'That's what's commonly believed. Everyone knows of cyanide tablets carried by wartime spies, for instance. But cyanide gas has also been used as a killing agent. You may remember that Saddam Hussein was suspected of using a form of cyanide gas in attacks on Kurdish villages.'

'Is it possible for the cyanide to have originated from a natural source?' Dirk enquired.

'Cyanide is found in a variety of edible plants, from lima beans to chokecherries. But it's most prevalent as an industrial solvent,' Sarah explained. 'Tons of the stuff is manufactured each year for electroplating, gold and silver extraction and fumigation. However, to answer your question, it's unlikely to exist in a natural gaseous state to any lethal degree. Sandy, what did you find in the historical profile of cyanide deaths in the US?'

'There's been a slew of them, but most are accidents or suspected homicides resulting from ingestion of solid cyanide.' Sandy picked up a manila folder she had brought along and skimmed through the pages inside. 'I found only two references to multiple deaths from suspected cyanide gas. A family of four died in Warrenton, Oregon, back in 1942, and in 1964 three men were killed by extraction solvents in a mining accident in Butte, Montana.'

Sarah jabbed her fork into a bowl of angel-hair pasta. 'So if it was a man-made airborne release, who did it and why?'

'I think the "who" was our friends on the trawler,' Dirk said drily.

'They weren't picked up by the authorities?' Sarah asked.

Dirk shook his head. 'No. By the time the local authorities arrived, they were long gone. The officials presumed they were poachers.'

'I suppose it's possible. I guess they could have released the gas from their boat upwind of a sea lion colony,' Sarah replied, shaking her head.

Dirk nodded. 'A fast way to do a lot of killing. Though poachers armed with AK-74's does seem a little extreme.' He looked at Sarah with concern. 'I hope that you two won't suffer any ill effects from the exposure.'

'Thanks,' Sarah replied. 'It was a shock to our system, but we'll be fine.'

Dirk pushed away a plate cleaned of Pasta Alfredo and rubbed his taut stomach with satisfaction. 'Excellent choice of restaurant.'

'We eat here all the time,' Sarah said, out-grabbing Dirk for the bill.

'I insist on returning the favour,' Dirk said, looking at her with a smile.

'Sandy and I have to travel to the CDC research lab in Spokane for a few days, but I'd love to take you up on that when we return,' she replied, intentionally leaving Sandy out of the equation.

Dirk smiled. 'I can't wait.'

CHAPTER 2

The twelfth hole of the Kasumigaseki Golf Club, south of Tokyo, stretched for 290 yards before it doglegged left to an elevated green guarded by a deep bunker. The US ambassador to Japan, Edward Hamilton, swung hard into the golf ball, sending it soaring down the fairway.

'Fine shot, Ed,' offered David Monaco, the British ambassador to Japan and Hamilton's weekly golf partner. The lanky Brit teed up his ball, then punched a long, arcing shot that rolled past Hamilton's ball before bounding into a patch of tall grass.

'Nice power, Dave, but I think you found the rough,' Hamilton said.

The two men proceeded to walk down the fairway while a pair of female caddies manhandled their golf bags a respectable distance behind them. Lurking nearby, four government bodyguards maintained a watch on the duo as they made their way round the course. The weekly outing was an effective but informal way for the two men to share information.

'I hear you're making progress with that economic partnership agreement with Tokyo,' Monaco began.

'It just makes sense for everyone to ease trade restrictions. I think even South Korea will forge a partnership with the Japanese shortly.'

'Speaking of Korea, I understand that some chaps in Seoul are going to issue another appeal in the Korean National Assembly next week for the removal of US armed forces.'

'Yes, we've heard that as well. The South Korean Democratic Labour Party is using the issue as a divisive wedge to gain more political power. Fortunately, they still represent only a small minority.'

'It's a damn mystery how they can think that way, given the past aggressiveness of the North.'

'True, but the DLP compares the US military presence to the occupations of Korea by the Chinese and the Japanese and it strikes a chord with the average man on the street. And we are pretty sure that at least some party officials are receiving support from the North,' Hamilton added. Taking a three-iron from his caddy, he lined up the pin, then knocked another straight shot that landed on the far side of the green.

'Support for reunification extends well beyond the DLP, I'm afraid,' Monaco continued. 'It's the potential economic gains. I heard the president of South Korea's Hyko Tractor Industries remark at a trade seminar that he could reduce costs if he had access to the North's labour force.' Monaco strode through the rough grass for a minute before locating his ball, then lofted a five-iron shot that bounced up onto the green.

'That's assuming a reunification would maintain free markets,' Hamilton replied as they approached the green. 'It's still clear that the North would have the most to gain, even more so if American forces are not in play.'

'I'm just glad we're working this side of the Sea of Japan,' said Monaco.

Hamilton nodded as he lined up a chip shot to the hole. But as he swung through the ball, there was a sudden thump, followed by a loud crack in the distance. The US ambassador's eyes rolled back and a shower of blood sprayed out from his left temple. As the British diplomat looked on in horror, Hamilton fell to his knees, his hands still clutching the club. A gurgle rolled from his lips, then he toppled stiffly onto the manicured grass.

In the bunker of the eighteenth hole, 600 yards away, a short, stout East Asian man with a droopy moustache got to his feet. The sun glared off his bald head and brightened a lifeless pair of coal black eyes. With the bored demeanour of a child putting away his toys, the man carefully disassembled an M-40 sniper rifle and placed the parts in a concealed compartment inside his golf bag. He then calmly three-putted to finish his round.

DIRK HEADED south from Seattle in the NUMA Jeep, enjoying the sights of the lush forested region of western Washington. He took a side road to Willapa Bay, then continued south along the shore. He found country drives relaxing, as they allowed his mind to roam freely.

Crossing the mighty Columbia river over the four-mile-long Astoria-Megler Bridge, Dirk exited at the historic fishing port of Astoria. As he stopped at a red light, a road sign caught his eye: WARRENTON 8 MILES. That was where Sandy had said the family of four had died from cyanide gas in 1942. He followed the sign west to Warrenton.

The small town at Oregon's northwest tip supported some 4,000 residents. It took Dirk only a few minutes of driving about the town before he found what he was looking for. Parking his Jeep on Main Street, he entered the Warrenton Community Library and walked up to a large desk. A fifytish woman with short blonde hair looked up suspiciously. A plastic badge pinned to her blouse revealed her name: MARGARET.

'Good morning, Margaret,' Dirk said with a smile. 'I wonder if you have copies of the local newspaper from the forties?'

The librarian warmed slightly. 'The *Warrenton News*, which went out of print in 1964. We do have original copies from the thirties through the sixties. Right this way,' she said, and walked to a cramped corner of the library, where she pulled out several drawers of a filing cabinet. 'What exactly is it that you're looking for?' she asked.

'I'm interested in the story of a local family that died suddenly from poisoning back in 1942.'

'Oh, that would be Leigh Hunt,' Margaret exclaimed. 'He was a friend of my father. Apparently, that was quite a shock around here. Let's see, I think it happened during the summer,' she said, flipping through the files. 'Did you know the family?'

'No, just a history buff interested in the mystery of their deaths.'

'Here we go,' the librarian said, pulling out an edition of the daily newspaper dated Sunday, June 21, 1942. It was the headline story.

FOUR DEAD ON DELAURA BEACH

Local resident Leigh Hunt, his two sons Tad (13) and Tom (11), and his nephew Skip were found dead on Saturday, June 20, on DeLaura Beach. The four went out clamming, according to Hunt's wife Marie, and failed to return home for dinner. County Sheriff Kit Edwards discovered the bodies, which showed no signs of a struggle or injury. 'Not finding any physical marks, we suspected smoke inhalation or poisoning,' Edwards stated. 'Leigh had a supply of a cyanide-based oil in his workshop that he used for tanning leather. He and the boys must have been exposed to a strong dose before they went to the beach, and the poison took effect when they got there. Funeral arrangements are pending examination of the bodies by the county coroner.'

'Is there a follow-up report on the coroner's findings?' Dirk asked.

Margaret riffled through another dozen editions before finding a small article in which it was reported that the coroner's office had confirmed accidental cyanide inhalation as the suspected cause of death. 'My father never did believe it was an accident,' she added, to Dirk's surprise.

'It doesn't make sense that they would have died later at the beach after inhaling the fumes in Hunt's work shed,' Dirk mused.

Margaret nodded. 'And the authorities never did consider the birds.'

'Birds?'

'Yes. About a hundred seagulls were found dead on the beach near where Hunt and the boys were found. Papa always suspected it was some sort of army experiment that accidentally killed them. Fort Stevens, the army base, was right near that beach . . .'

'Wartime secrets can be difficult to unlock sometimes,' Dirk replied. 'Thank you for your help, Margaret.'

Dirk returned to the Jeep, drove through the town to the coastal highway and turned south. Soon he approached an open pair of gates marked FORT STEVENS STATE PARK and drove in. The road narrowed through thick underbrush, and Dirk jammed the Jeep into low gear as he surged over a jagged ridge to a large abandoned gun emplacement overlooking the ocean. Battery Russell had been one of several coastal defence sites guarding the entrance to the Columbia River during the Civil War, and it had been updated during World War II with huge long-range guns.

From the emplacement, Dirk had a clear view of the shimmering blue waters at the mouth of the Columbia River, as well as the DeLaura Beach below. He took in a few deep breaths of the fresh sea air, then drove back out along the small road, pulling off into the brush at one point to let an oncoming black Cadillac pass by. Driving a quarter mile further, he stopped the car at a large historical marker along the roadside and got out. Inscribed on the massive grey slab of granite were the words:

On June 21, 1942, a 5.5" shell, one of 17 fired at Columbia River Harbor Defense Installations by the Japanese Submarine I-25, exploded here, the only hostile shelling of a military base on the US mainland during World War II and the first since the War of 1812.

Dirk studied the carving. It was the date that caught his eye. June 21. Just a day after Hunt and the boys were found dead on the beach.

He reached into the Jeep's glove compartment and pulled out a satellite phone. He dialled a number and after four rings, a deep and jolly voice boomed through the handset. 'Perlmutter here.'

'Julien, it's Dirk. How's my favourite nautical historian?'

'Dirk, my boy, so good to hear from you! Pray tell, how are you enjoying the Great White North?'

'We just finished in the Aleutians, so I am back in the Pacific Northwest. The islands were beautiful, but a little cold for me.'

'Heavens, I can imagine,' Perlmutter said. 'What's on your mind, Dirk?'

'World War Two-era Japanese submarines, to be exact. I'm curious about their record of attacks on the US mainland and any unusual weaponry in their arsenals.'

'Imperial submarines, eh? I recall they made some fairly harmless attacks on the West Coast, but I have not delved into my Japanese wartime files in some time. I'll have to do some nosing about for you.'

'Thanks, Julien. And one more thing. Let me know if you run across any references to the use of cyanide as an armament.'

'Cyanide. Now, that would be nasty, wouldn't it?'

DIRK CONTINUED on to Portland, where he found the antique auto auction he was looking for at a large fairground at the city's edge. Scores of people milled about among the gleaming autos, most from the forties, fifties and sixties. Dirk sauntered by the cars, admiring the restorations, before taking a seat in a large white tent where the auction was taking place.

Loudspeakers blared out the auctioneer's voice as he spat out bids like a rapid-fire machine gun. After several Corvettes and an early Thunderbird, a 1958 Chrysler 300-D was driven up onto the stage. Dirk sat up. The huge car was painted an Aztec turquoise, enhanced by gleaming chrome and a pair of rear tail fins that jutted into the air like the dorsal fin of a shark. Dirk felt his heartbeat quicken at the sight of it.

'Perfectly restored to concourse condition,' the auctioneer pitched, and Dirk was soon duelling for the car with an overweight man wearing yellow braces. Dirk quickly countered his opponent's bids, showing his intent to be serious. The tactic worked. The man shook his head after the third bid.

'Sold to the man in the NUMA hat!' the auctioneer barked as the surrounding crowd applauded politely.

Though it cost him several months' salary, Dirk knew it was a good buy. As he arranged to have the car shipped to Seattle, his cellphone rang.

'Dirk, it's Julien. I have some information for you.'

'That was fast service. What can you tell me, Julien?'

'After Pearl Harbour, the Japanese placed nine or ten submarines on station along the West Coast, primarily on reconnaissance missions, observing the major bays and harbours, though they did sink a handful of merchant ships early in the war. As for land attacks, the first occurred in early 1942, when the *I-17* lobbed a few shells near Santa Barbara, damaging a pier and an oil derrick. Then, in June of '42, the *I-25* fired upon Fort Stevens, near Astoria, Oregon. No fatalities were recorded. The Japanese lost five subs during the Aleutian battles as our sonar technology began to pick them out of the seas, then things were pretty quiet until the *I-403* was sunk off Cape Flattery, Washington, in January 1945.'

'Odd that one would get tagged off the West Coast at a point in the war when their navy was on its last legs.'

'It's even more queer when you consider that the *I-403* was one of their big boats, capable of carrying three planes. Apparently, it was planning an air attack when it was surprised by an American destroyer.'

'Did you find any indication of the use of cyanide weapons?'

'None that was recorded, but the Imperial Army's biological warfare unit in China experimented with biological and chemical weapons, I believe. It's possible the navy fooled around with cyanide artillery shells, but there's no official record of their use.'

'I guess there is no way to prove it, but I suspect the *I-25* launched a cyanide shell that killed four people before it attacked Fort Stevens.'

'It's possible. But with one exception, all the accounts I have seen indicate that Japanese vessels were armed only with conventional weapons.'

'And the exception?'

'The *I-403* again. I found a reference in a postwar army journal stating that a shipment of *Makaze* ordnance was delivered to the submarine in Kure prior to her last sailing. I could find no other references to *Makaze* in my files.'

'Any idea what the term means?'

'The best translation I can make of it is "Black Wind".'

A WEEK LATER, the fibreglass bow of the twenty-five-foot NUMA support boat *Grunion* plunged through the deep, wide swells off Cape Flattery.

'Now, you guys are sure Captain Burch isn't going to find out we borrowed his boat and are burning his fuel just for a pleasure dive?' Leo Delgado asked from the helm.

Standing alongside in the cramped cabin, Dirk and Jack Dahlgren were hunched over a small table. Dirk had phoned the two other men and and persuaded them to go on a hunt for the *I-403*.

'You mean this is his private boat?' he replied with mock horror.

'If he comes snooping, we'll just tell him that Bill Gates stopped by and offered us a few million stock options if he could take the *Grunion* out for a spin,' Dahlgren offered.

'Thanks. I knew I could trust you guys,' Delgado muttered. 'By the way, how good is your fix on the submarine's location?'

'Came right out of the official navy report on the sinking that Perlmutter faxed me,' Dirk replied, almost losing his balance as the boat rolled over a large swell. 'We'll start with the position that was recorded by the destroyer after she sank the *I-403*. She hadn't travelled far from shore when she engaged the sub, so their reported position ought to put us in the ballpark.'

When the *Grunion* reached the required spot, Delgado eased the throttle into neutral and began keying a search grid into the navigation computer. On the back deck, Dirk and Dahlgren unpacked a Klein Model 3000 sidescan sonar system from a plastic crate. As Dirk hooked up the cables to the operating system, Dahlgren reeled a yellow cylindrical sonar towfish out over the stern gunwale and into the water.

'The fish is out,' Dahlgren yelled from the back deck, whereupon Delgado applied a light throttle and the boat edged forward.

In a matter of minutes, Dirk had the equipment calibrated, and was back at the bridge watching a stream of shadowy images sliding across a colour monitor, representing the protrusions and cavities of the seabed.

'I have a one-mile-square grid plotted around the *Theodore Knight*'s reported position at the time she rammed the sub,' Delgado said.

'That sounds like a good starting range,' Dirk replied.

Delgado proceeded to steer the boat back and forth, making parallel tracks 200 metres long, while Dirk kept a sharp eye for a long, dark shadow on the sonar monitor that would represent the I-boat lying on the bottom.

Two hours went by and the only recognisable image that appeared was that of a pair of fifty-five-gallon drums. Finally, after three hours of searching, Dirk's voice suddenly cut the damp air.

'Target! Mark position.'

Gradually, the fuzzy image of an elongated object rolled across the screen, joined by two smaller protrusions near one end.

'Lord have mercy!' Dahlgren shouted, studying the image. 'Looks like a submarine to me.'

Dirk glanced at a scale measurement at the bottom of the screen. 'She's about three hundred and fifty feet long, just as Perlmutter's records indicate. Leo, can you park us right on top of her.'

'Can do.' Delgado punched the craft's location into the GPS system.

Dirk and Dahlgren hauled in the sonar towfish, then unpacked a pair of large dive bags.

'What's our depth here, Leo?' Dahlgren called out as he poked his feet through the leggings of a black neoprene wet suit.

'About one seventy feet,' Delgado replied, eyeing a humming fathometer.

'That will give us only twenty minutes of bottom time, with a twenty-five-minute decompression stop on the way up,' Dirk said.

'Not a lot of time to cover that big fish,' Dahlgren conceded.

'The aircraft armament is what I'm most interested in,' Dirk replied. 'According to the navy report, both aircraft were on deck when the destroyer attacked so I'm betting those two sonar images off the bow are the Seiran bombers. We should investigate them first.'

When Dirk and Dahlgren were suited up in their dive gear, Delgado threw out a small buoy tied to 200 feet of line. The two black-suited divers stepped off the rear dive platform and plunged into the ocean.

The cold Pacific water was a shock as they dropped beneath the surface.

'Damn, I knew we should have brought the dry suits,' Dahlgren's voice crackled in Dirk's ears. The two men wore full-face dive masks with integrated wireless communication systems.

'What do you mean, it feels like the Florida Keys,' Dirk joked.

He flipped over and began kicking towards the bottom, following the anchored buoy line. Dahlgren tagged along a few feet behind. At 120 feet, Dirk switched on a small underwater light strapped to his hood. Shortly after, a long, dark shape grew out of the depths.

The huge black submarine lay quietly on the bottom, a silent iron mausoleum for the sailors who had died on her. She had landed on her keel when she sank and now sat proudly upright as if ready to set sail again. As Dirk and Dahlgren drew closer, they were amazed at the vessel's sheer size.

'Dirk, I see one of the planes over here,' Dahlgren said, pointing towards a pile of debris lying off the port bow. 'I'll go take a look.'

'The second plane should be further back. I'll head in that direction,' Dirk replied, swimming along the deck.

Dahlgren could see that the wreckage was the remains of a single-engine floatplane, dusted in a heavy layer of fine silt. The Aichi M6A1 Seiran was a sleek-looking monoplane, but it had been made to look comical by the attachment of two huge pontoons braced several feet below its wings. Dahlgren could see only a split portion of one pontoon, as the left float and wing had been sheared off by the American destroyer. He swam in front of the plane, studying the undercarriage and underside of the wing. Moving closer, he fanned away an accumulation of silt to reveal a set of clasps that had secured the bomber's payload. They were empty of armament.

Dahlgren called Dirk on the radiophone. 'Say, old buddy, I'm at the business end of one of the floatplanes and it doesn't look like she had any weapons mounted when she sank.'

'I've found the remains of the second plane and she's clean as well,' Dirk replied. 'Meet me at the conning tower.'

Swimming back to the sub's topside deck, Dirk followed its length until he found a huge hole where the conning tower had been sheared off.

'Wow, you could drive your Chrysler through that hole,' Dahlgren remarked as he swam up alongside Dirk and surveyed the crater.

'She must have gone down in a hurry when the sail ripped off,' Dirk said.

The two men visualised the violent collision between the two war vessels and imagined the agony of the helpless crew as their submarine sank.

'Jack, why don't you take a pass through the hangar and see if you can eyeball any ordnance.' Dirk pointed towards a large twelve-foot-diameter tube, which stretched aft for more than a hundred feet and which had been the hangar for the aircraft. 'I'll go below decks.'

Jack glanced at his dive watch. 'We've only got eight more minutes of bottom time. I'll meet you back here in six,' he said, then disappeared with a kick of his fins through the gash in the hangar wall.

Dirk entered a crevice adjacent to the hangar, and descended into an open bay that he quickly identified as the remains of the control room. An array of radio equipment was fixed to one side, while an assortment of levers and controls protruded from another wall and the ceiling. Kicking his fins gently, he tried not to stir up sediment as he passed from one compartment to the next. Dining plates and silverware were strewn across the floor of a small galley; porcelain sake vials were still standing on cabin shelves.

At last he found his objective: the forward torpedo room. Thrusting ahead with a powerful kick, he advanced to the entrance.

Then he stopped dead in his tracks, wondering if his eyes were playing tricks on him. In the inky bowels of the rusting warship, Dirk saw a faint flashing green light.

He pulled himself through the hatch and into the torpedo room, which was pitch-black save for the beam of the tiny light, fixed at eye level on the far side, near the forward bulkhead with its round torpedo hatches. Lying in racks on either side of the room were six of the huge and deadly Type 95 torpedoes, that had proved more reliable than their American counterparts. Dirk shone his light on the floor and found two additional torpedoes that had been jarred out of their racks when the submarine had slammed into the bottom.

He floated over to the eerie green light, and soon saw that it came from a small digital clock at the end of the torpedo rack. Fluorescent green numbers flashed a row of zeros, indicating an elapsed time that had run out.

Dirk plucked the plastic clock off the rack and stuffed it in a pocket. He peered upwards. His air bubbles were not gathering at the ceiling as expected, but were trailing up through a shaft of pale light. He kicked up with his fins, and found a large hatch to the open deck that had been wedged open.

Jack's crackly voice burst through his earpiece. 'Dirk, time to go upstairs.'

'Come meet me on the bow, I need another minute.'

Dirk swam back down to the fallen torpedoes. Two wooden crates were crushed beneath one of them, split open like suitcases. Curiously, there was no silt covering them, unlike every other object on the submarine. Someone must have recently fanned away the sediment to reveal the crates' contents.

Dirk looked inside the closest crate. Six silver bombs were lined up in a custom-fitted case, like eggs in a carton. Each bomb was nearly three feet long and sausage-shaped, with a fin-winged tail. All six had been broken by the torpedo's fall. Running his hand over an undamaged section of one of the bombs, Dirk was surprised to feel that the surface was smooth like glass.

Kicking his fins gently, he glided over to the other crate and found another crate of damaged bombs. Only this time, he counted five bombs, not six. One was missing.

'Elevator, going up,' Dahlgren's voice suddenly crackled.

'Hold the door, I'll be right there,' Dirk replied, tugging on one of the less mangled bombs. It slipped out of its case but fell apart into three separate pieces in Dirk's hands. He gently placed the pieces into a large mesh dive bag, then, holding tight, kicked his way up to the open hatch.

Dirk joined Dahlgren, who was hovering above the sub's bow, and the two wasted no time in kicking towards their decompression stop. Tracking his depth as he rose, Dirk flared his body out like a sky-diver at forty feet to slow his ascent and purged a shot of air out of his buoyancy compensator. Dahlgren followed suit and the two men stabilised themselves at a depth of twenty feet to help lower the levels of nitrogen in their blood.

'That extra five minutes on the bottom cost us another thirteen of decompression time. I'll be sucking my tank dry before thirty-eight minutes rolls around,' Dahlgren said, eyeing his depleted air gauge.

Before Dirk could answer, they heard a metallic clang. 'Never fear, Leo is here,' Dirk remarked, pointing at the pair of silver scuba tanks with attached regulators that had been lowered by rope to the twenty-foot mark.

After hovering for a fifteen-minute decompression stop, the men grabbed the regulators and floated up to ten feet for another twenty-five-minute wait. When they finally surfaced and climbed aboard the boat, Delgado acknowledged them with a casual wave as he turned the boat for landfall.

As the boat motored into calmer waters, Dirk unwrapped the bomb canister fragments and laid them on the deck.

'Why would a canister crack open like that?' Dahlgren asked.

'Because it's made of porcelain,' Dirk replied, holding up a shard.

Dahlgren ran a finger over the surface, then shook his head. 'A porcelain bomb. Very handy for attacking tea parties, I presume.'

'Must have something to do with the contents.' Dirk rearranged the fragments like pieces of a jigsaw puzzle. Suddenly, several compartmentalised sections were clearly visible in the interior of the canister. 'Looks like different combustibles were to react together when detonated.'

'An incendiary bomb?' Dahlgren asked.

'Perhaps,' Dirk replied quietly. He then reached into a side pocket and pulled out the digital timer. 'Someone went to a fair amount of trouble to retrieve one of these bombs,' he said, tossing the timer over to Dahlgren.

Dahlgren studied the device. 'Maybe it was the original owner,' he finally said, as he showed Dirk the back of the clock. In raised lettering on the plastic case was an indecipherable line of Asian script.

LIKE A PACK of hyenas fighting over a freshly killed zebra, the president's security advisers were snapping at each other, each of them trying to dodge responsibility for the latest events in Japan. Ambassador Hamilton's assassination had been followed by that of Robert Bridges, the US embassy's deputy chief of mission, at the Tokyo Hilton Hotel.

'It's a breakdown of intelligence, clear and simple. Our consulates are not getting the intelligence support they need and two of my people are dead as a result,' the Secretary of State complained.

'We had no advance knowledge of an increase in terrorist activity in Japan. Diplomatic feeds reported that Japanese security forces were in the dark as well,' the deputy CIA director fired back.

'Gentlemen, what's done is done,' interjected President Garner Ward, who was widely admired for his common sense and pragmatic style, and had a low tolerance for finger-pointing and self-serving pontification. 'We need to understand the nature of the threat and the motives of our opponent, and then calculate a course of action,' he said simply. 'But first, we have to figure out who these characters are. Martin, fill us in on what we know so far.'

FBI Director Martin Finch, an ex-Marine, still sported a crew cut and spoke with the blunt voice of a drill sergeant. 'Sir, the assassinations of Ambassador Hamilton and Mr Bridges appear to have been performed by the same individual. Surveillance video from the Tokyo Hilton exposed a suspect dressed as a waiter who was not an employee of the hotel. Photographs from the video were matched to eyewitness descriptions of an individual seen at the golf course shortly before Ambassador Hamilton was shot.'

'And what of the suspect?' the Secretary of State asked.

'The Japanese authorities have been unable to provide an identification. He is not a known member of the Japanese Red Army, but there would seem to be little doubt that he is operating under their auspices.'

'The note left on Bridges's body. What did it say?' asked Dennis Jiménez, Secretary of Homeland Security.

Finch riffled through a folder, then pulled out a typewritten sheet. 'Translated, it says: "Be vanquished, American imperialists who soil

Nippon with greed, or death will blow her cold, sweet breath to the shores of America. JRA." Classic anti-imperialist rant.'

'What is the state of the Japanese Red Army?' President Ward asked. 'I thought they were essentially dissolved a number of years ago.'

'The Japanese Red Army grew out of a number of communist factions in Japan during the seventies. They seemed to lose support in the nineties and, by 2000, the known leadership of the organisation was behind bars.'

'Are we confident there is no Al Qaeda connection here?'

'It's not likely,' Finch replied. 'The method of assassination is not their style, and there has been no radical Islamic presence visible in Japan.'

'Where are we with the Japanese on this?' the president asked.

'We have an FBI counterterrorist team in-country working closely with the Japanese National Police Agency, who have assigned a large task force to the investigation.'

'And what are we doing elsewhere abroad to prevent any more shootings?' the president asked, addressing the Secretary of State.

'We have issued heightened security alerts to all of our embassies,' the secretary replied. 'We have also assigned additional security protection to our senior diplomats.'

'Any opinion that there is an imminent threat domestically, Dennis?'

'Not at this time, Mr President,' the Homeland Security Director replied. 'We've asked the Japanese Foreign ministry for a list of high-risk aliens, and we've tightened our border and immigration inspections on incoming traffic from Japan, but we don't feel that a domestic security alert is necessary.'

'Do you concur, Marty?'

'Yes, sir. All indications suggest that the threat is limited to Japan.'

The President looked round the table. 'All right, gentlemen, let's give it our all to find these murderers. I knew Hamilton and Bridges. They were good men. And allowing our diplomatic representatives to be gunned down without repercussion is not the message I want to be giving the world.'

ALTHOUGH KEITH CATANA had been in South Korea only three months, he had already identified his favourite watering hole. Chang's Saloon appeared little different from the other bars of 'A-Town', a seedy area on the fringe of Kunsan City that catered to American servicemen, but in Catana's eyes it attracted the best-looking working girls.

The twenty-three-year old master sergeant was an avionics specialist at the US air base, supporting the F-16 attack jets of the 8th Fighter Wing.

Located just a few minutes' flight time from the demilitarised zone, his squadron stood in constant preparedness for an aerial counterstrike should North Korea initiate an invasion of the south.

Catana was sitting in the saloon nursing his fourth beer when the most stunning woman Catana had ever laid eyes on strolled in. Her long, straight black hair accentuated a delicate, almost porcelain-skinned face, petite nose and mouth, and stunningly bold black eyes.

Like a tigress searching for prey, the woman surveyed the crowded bar before focusing on the airman sitting alone in a corner. She sashayed over to Catana's table and smoothly slipped into the chair facing him. 'Hello, Joe. Be a friend and buy me a drink?' she purred.

'Glad to,' Catana stammered in reply. If the heavens intended to drop this creature in his lap on payday, who was he to argue?

He took only one more quick beer before the harlot invited him back to her hotel room. They walked arm in arm to a seedy motel, where the woman unlocked the door to a small corner room.

After closing the door, the woman quickly stripped off her top, then embraced Catana in a deep, passionate kiss. He paid little attention to a noise near the closet as he soaked in her warmth, intoxicated by a combination of her beauty, the alcohol, and the expensive perfume she wore. His pleasurable delirium was suddenly interrupted by a sharp jab to his buttocks, followed by a hot searing pain. Whirling round, he was shocked to find himself facing a stocky bald man who grinned a crooked smile through his long moustache. In his hands, he held a hypodermic needle.

Pain and confusion overwhelmed Catana as his body went numb. It took just few seconds before a wave of blackness rolled over him.

Hours later, an incessant pounding jarred him from a state of unconsciousness. The pounding was not in his head, as he first imagined, but came from the motel room door. He noticed a warm stickiness enveloping him as he fought to clear the fog from his vision.

The banging ceased for a moment, then a loud blow struck the door, and a company of policemen stormed into the room, followed by two men with cameras. As his eyes adjusted to the sudden infusion of light, Catana saw the blood. It was everywhere. But mostly it was pooled about the prone figure of the nude woman lying dead beside him.

He instinctively lurched back from the body. 'What happened? Who did this?' he said in a daze, as two of the policemen pulled him off the bed and handcuffed his wrists.

He looked on in shock as a third policeman pulled back a sheet partially covering the woman, fully exposing her dead body. To Catana's further bewilderment, he saw that the body was not that of the beautiful woman he had met the night before but that of a young girl he did not know.

By noon that day, the story of the rape and savage murder of a thirteen-year-old Korean girl by a US serviceman was a countrywide horror. By evening, it had become a full-blown international incident.

THE HIGH NOONDAY sun shimmered brightly off the sapphire waters of the Bohol Sea, forcing Raul Biazon to squint as he gazed at the large research vessel in the distance. For a moment, the Philippine government biologist thought the sun's rays were playing a trick on his eyes. No scientific research ship could possibly be painted such a lively hue. But as the small launch in which he rode drew closer, he saw it was so: the ship was turquoise from stem to stern.

The pilot guided the launch alongside a stepladder suspended over the side of the ship and Biazon climbed aboard, nearly colliding with a tall, brawny man who stood at the rail.

'Dr Biazon? Welcome aboard the *Mariana Explorer*. I'm Captain Bill Stenseth.' The man smiled warmly through grey eyes.

'Thank you for receiving me on such short notice, Captain,' Biazon replied. 'When the local fishermen informed me that a NUMA research vessel was in the region, I thought you might be able to offer assistance.'

'Let's head to the bridge,' Stenseth directed, 'and you can fill us in on the environmental calamity you mentioned over the radio.'

'I hope I am not interfering with your research work?'

'Not at all. We've just completed a seismic mapping project off Mindanao and are taking a break to test some equipment before heading up to Manila. Besides,' Stenseth said with a grin, 'when my boss says, "Stop the boat," I stop the boat.'

As they reached the bridge wing, Stenseth pulled open the side door and the two men stepped through it. At the rear of the bridge, Biazon saw a tall, distinguished-looking man in shorts and a polo shirt bent over a chart table studying a map.

'Dr Biazon, may I present the director of NUMA, Dirk Pitt,' Stenseth introduced them. 'Dirk, this is Dr Raul Biazon, hazardous wastes manager with the Philippines Environmental Management Bureau.'

'Welcome aboard.' Pitt shook Biazon's hand with a firm grip. 'My underwater technology director, Al Giordino,' he added, gesturing towards a barrel-chested man standing in a corner of the wheelhouse.

Giordino smiled in greeting.

'As I told the captain, I appreciate your offer of assistance,' Biazon began. 'A few weeks ago, our office was contacted by a hotel on Panglao Island. Its management was upset because dead fish were washing up on the beach. My field team and I began monitoring the shoreline and have witnessed the fish kill growing at an alarming rate. We've sent samples to our lab in Cebu for analysis, but are still awaiting the results. We've failed to locate any heavy industrial businesses operating in the area. We also examined the coastline for obvious spills or illegal dump sites but came up empty.'

'Where exactly is the impacted area, Dr Biazon?' Pitt asked.

'Panglao is a small resort island off Bohol, about fifty kilometres from our present position.'

'I can have us there in under two hours,' Stenseth said.

Pitt nodded. 'We've got a ship full of scientists who can help find the answers. Bill, lay a course to Panglao Island and we'll take a look.'

'Thank you,' a visibly relieved Biazon said.

THE MARIANA EXPLORER cruised easily through a flat sea, arriving at Panglao Island in just over ninety minutes. Dirk Pitt Senior studied a navigational map of the area on a colour monitor. The NUMA chief had a tanned, muscular body that showed few indications of too much time spent behind a desk. His face was weathered and his ebony hair showed tinges of grey, but his opaline green eyes, the spitting image of his son's, sparkled with life.

'Bill, the current runs east to west through here, which would suggest that the hot zone is located at the eastern end of the box we're investigating. Why don't we start to the west and work our way east into the current, taking water samples at quarter-mile increments?'

Captain Bill Stenseth nodded. 'I'll run a zigzag course, to see if we can gauge how far from shore the toxin is concentrated.'

'And let's deploy the side-scan sonar. Might as well see if there are any obvious man-made object involved.'

Dr Biazon watched with interest as a towed sonar fish was deployed off the stern and the Mariana Explorer began following the dot-to-dot path laid out on the navigation screen. At intervals, a team of marine biologists collected sea-water samples, which were sent down to the shipboard lab for immediate analysis. On the bridge, Al Giordino tracked the signals from the side-scan sonar. The electronic image of the sea floor revealed a mixture of flat sand bottom and craggy coral as the ship sailed over the fringes of a reef. In a short time, Giordino's trained eye had flagged up a ship's anchor, an outboard motor and a propeller lying beneath the well-travelled waters.

Pitt glanced down at the water, where he spotted a sea turtle and scores of dead fish floating belly-up. 'We've entered the toxic zone,' he said.

As the research vessel ploughed west, the concentration of dead fish increased, then gradually fell away again.

'We're a half mile beyond Dr Biazon's grid,' Stenseth reported. 'Judging by the water, it looks like we're well clear of the toxic zone.'

'Agreed,' Pitt replied. 'Let's stand by here until we see what kind of results the lab has found.'

As the ship ground to a halt and the sonar towfish was retrieved, Pitt led Biazon to the ship's teak-panelled conference room, followed by Giordino and Stenseth. As they took their seats, a pair of white-coated marine biologists entered. A woman with brunette hair tied in a ponytail walked to a viewing screen at the front of the room, while her male assistant began typing commands into the projection system.

'We have completed an analysis of forty-four discrete water samples,' she said in a clear voice. As she spoke, an image appeared on the screen behind her: a zigzag line punctuated by forty-four large dots, most of them green, ran parallel to an outline of the Panglao Island shoreline. The biologist pointed to a row of yellow dots. 'As you can see from the chart, the concentration of positive readings increases as the samples moved east, with the highest reading registered here,' she said, tracing her finger past a few orange dots to a lone red dot near the top of the map.

'So the source is in an isolated location,' Pitt said, turning to his technology director. 'Al, do the results mesh with anything picked up on the sonar?'

Giordino walked over to the console and leaned over the operator's shoulder, typing in a quick series of commands. A dozen Xs suddenly appeared on the screen, at points along the zigzag tracking line.

'Al's "Dirty Dozen" hit lists,' he said with a smile, then retook his seat. 'We ran over twelve objects that appeared man-made. Mostly chunks of pipe, rusty anchors and the like. Only one item was located in the vicinity of the toxins—a ship's propeller. Looked like it was protruding from the reef. I couldn't make out any sign of the ship that went with it, though.'

All eyes found the X on the screen. It was right above the red dot.

'It would appear there's something more to it than just a propeller,' Pitt said finally. 'Leaking fuel from a submerged ship, or perhaps its cargo?'

'We did not detect abnormally high readings of petroleum compounds in the water samples,' the NUMA biologist stated.

'But you said you did identify toxins in the water, didn't you?' Biazon asked anxiously. 'What was it that you found?'

'Something I've never encountered in salt water before,' the biologist replied, shaking her head slowly. 'Arsenic.'

FEW THINGS in nature rival the beauty of a healthy coral reef, Pitt reflected as his eyes drank in the assortment of colours. Bright red sea anemones waved their tentacles lazily in the current amid a carpet of magenta sea sponges. Brilliant blue starfish glowed from the reef like neon signs, while dozens of pink sea urchins blanketed the sea floor. Floating just off the bottom, a pair of small clown fish darted into a crevice as a spotted ray cruised by.

'It should be slightly ahead and to the north of us,' Giordino's voice crackled through his ears, breaking the tranquillity.

The readings of arsenic in the water had startled everyone. There was only one way to find out what was happening down there, Pitt had declared, and that was to go down and take a look.

After mooring the *Mariana Explorer* over the site of the maximum toxin readings, Pitt and Giordino had donned rubberised dry suits with full faceplates to protect them from contamination. Dropping over the side, they had splashed into the clear, warm water and dropped 120 feet to the bottom.

Now, with Giordino at his side, Pitt checked his compass, then thrust his fins together and kicked himself at an angle across the current. To his right, a large underwater sand dune loomed up against the reef, its rippled surface stretching beyond his field of vision. Reaching the coral, he tilted his upper body towards the surface and propelled himself up and over its jagged edge. He was surprised to find that the reef dropped vertically away on the other side, creating a large crevasse. More surprising was what he saw at the bottom of the ravine. It was the bow half of a ship.

'What the heck?' Giordino muttered, spotting the wreckage.

Pitt studied the partial remains for a moment, then laughed through the underwater communication system. 'It's an optical illusion. The rest of the ship is there; it's just buried under the sand dune.'

Giordino saw that Pitt was right. The large sand dune neatly covered the vessel's stern, giving the impression that only half a ship existed.

Pitt swam away over the sand dune for several yards before it dropped sharply beneath him. 'Here's your propeller, Al,' he said, pointing down.

Beneath his fins, a section of the ship's stern curved down to a large brass propeller, which protruded from the dune like a windmill. Giordino kicked over and inspected it, then swam up the sternpost several feet and brushed away a layer of sand until the last few letters of the ship's name were exposed.

'Something MARU is the most I can get,' he said.

'She's Japanese,' Pitt said, 'and, by the looks of the corrosion, she's been here a long while.

Giordino followed Pitt as he swam towards the exposed front of the ship. She was listing to port, and her main funnel jutted nearly horizontally into the coral wall. From her small bridge section and long forward deck, Pitt could see that she was a common oceangoing cargo ship, slightly more than 200 feet long. As they swam over the angled top side, he could see that the wooden deck had disintegrated in the warm Philippine waters.

Pitt kicked past a brass deck rail and made his way along the deck until he reached a pair of large square hatch covers, the capstones to the ship's forward cargo holds. They tried to open one.

'Locked down tight as a drum,' Giordino said.

Pitt swam down the starboard hull and moved on towards the bow. He halted suddenly. Before him, a jagged four-foot-wide gash stretched nearly twenty-feet down the starboard hull to the very tip of the bow.

Giordino swam up to join him. 'Just like the *Titanic*,' he marvelled. 'Only she scraped herself to the bottom on a coral head instead of a chunk of ice. Outrunning a typhoon, probably.'

'Or maybe a navy Corsair. Leyte Gulf is just around the corner—where the Japanese fleet was decimated in 1944.'

The Philippine Islands were a hotly contested piece of real estate in World War II, Pitt recalled. More than 60,000 Americans had lost their lives in the failed defence and later recapture of the islands, a forgotten toll that exceeded the losses in Vietnam. The Leyte Gulf, just over a hundred miles from Panglao, was the sight of the largest air–sea battle in history. Days after MacArthur and his invasion force landed on Leyte in October 1944, the Japanese Imperial Navy appeared and came within a hair of destroying the Seventh Fleet, but were ultimately turned back in a devastating defeat that led, ultimately, to Japan's military collapse. Given the gash in the cargo ship's hull, it was easy to presume that the vessel was a victim of war.

'I think we definitely hit the jackpot,' Giordino said morosely.

Pitt turned to see his friend's gloved hand pointing towards the adjacent reef. Gone was the vibrant red, blue and green coral they had witnessed earlier. Here it was uniformly tinted a dull white. No fish were visible either.

Pitt grabbed a small flashlight clipped to his buoyancy compensator and ducked towards the gap in the hull. Edging his way into the ship, he flicked on the light and cast its beam across the black interior. The lower bow section was empty but for a coil of thick anchor chain.

Pitt moved towards the bulkhead that separated them from the forward cargo hold. At its lower edge, he found what he was looking for. The pressure from the collision with the reef had buckled one of the plates and created a window several feet wide. He eased up to the hole, stuck his head in and shone the flashlight around. His blood ran cold as he surveyed the interior. Scattered in mounds were hundreds of decaying artillery shells.

'A Welcome-to-the-Philippines present for General MacArthur?' Giordino said, peering in at his shoulder.

Pitt silently nodded, then pulled out a plastic-lined dive bag. Giordino obliged by reaching over and grabbing a shell and inserting it in the bag before Pitt sealed and wrapped it.

'I don't think they are ordinary artillery shells,' Pitt remarked as he noted a pool of brown ooze beneath a nearby pile of ordnance. 'Let's get this one back to the shipboard lab and find out what we've got.'

CHAPTER 3

At fifty-five-metres in length, the steel-hulled Benetti yacht was impressive even by Monte Carlo standards. The lush interior featured marble flooring, Persian carpets and rare Chinese antiques, while its glistening maroon and white exterior was more traditional, with inlaid teak decking and brass fittings. The vessel always turned heads on the Han River in Seoul, and an invitation aboard was highly desired, providing a rare opportunity to meet the boat's enigmatic owner.

Dae-jong Kang was an icon of South Korean industry and seemed to have a finger in every pie. Little was known of his background before his sudden appearance during the economic boom of the nineties as the head of a regional construction company. As Kang gobbled up companies in the shipping, electronics, semiconductor and telecommunications industries in a series of leveraged buyouts and hostile takeovers, Kang Enterprises remained a privately owned empire entirely controlled by Kang himself. Unafraid of the public spotlight, the fifty-five-year-old bachelor mixed freely with politicians and business leaders, yet he kept a veil of mystery over his private life. Much of his time was spent at his secluded estate on Kyodongdo Island near the mouth of the Han River on the western Korean coast, and it was unknown even to his closest associates that he still operated as an agent for the Democratic People's Republic of Korea, or North Korea as it was known by the rest of the world.

Kang had been smuggled into South Korea at the age of twenty-two and set up as a labourer at a small construction company. He quickly worked his way up to foreman, then arranged a series of 'accidental' site deaths that killed the firm's president and top managers. Forging a series of ownership transfer documents, Kang took control of the business within two years. With secret direction and capital from North Korea, the young communist entrepreneur slowly expanded his network of commercial enterprises. His primary objective, set out by his handlers, was to promote the reunification of the two Korean countries, on North Korea's terms.

Now the sleek Benetti yacht slowed its engines as it entered a narrow inlet off the Han River that wound, snakelike, into the calm waters of a lagoon. The vessel reached a floating dock, where a pair of black-uniformed men grabbed the bow and stern lines as the pilot finessed her the last few feet to the dock. A stepped platform was rolled to the yacht's side, and three men in dark blue suits stepped down from the boat, instinctively peering up at the immense stone house half-carved into the top of the cliff that rose nearly vertically above them. The building was capped by a deep, angular tiled roof. Surrounded by thick walls, it was accessible by steep steps carved into the cliff. A guard with an automatic rifle slung over his shoulder stood at the dock's entrance to ensure the inhabitants a high degree of privacy.

As the men in suits made their way along the dock, their host arrived to greet them. At six feet tall and weighing 200 pounds, Dae-jong Kang was physically imposing by Korean standards, but it was his stern face and penetrating eyes that indicated he was a man of power and not afraid to use it.

'Welcome, gentlemen,' Kang said in a smooth voice. 'I trust your voyage from Seoul was enjoyable?'

The three men, all leading party members in the South Korean National Assembly, nodded in unison.

The senior member of the trio, a balding man named Youngnok Rhee, replied, 'A trip down the Han River is a delight in such a beautiful boat.'

Kang smiled and motioned them past a small security station to a waiting elevator, the shaft of which had been carved into the cliff. The politicians followed obediently.

When the doors opened at the top, the men stepped out into an ornately decorated dining room. Beyond an elegant mahogany dining table, floor-to-ceiling glass walls offered a breathtaking view of the Han River delta, where the river's waters emptied into the Yellow Sea.

'An incredible view, Mr Kang,' said Won Ho, the tallest of the politicians.

'I enjoy it, for the vista encompasses both our countries,' Kang replied. 'Please be seated.'

He sat at the head of the table, and uniformed servants shuttled in an array of fine wines and gourmet dishes as the conversation drifted to politics. Kang played the gregarious host for a while, then applied the knife.

'Gentlemen, it's high time we took seriously the effort to unify our two countries. As a Korean, I know that we are one country in language, in culture, and in heart. As a businessman, I know how much stronger we could be economically in the global markets. It is time we threw off the shackles of foreign domination. Our destiny is as one.'

'The goal of unification beats strongly in all our hearts, but the military juggernaut of North Korea mandates that we tread with caution,' replied the third politician, a beady-eyed man named Kim.

Kang brushed aside the comment. 'As you know, I recently toured North Korea as part of a trip sponsored by the Ministry of Unification. The military forces we witnessed appeared ill equipped and low in moral,' he lied.

'But would reunification really benefit our economy?' Won Ho asked.

'The northern provinces offer an abundance of cheap labour and we would immediately become more competitive on the world markets. I have assessed the impact to my own enterprises and make no secret of the fact that my profits could be boosted dramatically. In addition, the northern provinces would provide a new market for South Korean goods.'

'We cannot simply achieve reunification unilaterally,' Won Ho stated.

'No,' Kim added. 'And the North Koreans have repeatedly insisted that US military presence be removed before reunification can be considered.'

'That is why,' Kang continued calmly, 'I am asking the three of you to support the resolution before the National Assembly demanding the removal of all American military forces from South Korea.'

A stunned silence fell over the room. The three politicians had known that Kang had brought them there for a reason, but they had not expected a demand so risky to their political careers.

Rhee cleared his throat. 'That particular resolution was introduced by a radical element. There is little chance it would ever pass a full vote.'

'There is if you three were in support of it,' Kang replied.

'That's impossible,' Kim stammered. 'I cannot support weakening our defence while North Korea boosts its military might.'

'You can and you will. With the recent murder of the girl by the American serviceman, there is a firestorm of animosity towards the US military. Now is the time to pressure our president to act.'

'But the American forces are essential for our security,' Kim argued.

'May I remind you,' Kang hissed, 'that I have paid your way into the position that you hold today.'

Rhee and Won Ho slumped back in their chairs and nodded gravely.

'Yes, it will be done,' Won Ho said meekly.

Kim appeared oblivious to Kang's rage. 'I'm sorry, but I cannot vote in favour.' He gave his fellow politicians a look of scorn.

The servants returned to clear away the dinner dishes and Kang whispered something into the ear of one of them, who walked quickly back to the kitchen. Seconds later, a side door opened and two security guards entered. Without a word, they strode to either side of Kim's chair, grabbed his arms, and yanked the politician to his feet.

'What is the meaning of this, Kang?' he cried.

'I will suffer your foolishness no more,' Kang replied coldly.

At a wave of his hand, the two thugs muscled Kim through a door that opened onto a verandah. As Rhee and Won Ho looked on in horror, the struggling Kim was pitched over the wall.

His screaming voice could be heard trailing away for several seconds as he plunged down the cliff. The two thugs calmly returned to the dining hall.

'Retrieve the body and plant it on a street near his residence,' Kang ordered nonchalantly. 'Make it look like a hit-and-run accident.'

As the thugs left the room, Kang turned to the ashen-faced politicians and asked with icy politeness, 'You will stay for dessert, won't you?'

LATER, KANG peered out of the dining-hall window and watched as Rhee and Won Ho anxiously boarded his yacht in preparation for the fifty-mile trek upriver to Seoul. Kim's body, wrapped in a brown blanket, had been dumped on the stern deck and covered with a tarp.

Kang turned as his administrative assistant entered the room, a pale, scrawny man in a worn blue suit and crisply starched white shirt.

'Your meeting was a success?' the man asked Kang.

'Yes, Kwan. Rhee and Won Ho are going to promote our initiative for the removal of US forces through the National Assembly. It was unfortunate that we had to eliminate Kim, but he had lost his loyalty to us. His death will send a strong message to the other two.'

'A sensible decision, sir.'

'Progress is being made. And our media payoffs will ensure continued press coverage of the US serviceman murder incident,' Kang added with a wry smile. 'We must implement the Chimera project quickly to maximise the Americans' strife. What is the latest from the biochemical laboratory?'

'The news is most promising. The lab team has verified that the virus was successfully rejuvenated and dispersed during flight release in the Aleutian Islands. The programme engineers are confident that the full-scale deployment system will be operationally successful.'

'Providing we can generate sufficient quantities of the virus. It was unfortunate that all but one of the canisters on the *I-403* was destroyed. How soon before recovery operations can commence at the second submarine?'

'The submarine must be located first. We are acquiring a submersible that will be required for the deep-water recovery operation. Once on site, we expect the recovery operation to be completed within ten days.'

'Very good,' Kang said, rubbing his hands together. He looked towards the rolling hills of North Korea, just north of the Han River. 'We must soon prepare for the coming offensive, Kwan. It is time we regain our country.'

'You will hold a place of honour in the new Korea.' Kwan started to leave, then stopped and turned. 'Sir, another item has cropped up, related to the Chimera project. The helicopter that was shot down in the Aleutians was operated by an US government research vessel from the National Underwater and Marine Agency. Our crew believed the pilot and crew were killed, which was initially confirmed by media reports of a fatal helicopter crash. However, our US field operations team later reported that the pilot, a special projects director named Pitt, and his copilot, had in fact survived.'

'That is of little consequence,' Kang replied irritably.

Kwan cleared his throat. 'Two days after their return, the NUMA men were seen in a small survey boat headed for the location of the *I-403*.'

'What? That's not possible,' Kang blurted in anger. 'How would they have any knowledge of our activities?'

'I do not understand it, either. Perhaps our recovery operation was witnessed by others. Or perhaps it is just a coincidence.'

'Perhaps. But this is no time to compromise the project. Have them both taken care of,' Kang directed.

'Yes, sir,' Kwan replied. 'It will be handled at once.'

'DIRK, I HAVE some terrifying news.' The fear in Sarah's voice was palpable, even over the telephone.

'What's wrong?'

'It's Irv. He's in the hospital in Anchorage and the doctors say that he has contracted smallpox. I just can't believe it.'

'Smallpox? I thought that had all but been eliminated.'

'Practically speaking, it has. If the diagnosis is correct it will be the first documented case in the United States in thirty years. The CDC is rushing vaccination supplies to Alaska in case an outbreak develops.'

'How's he holding up?'

'He's in a critical condition,' Sarah replied, nearly choking on the words. 'The next two or three days will be crucial.'

'I'm so sorry to hear that,' Dirk said with concern. 'Have you any idea how on earth he contracted smallpox?'

'Well,' Sarah replied, swallowing hard, 'the incubation period is approximately fourteen days. That would mean he became infected about the time we were on Yunaska and aboard *Deep Endeavor*. We need to work fast to check everyone who was on board and isolate those infected. The smallpox virus is remarkably contagious.'

'What about you and Sandy? Are you all right?'

'As CDC employees, Sandy and I were both vaccinated two years ago after concerns were first raised about smallpox as a potential bioterrorist threat. Irv was on loan to us from the State of Alaska's Department of Epidemiology and had not yet received his vaccination.'

'I'll contact Captain Burch. We'll check on all the crew immediately.'

'I'll be back from Spokane this evening. If you can assemble the crew at NUMA HQ, I can help the ship's doctor check for symptoms in the morning.'

'Consider it done. Sarah, I could use another favour from you. OK if I pick you up at your apartment in the morning?'

'Sure. And, Dirk . . . I pray that you are not infected.'

'Don't you worry,' he replied confidently. 'There's way too much rum in my blood to keep any bugs alive.'

As PROMISED, Dirk picked up Sarah the next morning, electing to make the journey to the NUMA field office in the big turquoise '58 Chrysler.

One by one, Sarah examined *Deep Endeavor*'s crew, concluding with Dirk and Captain Birch. When she had finished she gave a sigh of relief.

'Captain, just three of your crewmen are showing minor signs of flulike illness, which may or may not be preliminary symptoms of the virus. I request that these men remain isolated until we can complete their blood tests. Your remaining crew should avoid any contact for at least a few more days, but it appears there has been no outbreak among the ship's crew.'

'That is good news,' Burch replied. 'Seems odd to me that the virus did not spread easily through a confined ship.'

'Patients are most infectious after the onset of rash, typically twelve to fourteen days after exposure. Irv was working alone in Anchorage when he reached that stage. I'd ensure that his stateroom is thoroughly sanitised, along with all the ship's linen and dining ware, just to be safe.'

'I'll see that it's taken care of right away.'

'It would appear that the smallpox was contracted on Yunaska,' Dirk speculated. 'Our friends on the fishing boat may have been dabbling with something even nastier than cyanide. Which reminds me . . . the favour I asked?'

Dirk led Sarah to the Chrysler. Inside the trunk was the porcelain bomb canister from the *I-403*, carefully wrapped inside a milk crate.

Sara inspected the item with a quizzical look. 'OK, I give up. What is it?'

Dirk briefly explained his trip to Fort Stevens and the dive to find the Japanese submarine. 'Can you have your lab identify any remaining residue?' he asked. 'I have a hunch there may be something to it.'

'Yes, we can have it examined,' Sarah said in a serious tone. 'But it will cost you lunch,' she added, her face breaking into a smile.

DIRK DROVE SARAH to the State Public Health Lab on Fir-Crest Campus, where they left the fragmented bomb casing for analysis.

'Where shall we go to eat?' Sarah asked.

'I know a quiet spot with a nice water view,' Dirk replied with a grin.

'Then take me away in the green machine,' she said, laughing as she climbed into the turquoise Chrysler.

Dirk drove the car out of the laboratory's parking lot, easing past a strangely familiar-looking black Cadillac that sat with its engine running. Exiting the campus grounds, he drove south past Seattle's bustling downtown, then turned west, following a sign to the Fauntleroy Ferry Terminal, where he steered the Chrysler up a loading ramp onto a waiting car ferry.

It was a crystal clear day on Puget Sound, the kind that reminded local residents why they endured the long, drizzly Pacific Northwest winters. Sarah and Dirk climbed the steps to the open upper deck, and gazed at the Cascade and Olympic mountain ranges, which sparkled against an azure blue sky so intense it felt close enough to touch.

It was only a fifteen-minute ride to their destination, Vashon Island, and when the ferry began docking, Pitt and Sarah made their way back down to the Chrysler. As Sarah climbed into the passenger seat, Pitt glanced down the row of cars behind him. A black Cadillac sedan, four spaces back, caught his eye. It was the black Cadillac that had been parked at the Public Health Lab. And he had seen the same Cadillac, he now recalled, at Fort Stevens.

A long blast from the ship's horn drew Dirk's attention back to the docking procedure. Minutes later he was driving the Chrysler out of the covered car deck and into the bright sunshine.

Vashon Island is a thirty-seven-square-mile haven at the lower end of Puget Sound, just minutes from Seattle, reachable only by boat. Lowering the convertible top so that they could better enjoy the landscape, Dirk drove south along the Vashon Highway. In his rearview mirror, he watched the black Cadillac exit the ferry terminal and fall in line half a mile behind him.

Sarah stretched her arms above her head and let the cool wind rush through her fingers. 'This feels marvellous,' she said.

Dirk smiled to himself, having known too many women who despised riding in a convertible because it mussed up their hair. He slowed the car and turned east onto a small side road that petered out in front of a quaint waterside inn. Bright flowers sprouted in large pots and flower boxes, throwing a vast array of colours to the eye.

Sarah beamed. 'Dirk, it's beautiful. How did you discover this place?'

'One of our scientists has a summer home on the island. Claims they have the best king salmon in the state. I aim to find out.'

He led Sarah inside, and they took a table next to a large picture window that faced east across the sound. After ordering a local chardonnay, they admired the view. They could see Mount Rainier in the distance.

'Reminds me a little of the Grand Tetons,' Sarah said, fondly recalling the craggy peaks of northwest Wyoming. 'As a child I used to ride horses for miles around Lake Jackson.'

'So tell me, how did a nice girl from Wyoming end up working at the Centres for Disease Control?'

'Growing up on my parent's ranch, I was always nursing a sick calf or mending a lame horse. I just loved helping animals. So I studied veterinary medicine in school and then snagged the job with the CDC.' She smiled. 'Now I travel the world, and I even get paid for it.'

A waiter appeared, bringing mesquite-grilled king salmon fillet for Dirk and Alaskan scallops for Sarah. After sharing a fresh raspberry cheesecake for dessert, they took a short stroll hand in hand along the water's edge.

Sarah sighed. 'It's gorgeous here, but we should be getting back,' she said. 'We should have the blood test results on your sick crewmen by now.'

As they approached the car, she turned and hugged Dirk. 'Thanks for a lovely lunch.'

'Kidnapping beautiful women in the afternoon is a speciality of mine.'

He smiled, then took her in his arms and gave her a long, passionate kiss. She responded, wrapping her arms tightly round him.

Dirk eased the car out of the parking lot, and drove past the Cadillac, which was parked in a side alley. As he watched in the rearview mirror, he was surprised to see the black sedan turn and follow immediately behind him. There was no attempt at an invisible tail. Not a good sign.

The Cadillac followed until they reached the intersection of the Vashon Highway. As he stopped, Dirk glanced again in his mirror and saw the passenger in the Cadillac was reaching down for something. A sick feeling hit him in his stomach and he pushed down on the accelerator. With tyres squealing, the Chrysler whipped onto the highway and sped north.

'Dirk, what are you doing?' Sarah asked in bewilderment.

In an instant, the Cadillac screeched onto the highway behind them and moved into the vacant oncoming traffic lane in order to pull alongside.

'Get down on the floor!' Dirk yelled at Sarah as he watched the black car approach in his side mirror.

Confused, Sarah slipped down into the footwell of the Chrysler and rolled into a ball. Dirk eased off the accelerator and looked to his left as the Cadillac came alongside. The passenger window was rolled down and a young tough with East Asian features and a straggly goatee beard raised a submachine gun from his lap and levelled it at Dirk's head.

The gunman may have been younger but Dirk's reflexes were faster. By the time the killer pulled the trigger, Dirk was standing on the brakes. A burst of fire ricocheted harmlessly across the Chrysler's hood as it suddenly fell back from the speeding Cadillac in a cloud of burnt rubber. The wheels locked up for a moment before Dirk eased off the brakes. He paused a second then, as the brake lights of the Cadillac lit up, he punched the automatic transmission into second gear and stomped the accelerator to the floor. A flood of raw gas charged into the Chrysler's twin carburettors and, showing no signs of its age, the big automobile roared off down the road.

The would-be assassins were caught off guard. The gunman made an attempt to fire another burst as the Chrysler accelerated past, but was too late with his aim, emptying the clip uselessly into the woods.

'What's happening? Why are they shooting at us?' Sarah cried.

'Some relatives of our old pals in Alaska, I'm betting,' Dirk yelled over the roar of the engine. 'Been following us for some time now.'

'Can we escape?' Sarah asked with fear in her voice.

'We can hold our own on the straight but they'll gain on us on the curves. If we can get close to the ferry and more people, they should back off.'

The Chrysler's speedometer needle was tickling 125 miles per hour, and a wide gap had opened between the two cars.

'How much farther?' Sarah asked, still low on the carpeted floor.

'Just a couple of more miles. We'll make it,' Dirk replied confidently, but inside he was cursing himself for placing Sarah in such a position of danger.

The Vashon Highway became a series of bends at the northern end of the island as it approached the ferry terminal. Dirk braked hard into a sweeping left curve, fighting to keep the big convertible on the road. The more agile Cadillac easily made up lost ground and was soon within a few yards of Dirk's bumper. Once more, he heard the sputter of machine-gun fire and ducked down, feeling a round nearly graze his cheek as it whizzed by before smashing into the dashboard. As he slid the car through a right turn, a ribbon of holes appeared down the hood. One bullet punctured the radiator, sending a plume of steam hissing out of the grille. Time was short now, Dirk realised. Without coolant, the engine would overheat and seize up.

The two cars had reached the top of the last rise. From there, the road snaked downhill towards the water's edge and the ferry landing.

Dirk gave Sarah a quick glance and forced a grin. Her soft eyes showed a mixture of fear and trust. He gripped the steering wheel tightly, more determined than ever to shield her from harm.

But the old Chrysler was on its last legs. Smoke billowed from under the hood, and the temperature gauge, Dirk noted, had been pegged in the red for several minutes. His eyes raced over the landscape, searching for a sheriff's car, a security guard, any sort of help he might solicit. But all he saw was quaint little bayside homes with flower gardens.

Then, looking down the hill towards the ferry terminal, he had an idea. Highly improbable, he figured, but at this point they had nothing to lose.

Sarah looked up and noticed an expression of confident resolve appear on his face. 'What is it, Dirk?' she yelled above the din.

'Sarah, my dear,' he replied, 'I think our ship has come in.'

ONCE THE FINAL car in line, a 1968 Volkswagen bus, was safely aboard, Larry Hatala, the Vashon Island terminal attendant, lowered a wooden orange and white barrier that halted any waiting traffic at the end of the pier. His work complete until the next boat arrived in thirty minutes, he threw a cheerful wave to a fellow employee on the departing ferry.

The pilot let loose a deep blast from the air horn, and it had barely ceased echoing across the water when Hatala's ears detected the sound of tyres screeching violently on asphalt. He peered up the road, then stared in astonishment as two cars, a big turquoise Chrysler and a sleek black Cadillac sedan, roared down the hill. A young Asian man was dangling out of the Cadillac's passenger window, wildly firing an automatic weapon. And, to Hatala's horror, the convertible was headed for the pier.

BY RIGHTS, the old Chrysler should have died long before. A rain of lead had cut through wires and hoses. Burning oil mixed with radiator fluid spewed from the red-hot motor. But the car offered one last gasp of power.

'Dirk, where are we now?' Sarah asked from the floor.

'We have a boat to catch,' Dirk said, grimacing. 'Hang on tight!'

He could see a man waving his arms wildly at the end of the pier, some fifty yards ahead. Beyond the pier's edge, the boat was pulling away from the dock. It was going to be close.

Dirk accelerated hard, and held his breath. The end of the pier was now just a few yards away. Beyond it the ferry inched further into the Sound.

To Dirk's surprise, the man at the end of the pier stopped waving and raised the orange and white barrier, apparently realising the futility of trying to stop the barrelling mass of Detroit iron that was charging his way. As he roared by, Pitt nodded the guy thanks and threw him a jaunty wave.

The big convertible stormed up the ramp at the end of the pier and burst into the air. Dirk gripped the steering wheel hard and braced for the impact as he watched a ribbon of blue water pass beneath the car. Screams filled the air as shocked passengers on the rear of the ferry scrambled to avoid the green monstrosity hurtling towards them.

Gravity eventually took hold and the massive old car slammed down onto the ferry, bounced twice, then skidded slowly to a stop just twenty feet from where it had struck the deck, lightly smacking the pea-green Volkswagen bus.

The black Cadillac did not fare so well. Just a few seconds behind, its driver saw too late that the ferry had left the dock. The gunman gave a blood-curdling scream, and the Cadillac soared gracefully into the sky before nosing hard into the stern of the boat with a thunderous crash. The car crumpled like an accordion and a large spray of water flew up as the mangled wreckage plopped into the Sound and sank, carrying its crushed occupants to a watery grave.

CHAPTER 4

After twelve hours at Sarah's hospital bedside in Seattle, Dirk finally convinced doctors to release her the following morning. She was fortunate in that the break to her tibia, or shinbone, did not require any rods or screws, but the medical staff were concerned about trauma from the accident and had kept her overnight for observation.

'Guess I can't take you dancing anytime soon,' Dirk joked as he pushed her out of the hospital exit in a wheelchair.

'Not unless you want a black-and-blue foot,' she replied, grimacing at the heavy plaster cast round her lower leg.

Dirk took Sarah home to her apartment in Seattle's Capitol Hill district, where he gently carried her to a leather couch and propped her broken leg up on a large pillow.

'Afraid I've been called back to Washington,' he said, stroking her silky hair as she adjusted the pillows behind her back. 'Have to leave tonight. I'll make sure Sandy checks in on you.'

'I probably won't be able to keep her away,' she said, grinning. The drugs made her feel as if her mind were coated in honey, and she fought against the overwhelming desire to sleep. 'But when will I see you again?'

'Just a quick trip to headquarters. I'll be back before you know it.'

'You better,' she replied, her eyelids drooping low.

Dirk leaned over and brushed her hair aside, then kissed her gently on the forehead. As he stood up, he could see that she had already fallen asleep.

DIRK SLEPT SOUNDLY on his cross-country, red-eye flight, popping awake well rested as the wheels of the NUMA jet touched down at Ronald Reagan National Airport near Washington, DC, at just after eight in the morning. An agency car was waiting for him at the terminal, and he drove himself the short distance to the towering green glass building that housed NUMA headquarters. Passing through a security gate, he pulled into an underground garage and parked. Opening the car's trunk, he pulled out a large duffle bag, hoisted it over his shoulder, then rode the employees' elevator to the tenth floor. The doors opened onto an elaborate maze of computer hardware.

The NUMA Ocean Data Center, established with a budget that would make a third world dictator whimper, housed the finest collected of oceanographic research resources in the world.

'Well, the young Mr Pitt,' Hiram Yaeger declared, grinning warmly.

'Hiram, how are you?'

'Not having smashed my car or destroyed an agency helicopter, I'd say I'm doing quite well,' he joked. 'So, to what do I owe the pleasure of your visit?'

'I'd like a little time with you and Max before my meeting with Rudi Gunn later this morning,' Dirk replied.

'Now, that I can approve,' Yaeger replied as he applied both hands in a finger dance over the keyboard to conjure up his research assistant, Max.

An artificial intelligence system with a virtual interface in the form of a holographic image, Max was Yaeger's brainchild. Cleverly modelled on his wife, she even had a sensual voice and saucy personality.

On a platform opposite the horseshoe-shaped console the 3-D image of an auburn-haired woman suddenly appeared, dressed in a skimpy halter top and short leather skirt. 'Good morning, gentlemen,' she murmured.

'Hi, Max. You remember the younger Dirk Pitt?'

'Of course. Nice to see you again, Dirk.'

'Dirk, what is it you'd like to ask Max?' Yaeger prompted.

'Max, what can you tell me about the Japanese efforts at chemical and biological warfare during World War Two?' Dirk asked.

Max hesitated as the question generated a massive search through thousands of data bases, then consolidated the data into a concise reply. 'The Japanese military conducted extensive research and experimentation into chemical and biological weaponry both during and preceding World War Two. Primary research and deployment occurred in Manchuria, under the direction of the occupying Japanese Imperial Army after they seized control of northeast China in 1931. Numerous test facilities were constructed, to which criminals and derelicts were sent and used as subjects. Few survived. Chinese prisoners, and even some Allied prisoners of war, were routinely injected with an assortment of deadly pathogens, as their captors sought to determine the appropriate lethal dosage.'

'What pathogens and chemicals did the Japanese work with?' Dirk asked.

'It might be easier to ask what they *didn't* experiment with. Their known research in bacteria and viruses included anthrax, cholera, bubonic plague, smallpox and typhus. Among the chemical agents employed were phosgene, hydrogen cyanide, arsenic trichloride, sulphur mustard and lewisite. It is unknown how much was deployed in the field, since the Japanese destroyed most of their records as they retreated from China at the end of the war.'

'Max, are you aware of the use of porcelain as a bomb-casing material for these chemical or biological agents?'

'Why, yes. Upon explosion, steel bombs generated excessive heat, which destroyed the biological pathogens, so the Japanese turned to ceramics.'

Dirk felt a knot in his stomach. The *I-403* had indeed been on a mission of death in 1945. Fortuitously, the submarine had been sunk, but was that, in fact, an end to the danger?

Yaeger broke his concentration. 'Max, this is all new history to me. Were those weapons ever employed outside of China, against American forces?'

'Limited instances of their usage were reported in Burma, Thailand and Malaysia. My data sources show no recorded use of biological or chemical agents in battle with western Allied forces, but of course Dirk's father's discovery proves that chemical munitions were being stockpiled in the Philippines for possible deployment in defence of the islands.'

'My father's discovery? I don't understand,' Dirk muttered.

'I'm sorry, let me explain. I received a toxin assessment taken from an ordnance sample recovered by your father on the *Mariana Explorer*.'

'What's the connection?' Dirk asked, still confused.

'Your father and Al Giordino traced a toxic leak to an old cargo ship that sank on a coral reef near Mindanao during World War Two. The toxin was leaking from artillery shells carried in the ship's hold,' Yaeger explained.' They would have been used by the Japanese Imperial Army, and the content was a mixture of sulphur mustard and lewisite—an arsenic derivative. The Japanese produced thousands of mustard/lewisite shells in Manchuria.'

'Max, I'd like to explore the Naval Ministry records for information on the mission of a particular Japanese submarine, the *I-403*,' Dirk said, as he digested this new information.

'I'm sorry, Dirk, but I don't have access to that portion of the National Archives' data records.'

Dirk turned to Yaeger and gave him a long, questioning look.

'The National Archives, eh? Well, that should be a lot less dangerous than tapping into Langley,' Yaeger acceded with a shrug.

Dirk laughed. 'That's the old Silicon Valley hacker I know and love.'

'Give me a couple of hours, and I'll see what I can do.' Yaeger's fingers were already flying over his keyboard.

'Max,' Dirk said, looking the transparent woman in the eye, 'thank you for the information.'

'My pleasure, Dirk,' she replied seductively.

AT TEN O'CLOCK prompt, Dirk entered a plush executive conference room, still carrying the large duffle bag over his shoulder. Seated at the table, two stony-faced men in dark suits were listening attentively as a diminutive man in horn-rimmed glasses discussed the recent events in the Aleutian Islands.

Rudi Gunn stopped in midsentence as Dirk entered the room. 'Dirk, good of you to return to Washington so quickly,' he said, popping to his feet. 'Glad to see your ferry landing injuries were minor,' he added, eyeing the dressing on Dirk's bandaged cheek.

'My companion broke her leg, but I managed to escape with just a fat lip. It's good to see you again, Rudi,' he added, shaking the hand of NUMA's longtime assistant director.

Gunn escorted him over and introduced him to the other two men. 'Dirk, this is Jim Webster, Department of Homeland Security Special Assistant, Information Analysis,' he said, waving a hand towards a pale-skinned man with cropped blond hair. 'And Rob Jost, Assistant Director of Transportation Security Administration, under DHS.' A rotund, bearlike man nodded at Dirk. 'We were discussing Captain Burch's report of your rescue of the CDC team on Yunaska Island,' Gunn continued.

'A fortunate thing we happened to be in the area. I'm just sorry we couldn't reach the two men from the Coast Guard weather station in time.'

'Given the apparently high levels of toxins that were released near the station, they never had much of a chance,' Webster said.

'Have you uncovered any information on the boat that fired at us, and presumably released the cyanide?'

After a pause, Webster replied. 'No additional information has been obtained. It is not believed to have been a local vessel, and we are now working with the Japanese authorities to investigate leads in their country.'

'So you believe there is a Japanese connection. Any ideas on why someone would launch a chemical attack on a remote weather station?'

'Mr Pitt,' Jost interrupted, 'did you know the men who tried to kill you in Seattle?'

'Never saw them before.'

Webster opened a file on the table before him and slid over a crinkled black and white photograph of a Japanese woman of about fifty, who glared into the camera lens. 'Fusako Shigenobu, former revolutionary leader of the JRA,' Webster continued. 'We found this in the wallet of one of your would-be assassins after we fished them out of the Sound.'

'What's the JRA?' Dirk asked.

'The Japanese Red Army. An international terrorist cell that dates back to the seventies. They appear to have staged a revival. Indeed, they have claimed responsibility for the recent assassinations of our ambassador to Japan and deputy chief of mission.'

'We suspect they were behind the cyanide attack on Yunaska Island, as a prelude to a more deadly strike in a major urban area,' Jost added.

'And the smallpox infection of the Yunaska scientist . . .' Dirk began.

'We have not established that link,' Webster countered. 'Japanese authorities do not believe the JRA is sophisticated enough to obtain and disperse the smallpox virus.'

'I might think otherwise,' Dirk cautioned.

'Mr Pitt, we are not here to gather your conspiracy theories,' Jost remarked in a belittling tone. 'We are just interested in learning why two JRA agents tried to kill a NUMA diver.'

'That's special projects director to you,' Dirk replied as he hoisted the duffle bag onto the conference table. Then giving it a strong shove, he pushed the bag across the table in the direction of Jost, who had to scramble to push a cup of coffee out of the way before the bag slid up against his chest. 'You're answer is in there,' Dirk stated brusquely.

Webster stood and unzipped the bag as Jost and Gunn looked on. Carefully wrapped in foam padding was a large section of the porcelain bomb canister that Dirk had recovered from the *I-403*.

'What is it?' Gunn asked.

'Part of a sixty-year-old dirty bomb,' Dirk replied. He retold the story of the World War II attack on Fort Stevens, his discovery of the submarine and the retrieval of the canister. 'I had the CDC lab try to find out what was in it.'

'It's made of porcelain,' Webster noted.

'Used to protect biological agents. The nose cone had a simple explosive, designed to detonate at a prespecified altitude to disperse the main payload. The charge was large enough to shatter the porcelain casing but not damage the payload with undue heat or pressure.' Dirk pointed to the segmented compartments. 'It's clear that the bomb could carry multiple compounds—even a combination of biological and chemical agents. The CDC lab found a trace of cyanide in one of the compartments on this particular bomb.'

'But why utilise more than one agent?' Webster queried.

'Perhaps because in combination they would be more lethal.'

'So what additional agents were on this bomb?' Gunn asked.

'We don't know. The lab technicians detected no trace elements in the other compartments. We know that the Japanese experimented with all kinds of organisms, so it could be anything from bubonic plague to yellow fever.'

'Or smallpox?' Gunn asked.

'Or smallpox,' Dirk confirmed.

Jost's face glowed beet red. 'This is a preposterous fantasy,' he grumbled. 'The Japanese Red Army is a small organisation of limited sophistication. Political assassination and planted explosives are within their means. Deep-sea salvage and microbiology are not.'

'I have to agree with Rob,' Webster added in a muted tone. 'Although the cyanide is an interesting coincidence with the Yunaska attack, there is no evidence supporting the smallpox theory. And we don't know if the missing bomb canister you reported was even on board the sub in the first place.'

Dirk reached over to the duffle bag and pulled out the still-blinking digital timer. 'Maybe you can at least find out where this came from,' he said, handing it to Webster. 'I found it in the sub's torpedo room.'

'Could have been left behind by a diver,' Jost noted.

'One with a possessive disposition, apparently,' Dirk remarked drily. 'I've been shot at twice since I retrieved this.'

'I assure you, we have a full investigation under way,' Webster stated. 'We will find out who caused the death of the weather station men.' The hollow tone in his voice revealed a lack of confidence. 'We can offer a safe house for you, Mr Pitt, until we have made an arrest,' he added.

'No thanks. After all, if these people are who you say they are, then I should have nothing to fear, should I?' Dirk asked with a penetrating glare.

'We appreciate your investigation into the loss of our helicopter,' Gunn interrupted diplomatically, as he gently ushered the DHS men to the door.

'Please keep us advised of any new developments, and, of course, NUMA will be happy to assist in any way we can.'

After they left the room, Dirk sat silently shaking his head.

'They've hushed up the Yunaska incident because they are getting so much flak for the unsolved assassinations in Japan,' Gunn said.

'The evidence may be weak, but there is no reason to foolishly ignore an attack on our own soil,' Dirk stated.

'I'll speak to the admiral about it. He'll make sure it doesn't get brushed under the carpet.'

They were interrupted by a knock on the door, then Hiram Yaeger poked his face in. 'Sorry to intrude, Dirk, but I found a log of operations orders for the Japanese Sixth Fleet covering the last six months of 1944.'

'Including the *I-403*?' Dirk asked.

'Yep.' Yaeger took a seat at the table, pulled a sheet of paper from a folder and read aloud. 'Proceed northerly route to Pacific West Coast, refuelling Amchitka. Initiate aerial strike with *Makaze* ordnance earliest practicable. Primary targets: Tacoma, Seattle, Vancouver, Victoria.'

'That's an ambitious target list for two planes,' Gunn remarked.

'Think about it, though,' Dirk said. 'The cities are close enough to be reached on a single fly-past. Two or three biological bombs per city would wreak havoc. Hiram, any information on what this *Makaze* was?'

'I was curious about that myself,' Yaeger replied. 'All I found was that the literal translation is "evil wind" or "black wind". But there is no additional information in the naval records.' He sat back in his chair with a knowing look. 'It was Max who finally hit pay dirt. In a Japanese genealogy data base, she located the diary of a sailor who served aboard the *I-403* during the war.' Holding up a print-out he continued, 'Mechanic First Class Hiroshi Sakora was a lucky devil. He came down with appendicitis while the sub was crossing the Pacific on its last, fateful voyage in December of 1944, and was transferred onto the refuelling ship in the Aleutian Islands.'

'And he made mention of the *I-403*'s mission?' Dirk asked.

'In vivid detail. It turns out that the young Mr Sakora was also in charge of ordnance for the submarine's planes. He wrote that before they left Japan an army medical officer named Tanaka had brought aboard an unusual type of aerial bomb that was to be used on the mission, and there was much mystery and speculation about it. Tanaka apparently gave nothing away, but just before he was transferred off the sub, Sakora was able to prise the information out of one of the pilots. The secret payload was smallpox.'

'Good God, so it's true!' Gunn exclaimed.

'Apparently so. He wrote that the payload was a freeze-dried virus, which was to be disbursed at altitude above each city. The Japanese figured the resulting panic would allow them to negotiate a peace settlement.'

'You mentioned that the virus was freeze-dried,' Dirk noted. 'So they had the ability to store the virus for long periods and then reactivate it.'

'Yes. According to Max, the Japanese perfected a way of freeze-drying the virus, for easier handling and longer storage. To activate, insert a little H_2O and you're in business.'

'So the virus could still be a viable danger, even after sixty years at the bottom of the sea,' Gunn remarked.

'Since they're made of porcelain, the canisters could survive intact for centuries underwater, if they didn't crack during sinking,' Dirk said. 'Might also explain the various interior segments to the bomb. A compartment with water was needed to rejuvenate the virus.'

'Perhaps it was more fortunate than we know that all but one of the canisters were demolished on the *I-403*,' Gunn remarked.

'That still leaves one unaccounted for,' Dirk replied.

'Yes, as well as the other sub's ordnance,' Yaeger added.

Dirk and Gunn looked at each other. 'What other sub?'

Yaeger felt their eyes boring right through him. 'There was a second submarine, the *I-411*. It, too, was armed with the *Makaze* ordnance and was ordered to attack the eastern seaboard of the United States.'

SOME DAYS LATER, Dirk Pitt Junior passed quickly through the customs checkpoint at Osaka's Kansai International Airport, relieved to be freed from the cramped airline seating, and entered the busy main terminal. It took him just a moment to pick out the woman he was looking for.

Standing nearly six feet tall with shoulder-length flaming red hair, Dirk's twin sister, Summer, towered like a beacon above a sea of black-haired Japanese. Her pearl-grey eyes glistened and her soft mouth broke into a grin as she spotted her brother and waved him over.

'Welcome to Japan,' she gushed, hugging him. 'How was your flight?'

'Like riding in a sardine can with wings.'

'Good, then you'll feel right at home in the cabin I scraped up for you on the *Sea Rover*,' she said, laughing.

Dirk collected his luggage. 'I was afraid you wouldn't be here yet,' he remarked, as they made their way to the parking lot.

'When Captain Morgan received word from Rudi that we were to assist in an emergency search-and-recovery mission, he wasted no time in responding. Fortunately, we were working on our pollutants study off Shikoku when we got the call, so we were able to reach Osaka this morning.'

Like her brother, Summer had possessed a deep love of the sea since childhood. After obtaining a master's degree in oceanography from the Scripps Institute, she'd joined her brother and father at NUMA. As headstrong and resourceful as her sibling, she'd gained respect in the field through her knowledge and hands-on ability.

Summer jumped into the driver's seat of her Suzuki hire car, then threaded her way out of the parking lot and onto the Hanshin Expressway, heading for the city's port terminal. Half an hour later the pair were pulling up in front of the *Sea Rover*.

The NUMA research vessel was a slightly newer and larger version of *Deep Endeavor*, with a matching turquoise paint scheme. Dirk's eyes were drawn to the stern deck, where a bright orange submersible called the *Starfish* sat glistening like a setting sun.

'Welcome aboard, Dirk,' boomed Robert Morgan, the bearded master of of the *Sea Rover*, who had joined NUMA for the pure adventure of sailing the globe. 'Grab a cup of coffee then come and tell me about this urgent search-and-recovery mission. Gunn was rather vague over the satphone.'

Dirk stored his bags and went directly to the ship's conference room, where they were joined by First Officer Tim Ryan. Dirk recapped the Yunaska incident and the recovery of the *I-403*'s bomb canister and what had been learned of the sub's failed mission.

'When Hiram Yaeger reviewed the Japanese naval records,' Dirk concluded, 'he discovered that a duplicate operations order had been issued to a second submarine, the *I-411*, only that sub's mission was to cross the Atlantic and strike New York and Philadelphia on the east coast. Apparently she failed to appear for a refuelling rendezvous near Singapore and was presumed lost in the South China Sea. I contacted St Julien Perlmutter, who found that an official Japanese naval inquiry had placed the loss in the middle of the *East China Sea* sometime in the first few weeks of 1945. Perlmutter noted that those facts matched a report from the US submarine *Swordfish* that she had engaged and sunk a large enemy submarine in that region during that time frame. Unfortunately, the *Swordfish* was later destroyed on the same mission, so the full accounting was never documented. Their radio reports did provide an approximate coordinate for the sinking, however.'

'So it's up to us to find the *I-411*,' Morgan said matter-of-factly.

Dirk nodded. 'We need to confirm that the biological bombs were destroyed when the submarine sank, or recover them if they're still intact.'

'Dirk, Rudi Gunn briefed us about the Japanese Red Army. Could they have already recovered these weapons?' Summer asked.

'It's a possibility. Homeland Security doesn't seem to think the JRA has the resources to conduct a deep-water salvage operation, but all it would take is money, and who's to say how well funded they are.'

The room fell silent as they all visualised the consequences of the deadly cache falling into the wrong hands.

'You've got NUMA's best ship and crew at your disposal,' Morgan finally said. 'Let's get under way.'

DAE-JONG KANG relaxed into the leather back seat of his red Bentley limousine, and allowed a feeling of self-congratulation to overtake him. The plan was going better than expected. Numerous protests were being held outside US military bases, demanding the removal of all foreign armed forces, while riotous students had marched on the US embassy. And Kang's bribery of several National Assembly leaders had initiated the political opposition that South Korea's president would soon have to contend with. Now he was turning his attention to the business leadership community, which had real clout with both the media and the members of the National Assembly.

The Bentley drove into downtown Seoul, turning through the gates of a nondescript low-rise building marked with a sign stating, simply: KANG ENTERPRISES—SEMICONDUCTOR DIVISION. The luxury car continued down a small alleyway that led to a private dock at the back of the building, where Kang's Italian motor yacht was tied up. A servant welcomed Kang and his bodyguard aboard as the engines were started, and the yacht headed back along the Han River, to Kang's estate.

Kang's assistant, Kwan, bowed as the tycoon entered the small cabin that he used as an office aboard the boat. Kang scanned the reports stacked on the table. After addressing a number of business issues, he rubbed his eyes.

'Have we managed to get the submersible yet?' he asked.

Kwan's face visibly paled. 'We have a problem. The Japanese submersible we leased was damaged while being transported to the *Baekje*. It was the fault of some careless dockworkers.'

A vein stood out on Kang's temple and began throbbing violently. 'This bungling must stop! How long before repairs can be completed?'

'At least three months,' Kwan said quietly. 'The only other available submersible suitable for the recovery is a Ukrainian vessel currently operating in the Indian Ocean. It will take three weeks to have her on site.'

'We have a timetable to adhere to,' Kang replied with agitation. 'The momentum we have built in the National Assembly for the referendum is peaking. I need not remind you that we had committed to strike during the G8 assembly,' he said, his eyes simmering with anger.

'Sir, there may be another option,' Kwan ventured. 'We were told that a NUMA research vessel is operating in Japanese waters with a deep-sea submersible capable of deep-water recovery. It is at this moment taking on fuel in Osaka.'

'NUMA again?' Kang mused, contemplating the risk of delay. Finally, he nodded at Kwan. 'Obtain the NUMA submersible, but do it without incident.'

'Tongju is there to lead the operation,' Kwan replied confidently. 'At your instructions, he will proceed. He will not fail us.'

SIX-FOOT SWELLS topped with white foam pushed at the *Sea Rover*, causing her decks to roll gently. Dirk stood at the bow rail and breathed in a deep lungful of sea air. After watching a pair of gulls arc lazily above the ship in search of a morning meal, he made his way aft and climbed up to the bridge.

Captain Morgan thrust a mug of steaming coffee into his hand. 'You're up early,' he boomed with a jovial grin on his face.

'Didn't want to miss out of any of the fun,' Dirk replied, taking a sip. 'I figured we're approaching the search area.'

'Pretty near,' Morgan said. 'We're forty minutes from where the *I-411* is thought to have sunk.'

A young helmsman in a blue jumpsuit eyed the depth monitor and crisply announced, 'Depth 920 feet, sir.'

'Looks like territory for a deep-water AUV search,' Dirk said.

'I'll have Summer wake up Audry and get her ready for work,' Morgan replied with a grin.

Audry, as the NUMA scientists who built her had dubbed their 'Autonomous Underwater Data Recovery Vehicle,' was a state-of-the-art self-propelled sensor containing a side-scan sonar, a magnetometer and a sub-bottom profiler, all packaged into a fish-shaped casing which was simply dropped over the side of the ship. The sensor could map the sea-bed and operate at a depth of 5,000 feet, propelled by a powerful battery pack.

As the *Sea Rover* approached the search area, Dirk assisted Summer in downloading the search parameters into Audry's computer. 'We'll use the side-scan sonar only,' he instructed. 'If the *I-411* is out there, we ought to be able to see her sitting up off the bottom. Let's set the search grid at five by five miles initially.'

Once Audry's software program was reconfigured, Summer and Dirk watched the eight-foot-long, lemon-coloured survey vehicle being lowered over the side rail into the water. A plume of spray from the tail indicated that Audry's small propeller was churning, then the grips from the winch were let go, and she disappeared into the depths.

While Audry motored back and forth down neat imaginary lanes 100 feet above the sea floor, her progress was monitored on a computer display. A pair of transducers had been dropped into the water at either end of the search grid. At twenty-minute intervals, a digital data upload was transmitted to the ship from the transducers, then converted into an image of the sonar readings. Dirk and Summer took turns scanning through the images of the seabed, searching for shapes that might signify a shipwreck.

Summer had adjusted the colour images to a golden hue so that the occasional rock or mound on the bottom cast a brown-tinted shadow. She studied the monitor closely, watching the same monotonous sea bottom glide by. Then, suddenly, a dark smudge appeared at the top right of the screen. The smudge was a shadow, she quickly realised, created by a long tubular shape that was crisply defined in a dark shade of russet.

'My word, there it is!' she squealed.

A small crowd gathered round her as she replayed the image several times. Summer measured the object at well over 300 feet.

'Sure looks like a submarine, and a big one,' she said.

'That's our baby,' Dirk said confidently.

'Nice work, Summer,' Morgan offered as he approached.

'Thanks, Captain, but Audry did all the work. We better pull her aboard before she makes her way to China.'

Summer typed in a new handful of commands and a signal was relayed from the transducers to the underwater vehicle. In a matter of seconds, Audry was breaking the water's surface a quarter mile away from the *Sea Rover*. Summer, Dirk and Morgan watched as a retrieval team in a rubber Zodiac scooted over to the idling yellow sensor.

As Audry was hoisted out of the water and replaced in her cradle on the stern deck, Dirk noticed a large exploration vessel that was inching past them a mile away, a Japanese flag on its bow platform.

'Cable-laying ship,' Morgan said, catching Dirk's gaze. 'She followed us out of the Inland Sea.'

'She's a beauty. Doesn't appear to be in any hurry,' Dirk said.

'Must be operating under a daily billing rate contract.' Morgan laughed, then turned his attention to hoisting the transducers aboard.

'Maybe,' Dirk replied, worry tugging at the recesses of his mind.

THE CREW of the *Sea Rover* wasted no time in making preparations to investigate the sub. Captain Morgan brought the ship around and positioned it above the target, while Dirk, Summer and First Officer Ryan carefully worked through a pre-dive checklist for the *Starfish,* a high-tech submersible specifically designed for deep-water exploration. Resembling a giant translucent ball on a forklift, the *Starfish* carried two operators in a six-inch-thick reinforced acrylic bubble that offered a panoramic view of the sea. Wedged into a bright orange supporting buttress, the sphere was filled with sensors, still and video cameras, and coring devices. Four sets of thrusters were mounted behind and beneath the bubble, which provided the sub with a high degree of manoeuvrability, and it had a pair of steel articulated arms that could be used for collecting samples.

'I think we're set,' Summer said, eyeing the last item on her clipboard. 'You ready to get wet?'

'Only if I get to drive,' Dirk replied, grinning.

Clad in aqua-coloured NUMA jumpsuits, the siblings threaded their way into the tiny chamber through a hatch in the rear, and sat in the two captain's chairs that faced out of the front of the bubble. Dirk slipped on a communications headset and spoke to First Officer Ryan.

'This is *Starfish,*' he said. 'Ready when you are, Tim.'

'Prepare for deployment,' Ryan's voice rang back.

An overhead boom reeled up a thick cable attached to the submersible and suspended her three feet above the deck. As the *Starfish* hung in the air, Ryan pushed a button on a console and the deck suddenly split open, exposing the pale green water of the East China Sea. Ryan hit another switch and the orange submersible was slowly lowered through the hole and into the water. The lifting cable was released after Dirk confirmed that all systems were operational.

'You are free to swim. Happy hunting, guys,' Ryan's voice announced over Dirk's headset.

As the submersible dropped into the depths, Summer flicked a switch and a powerful bank of xenon arc lights illuminated their path. It would take about fifteen minutes to make the 1,000-foot descent to the sea floor.

At 900 feet, Summer tweaked the buoyancy level to slow their descent. Gradually, through the murk, a dark shape loomed up beneath them.

'There she is,' Dirk said. 'We're right on her.'

The shadowy black superstructure of the *I-411*'s conning tower reached out to them like a tiny skyscraper as the *Starfish* descended amidships of the giant submarine.

'She's enormous!' Summer exclaimed.

'Definitely not your run-of-the-mill World War Two U-boat,' Dirk replied. 'Let's see where she got hit.'

Manoeuvring the thrusters, Dirk propelled the submersible along the starboard flank of the submarine, gliding just a few feet above it. They had travelled about fifty feet when a huge gash appeared in the hull.

'Torpedo hit number one,' Dirk called out, eyeing the fatal impact from one of the *Swordfish*'s torpedoes. Inside the hole they could see a circular mass of twisted and jagged metal, like the open jaws of an iron-toothed shark. The submersible crept along the silent wreck for another thirty feet before a second opening appeared.

'Torpedo hit number two,' Dirk said. 'Pretty good firing from the *Swordfish*. They must have caught her at night, while she was running on the surface.'

'Is that the aircraft hangar?' Summer asked, pointing to a tubular appendage that ran the length of the rear deck to the conning tower.

'Yes. Looks like it was blasted open in the explosion,' Dirk said as they glided over towards the opening.

A twenty-foot section of the hangar adjacent to the deck had simply disappeared. Under the beam of the floodlights, they could see a three-bladed aircraft propeller mounted on the hangar wall.

'We've found the Easter Bunny,' Dirk said. 'Now let's hunt for the eggs.'

Applying power to the thrusters, Dirk turned the vehicle and zoomed forward, gliding past the *I-411*'s conning tower and hovering off the bow near one of the large diving planes, which sprouted off the submarine like a giant wing. He spotted what he was looking for.

'There's the forward hatch to the upper torpedo room. If it's like the *I-403*, that's where the biological ordnance would have been stored.'

Dirk manoeuvred the *Starfish* in front of the hatch before setting the submersible down onto the deck of the *I-411* and killing the thrusters.

'How are your breaking and entering skills?' he asked Summer.

Unlike on the *I-403*, the forward hatch was closed and battened tight by a flush-mounted wheel. Summer activated a joystick control and, with the precision of a surgeon, extended the clawlike hand of the submersible's arm and dropped it down to the hatch, wedging the fingers into the open slots of the hatch wheel on the first attempt.

'Nicely done,' Dirk said admiringly.

At the flick of a toggle control, the articulated grip of the mechanical claw began to twist. Dirk and Summer pressed their faces to the bubble window, both intent on seeing the wheel turn. But the seal that had been locked for sixty years didn't budge. Summer toggled the grip back and forth half a dozen more times before the seal finally broke, and she was able to spin the locking wheel to its stops. Dirk then backed the *Starfish* away, and, with Summer holding on, the hatch finally swung up and open.

'I guess this is a job for *Snoopy*,' she said. 'You have the controls.'

Dirk pulled out a laptop and pressed the POWER ON button. 'Go fetch,' he murmured, while pressing a switch that engaged a tiny thruster.

From a cradle tucked beneath the acrylic bubble, a small Remote Operated Vehicle popped out. No larger than an attaché case, the tiny ROV was little more than a video camera wedged against a small set of electronic thrusters, designed to probe the deep and dangerous niches of submerged wrecks.

Summer watched as *Snoopy* ducked into the open hatch amid a spray of small bubbles. Watching the live video feed from the ROV that appeared on a colour monitor, Dirk steered the vehicle around the now-familiar torpedo room. The *I-411* was clearly not anticipating battle when the *Swordfish* surprised and sank her: all ten huge steel torpedoes were still stored in their racks on either side of the bay.

'No sign of the canisters or their crates,' Dirk said. 'But there is a second torpedo room below.'

He aimed *Snoopy*'s camera-lens eye onto an open hatch in the floor. Dropping down to the deck below, *Snoopy* entered the second bay of warheads, and, just as before, the camera showed all ten of the deadly Type 95 torpedoes resting peacefully in their racks. Nothing else.

'We may not know where they are, but we know where they ain't,' Dirk muttered. 'Now, if it was me, I'd want to keep those eggs close to the hen.'

Summer took a second to digest this comment, then her face brightened. 'The deck hangar? Where the aircraft are stored?'

'The deck hangar,' Dirk replied. 'And the *Swordfish* was even kind enough to leave the door open for us.'

Once *Snoopy* was securely back in its cradle, Dirk activated the main thrusters and the *Starfish* shot off down the deck of the submarine towards the site of the second torpedo blast. The detonation hole was large enough to allow the *Starfish* to drop into the interior, but the hangar was fractionally too tight to allow any room for it to manoeuvre further. So Dirk slowly guided the submersible forward and down until her supporting skids tapped onto firm decking just inside the hangar.

As he switched off the *Starfish*'s thrusters, silence filled the submersible. The hangar stretched in front of them like an endless tunnel. Then the quiet was broken by a muffled metallic clunk that rang through the water.

'Dirk, the propeller!' Summer shouted, pointing to her right.

The mounting bracket that held the spare, three-bladed Seiran bomber propeller had long ago corroded in the salt water, yet it had somehow maintained sufficient integrity to hold the heavy blade onto the wall for sixty years. Now, blasted by the stirred waters from the *Starfish*'s thrusters, it decided to give up its mission and crumble from the wall. As the bracket fell away, the heavy propeller dropped to the deck, landing on the tips of its lower two blades with a clang.

Dirk and Summer watched in helpless fascination as the propeller tipped forward in slow motion, until the blade and nosepiece came to rest upon the *Starfish*'s front skid plates. A cloud of brown sediment rose and obscured their vision for a moment, then, as the water cleared, Summer noticed a trail of dark fluid rising up in front of them, as if the *Starfish* were bleeding.

'We're pinned,' she gasped.

'Try the right arm. See if you can lift the blade up and I'll try to back us out,' Dirk directed as he powered up the thrusters.

Summer grasped the joystick and toggled it back to raise the arm, but there was no response. 'No good,' she said calmly. 'The blade must have cut the hydraulics. The right arm is as good as amputated.'

'That must have been the fluid we saw. Try the left arm.'

Summer applied power to the submersible's left mechanical arm, bending and twisting it until she finally had the edge of the propeller blade in the grasp of the claw. 'I've got a grip, but it's at an awkward angle. I don't think I'll be able to exert enough pressure,' she said.

Her words fell true. She pushed at the controls but nothing budged. Several further attempts met with the same result.

'Guess we'll have to barge our way out,' said Dirk.

Gritting his teeth, he applied full throttle power to the thrusters, trying to elevate the *Starfish* and slip back and away from the fallen propeller. The electronic thrusters vibrated violently as they clawed at the water with all their might, but the weight of the propeller was just too great. After several attempts, Dirk shut off the thrusters to conserve power.

'How much time do we have?' Summer asked, as the desperation of their situation began to sink in.

Dirk glanced at a row of gauges. 'It'll be lights out in about three hours, then another hour or so for the air to go. We better contact the *Sea Rover*.' His voice was matter-of-fact.

Summer activated the communication system and called Ryan.

'We do not copy, please repeat, over,' came a faint call from Ryan.

'Our com signal must be blocked by the submarine's bulkheads,' Dirk said. 'We can hear them, but they can't hear us.'

He shut down all nonessential electronics in order to conserve battery power. His hand came to the controls that powered *Snoopy* and he hesitated. 'Any objection to taking *Snoopy* for a walk?'

'We came here to determine if the biological weapons are in the hangar, so we might as well finish the job.'

'My thoughts exactly,' Dirk said as he powered up the tiny ROV.

He worked the vehicle out of its cradle and sent it sailing into the darkened hangar. Both of them watched *Snoopy*'s field of vision on the colour monitor as it moved away. Silt-covered objects began to materialise: a spare aircraft engine, storage bins for tools. Then the camera lens glided up to what was clearly the fuselage of a Seiran floatplane.

'Wow,' Summer murmured, impressed by both the size and condition of the twin-seat bomber. 'It's still amazing to me that they could store, launch and retrieve aircraft from a submarine.'

'A trained crew were capable of assembling and launching a plane in under thirty minutes,' Dirk commented.

Gliding past the fuselage, *Snoopy*'s cameras revealed a pair of the plane's giant pontoons strapped to a wooden pallet on the deck. The hangar was empty for several feet, then a set of low-slung racks grew out of the darkness on either side, holding what Dirk immediately recognised as aerial torpedoes. At 1,300 pounds each, they were much smaller than the massive submarine-launched torpedoes below decks.

'Let's keep going,' Dirk said. 'There should be at least one more plane.'

The ROV moved on, and seconds later a second Seiran bomber emerged into view, complete with folded wings. Just beyond, near the bulkhead dividing the hangar from the forward deck, was the plane's matching pair of floats, strapped to the deck by cables.

'Well, that's it,' Dirk said solemnly. 'We've covered the length of the hangar and no sign of any canisters.'

Summer bit her lower lip. 'Well . . . there's no indication of a forced entry anywhere, nor did the silt appear to have been disturbed recently. Perhaps they were destroyed in the torpedo blast.'

'Could be.' Dirk silently cursed their bad luck as he steered *Snoopy* back towards the submersible.

As the ROV approached the first plane's set of pontoons again, a quizzical look fell over Summer's face. 'Dirk, hold it there for a second,' she said quietly, focusing on the monitor.

'What is it?' he asked, neutralising the position of the ROV.

'Look at the pontoons. The pair at the end of the hangar were tied directly to the deck,' she said. 'But these two have a platform under them.'

He looked at the images and his brow furrowed. Each of the pontoons sat balanced on a square-shaped platform roughly two feet high.

Dirk eased the ROV next to one of the platforms. Spinning *Snoopy* around, he applied the thrusters for a few seconds, then repositioned the ROV. When the resulting cloud of sediment had subsided, they could clearly see an exposed section of a hardwood crate.

'But God, that's got to be it,' Dirk exclaimed. 'The exterior is the same construction as the crates that I found on the *I-403*.'

Summer made a notation on the video files, stating the crates' location.

'It's going to take some doing to get these out of here,' Dirk said.

'Us, too, for that matter,' Summer replied glumly.

Dirk guided the ROV back towards the *Starfish*. But as it approached, the ROV suddenly hung suspended, failing to move the last few feet. *Snoopy's* cable had snagged on some sort of debris about twenty feet in front of them.

Reversing direction, Dirk backed up the ROV until the cable straightened, tightening itself round what looked to be a small engine sitting in a tubular frame. 'A gas-powered compressor, I bet,' he said, noticing a pair of decayed hoses connected to the motor.

'What's with the big handle?' Summer asked, eyeing a large metal rod protruding from one side of the block.

'It has an old mechanical starter,' Dirk said, staring at it thoughtfully. 'Kind of like pulling the cord on a lawn mower to crank the motor.' Suddenly there was a gleam in his eye. 'And it may help get us out of here.'

IT HAD BEEN nearly ninety minutes since the *Sea Rover* had last communicated with the *Starfish*, and Captain Morgan was anxiously preparing to call in an emergency rescue.

'Ryan, let's contact the navy's Deep Submergence Unit. Notify them of our situation and request the ETA on a deep-water rescue vehicle,' he barked, silently dreading the thought. If Dirk and Summer were in real trouble, he knew the pair now had only a matter of minutes, not hours. Their chances of rescue were slim.

DIRK GENTLY moved the ROV in a circular motion above the compressor, letting the slack cable wrap loosely round the protruding handle like an anaconda coiling about its prey. After successfully engineering five loops about the handle, he tightened them by drawing the ROV up and away.

'OK, activate the take-up spool and I'll pull with *Snoopy*.'

'That compressor must weigh three hundred pounds. You'll never budge it,' Summer replied, wondering if he lost his mind.

'It's not the compressor I'm after, it's the handle.'

Toggling the ROV's controls, he increased the power to *Snoopy*, and the ROV's power cord tightened round the metal handle. Catching on to what Dirk was trying to do, Summer joined in, reeling in the other end of the cable with the automatic take-up spool until the cord went taut round the handle. That did the trick. The metal bar slid off the sprocketed knuckle and the whole handle slipped free of the compressor.

'And what exactly is it that you have in mind?' Summer asked as she watched the handle gliding through the water towards them.

'Why, just a little bit of leverage, my dear sister. If you'd be so kind as to grab my newfound crowbar with the left mechanical arm, you'll see.'

Working in unison, they brought the two devices together until Summer could securely snatch one end of the handle with the claw of the mechanical arm. Dirk then unravelled the ROV cable from the free end of the handle, and returned *Snoopy* to its cradle on the *Starfish*.

'Let's do this on one try. Purging tanks,' he said, pushing a button that pumped water out of the ballast tank to increase the submersible's buoyancy.

He then powered up the main thrusters, while Summer gently shifted the controls and worked eight inches of the metal handle under the tip of the fallen propeller. Using the hydraulic power of the arm, she leveraged the handle against the deck, and the propeller blade rose an inch, then two, then a few more. Dirk could feel the rear of the submersible tilt off the deck slightly as it was released. When Summer had safely jemmied the blade off the front skids, he slammed the power controls to maximum reverse thrust, and the *Starfish* gave a slight jerk as it backed tail first off the sub's deck, away from the grasp of the propeller blade.

'Nicely done, sis. What do you say we go get some fresh air?'

'WE WERE AFRAID you got lost down there,' Morgan smiled, when the two stepped onto the *Sea Rover*'s deck a quarter of an hour later. He looked quizzically at the compressor handle that was still in the grip of the mechanical arm.

'That's our walking stick,' Summer explained. 'We took a walk where we ought not to have gone and had trouble getting back out.'

'Well,' Morgan asked, unable to refrain from voicing his other concern, 'what did you find?'

'Two cartons of eggs waiting to be delivered,' Dirk said with a grin.

While Dirk and Summer told Morgan about the crates they'd seen, the *Sea Rover*'s crew worked feverishly to repair the *Starfish*'s mechanical arm and replenish the submersible's drained batteries.

Dirk and Summer grabbed a few hours rest, then they were back on the bridge ready to formulate a salvage strategy with Morgan. Reviewing the video footage recorded by *Snoopy*, they calculated that if they worked through the night, they should have the recovery operation complete by morning.

LESS THAN A MILE away, Tongju, Kang's personal executioner, peered at the NUMA vessel through a pair of high-powered marine binoculars. For nearly forty minutes he studied the *Sea Rover*, making careful mental notes on passageways, stairwells, hatches, and other elements of the ship. At last satisfied with his observations, the bald assassin entered the *Baekje*'s bridge and walked into a small side anteroom, where he found a pug-faced man with short-cropped hair.

'Sir, the assault team has studied the plans to the NUMA research vessel,' Ki-Ri Kim reported in the clipped, blunt tone expected of a former special operations commando of the Korean People's Army. 'We have formulated an assault and seizure strategy and are prepared to commence at your directions.'

'From the bits of communication that we have been able to intercept, it appears that they have located the weapons and are in the process of retrieving them from the seabed,' Tongju said in a quiet voice. 'I have notified the captain that we will be launching the operation tonight. We will commence the strike at oh-two-hundred hours.'

SHORTLY AFTER MIDNIGHT, after its third descent into the ocean depths, the *Starfish* bobbed to the surface. Dirk and Summer stood watching on the deck as the submersible was hoisted from the water and parked gently on a platform. A pair of technicians rolled a portable hoist to the submersible's front skids and began the delicate process of removing the three porcelain bombs wedged into the mesh basket suspended from the *Starfish*.

Dirk opened the rear entry hatch and lent a hand as Ryan and an engineer named Mike Farley squirmed their way out of the cramped compartment.

'Nice work, Tim. That makes a total of nine. I take it you accessed the second case without any problems?' Dirk asked.

'Piece of cake. Mike deserves the credit, though. He operates those mechanical arms like a surgeon.'

Farley grinned modestly. 'The second crate fell apart like it was made of mashed potatoes. But all six bombs were lying there intact. We snatched the first three, and the remaining three are readily accessible. Be mindful of the current, though, it seems to have picked up since our last dive.'

'Thanks, Mike, will do.'

Dirk helped the technician crew change the batteries on the *Starfish*, then worked through the pre-dive checklist. Shortly after 1 a.m., he and Summer squeezed back into the submersible for their last dive to the *I-411*.

THEY CAME OUT of the darkness like demons. Black-clad men in black rubber boats dashing silently across a blackened sea. Tongju led the assault in the first boat, accompanied by five heavily armed commandos, while Ki-Ri Kim led the second team. Together they raced towards the *Sea Rover*, propelled by high-power electric motors that emitted barely a hum.

The two crafts throttled back as they got within 100 metres of the NUMA ship, covering the remaining distance at a crawl. Tongju brought his boat alongside the *Sea Rover*'s starboard flank, while Kim's eased up on the port side. In unison, a pair of rubber-coated grappling hooks sailed up from the two boats, catching secure grips round the *Sea Rover*'s lower-deck railing. The commandos scrambled up the narrow rope ladders that trailed off the grappling hooks, then moved silently forwards along the deck.

On the bridge, the *Sea Rover*'s helmsman and second officer were discussing football. Without warning, Tongju and two of his men burst through the starboard wing door, aiming their weapons at the men's faces.

'Down on the deck!' Tongju yelled in clear English.

The second officer quickly dropped to his knees, but the helmsman panicked and bolted for the port wing in a futile attempt at escape. Before Tongju or his men could cut the man down, one of Kim's commandos appeared in the doorway, striking the man in the chest with his assault rifle. The helmsman withered to the deck, groaning in agony.

Tongju nodded at one of the commandos to stand guard over the communications equipment, then walked towards the door to the captain's cabin, at the back of the bridge. With a nod, he ordered one of his men to charge in.

Morgan was asleep when the commando burst in and levelled an AK-74 at his head. He sprang out of his bunk clad only in T-shirt and boxers.

'What's this all about?' he barked.

The startled commando hesitated in the doorway as the burly captain bore down on him. With a nearly invisible flick of his arm, Morgan knocked the muzzle of the firearm away, then, with his other hand, sent the commando sprawling backwards.

The commando was still sliding on his backside across the deck when Tongju levelled his Glock 22 and fired a single shot at Morgan's left thigh. The captain cursed as he grabbed his leg before crumpling to the deck.

'This is a United States government vessel,' he hissed defiantly.

'It is my ship now,' Tongju replied coolly. 'Any more insolence from you, captain, and I shall place the next bullet in your skull.' To emphasise his words, he stepped forward and kicked the kneeling captain, the heel of his black boot striking Morgan on the cheekbone and sending him sprawling.

The captain slowly got back onto his knees and stared quietly at his captor. He could only watch helplessly as the intruders took over his ship.

A THOUSAND FEET beneath the *Sea Rover*, Summer was carefully securing the twelfth and last bomb canister into the mesh basket.

'You may take us home now, Jeeves,' she said to her brother.

'Yes, m'lady,' he replied with a smile, then he activated the submersible's thrusters and backed out of the tight confines of the hangar.

As they cleared the deck of the *I-411*, Summer radioed up to the *Sea Rover*'s control room. '*Sea Rover*, this is *Starfish*. Have secured the last batch and are preparing to ascend with the goods, over.'

The call met with silence. 'Ryan must be asleep at the wheel,' Dirk said, as they began their ascent.

'Can't blame him,' Summer replied while suppressing a yawn. 'It is two thirty in the morning.'

As they neared the surface, they manoeuvred the *Starfish* into the centre of the ring of lights, paying scant attention to the shadowy figures on deck as the hoist was attached to the submersible. It was only when they were jerked roughly out of the water and swung wildly to the stern deck that they realised something was amiss.

'Who the hell's working the crane?' Summer cursed as they were set down harshly on the deck. 'Don't they know we've got bombs aboard?'

'It sure ain't the Welcome Wagon,' Dirk said drily.

Directly in front of them, an East Asian man in a black paramilitary outfit with a crooked yellow grin and cold, black eyes stood holding an automatic pistol to the stomach of Captain Morgan.

Summer gasped. A makeshift bandage was wrapped about the captain's left thigh but failed to cover the dried blood splattered down his leg. His cheekbone was bruised and swollen and his eye had begun to blacken.

A pair of commandos suddenly jumped in front of the *Starfish*'s acrylic bubble, waving their AK-74s to indicate that Dirk and Summer should exit the submersible. Gun muzzles were poked in their faces as they climbed out and were marched over to Morgan and Tongju.

'Mr Pitt,' Tongju said in a low voice. 'Good of you to join us.'

'I don't believe I've had the pleasure of your acquaintance,' Dirk sneered.

'A servant of the Japanese Red Army whose name is unimportant,' Tongju replied with feigned graciousness, bowing his head slightly.

'I didn't realise there were any of you fruitcakes left outside of jail.'

Tongju held his grin. 'Unload the final ordnance,' he said calmly, raising the muzzle of the Glock pistol to the captain's right temple.

Dirk glared at the madman but the delicate touch of Summer's hand on his shoulder dispelled any thoughts of rash action.

Reluctantly he began to transfer the porcelain bombs from the *Starfish* into empty storage containers that had been rolled out onto the deck on a wheeled cart. As he worked he watched Morgan being roughly manhandled to the stern hold. The big man seemed to stumble and fall against the bulkhead before being unceremoniously pitched down the steps. The remainder of Morgan's men soon followed at gunpoint, and a massive steel hatch was closed over the rear hold, imprisoning the entire crew in darkness below.

'Our intelligence heads apparently underestimated this Japanese Red Army,' Summer whispered. 'These guys didn't look like a rogue band of ideological extremists.'

'No, it's apparent they're well-trained, military professionals. Whoever's running their operation is obviously skilled and well funded.'

'I wonder what they intend to do with the bombs?'

'I guess we can't worry about that for now. We've got to figure out a way to save the crew. I counted eight commandos, and there are no doubt a few more elsewhere on the ship.'

When the last ordnance was secured in a container, Tongju turned his attention back to Dirk and Summer. 'You two, back in the submersible,' he commanded in English, the muzzle of his Glock pointing the way.

As they obeyed, they noticed for the first time that the Japanese cable-laying ship the *Baekje* had come alongside the *Sea Rover*, towering over her. A huge crane on the larger ship's stern deck swung over the *Sea Rover*'s side rails, trailing a cable from which an empty pallet hung, spinning lazily in the breeze. They watched as the pallet was dropped to the deck beside them. A trio of black-clad commandos then rolled the storage containers holding the other nine biological bombs out of the *Sea Rover*'s lab where they had been stored, and secured a couple to the pallet.

The *Baekje*'s crane operator quickly transferred the pallet back and forth several times in the predawn darkness until all the bomb containers were aboard the Japanese ship. The empty pallet then became a bus, ferrying the commandos to the ship a handful at a time. From below decks a black-clad gunman appeared and conversed briefly with Tongju, who smiled, pointed towards the submersible and barked out an order. The cable hook was released from the pallet and attached to the *Starfish*.

'Guess we're changing rides,' Dirk commented when the cable was pulled taut and they felt the submersible being hoisted smoothly into the air.

Dirk and Summer watched the *Sea Rover* fall away beneath them as they were carried over the water and deposited on a high stern deck of the *Baekje*. Climbing out of the submersible, they were welcomed by a pair of armed thugs, who prodded them towards the ship's railing with their guns. From this vantage point, they watched as Tongju and his commandos were ferried over on the pallet.

'Dirk, is it my eyes or is the *Sea Rover* sitting lower in the water?' Summer asked with alarm in her voice.

'You're right,' he agreed, studying the ship. 'They must have opened the sea cocks. She's listing a little to starboard as well.'

The pallet carrying Tongju swung over the deck and the commando leader jumped lightly off it onto the *Baekje*. He strode over to Dirk and Summer.

'The crew is trapped in the hold, you murderous swine!' Summer cried.

Tongju thrust his face close to hers and spoke in a voice dripping with menace. 'I shall enjoy watching you die in the manner of your shipmates,' he said, then turned and walked away.

The remaining commandos herded Dirk and Summer down a stairwell into a small twin-bedded cabin, and its door was locked from the outside.

Dirk and Summer pressed their faces against a porthole . They could see the *Sea Rover* still floating alongside the *Baekje*, but there was no sign of life on her decks.

Beneath their feet, they felt a rumbling as the *Baekje*'s engines were engaged and the big cable ship slowly increased its speed. The predawn light had yet to edge over the black night sky as they watched the twinkling lights of the NUMA vessel dissolve over the horizon.

CHAPTER 5

'Sir, we seem to have lost all contact with the *Sea Rover*.'

Rudi Gunn looked up from his desk, his bespectacled blue eyes boring into the NUMA field support analyst standing nervously before him. 'How long ago?' Gunn probed.

'Our communications link fell nonresponsive a little over three hours ago. We continued to receive a digital GPS position update, which showed they were still on site in the East China Sea. That signal was lost approximately twenty minutes ago.'

'Did they issue a distress call?'

'No, sir. We've requested satellite imagery from the National Reconnaissance Office and we should have something within the hour.'

'I want search and rescue craft in the air now,' Gunn barked. 'Contact the air force and navy. Get them moving. Quick!'

'Yes, sir,' the analyst replied, nearly jumping out of Gunn's office.

Gunn mulled over the situation. NUMA research ships had the latest in satellite communications equipment. They wouldn't just disappear without warning. And the *Sea Rover* had one of the most experienced crews in the NUMA fleet. Dirk must be right, he feared. There must be a powerful operation that was pursuing the biological bombs on board the *I-411*.

With a sense of foreboding he picked up his telephone and buzzed his secretary. 'Darla, get me the Vice President.'

SECONDS AFTER the massive steel hatch cover had been slammed down above their heads, thrusting the storage hold into complete darkness, Captain Robert Morgan took command of his shaken crew. 'Don't panic,' he told them. 'Ryan, are you in here?'

'Over here,' Ryan's voice rang back from a corner.

'There should be a spare lightweight ROV secured in the rear. Find some batteries and see if you can't get the lights rigged,' he ordered.

A dim light suddenly glowed in the back of the hold—the narrow beam of a torch clasped in the fist of the chief engineer, a red-haired salt named McIntosh. 'We'll get it done, Cap'n,' he growled.

Ryan and McIntosh located the spare ROV in a storage cradle, and further rummaging produced a stockpile of battery packs. Ryan cut one end of the ROV's power cable and spliced several internal lines to the battery pack terminals. Once he configured a complete circuit, the ROV's bright xenon lights flashed on, sending a surge of luminescence into the blackened hold.

'Nice work, Ryan. Now, then, is anybody hurt?' the captain said, ignoring his own injuries.

A quick tally revealed a score of cuts, and bruises but nothing serious.

'We're going to get out of this,' Morgan asserted. 'We just need to figure out a way.'

As he ran through the possibilities in his mind, a gushing noise drifted up from the bowels of the ship. In a few minutes, it had doubled in intensity.

McIntosh stood and addressed the captain in a sombre voice. 'Sir, they've opened the sea cocks. They mean to sink her.'

Several voices gasped in horror at his words. Morgan ignored them.

'Well, let's get on with it then. There's a small venting hatch located in that corner that those thugs might have forgotten about when they locked us in. One of you men climb up the ladder and check.'

'DON'T QUOTE me on this, but I don't think we're headed to Japan.' Dirk said, as he sat gazing out of the porthole.

'How can you tell?' Summer asked.

'I've been observing the sun and the shadows cast off the ship. We should be heading north-northeast if we were travelling to Japan, but it appears to me that our course has been more to the northwest.'

'Then do you think we're sailing to China?' she replied, picturing a map of the region in her head.

'Could be. The Japanese Red Army might have a base of operations in

China. But there's another possibility. The two hoods who shot up my Chrysler—a forensics doctor at the county morgue thought that the men looked Korean.'

Summer furrowed her brow. 'Korea?' she asked.

'Korea.'

ED COYLE'S eyes had long since grown weary of scanning the flat grey sea for something out of the ordinary, and at first the copilot of the Hercules search-and-rescue plane nearly didn't trust his eyes when saw a small light in the sky dragging a wispy white tail. 'Charlie, I've got a flare at two o'clock,' he said into his microphoned headset.

'I got her,' Major Charles Wight replied, peering out of the cockpit. The pilot gently banked the aircraft towards the fading wispy smoke and slightly reduced airspeed. 'Looks like we've got us some lifeboats,' he stated as a line of white dots slowly appeared on the horizon and grew into distinguishable shapes.

'Seven of them,' Coyle confirmed, counting the small boats.

Morgan had rounded up all the lifeboats and lashed them together, bow to stern, in order to keep the survivors together. As the Hercules flew in low over them, the crew of the *Sea Rover* waved wildly and let out a cheer.

'Roughly sixty heads,' Coyle estimated as Wight brought the plane around in a slow circle. 'They look to be in pretty good shape.'

'Let's drop an emergency medical pack, and order up a sea pick-up.'

At Coyle's command, a loadman at the back of the Hercules lowered a big hydraulic door, and shoved out several emergency medical and ration packs, which drifted down suspended from small parachutes. An airborne communications specialist had meanwhile issued a distress call over the marine frequency. Within seconds, several ships answered the call, the closest being a container ship bound for Hong Kong. Wight and Coyle continued to circle the lifeboats until the container ships arrived on the scene and began taking aboard the survivors. Satisfied they were now safe, the pilot banked the Hercules southeast towards its home base on Okinawa.

AFTER SAILING north for a day and a half, the *Baekje* was gradually turning onto an easterly heading. Landfall was spotted at dusk, and the ship waited until dark before creeping into a large harbour. Dirk's guess was correct. They were in South Korea's large port city of Inchon.

The cable-laying ship moved slowly past a container-ship terminal and approached the entrance to a small side channel, beneath a rusting sign that proclaimed, in Korean: KANG MARINE SERVICES—PRIVATE.

The *Baekje*'s captain manoeuvred the ship along the winding channel until it opened out into a small lagoon. A massive pair of hangars sat at the far end, and the captain inched the ship into one of them. A large hydraulic door then quietly slid shut, concealing the vessel from outside eyes.

Under bright halogen lamps, a crane swung over and half a dozen crewmen began unloading the ordnance containers, which were lowered to the dock under Tongju's supervision. Once all the bomb canisters were stacked on the deck, a large white truck backed down the dock. It had the blue bolt of lightning logo of the Kang Satellite Telecommunications Corporation emblazoned on its sides. Another group of men, wearing powder-blue lab coats, carefully loaded the weapons into the back of the truck, then drove away from the ship.

Kim approached as Tongju watched the truck exit the hangar through a guarded doorway. 'Mr Kang will be pleased when he learns that we have recovered all of the ordnance,' Kim stated.

'Yes, the mission was successful. I am taking the prisoners to Kang for him to interrogate them. I trust you will begin the reconfiguration of the vessel immediately. The sooner we get to sea, the better our chances of success.'

'Of course. But we have surprise on our side. There is no way we can fail,' Kim said confidently.

Tongju knew otherwise. 'Let us just hope that our deception endures,' he replied thoughtfully.

BELOW DECKS on the *Baekje*, a thick-necked guard handcuffed Dirk and Summer's wrists behind their backs before marching them at gunpoint to where Tongju awaited them.

'It was a lovely cruise. Though you never did show us where the shuffleboard court was located,' Dirk said to the assassin.

'The American sense of humour is hardly amusing,' Tongju grunted.

'By the way, what exactly is the Japanese Red Army doing in Inchon, Korea?' Dirk asked bluntly.

Tongju's brow arched. 'Most observant, Mr Pitt.' Then, ignoring his captives, he turned to Thick-Neck, who held an AK-74 levelled at the pair. 'Take them to the launch and lock them in the forward berth,' he barked.

Dirk and Summer were marshalled down a gangplank and across the dock to where a sleek, teal-coloured catamaran was tied up.

'Now, this is more my style,' Summer commented as they were prodded aboard and locked in a plush centre berth. 'No windows this time. Guess Mr Hospitality didn't like your Inchon gibe,' Summer added as she curled herself into a chair.

'Me and my big mouth.'

'These guys certainly have some deep pockets for a second-rate terrorist organisation,' Summer said, admiring the expensive artwork on the walls.

'Apparently, they have some friends at Kang Enterprises.'

'The shipping company?'

'A large conglomerate. I've seen their commercial freighters around for years. They're also involved in some other high-tech businesses as well, though I'm only familiar with their shipping division. This has to be their repair and storage facility.'

'Why would a South Korean business be mixed up with the JRA? And what do they want with us?'

Summer's words were interrupted by the throaty roar of the catamaran's diesel engines as they were fired up astern.

'I guess we'll soon find out.'

TONGJU BOARDED the catamaran as the ropes were cast off, and the huge hangar door slid to the side, allowing the catamaran to exit the enclosed building. As it slipped out, Tongju glanced back at the big cable ship. Workmen were already crawling over the *Baekje* and a heavy-duty crane was removing the giant cable-laying wheel from the stern deck, while construction crews were cutting up the superstructure and adding compartments and bulkheads. In just a matter of hours, the entire ship would be transformed. It would be as if the *Baekje* had never existed.

ADMIRAL James Sandecker marched through the corridors of NUMA's headquarters as if he owned the building, which he essentially did. The diminutive man with fiery red hair had founded the agency several decades before, and was revered throughout its offices and laboratories.

'Hello, Darla, you're looking stunning today,' he said graciously to a woman typing on a computer. 'Is Rudi in the conference room?'

'Good to see you again, Admiral,' the woman said, beaming. 'Yes, Mr Gunn is waiting for you inside.'

Though still regarded as 'the admiral' by his NUMA comrades, the rest of the world knew him as Vice President Sandecker. Despite a lifelong aversion to the world of politics, Sandecker had been persuaded by President Ward to fill the shoes of the vice presidency when the elected veep unexpectedly died in office. The fiery admiral immediately broke the mould. Far from being a passive figurehead, he vigorously spearheaded defence and security reforms, increased funding to government-sponsored scientific research and led new conservation initiatives.

Sandecker burst through the door to the conference room, immediately hushing the group of NUMA officials discussing the loss of the *Sea Rover*.

'Thanks for coming over, Admiral,' Gunn said, jumping up and showing his boss to the head of the table.

'What's the latest information?' Sandecker asked.

'The *Sea Rover* was sunk after being attacked in the East China Sea by a small armed force that infiltrated the vessel. Miraculously, the crew escaped from a locked storage hold minutes before the ship went under. They were able to make it into the lifeboats and were spotted by an air force search-and-rescue plane. The crew were picked up by a nearby freighter, and are en route to Nagasaki as we speak. All but two have been accounted for.'

'She was boarded by force?'

'A stealth commando team of unidentified nationality boarded her at night.'

'That's Bob Morgan's ship, isn't it?'

'Yes. He apparently took a gunshot wound to the leg during the struggle, but he's expected to pull through in good shape. According to First Officer Ryan, the boarders claimed to be with the Japanese Red Army. They made their escape in a cable-laying ship bearing the Japanese flag.'

'Odd choice of attack ship,' Sandecker mused. 'I take it they absconded with the biological bombs from the *I-411*?'

'Ryan confirmed as much. The *Starfish* was missing when the crew escaped from the hold, and Ryan believes it was hoisted onto the attack ship, perhaps with the submersible's missing pilots.'

'I'll call the State Department and request an immediate dragnet search by the Japanese naval authority. Shouldn't be too difficult to peg a cable ship when she slips into port.' He pulled a cigar from his breast pocket and lit it, sending a thick plume of smoke towards the ceiling. 'I'll brief the president this afternoon. Someone is going to damn well pay for destroying an American government vessel,' he snarled.

The inhabitants of the conference room nodded in agreement.

'By the way, who are the two missing crewmen?' Sandecker asked.

Gunn swallowed hard. 'Summer and Dirk Pitt.'

Sandecker stiffened in shock. 'Good Lord. Does their father know?'

'Yes. He's in the Philippines trying to contain an underwater environmental hazard. I spoke with him by satellite phone.'

Sandecker leaned back in his leather chair and gazed at the cloud of blue cigar smoke drifting above his head. God have mercy on the fool that would harm that man's offspring, he thought.

SEVEN THOUSAND miles away, the blue catamaran ripped across the coastal waters west of Korea. After two hours of hard running, the vessel turned inland and slowed as it threaded its way through the small islands dotting the mouth of the Han River. The pilot manoeuvred the boat upriver for another hour until he spotted the hidden channel that curled into Kang's Kyodongdo Island lair. The catamaran inched to a stop beside the floating dock, and was tied up behind Kang's gleaming white Benetti yacht.

Dirk and Summer remained locked in their cabin as Tongju strode off the craft and rode the elevator up the cliff to Kang's private residence. Kang was sitting in his cherrywood-panelled office with Kwan, studying some financial statements, when Tongju entered and bowed.

'Captain Lee of the *Baekje* has sent word that your mission was a success,' Kang stated through tight lips.

Tongju nodded. 'We acquired the ordnance after it was salvaged by the American vessel. The devices were immediately transferred to the biological research laboratory upon our arrival at Inchon. The lab chief assured me that the necessary refinement will be complete within forty-eight hours.'

'By which time the *Baekje*'s reconfiguration will be complete?'

Tongju nodded. 'She will be ready to set sail on time.'

'We cannot tolerate another miscalculation,' Kang said coldly. 'The mission must be achieved before the National Assembly referendum vote.'

'I have brought two of the captives from the American vessel with me. One of them is the man responsible for the death of our two agents in America. I thought perhaps you might wish to entertain him personally.'

'Ah, yes, the two missing crew members from the NUMA ship.'

'Missing crew members?'

Kwan stepped forward and thrust a news story gleaned from the Internet into Tongju's hands. 'It is all over the news,' he said. 'Research vessel sunk in East China Sea; all but two saved,' he quoted from Korea's largest newspaper.

Tongju's face went pale. 'That is impossible. We sank the vessel with the crew sealed in a storage hold.'

'Well, they escaped,' Kang said. 'A passing freighter picked them up and took them to Japan. Did you not watch the ship sink?'

Tongju shook his head. 'We were anxious to return with the salvaged material at the earliest possible moment,' he said.

'Perhaps your failure to dispose of the crew was not a bad thing,' Kang stated. 'It will keep American intelligence effort focused on Japan.' Kang perused a leather-bound schedule book. 'I am travelling to Seoul for an engagement with the Minister of Unification this evening and shall return tomorrow. Keep the two Americans alive until then.'

HALF A MILE from the dock in Inchon where *Baekje* was undergoing its cosmetic refit, two men in worn coveralls and grease-stained baseball caps were discreetly patrolling a secret facility. The dilapidated exterior of the building hid a high-tech engineering workshop filled with the latest supercomputing technology that was dedicated to developing Kang's satellite communications business. In the basement, heavily guarded, was a small microbiology laboratory whose very existence was known to only a handful of Kang employees. The scientists who worked in the lab had mostly been smuggled in from North Korea and had little choice in accepting the nature of their work with hazardous biological agents.

The *I-411*'s deadly bombs had been quietly transferred into the lab, where an ordnance expert had assisted the biologists in separating the powdery smallpox virus from the compartmentalised bombs. The freeze-dried virus, inert until hydrogenated, was still every bit as potent as when it had been loaded, sixty years before.

Placing samples of the powder into a biosafe container, the biologists carefully initiated a reconstitution of the virus using a water-based diluent. Under a microscope, the dormant microorganisms could be seen waking from their long slumber.

The research lab was run by a highly paid Ukrainian microbiologist named Sarghov. A former scientist with the agency that had run the Soviet Union's biological weapons programme, Sarghov had fled his homeland after being caught in bed with the wife of a Politburo member, and had sold his skills to the highest bidder. In Inchon, he had set up a high-tech research laboratory stocked with the tools necessary for isolating, splicing and recombining the genetic material of one microorganism with another. Yet he still felt he had one hand tied behind his back. The bacterial and viral agents available to him were common, easily acquired—nothing like the deadly Ebola, smallpox and Marburg viruses he had worked with in Oblensk. What he needed to create a knockout killer agent was a truly lethal pathogen. And, finally, it had come from an unexpected source.

Sarghov was not content simply to regenerate the supply of smallpox that had been delivered to him, however. By combining it with a sample of the HIV-1 virus, he was attempting to grow a new, mutated bug. A supervirus. Microbiologists sometimes refer to the result of this process as a chimera.

The lethal mixture was now delicately packed into lightweight tubular containers, which were then sent upstairs, where a team of mechanical engineers took over, inserting the tubes into larger stainless-steel cylinders. Five of these were assembled and had been placed into large shipping crates.

Sarghov grinned in delight. In less than forty-eight hours, his biologists had processed the sixty-year old virus into an entirely new killer, the likes of which the world had never seen before.

'WHAT DO you mean the ship has yet to materialise?' Gunn rasped in dismay.

The chief of the FBI's International Terrorism Operations Section, a man named Tyler, opened a file on his desk and perused the contents. 'The Japanese police have been monitoring shipping traffic in every port, and an international notice has been posted by Interpol. At this time, we've had no information on the whereabouts of the cable ship *Baekje*. There's a million places she could be hiding, Rudi, or she could have been scuttled.'

'What about satellite imagery of the site where the *Sea Rover* was sunk?'

'Bad timing there, unfortunately. With the recent flare-up of political tensions in Iran, the East China Sea is only covered by periodic scans from non-geosynchronous satellites. Which all means that the *Baekje* could move five hundred miles between covering passes. I'm waiting for the images from the last few days, but have been told not to be too hopeful.'

Gunn's anger softened as he realised that the FBI man was a professional doing the best he could. 'Any headway on the ship's history?' he asked.

'Your man Hiram Yaeger gave us a good head start on that one. Yaeger was the one who tentatively identified the ship as the *Baekje*, based on a worldwide review of ship registries in his NUMA computer bank. Owned and operated by Kang Shipping Enterprises, Inchon, South Korea, from 1998 to 2000, the *Baekje* has been under lease to the Nippon Telegraph and Telephone Corporation, Tokyo, since 2000, for cable-laying services in and around the Sea of Japan.' Tyler stared at Gunn. 'NTT's operating lease expired six months ago, at which time the *Baekje* sat unutilised in a

Yokohama dock. Port records show the vessel has since been unaccounted for until she was sighted a fortnight ago in Osaka, where she apparently tailed the *Sea Rover* to the East China Sea.'

'Any known links with the Japanese Red Army?'

'None that we've established yet, but we're looking into it.'

Gunn shook his head. 'So we've got a four hundred-foot ship that has vanished into thin air, a US government vessel sunk, and two of my people kidnapped—and we have no idea where to look for them.'

'We're frustrated, too, Rudi, but we'll get them eventually. Sometimes, these things just take time.'

Time, Gunn thought. Just how much time did Dirk and Summer still have, if any at all?

THE HOT SHOWER felt delicious. Summer let the steaming water pelt her body for twenty minutes before finally turning it off and reaching for a towel. After an uncomfortable night's sleep in the catamaran, she and her brother had been marched ashore at Kyodongdo Island, and prodded into the rock-enveloped elevator. They had ridden up to an interior corridor beneath the main quarters and then been escorted to a pair of plush guest rooms. 'Prepare for dining with Mr Kang, two hour,' a guard had barked.

As Summer dried her wet hair, she briefly allowed herself to enjoy the luxury of her surroundings. She sniffed at an array of exotic lotions and perfumes aligned on the marble counter, then walked over to a rack of silk clothing in the corner. Running her fingers through the collection of robes and dresses, she spotted a flaming red dress with matching short jacket that looked like it might fit. Squirming into the silk dress, she looked at herself in the mirror and couldn't help but admire the results. Wedging on a pair of black low-heeled shoes, she cursed as she broke a thumbnail. She rummaged through the bathroom cabinet, finally discovering a metal nail file, which she absently stuck in a jacket pocket after filing her thumbnail.

An instant later there was a pounding at the door. Exiting the bathroom, Summer found Dirk standing with two rifle muzzles pointed at his back.

He looked at his sister in the stunning silk dress. 'I'm afraid we've only got a few rats to guide your chariot tonight, Cinderella,' he joked, jerking his thumb in the direction of the two guards behind him.

'I see you've stuck with the Mr Goodwrench look,' she countered, observing the stained NUMA jumpsuit he'd worn since they were abducted.

'Afraid my available wardrobe was a little on the short side,' he said.

Annoyed with the chattering, the guards forcefully guided the twins to the elevator, where they rode up one floor. The doors opened onto Kang's impressive dining room, with its broad vista shimmering through picture windows. Kang sat at the head of the dining table, reviewing the contents of a leather-bound folder. Tongju stood at his left shoulder.

Dirk and Summer were escorted to the table, where their eyes briefly drank in the scenic riverscape before settling on their host.

'The submersible operators from the NUMA vessel,' Tongju said to his boss with a touch of disdain.

The Korean magnate's steely slate eyes darted upwards, then he motioned for Dirk and Summer to sit down. The guards eased back to a side wall, while Tongju sat opposite Dirk.

'Mr Pitt, here, was responsible for the death of our two men in Seattle.' Tongju said, his eyes narrowing.

Dirk nodded in satisfaction at this confirmation of the connection between the salvage efforts on both Japanese submarines and the murder attempt on Vashon Island.

'A tragic accident, really,' he replied. 'You must learn to recruit employees with better driving skills.'

'Very fortuitous that you survived, Mr Pitt, otherwise we may have lost your generous assistance in salvaging the *I-411*,' Kang said. 'I am most curious as to what led you to the submarines?'

'Luck, mostly. I discovered that a Japanese submarine had launched a few cyanide shells at the Oregon coast and wondered if someone had recovered some similar shells and used them in the Aleutians. It wasn't until I discovered the remains of the biological bombs on the *I-403*, though, that I realised there was something more afoot.'

'A shame the bombs were damaged during the vessel's sinking,' Kang said. 'They'd have been much easier to recover than those from the *I-411*.'

'But you did recover one bomb canister intact, which you discharged in the Aleutian Islands.'

'Of course,' Kang replied. 'Rather interesting how the Japanese combined a chemical and biological agent in one weapon. Our test release revealed that the efficacy of the biological agent was hampered by the dual release.'

'It was potent enough to kill two men,' Summer commented.

Kang shrugged. 'How do you know of these? Were you there?'

Summer shook her head in silence.

Dirk spoke up. 'I was piloting the helicopter your "trawler" shot down.'

'You are rather a resilient man, Mr Pitt,' Kang stated.

Before Dirk could respond, a door swayed open and two men in white jackets glided over to the table holding large silver trays. An array of seafood dishes was spread before Dirk and Summer who, having not eaten a full meal in days, attacked the food as the conversation continued.

'Your government . . . is rather displeased with the Japanese, I suspect,' Kang prodded.

'Your shady activities under the guise of the JRA was a clever ruse but uncovered for what it was by my government. Your two flunky hit men were easily traced to Korea,' Dirk lied. 'I suspect the authorities will be banging on your door any minute now, Kang.'

Kang smiled. 'A commendable effort. But the truth is that the two men had no idea themselves who their employer was. No, I think it is apparent that you know nothing of our intent.'

'The animosity of Korea towards Japan for their many years of brutal colonisation is well known,' Dirk said. 'It would be no surprise if the warped minds in possession of these weapons planned to use them on a historical adversary.'

A thin smile crossed Kang's lips. 'Your guess is quite off the mark.'

'What *is* your intended target for the weapons?' Summer asked.

'Perhaps your own country,' Kang teased as the colour drained from Summer's face. 'Or perhaps not. That is neither here nor there.'

'The smallpox vaccine is readily available in the United States,' Dirk countered. 'Tens of thousands of health workers have already been inoculated. A release of the smallpox virus might create a minor panic, but there's not much risk of an epidemic.'

'Certainly a release of *Variola major* would register only a small nuisance. But your vaccinations would be useless against a chimera.'

'A *chimera*? Of Greek lore? A monster—part lion, part goat, part serpent?'

'Indeed. Another monster would be a hybrid mix of virulent agents. A biological weapon against which your vaccinations would be impotent.'

'But, in God's name, why?' Summer cried.

Kang calmly finished his meal and set his napkin on the table. 'You see, my country has been divided against itself since your incursion in the fifties. What you Americans fail to understand is that all Koreans dream of the day when our peninsula will be united as one nation. Constant interference from outsiders keeps us from achieving that dream. As does the presence of foreign military forces.'

'The American military presence in South Korea ensures that the dream of unification will not be realised at the point of a North Korean bayonet,' Dirk replied.

'The military power of North Korea offers the leadership and stabilising force necessary to restore order during reunification,' Kang countered.

'In other words, once the US military is removed, the forces of North Korea will march south and unify the country by force,' Dirk muttered.

'Military estimates suggest that eighty per cent of the South Korean Peninsula can be overrun within seventy-two hours. The country will be unified under Workers' Party rule before the United States, Japan, or any other outside force can react.'

Dirk and Summer sat in stunned silence. Their fears of a terrorist plot using the smallpox virus had been well founded, but they had no suspicion of its magnitude: nothing less than the overthrow of the Republic of Korea and the death of millions of Americans.

'I think you underestimate the resolve of the United States,' Dirk retorted. 'The intelligence community will ultimately see past the Red Army façade and trace the actions back to you and your communist pals up north.'

'Perhaps. But how long will that take? How long has it taken for your government to solve the anthrax killings in your own capital?'

'Aren't you overlooking your own business interests?' Dirk said to Kang. 'There won't be a nation around that will be interested in purchasing the ill-gotten goods of a totalitarian regime. Face it, Kang, you're on the losing end. There's no longer room for warped despots who screw their own countrymen for personal wealth. At the end of the day, you'll be steamrolled by a concept foreign to you: "freedom".'

Kang sat stiffly for a moment, a look of annoyance settling over his face. 'Thank you for the lecture. It was most enlightening. Goodbye, Miss Pitt, goodbye, Mr Pitt,' he said coldly.

A glance to the guards instantly brought them over.

'Take them to the river cave,' Kang barked. And three of the guards pushed the pair towards the elevator.

Dirk knew that if they were to make it out of Kang's grasp alive they would have to act soon. The immediate problem was Tongju and the Glock 22 that the assassin kept aimed at them.

To Dirk's relief, Tongju and one of the guards remained standing in the dining hall when the elevator doors slid shut.

Dirk glanced at Summer and nodded ever so slightly. His sister caught on and acknowledged the silent message with a quick wink. She clutched her stomach urgently and groaned, leaning forwards as if she were about to vomit. The nearest guard took the bait and bent down slightly towards her. Like a cat, she sprang upright, jerking her knee into the man's groin with all her might, and he doubled over in agony.

As the attention of all three guards turned to Summer, Dirk launched an uppercut that connected squarely with the jaw of guard number two, nearly lifting him out of his shoes. The man's eyes rolled to the back of his head and he slumped to the floor unconscious.

Guard number three took a small step back as the fighting broke out and attempted to raise the muzzle of his rifle at Dirk. Summer reacted by grabbing the shoulders of the man she'd kneed and shoving his hunched-over body towards the standing guard. The shove had just enough force to offset the other man's balance, allowing Dirk to let go a left cross that landed on the gunman's chin. The blow threw the man against the back of the elevator, where he slid to the floor.

'Nice work, Smokin' Joe,' Summer praised.

'Let's not wait for round two,' Dirk gasped as the elevator slowed. He prepared to leap out as the doors opened. Only there was nowhere to go.

As the doors opened, the muzzles of three AK-74s were thrust into their faces. A security guard sitting at a bank of television monitors had witnessed the fracas in the elevator over closed circuit video and quickly dispatched a cadre of guards to the vicinity.

Dirk and Summer froze in their tracks, and Dirk gently dropped his rifle to the ground. He sensed a stirring in the elevator behind him. Too late, he turned to see the butt of a rifle swinging towards his head, where it collided with a thump.

For an instant he saw a blinding light, but that soon gave way to a fading darkness as he crumpled to the ground in a limp heap.

As CONSCIOUSNESS slowly seeped back into Dirk's brain, his mind registered pain signals from his wrists, arms and shoulders that were easily outclassed by the agonising pangs from his head. More confusing to his senses was the feeling from his feet and legs that he was standing in water. He opened his eyes to see a wet and gloomy cave.

'Welcome back to the land of the living,' Summer's voice echoed through the dark cavern.

'Where the hell are we?' Dirk asked.

'A cavern just off Kang's floating dock. That cool water nibbling at your naval is the River Han.'

His vision now restored, Dirk could see that he and Summer had their feet cuffed to two barge anchors—large blocks of concrete with a rusty iron mooring ring protruding from the top. They stood adjacent to each other, their arms stretched wide with each wrist handcuffed to adjoining blocks.

Dirk's eyes wandered about the dim cavern until he found the high-water mark, which, he noted uncomfortably, was two feet above their heads.

'Death by slow drowning,' he muttered.

Summer gazed fearfully at her brother. 'The water's rising pretty fast.'

Seeing the despair in his sister's eyes, Dirk's mind engaged in high gear to determine a means of escape.

'I just remembered something,' Summer said, crinkling her brow. 'I've got a small nail file in my pocket. Might be like trying to kill a pterodactyl with a fly-swatter, but it might help.'

'Sure, toss it over,' Dirk replied.

'This mooring ring looks pretty mangy,' she said, tugging at her left wrist. 'If I could just get one hand free.'

'Maybe I can help.' Dirk slid his legs towards Summer and raised one, placing the sole of his shoe on the iron ring. Applying as much pressure as he could, he pushed his weight hard against it.

Nothing happened.

Shifting his foot so that his heel was against the ring, he pushed once more. This time, the ring bent a fraction towards Summer. Gradually he forced the ring to bend over nearly ninety degrees.

'OK, now I'll need your help in pushing it back upright,' he said.

For twenty minutes, they toggled the ring back and forth, the movement gradually becoming easier as the old iron weakened. With a last strong kick by Dirk, the ring finally snapped off, freeing Summer's left arm.

She immediately dug her hand into the pocket of her silk jacket and produced the nail file. 'Should I try on the handcuff or the mooring ring?'

'Go for the ring. Even though it's thicker, it will be much softer to cut through than the hardened stainless-steel handcuffs.'

Using the small file like a hacksaw, Summer began grinding away at the base of the mooring ring, and after several minutes of hard effort her right hand was free. Next, she tackled the rings holding the cuffs to her ankles. Working the file with any degree of accuracy beneath the murky river water was a Herculean task. The rising water was soon level with her chest.

Millimetre by millimetre she progressed until she at last broke through the ring and freed herself. 'Got it!' she exclaimed in victory.

'Mind if I borrow that file?' Dirk asked calmly, but Summer had already swum her way over and begun cutting into the ring grasping his right hand. As she worked the file, she mentally noted that it had taken her roughly thirty minutes to cut through the first rings and that the water level was now nearly to their shoulders. The water was rising faster than she anticipated and would be well above Dirk's head in less than an hour.

Summer sawed tirelessly on, but it seemed no time before Dirk had to strain to keep his face out of the water while applying alternating tugs and shoves on the ring. A muffled metallic *ting* finally echoed beneath them as the first ring broke loose under their combined pressure.

'Three down, one to go,' Summer gasped, taking in a lungful of air after being submerged for several seconds.

'Save your strength for getting out of here,' Dirk told his sister.

Summer said nothing, but simply plunged back beneath the surface. Dirk half-floated with his head tilted back, his face barely out of the water, drawing a few deep lungfuls of air before holding his breath. His ears began pounding with each beat of his heart as a minute, two minutes passed. In the murkiness, he could feel that Summer was no longer by his side. Perhaps she had finally taken his advice and sought escape.

Light-headedness fell over him as spots began to creep into his vision. He exhaled what remaining air was left in his lungs and fought the temptation to open his mouth and gulp in. A white veil was being drawn across his vision and a distant voice inside was telling him to let go. Then his ringing ears detected a deep thump, and a strange vibration rippled up his arm just before his mind tumbled into a dark and empty void.

CHAPTER 6

Summer had known that they were at least twenty minutes from filing through the last of the iron rings and that there would have to be another way to free her brother. Abandoning Dirk, she had dived to the cavern floor, searching for anything that would help to break the manacle. But the flat, sandy bottom yielded nothing, just the row of mooring weights, one after another. Then, kicking ahead along the blocks of concrete, she touched a large chunk of concrete that had broken off one of the weights when it had been dropped. It might be the answer.

After kicking up for a quick breath of air, she dived back down and muscled the block off the floor and up to her chest. It had to weigh around ninety pounds. Fighting to keep the chunk balanced, she shuffled down the row of weights to her brother. Feeling rather than seeing Dirk, she turned and backed into her brother, pushing his body away from the block that held his left wrist then lunging forwards, throwing herself and the broken chunk of concrete at the iron ring. Her timing was perfect. An audible clang told Summer that she was on target. The rusty mooring ring, weakened by the filing, succumbed to the weight of the block and snapped off its anchor.

Summer grabbed Dirk's limp arm and pushed him to the surface, towing his limp body to a small rock ledge and pulling him out of the water. She knelt to administer CPR when his body suddenly stirred, his head turning to one side. With a groan, he expunged a small flood of water from his mouth and replaced it with a heaving lungful of air.

Rising unsteadily to his elbows, he turned to Summer and gasped, 'I feel like I drank half the river. Remind me to stick to bottled water next time.'

He sat up and rubbed his left wrist. He was pleased to see that his sister appeared unharmed and in good spirits.

'Thanks for pulling me out,' he said. 'How did you finally get the ring off?'

'I found a loose chunk of concrete and flung it against the stanchion. Thankfully, I didn't take your hand off in the process.'

'Much obliged for that,' he muttered.

They rested for nearly an hour, slowly regaining their strength. The cavern was now in near total blackness.

'Do you know the way out of here?' Dirk asked once he felt fit to move.

'The mouth of the cave is less than fifty metres away,' Summer said.

'How'd we get in here?'

'In a small skiff.'

'We'll have to borrow it if we want to get off this rock,' Dirk said. 'You know the way out, so lead on.'

Summer ripped the side seam of the silk dress up to her hip to allow more freedom for swimming, then slipped back into the cool water. Dirk followed as they swam and groped their way along the narrow cavern towards a pale patch of light. As they swam round a tight bend, the mouth of the cavern opened up before them, the night sky twinkling with starlight while the reflection of Kang's dockside floodlights danced on the water's surface.

Dirk and Summer swam out of the cavern to a small rock outcropping a few yards away. It afforded a safe vantage point. The skiff was pulled up onto the shore, adjacent to the dock.

'That's awfully close to the guardhouse,' Summer noted.

Dirk glanced at the hut at the base of the cliff. A guard was sitting in it. 'Stealth it will have to be,' he said.

They swam widely round the docked boats to approach the rocky beach.

Inching out of the water, Dirk crawled on his belly towards the skiff, which was wedged between two rocks about twenty feet from the shoreline. Using the boat as a shield between him and the guardhouse, he reached over the gunwale for the bowline, unfastened it, then crawled back over the pebble beach to the boat's stern, which faced the water. Running his hand along the top of the transom, he felt a bolt hole for attaching an outboard motor and ran one end of the line through, tying it securely.

Scurrying on his belly into the water, he played out the line until he was crouching in about four feet of water. Summer followed close behind him.

'We'll reel it in like a marlin,' Dirk whispered. 'If anybody gets wise, we can duck back behind those rocks by the cavern,' he said.

They gradually began applying tension to the line, and as it drew taut a grinding noise pierced the silence as the hull scraped across its rocky berth. They quickly eased off the line and stared towards the guardhouse. Inside, the guard still had his nose stuck in a magazine, so they continued to reel the boat towards them, a foot at a time, stopping periodically to ensure they had not attracted any attention. When they had towed the little skiff a hundred metres from the shoreline, Dirk tossed the line into the boat and pulled himself over the side, then grabbed Summer's hand and pulled her aboard.

Spying a pair of oars under the bench seat, he popped the shafts into the side rowlocks and began pulling heavily on the oars, propelling the small boat swiftly into the centre of the cove.

'It's about a mile to the main river channel,' Summer estimated. 'Maybe we can find a friendly Coast Guard vessel on the river.'

'I'd settle for a passing freighter.'

'As long as it doesn't have a Kang Enterprises lightning bolt on the funnel.'

Glancing towards the shoreline, Dirk suddenly detected a movement across the water. As his eyes focused, he grimaced. 'I'm afraid it's not going to be a freighter offering us the first lift,' he said, tightening his grip on the oars.

THE DOCKSIDE guard had grown bored with his magazine and decided to patrol the moored boats. He would never have noticed that the skiff had disappeared if he hadn't seen the scarred indentation made by the boat as it had been dragged across the pebbly beach.

He quickly radioed his discovery to the central security post and, in an instant, two heavily armed guards came running from the shadows. After a brief but heated exchange, several flashlights were produced, their yellow beams waving rapidly over the water and rocks in a frantic search for the skiff. But it was the guard on the stern of Kang's catamaran who located the two escapees. Shining a powerful marine spotlight across the water of the cove, he pinpointed the small white boat lurching across the waves.

Tongju, awakened by the commotion, burst out of his cabin on the catamaran and began barking enquiries at one of the guards. When he understood what had happened he rushed into the cabin of the catamaran's pilot, and barked, 'Start the engines. Get us under way immediately.'

DIRK GRUNTED as he pulled on the oars, his heart pounding fiercely. In the distance, he could hear the deep, muffled exhaust of the catamaran as its engines were revved. They had reached the far end of the cove, and Summer was relieved to see Kang's compound and boats suddenly drift from view as they began threading their way through the S-curved inlet.

'We've got maybe five minutes,' Dirk exhaled between strokes. 'If we can make it to the main channel, we may have a chance.'

The inlet grew dark as they made their way past the first bend and the lights of the compound were shielded by the surrounding hills. Dirk continued his even stroke, while Summer suggested subtle course changes to guide them through the channel along the shortest route possible. Though his limbs ached, Dirk seemed to grow stronger as the drone of the catamaran's engines grew louder behind them. Ebony darkness fell around them as they rounded the last bend of the inlet and rowed into the expansive breadth of the Han River. Patches of starry lights twinkled across the horizon, shining from small villages scattered along the river and hillsides, but night traffic on the river was almost nonexistent.

'Afraid I don't see any passing water taxis,' Summer said.

As Dirk rowed towards the centre of the river, he could feel the current pushing them downstream. He eased off the oars for a moment to survey their options. A brightly illuminated dredge ship was slowly making its way upstream on the far side of the river, about four miles away. It looked appealing, but they would have to fight the crosscurrent to reach it, which would be near impossible once they started swimming. Peering downriver, he spotted a small cluster of yellow lights on the opposite shore.

'Let's try for the village there,' he said, pointing an oar in the direction of the lights, about two miles downstream. 'If we swim directly across the river, the current should carry us pretty close.'

Unbeknownst to both of them, the Korean demarcation line ran through this section of the Han River delta. The twinkling lights downriver were not a village at all but a North Korean military base.

Suddenly the catamaran burst out of the inlet. A pair of bright spotlights flared from its wheelhouse, sweeping back and forth across the water.

'Time to exit stage right,' Dirk said, swinging the boat round so that the bow pointed downstream.

Summer quickly slipped over the side. Dirk hesitated a moment, then flung a pair of life jackets away from the boat before rolling into the water.

As the clatter of machine-gun fire suddenly tore through the night air, Dirk and Summer ducked under the water, kicking down to a depth of four feet before angling into the powerful current. After thirty seconds, Dirk eased slowly to the surface. Just ten feet away, Summer's face emerged and Dirk could hear her breathing deeply. They glanced at each other, then at the skiff; they were already nearly 100 metres away from it. Kang's catamaran had barrelled in on the skiff with guns blazing and was creeping close to assess the damage. Dirk and Summer gulped more air and resubmerged.

TONGJU ORDERED his gunmen to cease firing. He expected to find the two escapees sprawled dead in the bottom of the bullet-ridden skiff, but as they pulled alongside it was clear that the small boat was empty.

'Search the surrounding water and shoreline,' Tongju ordered.

The catamaran circled round the skiff while the spotlights were swept across the water, all eyes peering intently into the darkness.

Suddenly, a gunman yelled out, 'There, in the water . . . two objects!'

This time they are finished, Tongju thought with ruthless satisfaction.

HAVING DISTANCED themselves from the skiff by almost 400 metres, Dirk and Summer took a moment to rest.

'We can swim on the surface for the time being,' Dirk said between deep breaths. 'Give us a chance to see what our friends are up to.'

Summer followed her brother's lead and rolled onto her back, kicking into a backstroke that allowed her to watch Tongju circling the catamaran. A shout erupted from Kang's boat and the catamaran suddenly raced downriver a short distance. Gunfire exploded again, then ceased as the boat stopped in the water, and Tongju discovered the bullet-ridden life jackets that Dirk had tossed into the water. After a while, the boat began to search around the skiff and life jackets in an ever-expanding spiral.

'Won't be too many more minutes before they work their way in our direction,' Summer lamented.

Dirk scanned the horizon. They were still barely a quarter of the way across the vast waterway. They could turn back and make for the nearest shoreline, but that would entail crossing the path of the advancing catamaran. Or they could continue with their original plan of traversing the river towards the lights on the opposite shore. But fatigue was beginning to creep up on them, and another three-mile swim would be a tall order.

There was a third option. A small vessel with an array of coloured lights was approaching from upriver, about a half mile away. In the darkness, Dirk had trouble identifying the boat, but it appeared to be a wooden sailing vessel of some kind with a small red sail.

'Sister, I think it's time for Plan B,' he said. 'Stick out your thumb and start hitchhiking.'

As the sailboat crept closer, Dirk could see that it was a three-masted Chinese junk about twenty-five metres in length. A string of multicoloured lanterns hung gaily from bow to stern, lending a partylike atmosphere to the boat, yet there was not a soul to be seen on deck.

'Ahoy! We're in the water. Can you help?'

Dirk's shout went unanswered. Swimming closer, he thought he detected a shadowy movement on the stern, but the junk slipped by, strangely impervious to their voices. Just as Dirk had abandoned hope, he was startled by a sudden splash in the water near his head. It was an orange plastic float tied to a rope trailing back to the stern of the junk.

'Grab hold and hang on tight,' he instructed his sister, making sure Summer had a strong grip on the line before grasping it himself.

The line drew taut, and they were dragged along the river's surface like fallen waterskiers. Dirk slowly began pulling himself up, hand over hand. Reaching the high, blunt stern of the junk, he shimmied up the rope almost vertically until he reached the stern railing. A pair of hands emerged from the darkness, yanking him over the rail and onto the deck.

'Thanks,' Dirk muttered, paying little heed to a tall figure in the shadows.

'My sister is still on the line,' he gasped, grabbing it and pulling.

The tall man stepped up behind him and together they hoisted Summer up like a flounder until she flopped onto the deck in a soggy heap. A high-pitched bark erupted and a small black and tan dachshund raced over to Summer and began licking her face.

'Dark night for a swim, isn't it?' the stranger said in English.

'You're American,' Dirk stated with surprise, and studied the man beside him for the first time.

He stood six foot three, nearly matching Dirk's own height, though he carried a good twenty pounds more. A wave of unruly white hair and a matching goatee indicated that he was at least forty years Dirk's senior, yet the man's blue-green eyes seemed to twinkle with mischief. Dirk felt as if he was looking at an older version of his own father, he finally decided.

'We're in great danger,' Summer interjected, rising to her feet. 'Our research vessel was sunk by murderers and they mean to kill us.'

'I heard the machine-gun fire,' the man replied as he looked the pair up and down. Summer, soaked but elegant still in her ripped silk cocktail dress, appeared an unusual companion for Dirk, who was battered and bruised in a shredded blue jumpsuit. Neither attempted to conceal the hand-cuffs that dangled from their wrists.

A slight grin fell across the man's lips. 'I guess I'll buy it. We better hide you below decks until we get past that cat. You can stay in Mauser's cabin.'

'Mauser? How many people are aboard?' Dirk asked.

'Just me and that fellow who's kissing your sister,' he replied.

Dirk turned to see the small dachshund happily licking Summer's face.

The junk's owner quickly led them down to a cabin. 'There are towels and dry clothes in the closet. And, here, this will warm you up.'

He poured them each a glass of clear fluid. Dirk downed a shot quickly.

'*Soju*,' the man said. 'A local rice brew. Help yourself while I try to get us past your friends in the cat.'

'Thank you for helping us,' Summer replied. 'By the way, my name is Summer Pitt, and this is my brother, Dirk.'

'Pleased to meet you. My name is Clive Cussler.'

CUSSLER returned to the junk's wheel, slipped the engine into gear and nosed the bow further towards the middle of the river. It was only a few minutes before the catamaran approached from downstream, pulling along-side and washing the junk in a flood of spotlights.

Cussler slipped on a conical straw peasant's hat and hunched his tall frame low at the wheel. Through the glare of the lights, he could see several automatic weapons pointing at him as an unseen man on the bridge barked a question through the boat's PA system. Cussler replied by shaking his head. Another command echoed from the catamaran and Cussler again shook his head. For several minutes, the catamaran held steady at the junk's side as if waiting to board. Then, with a sudden blast of its engines, it roared away.

Cussler guided the junk down the last vestiges of the Han River until its waters were swallowed by the Yellow Sea. As the sea lanes opened out, he punched in a handful of electronic controls. The small diesel motor was switched off, and the red, square-shaped lugsails were raised to the peak of the main- and mizzenmasts, causing the old junk to leap through the waves.

'You've got a beautiful vessel,' Dirk said, emerging from below decks dressed in jeans and a polo shirt.

Summer followed, clad in a pair of coveralls and a man's work shirt.

'She was built in Shanghai in 1907 for a wealthy tea trader,' Cussler said. 'She's made entirely from teak and is surprising seaworthy.'

'You sail her by yourself?' Summer asked.

'She's been modified with a strong diesel engine and hydraulic lifts for the lugsails, which are linked to a computerised automatic pilot. She's a breeze to manage, and I'm planning to work my way down to Wellington in her.'

'Do you have a satellite phone aboard?' Dirk asked.

'Afraid not. A ship-to-shore radio is the best I can offer you. I didn't want any phone calls bothering me on this cruise.'

'Understandable. What is our position now?'

Cussler pulled out a marine navigation chart and held it under a weak light. 'We're entering the Yellow Sea about forty miles northwest of Seoul.' He ran a finger across the chart. 'How about Inchon? I can drop you there in about eight hours. I believe there's a US air force base located somewhere nearby.'

'That would be great. Anywhere we can find a phone and get hold of someone at NUMA headquarters.'

'NUMA,' Cussler said, mulling over the word. 'You're not from the NUMA ship that sank southwest of Japan?'

'Yes, we are. How did you know about that?' Summer asked.

'It was all over CNN. I saw them interview the captain. He told how the crew was rescued following an explosion in the engine room.'

Dirk and Summer stared at each other in disbelief.

'Captain Morgan and the crew are alive?' Summer blurted.

'Yes, that was the fellow's name.'

Summer told Cussler the story of the attack on their ship and their abduction by Kang's men.

'Well, you're safe for now,' he said when she had finished. 'There's some sandwiches and beer in the galley. Why don't you two grab a bite and get some rest. I'll wake you when we reach Inchon.'

'Thanks, I'll take you up on that,' Summer replied, heading below.

Dirk lingered a moment, standing at the rail and watching the first glimmer of daybreak painting the eastern horizon. As he contemplated the events of the past three days, resolve surged through his exhausted body. If what Kang had told them was true, then millions of lives were at risk. The madman would have to be stopped, and quick.

CHAPTER 7

Though it was a cool, damp Southern California morning, Danny Stamp could feel the sweat beginning to drip from his underarms. The veteran engineer was as nervous as a teenager on prom night. He always was when one of his babies was on the move. And his baby today was a 209-foot Zenit-3SL rocket that was in the process of being transferred to its launch platform. As the $90 million rocket rolled into view, a huge white cylinder on a centipede-like cradle, Stamp's eyes were drawn to the large blue letters emblazoned on its side: SEA LAUNCH.

Sea Launch was an international consortium formed to provide rocket-launch services primarily for satellite telecommunications operators. The American aerospace giant Boeing was the main founder, but more recently a pair of Russian companies had joined by providing the actual rockets, or 'launch vehicles', as they are known in the parlance. Ex-military rockets that once carried nuclear warheads, the Zenits were perfectly suited to commercial applications. But it was a Norwegian firm, Kvaerner, that provided perhaps the most unique asset to the venture: a floating launch pad called the *Odyssey*, based on a used North Seat oil platform, which could be positioned in almost any ocean of the world.

For a geosynchronous satellite, which remains in a fixed orbital position following the earth's rotation, there is no more direct or fuel-efficient path to orbit than from the equator. So Sea Launch specialised in integrating a satellite into a launch vehicle in Long Beach, then sailing the rocket to the equator for launch. And the concept had grown from an intriguing idea to an efficient business model in the high-stakes, high-risk game of commercial space operations.

A handheld radio fastened to Stamp's belt suddenly cracked with static. '*Sea Launch Commander*, this is *Odyssey*. Ready to transfer launch vehicle.'

Stamp nodded to a short fellow standing besides him, a bearded man named Christiano who captained the *Sea Launch Commander*.

Christiano spoke into his own radio. 'This is *Commander*. Proceed with transfer. Good luck, *Odyssey*.'

Stamp glanced across at the floating launch platform that had been positioned just aft of them. Its huge crane swung over until it hung directly above the horizontal rocket, where teams of engineers in hard hats attached the cables to a series of slings along the rocket's length. Seconds later, the cable lines drew taut and the Zenit rocket was hoisted high into the air above the decks of the *Commander*. It was then gently swung towards the *Odyssey* and lowered into a wheeled cradle on the *Odyssey*'s high deck.

'Launch vehicle secure. Well done, gentlemen. The beers are on me tonight. *Odyssey* out.'

Stamp visibly relaxed, a broad grin spreading across his face. 'Piece of cake,' he said to Christiano, as if the outcome had never been in doubt.

'Looks like we'll make the scheduled launch date in seventeen days after all,' Christiano replied as he watched the empty rocket cradle slide back into the ship's lower-deck hangar. 'After further checks and fuelling, the *Odyssey* can depart in four days and we'll follow forty-eight hours later. We'll easily catch up with her before reaching the launch site.'

'A good thing, too,' Stamp said with relief. 'There's a penalty clause in the customer contract that's a killer if we're late to launch. But the rocket team must have set a new record for assembly time. Even with our paranoid customer shielding the mission payload from everyone.'

'What's so terribly secretive about a television satellite?'

'Search me,' Stamp said, shrugging his shoulders. 'The whole operation makes no sense. They could have easily launched off the Chinese Long March rocket for a couple of million dollars less than our fees.'

'Apparently the head of the telecommunications firm is a real maverick. Owns the company outright, doesn't he?' Christiano asked.

'Yep,' Stamp replied. 'Dae-jong Kang is one rich and powerful man.'

KANG LEANED back in the padded leather chair in his cherrywood study and listened intently as an engineer from his Inchon facility provided a technical briefing. Tongju sat silently at the back of the room while the slight, dishevelled man with glasses spoke in a rasping voice.

'As you know, the Koreasat 2 satellite was delivered to the launch provider's facility approximately three weeks ago, where it was encapsulated inside the payload fairing, or nose-cone section, of the Zenit rocket. The entire launch vehicle has since been loaded onto the self-propelled launch platform, which is departing soon for the equator. The Sea Launch team suspects nothing. To all external appearances, the satellite is designated for television broadcast services.'

'The aerosol device . . . it was verified as operational?' Kang asked.

'Yes. As you know, we made a number of modifications from the small-scale model that was tested in the Aleutian Islands. There is no longer a dual agent capability, as the deployment of the cyanide mixture was eliminated from the mission. Plus, the system was redesigned with removable canisters that will allow us to arm the payload with the bio-agent just hours before launch. We conducted a final test before the satellite was encapsulated into the nose cone. The results were flawless. We are confident the aerosol system will operate as designed over the target.'

'And you have determined the optimal flight path to achieve maximum dispersal of the agent?' Kang asked.

'As there is no guidance system for the suborbital payload, we are relying on wind, thrust and launch positioning to reach the strike zone. Utilising normal Pacific wind conditions, our Ukrainian engineers have determined that positioning the launch platform approximately four hundred kilometres uprange of the target will maximise the accuracy of delivery. Adjusting for atmospheric conditions at the time of launch, we can expect the payload to disperse from within a five-kilometre radius.'

'Are we positive the US missile defence systems pose no risk?'

'The American antiballistic system is still in its infancy. It is geared towards intercontinental ballistic missiles that are launched from thousands of miles away. They will have no time to react. No, sir, there will be no stopping the payload deployment once we have launched.'

'I am expecting the countdown to occur while the G8 leaders are in the target area,' Kang stated bluntly.

'Weather permitting, we have scheduled the launch to coincide with the pre-summit assembly in Los Angeles,' the engineer said.

'You have done exceptional work.' Kang nodded, indicating that the briefing was over.

The engineer bowed and quietly shuffled out of the study. Tongju rose from his seat and stepped to the front of the large mahogany desk.

'You're assault team is in place?' Kang asked his quiet enforcer.

'Yes, they remained aboard ship in Inchon. I have arranged for a company jet to fly me to an abandoned Japanese airstrip in the Ogasawara Islands, where I will rejoin the *Koguryo* for the operation.'

'Yes, I expect you to lead the assault phase.' Kang paused for a moment. 'We have come too far to risk failure now,' he said sternly. 'I will hold you responsible for the continued secrecy of our operation. That means the Japanese must continue to be painted as the responsible party. And you must destroy the ship after the launch.'

Tongju arched a brow. 'My assault team will be on the ship, as well as your many satellite telecommunications experts . . .'

'It is the way it must be, Tongju,' Kang said. 'Under no condition must the *Koguryo* be apprehended with the crew aboard.'

Tongju nodded, accepting the assignment without question.

'Good luck,' Kang said, rising and escorting him to the door. 'Our homeland is counting on you.'

THE G8 SUMMIT meeting is a forum that was created by former French president Giscard d'Estaing in 1975. It was designed as a conference for the leaders of the major industrialised nations to come together once a year to discuss, in a private and informal setting, global issues like world health, the environment and terrorism.

President Ward of the United States had selected the scenic and tranquil setting of Yosemite National Park as the site of the 2007 summit, which he was hosting, with a glamorous pre-summit reception at a Beverly Hills hotel the day before, to be attended by the current crop of top movie actors and film industry moguls.

What the president and his security advisers had no way of knowing was that the G8 reception in Beverly Hills was ground zero for Kang's missile.

Arcing across the sky from a launch position in the Pacific Ocean, the aerosol dispenser would commence release of its payload as it passed over Santa Monica beach, dumping its deadly agent in a swath across Los Angeles. Over the next twenty-four hours, the virus would disperse and silently launch its internal cellular attack upon unsuspecting victims. There would be no symptoms during the two-week incubation period. Then, suddenly, a frightening horror would strike. With smallpox having been eradicated for over thirty years, health professionals would be slow to identify the culprit.

Kang's scientists had conservatively estimated that twenty per cent of those exposed to the released vapour would succumb to infection. The payload's flight path would expose around 200,000 people to the virus, infecting some 40,000. And they would spread the contagious germs unknowingly during the first few days. In a month, nearly half a million people in Southern California would be fighting the lethal disease.

Fear would spread faster than the smallpox infection itself, in the wake of the shocking images of the president and other G8 world leaders fighting the lethal disease. Federal authorities would assure the nation that sufficient smallpox vaccinations were on hand to inoculate the entire population. But to those already exposed to the virus, the vaccinations would come too late to be of any help. And for everyone else it would turn out to be useless. By virtue of its recombinant strength, the killer bug would prove itself largely immune to the US stockpiled vaccinations.

Tourists and travellers from Los Angeles would unknowingly carry the virus all over the United States and the world at large. With the vaccinations proving ineffective, authorities would resort to mass quarantine. Public gatherings would be banned, travel restrictions imposed. Businesses would be forced to close while local governments curtailed services to avoid debilitating their entire work force. Those who ventured out for food or medicine would only do so clad in rubber gloves and surgical masks. The economic impact would be devastating. Industries would shut down overnight, and in a few short weeks the national output would fall to the level of a third world country.

The highly contagious disease would rip through the armed forces, infecting thousands of soldiers and sailors living in close quarters. For the first time in nearly two centuries, the country's ability to defend itself would be seriously endangered. And the horror would not end there. For hidden in the smallpox outbreak would be the spectre of HIV. Slower acting and less detectable, the HIV would not only made the chimera virus resistant to the smallpox vaccine but it would also wreak further destruction in the surviving victims. Thriving in a weakened immune system, the virus would destroy and alter cells in a barbaric invasion. Yet another wave of death would surge across the country. While the smallpox pandemic would claim a thirty per cent mortality rate, the HIV death rate would reach near ninety per cent.

By the time the chimera ran its course, tens of millions would lie dead in the United States, with untold more deaths around the world. And on the far side of the globe, when South Korea was overrun by its totalitarian neighbour to the north there would be little response from the devastated US aside from a feeble cry of protest.

CUSSLER CAREFULLY threaded the Chinese junk through a maze of midmorning commercial traffic in Inchon Harbour before easing into a small public marina nestled between two large cargo docks. He gave a quick knock on the spare cabin door to wake its slumbering occupants, then brewed a large pot of coffee in the galley as a marina employee refilled the junk's fuel tank.

Summer staggered out into the sunshine on the aft deck, holding the dachshund in her arms. Dirk followed behind, trying to suppress a yawn. Cussler put mugs of coffee in their hands, then ducked below decks for a moment before emerging with a hacksaw.

'Might be a good idea to off-load those handcuffs before going ashore,' he said, grinning.

'I'll be only too happy to dispose of them,' Dirk said as he picked up the hacksaw and began cutting into the shackle on Summer's left wrist. 'You saved our lives back there. Is there anything we can do to repay you?'

'You don't owe me anything,' Cussler replied warmly. 'Just let the government take care of those hoodlums.'

'Can do,' Dirk replied. After sawing through both of Summer's shackles, he relaxed while she and Cussler took turns cutting through his.

'There's a phone in the marina restaurant you can use to call the American embassy if you like. Here, take some Korean *won*. You can use it to make the call and buy a bowl of *kimchi*,' Cussler said, passing Summer a few purple-coloured bills of the national currency.

'Thanks, Mr Cussler. And good luck on your voyage,' Dirk said, shaking the man's hand.

Summer leaned over and kissed the old sailor on the cheek. 'Your kindness was overwhelming,' she told him, then patted the dog goodbye.

'You kids take care. Be seeing you.'

Dirk and Summer stood on the dock and waved as the junk eased out into the harbour. Then they made their way up a set of worn concrete steps to a building that was a combination of marina office, store and restaurant.

Dirk found a phone on the wall in the back and rang NUMA headquarters in Washington. The NUMA operator required only minimal convincing before patching the call through to Rudi Gunn's home line. Gunn had been in bed asleep, but answered the phone on the second ring. After several minutes of animated conversation, Dirk hung up the phone.

'Well?' Summer asked.

Dirk glanced towards the restaurant. 'Let's sample some *kimchi* while we wait for a ride,' he replied, hungrily rubbing his stomach.

They had just finished their meal of hot soup, rice, tofu flavoured with dried seaweed, and *kimchi*, the omnipresent side dish of fermented vegetables, when a pair of US air force security police strode sternly into the restaurant to pick them up and take them to Osan Air Base.

Two hours later, Dirk and Summer were climbing aboard a grey air force transport jet bound for McChord Air Force Base, from where a government plane would transport them on to Washington, DC.

As they settled into their seats, Dirk found an eye mask and a pair of earplugs in the seat back in front of him. Donning the sleep aids, he turned to Summer and said, 'Please don't wake me till we're over land. Preferably land where they don't serve seaweed for breakfast.' He then pulled down the eye mask, stretched out flat in the seat, and promptly fell fast asleep.

THE FIRE was minuscule, burning for less than twenty minutes before it was brought under control, yet the damage had been carefully calculated. Planted by one of Kang's men days before and ignited by a small timer, the tiny fire bomb had splattered its flaming goo about the conduit room, sabotaging the overhead sprinkler system. It was enough to delay the *Sea Launch Commander* from sailing for several days, but not enough to raise suspicions that the cause was anything but accidental.

The pungent smell of an electrical fire still hung over the ship when Danny Stamp arrived at the launch control centre, having been summoned by Captain Christiano. He shook his head as he listened to the damage assessment from the computer operations manager.

'You couldn't have picked a worse place for a fire to break out,' the systems man said in frustration. 'Literally every launch ops computer on the ship runs through the conduit room, as well as most of the test and tracking monitors. We'll have to rewire the whole works.'

'What about the actual hardware?' asked Stamp.

'Well, if you want to call that the good news, there was no damage to any of our hardware resources. Thankfully, our own crew put out the flames before any fire department hoses were let loose on board.'

'In order to go operational, then, we're just talking about restringing the hardware. How long will that take?'

'Three or four weeks at best.'

'You've got eight days,' Stamp replied.

The man nodded slowly. 'Guess I've got to get a few people out of bed,' he muttered, slipping out through a side door.

'Do you think he can do it?' Christiano asked once the door had closed.

'If it can be done, then he'll get us close.'

'What about the *Odyssey*? Do we hold her in port until the damage to the *Commander* is repaired?'

'No,' Stamp said. 'The Zenit is loaded and secured aboard the *Odyssey*, so we'll send her out as planned. We can still make the equator with the *Commander* in half the time the platform will take to get there. And there's no harm in having the *Odyssey* wait on station a few days. It will just give the platform crew more time to prep for the launch. I'll notify the customer of our revised plans. I'm sure I'll have to do a Kabuki dance to keep them calm.'

At six the next morning a NUMA van whisked Dirk and Summer from Andrews Air Force Base through the light early-morning traffic to the head-quarters building.

'Thank God you're safe,' Gunn exclaimed as he greeted them in his office. 'We were turning Japan upside-down looking for you.'

'Nice idea but wrong country,' Summer said.

'There's some folks here who'd like to hear about your ordeal first-hand,' Gunn continued quickly. 'Let's go to the meeting room.'

Gunn led them to a large corner office overlooking the Potomac River where two men were seated on a couch discussing coastal security, while Special Assistant Webster sat in a chair across from them, reviewing a file.

'Dirk, Summer, you remember Jim Webster from Homeland Security. This is Special Agent Peterson and Special Agent Burroughs, from the FBI's counterterrorism division,' Gunn said, motioning a hand towards the two men on the couch. 'They're interested to know what happened to you after the *Sea Rover* was sunk.'

Dirk and Summer settled into a pair of chairs and proceeded to describe the entire course of events, from their imprisonment on board the *Baekje* to their escape on the Chinese junk.

'I just can't believe it,' Webster muttered when they had finished. 'Every shred of evidence we had pointed to a Japanese conspiracy.'

'A well-designed deception,' Dirk stated. 'Kang is a powerful man with considerable resources at his disposal.'

'You are certain he aims to target the United States with a biological attack?' asked Peterson.

'That's what he insinuated and I don't believe he was bluffing. The incident in the Aleutians would seem to have been a test of the technology they've designed to disperse a bioweapon into the air.'

'Only now they've created a deadly combination of viruses—a chimera,' Summer added.

'If the strain is immune to our vaccines, an outbreak could kill millions,' Peterson muttered, shaking his head. The room fell silent for a moment.

'The attack in the Aleutian Islands proves they have the means to disperse the virus. The question is, where would they target a strike?' Gunn asked.

'If we can stop them before they have the chance to strike, then it doesn't matter. We should be raiding Kang's palace, his shipyard and his other businesses right now,' Summer said passionately.

'She's right,' Dirk said. 'For all we know, the weapons are still on board the vessel at the Inchon Shipyard and the story can end there.'

'We'll need to assemble more evidence,' the homeland security man said flatly. 'The Korean authorities will have to be convinced of the risk before we can assemble a joint investigative force.'

Gunn quietly cleared his throat. 'We may be on the verge of providing the necessary evidence,' he said. 'Vice President Sandecker has obtained approval to send in an underwater special ops reconnaissance mission—a SEAL team—in the hope that we'll be able to locate a smoking gun. Unfortunately, with the ruckus over our military deployment in Korea, it's a sensitive time to be nosing around our ally's backyard.'

'All they need to do is snap a picture of the *Baekje* sitting at Kang's dock and we've got proof positive,' Dirk said.

'That would certainly boost our case. When are they going in?' Webster asked.

Gunn looked at his watch, calculating the fourteen-hour difference between Washington and Seoul. 'In about two hours. We should know something early this evening.'

Webster gathered his papers, then stood up. 'I'll be back later for a full debriefing,' he grumbled, then made his way towards the door. As he left the room and vanished down the hall, the others could hear just a single word being muttered repeatedly: 'Korea.'

CHAPTER 8

Webster, Peterson and Boroughs returned to NUMA headquarters at six o'clock that evening and found a subdued scene in Gunn's office. The results of the SEAL team's reconnaissance had just been received, and Gunn, Dirk and Summer sat discussing the report.

'Disappointing news, I'm afraid,' Gunn said. 'The cable ship wasn't there. In fact the dock was completely empty, save for an old tugboat.'

'How could it come and go without being seen?' Webster wondered. 'We've got Interpol and customs authorities on the lookout for that vessel throughout Asia. We're certain the SEAL team didn't misidentify anything?'

'A video feed of the surveillance is being sent by satellite right now, so we can take a look for ourselves on the viewing monitor,' Gunn replied.

For the second time that day, he led a procession to the meeting room. As he approached, he was surprised to hear a familiar laugh emanating from the room as a hazy cloud of smoke drifted out of the open door.

Inside Gunn found Al Giordino sitting on the couch. The NUMA director of underwater technology sat with his legs up on the coffee table, a cigar dangling from his lips. He was dressed in a worn NUMA jumpsuit and, with his dark curly hair askew, looked like he had just stepped off a boat.

'Rudi, we're flogging the crew a little late tonight, aren't we?' Giordino asked before blowing a puff of smoke skywards.

'Somebody's got to mind the store while you're out basking on a warm tropical beach.'

Dirk and Summer grinned as they entered. Giordino was like a favourite uncle. They didn't immediately see their father, who stood at the far end of the corner suite gazing at the lights across the Potomac.

'Dirk, Summer!' Dirk Pitt Senior gave a broad grin, his green eyes glowing with warmth as he threw his arms round his children.

'Dad, we thought you and Al were still in the Philippines,' Summer said, after giving her father a hug and a peck on the cheek.

'Are you kidding?' Giordino piped up. 'The old man practically swam across the Pacific to get here when he heard you were missing.'

The elder Pitt smiled. 'I was just jealous of you two taking a tour of Northeast Asia without me,' he said, grinning.

In the presence of his two kids, Pitt seemed radiant. His professional life had seen much upheaval recently. With Admiral Sandecker unexpectedly taking the vice presidency, Pitt had suddenly been thrust into the top spot at NUMA. As special projects director, he had experienced several lifetimes' worth of adventure and challenges. The hazards had taken a toll on him, both physically and mentally, and he was glad to be easing back from the more vigorous demands of the job. As NUMA's chief director, his administrative and political duties often exceeded his interest in them, but Pitt ensured that he and Al still spent plenty of time in the field.

'Dad, what's the situation with the toxic Japanese cargo ship in the Philippines?' Dirk asked. 'I understand that it was leaky chemical munitions causing the reef kill.'

'That's right, a mixture of mustard and lewisite left over from World War Two. We have the leak contained. Nobody was volunteering to conduct a costly removal of the munitions, so we did the next best thing—bury them.'

'As long as nobody goes digging around down there, there should be no more toxic leakage and the reef should rejuvenate in a few years,' said Al.

An administrative aide poked her head through the door and spoke to Gunn. 'Sir, the video feed from the Pentagon is available for viewing now.'

Gunn seized the moment to introduce the Homeland Security and FBI men to Pitt and Giordino, then herded everyone towards a large, flat monitor and typed in a few quick commands on a keyboard. The screen was suddenly illuminated with the image of a large, enclosed dockyard. The camera's eye panned round the facility, showing a series of empty berths. After less than a minute, the video ended and the screen went blank.

'That's Kang's facility, no doubt about it. But there's no sign of the *Baekje*,' Dirk said.

'Interpol and the Korean National Police confirm that no vessel matching the *Baekje*'s description has been seen entering or departing Inchon port,' Webster said.

'Someone's on the take,' Giordino sneered.

Webster gave an indignant look. 'A remote possibility but not likely. Inchon is not a large port. Somebody should have seen her depart.'

'She may have made a stealthy getaway right after Dirk and Summer left the ship,' Gunn conjectured. 'Before the Interpol alert.'

'There's another possibility,' Pitt suggested. 'The ship may have been camouflaged, and may have sailed out of port in broad daylight.'

'The fact remains that without the ship we have insufficient evidence to make a move against Kang,' Webster said. 'The proof has to be ironclad as there's a serious political problem with South Korea right now. The threat of losing our military presence in Korea is very real, and nobody wants to jeopardise a precarious situation at this juncture.'

'What does the admiral have to say about this?' Pitt asked.

Gunn shook his head. 'Admiral . . . er, Vice President Sandecker has informed me that intelligence reports have revealed secret business dealings between Kang and the president of South Korea, but President Ward is afraid that instigating an investigation might lose him the National Assembly vote to keep US troops in South Korea.'

'Doesn't he understand the magnitude of the risk involved with the weapons Kang possesses?' Summer asked incredulously.

Gunn nodded. 'The President has stated that once the resolution has been voted upon, he will request a full investigation into the sinking of the *Sea Rover* and Kang's connections to North Korea. In the meantime, he has authorised Homeland Security to introduce heightened security, with emphasis on aircraft and marine traffic arriving from Japan and South Korea.'

The younger Pitt began pacing the room in frustration. 'Promoting the removal of US forces from South Korea is part of Kang's strategy, using the perceived terrorist threat from Japan as a diversion. Don't you see? If he's going to attempt a strike on the US, it will happen before the vote comes up in the National Assembly.'

'Which is just ten days from now,' Gunn said.

'Then we have to anticipate Kang's next move,' Pitt Senior injected calmly. 'We know he operates a large shipping line, so it would figure that he would try to bring the weapons in via a commercial freighter.'

'Much easier than smuggling them in on a plane,' Giordino agreed. 'Probably send them over on a Japanese-flagged carrier.'

'Or perhaps the elusive *Baekje*,' Dirk added.

'I'll see that customs are primed for the necessary port inspections,' Gunn said.

'That may still be too late,' Pitt replied. 'They could release the agent as they're sailing into port.'

'Or even before that. The release in the Aleutians was launched by boat offshore,' his son added. 'Can the Coast Guard board and inspect offshore commercial vessels?'

'I do not believe that the Coast Guard's resources are sufficient for that to be considered part of their security mission.'

'There is another option,' Pitt said, reaching into a desk drawer and withdrawing a daily report of NUMA research vessel assignments. 'Let's see. The *Pacific Explorer* just arrived in Vancouver, the *Blue Gill* is conducting a marine survey off San Francisco, and *Deep Endeavor* is testing a submersible in San Diego. I could reassign those three vessels to be in position off the major West Coast ports, assisting the Coast Guard, in two days.'

'I'm sure they would be grateful for the support,' Webster said.

'Call it a temporary loan,' Gunn added, eyeing Webster with a sharklike grin. 'Until we can work out some sort of compensation.'

'It's settled then,' Pitt concluded. 'The NUMA fleet will initiate offshore bomb-sniffing exercises at once.'

THE *KOGURYO* raced across the Pacific like a greyhound, her four diesel engines propelling her along at twenty-one knots. Since departing Inchon she'd made only one diversion—to the Ogasawara Islands to retrieve Tongju.

On board, the large team of engineers and technicians readied themselves for the coming Zenit rocket launch. A launch control centre, nearly an exact duplicate of the control room on the *Sea Launch Commander*, had been constructed on the lower deck and was the site of continuous activity. Told only that they would be controlling the launch of a Kang satellite from a floating platform, the team had no idea of their illicit mission.

Tongju utilised the time at sea to hone his tactics for the assault on the *Odyssey*. He and his commando team pored over blueprints of the launch platform, calculating strike positions and coordinating movements until they had a minute-by-minute plan of attack. After an evening meal with his assault team, Tongju invited his second-in-command, Kim, back to his cabin. There he explained Kang's order to scuttle the *Koguryo*.

'I have provided Captain Lee with the position for the rendezvous with the waiting freighter. I did not inform him of the plan to sink his ship, only that we would be transferring the launch crew to the other vessel for safety.'

'You do not trust his obedience to Kang?' Kim asked, unaffected by the prospect of murdering 200 of his fellow shipmates.

'No, it is not wise. No sea captain desires to sink his own ship and abandon his crew. We shall make our escape without him.'

'How is the ship to be destroyed?'

Tongju reached under his cot and pulled out a small satchel, which he handed to Kim. 'Semtex plastic explosives with wireless detonators. I intend to activate the charges while the ship is in motion.'

'And what about us?' Kim asked, uncertainty creeping into his voice.

'You and two others will leave with me on the assault boat. I will convince Lee to let us depart the ship for an advanced surveillance check once the attack on the *Odyssey* is complete. When he has brought the *Koguryo* up to speed and turned for home, we will detonate the charges.'

'It will not be easy to abandon my assault team,' Kim said quietly.

'They are all good men but expendable. I will leave it to you to pick the two to join us. But first you must get the explosives planted. Set the charges in the forward bow. And don't let any of the ship's crew observe you.'

'It will be done,' Kim said, then left the cabin, grasping the satchel tightly.

THE *ODYSSEY* cruised due west of San Diego shortly before midnight and soon afterwards departed the territorial waters of the United States. Towering nearly 100 feet above the water, the converted North Sea oil platform rode atop five thick support columns. The base of the columns rested upon a huge pair of underwater pontoons, each over 400 feet in length, making the *Odyssey* the largest catamaran-style vessel in the world.

By the end of her third day at sea, the *Odyssey* shared a desolate section of the Pacific Ocean with only one small dot of a vessel on the northeast horizon. In the fading dusk, Captain Hennessey watched with interest as the distant speck slowly grew larger, bearing down on them on a southerly heading. When it approached within five miles, he aimed his binoculars at it and saw a stout blue ship that looked more like a special purpose research vessel than a commercial freighter. He noted with annoyance that the ship was on a collision course with the *Odyssey*'s current heading.

'The whole empty Pacific Ocean around us and he's got to run right down our path,' he muttered, shaking his head.

For the next hour he watched the other vessel inch to within a mile of his starboard flank before slowing and changing course towards the southwest.

The thought never occurred to him that it was anything more than a coincidental encounter. Nor would he ever suspect that a trusted crewman—one of a handful of Kang's men working on board as launch technicians—was feeding the *Odyssey*'s exact position to the *Koguryo* using a simple portable radio transmitter.

As the lights of the unknown ship twinkled off the *Odyssey*'s port stern, Hennessey put it out of his mind and focused on the empty blackness before him. They were still nearly ten days away from the equator, and there was no telling what other obstacles might cross their path.

THE ASSAULT TEAM came quickly, in the dark of night. After shadowing the *Odyssey* for most of the evening, the *Koguryo* had suddenly stopped its engines, letting the launch platform churn on towards the horizon.

Far from changing course, the *Koguryo* had stopped to launch its high-speed tender. The open-decked thirty-foot boat was a luxurious assault craft for Tongju, Kim and a dozen other men dressed in black commando outfits, and a fast and stable means of crossing open water to attack the platform. As the tender bounded across the rolling waves under a bright canopy of stars, it gobbled up the distance to the moving platform, which was lit up against the night sky like Times Square.

As the tender's pilot approached the shadow of the platform, he steered the boat under the massive structure, threading between the *Odyssey*'s twin pontoons. Slowing to match speed with the launch platform, he steered to where a salt-encrusted steel stairway led to the heights above. When he had edged to within a few feet of it, one of the commandos leapt from the bow and quickly tied a line to the stairwell post. One by one, the remaining commandos jumped onto the stairwell and began the climb to the platform above, pausing at the top to regroup before Tongju nodded his head to proceed. The stairwell door had been left unlocked by one of Kang's men, and the commandos quickly slipped through and fanned out across the deck.

Most of the forty-two-man crew aboard the *Odyssey* had little to do until the platform reached the launch site, and they were idly reading, playing cards, or watching movies. When a group of commandos struck the crew's quarters, the confused technicians were too stunned to react as they were rounded up at gunpoint.

In the hangar, it was a similar story. A small commando team swept through the building that housed the cradled Zenit rocket, rounding up the handful of engineers without a fight. On the bridge, the two men manning the helm couldn't believe their eyes when Tongju walked in and levelled his Glock pistol at the executive officer's ear. Even Captain Hennessey was roughly bound and forced to the galley in shock, with the rest of his crew. In less than ten minutes, the entire platform had been secured by Tongju's men without a shot being fired.

On the bridge, Tongju radioed the *Koguryo* that the platform had been taken with no resistance. Examining a navigation chart left on a side table, he barked at Kang's crewman, who was now manning the helm.

'Revise bearing to fifteen degrees north-northeast. We are diverting to a new launch site.'

IT TOOK just under twenty-four hours to convert the Zenit rocket's payload into a weapon of mass destruction. The engineering team carefully replaced the inner workings of the mock satellite with small electric pumps, which would drive the aerosol system. Lines and fittings were attached to the phoney solar panels, which would open in flight to spread the rejuvenated virus, disseminating it as a fine mist across the California sky.

Working in protective suits, the technicians performed the final step of the operation: inserting the chimera into the payload vehicle. Under Tongju's supervision, the deadly virus had been carefully transferred across from the *Koguryo* in special canisters, along with a dozen payload specialists. When activated, a software-controlled procedure would vacuum-mix the powdered substance with purified water, ready for transfer into the atmosphere.

With the deadly cocktail loaded aboard, the payload fairing was reassembled around the satellite. Propellant explosives were inserted at key points inside the fairing to blast the payload doors away at the appointed moment during flight. Then the final section of the nose cone was sealed into place. A few precious hours of sleep was all the tired engineering team could allow themselves before the start of the final countdown.

AT VICE PRESIDENT Sandecker's insistence, all available Coast Guard cutters were put to sea along the West Coast, concentrated around the commercial hubs of Seattle, San Francisco and Los Angeles, and ordered to board and search all Japanese- or Korean-flagged inbound ships.

In San Francisco, Rudi Gunn coordinated NUMA's interdiction support with the local Coast Guard commandant. The research vessel *Blue Gill* was assigned to picket duty ten miles off the Golden Gate Bridge.

Meanwhile, Dirk and Summer flew to San Diego, and quickly joined *Deep Endeavor*, which was moored on a large municipal dock. As they approached the ship, Dirk noticed that an odd-shaped submersible, painted bright red, sat on the vessel's stern deck.

'Well, if it isn't the Prisoners of Zenda,' Jack Dahlgren called from the bridge upon spotting the twosome boarding the ship. 'Heard you two enjoyed a seaside tour of the Korean Peninsula!' Dirk's friend hopped down a stairwell and met them at the head of the gangway, where he shook Dirk's hand firmly, then gave Summer a hug. 'So, let's do a little search-and-seizure work. We're ready to shove off.'

'Good. Let's get after it.'

Dahlgren escorted Dirk and Summer up to the bridge, where they were greeted by Leo Delgado and Captain Burch, then introduced to a uniformed Coast Guard marshal with cropped blond hair, named Aimes.

'What's our intercept procedure, Lieutenant?' Dirk asked, noting the insignia on Aimes's uniform.

'Call me Bill,' replied Aimes. 'We'll be assisting the regional Coast Guard vessels, when and if commercial traffic gets heavy. Otherwise, we'll be assigned to ad hoc reconnaissance. I will lead all boardings and searches with my team but will be assisted by your crewmen. We have been ordered to patrol a quadrant southwest of the Port of Los Angeles and, once on site, we'll coordinate our positioning through *Icarus*.'

'*Icarus*?' Dahlgren asked.

'Our all-seeing eye in the sky,' Dirk said with a knowing smile.

DEEP ENDEAVOR steamed up the California coast for three hours before turning out to sea. Dirk stood on the bridge, watching the ship's progress on a colour navigation monitor. As the coastline fell away, he observed the island of San Clemente scroll up on the map.

He turned to Aimes. 'I thought your interdictions were to be restricted to no more than twelve miles from the coast. We're headed by San Clemente Island, which is over fifty miles from the mainland.'

'For normal coastal duty we recognise the twelve-mile limit. The Channel Islands are technically a part of California, however, so legally we can operate within a twelve-mile range of them.'

Two hours later, they cruised beyond the large island of Catalina and the engines slowed as they began their patrol.

'We are positioned well south of the main shipping lane to LA and not likely to catch much night traffic in this quadrant,' Aimes said. 'We'll get tossed into the fray in the morning when *Icarus* shows up. In the meantime, I suggest we take shifts and get some sleep.'

BY 9.00 P.M. the *Odyssey* was approaching her new launch position. Tongju, catching up on some lost sleep in Captain Hennessey's cabin, was startled awake by a rapid pounding at the door.

An armed commando entered the room and bowed. 'So sorry to intrude,' he apologised. 'Captain Lee has requested that you return to the *Koguryo* at once. There is some sort of dispute with the Russian launch engineers.'

Tongju nodded, and made his way to the pilothouse, where he radioed for the *Koguryo*'s tender. A short ride took him to the nearby support ship.

Captain Lee was waiting for him. 'Come with me to the launch control centre. It's those damn Russians,' the captain cursed. 'They can't agree on where to position the platform for launch.'

The two men made their way down a flight of stairs and along a passageway. As Lee opened a door, a loud staccato burst of foreign swearing met their ears. At the centre of the room, a group of engineers was in a huddle with two Ukrainian launch specialists, arguing violently. The group parted as Tongju and Lee approached, and fell silent.

'What is the issue here?' Tongju growled.

One of the Ukrainians answered: 'It is the weather. The high-pressure front over the eastern Pacific has stalled because of the push from a low-pressure system in the south, causing the normally prevailing high-altitude easterly winds to reverse. As a result, we are facing a strong head wind, which has thrown off our planned mission flight profile by a considerable margin.' He pulled out a sheet of paper bearing handwritten calculations. 'Our planned launch position was three hundred kilometres west of Los Angeles. We now have two options: wait for the low pressure front to yield to the prevailing winds or reposition the launch platform closer to the target.'

'There's a third option,' the other Ukrainian stated irritably. 'We can increase the fuel load in the Zenit to reach the target from the original launch position.' As he spoke, his counterpart shook his head silently.

'What is the risk of that?' Tongju asked the doubter.

'Sergei is correct in that we can adjust the fuel load to reach the target from the original launch position. However, I have grave doubts about the accuracy that we would achieve. We do not know the wind conditions for the entire flight trajectory. The launch vehicle could easily be diverted from the target by a large deviation.'

Tongju contemplated the matter for a moment, then made his decision. 'We can ill afford to sit and wait for the weather to change, nor can we risk diluting the target strike. We shall move the platform closer to the target and initiate countdown as soon as possible.'

'Based on our latest wind measurements, we must position ourselves one hundred and five kilometres from the coast.'

Tongju thought for a minute. The proposed position was dangerously near the coastline, and there were offshore islands in close proximity. But they could reach the spot and still launch within Kang's desired time schedule. 'Alter course at once. We will position both vessels at the new position before dawn and initiate launch countdown at daybreak.'

'You've got to be kidding me. A blimp?' Giordino shook his head at Pitt. 'You dragged me all the way to LA to go for a ride in a blimp?'

He had wondered what Pitt had up his sleeve after the two had arrived at Los Angeles airport after a flight from Washington. Rather than head south towards the Port of Los Angeles, Pitt had driven their rental car north. Now they were entering the tiny Oxnard Airport.

'I believe the preferred term is *airship*,' Pitt said, throwing his partner a look of mock indignation as he parked the car. 'And I'll have you know that it's the latest in surveillance and tracking technology.'

Unlike the rigidly framed dirigibles of the twenties and thirties, which relied on highly flammable hydrogen for lift, the 222-foot long Sentinel 1000 suspended in front of them used the safer element of helium. 'She's fitted with a LASH optical system,' Pitt continued. 'NUMA is testing her out for possible use on coral reef and tide surveys. The system has already been used successfully to track migrating whales.'

'What is a LASH system?'

'Stands for Littoral Airborne Sensor-Hyperspectral. It's an optical imaging system that uses a breakdown in the colour band to detect and track targets that the eye cannot see.'

A ground crewman wearing a NUMA identification badge climbed out of the gondola of the silver-skinned airship as Pitt and Giordino approached.

'Mr Pitt? We've installed the radio set that the Coast Guard sent up, so you'll be able to conduct secure communications with their vessels. *Icarus* is also fitted with a water ballast system and an experimental fuel dump release, should you need emergency lift.'

'How long can we stay aloft?' Giordino asked, eyeing a pair of ducted propellers jutting from either side of the gondola's aft section.

'Eight to ten hours, if you go easy on the throttles. Enjoy your flight. She's a joy to fly,' he said, bowing slightly.

Pitt and Giordino climbed through the gondola door and into a spacious passenger cabin. Squirming through a forward opening into the flight compartment, Pitt took up the controls while Giordino dropped into the co-pilot's seat.

'Ready for take off, Wilbur?' Pitt asked.

'Ready when you are, Orville.'

Pitt started the pair of turbocharged Porsche 930 air-cooled engines and they gave a muffled roar. Outside the gondola, *Icarus*'s support crew took up positions round the airship. A pair of ropes attached to its nose were pulled taut by three men standing off either side of the bow, while four additional men grabbed onto side rails running the length of the gondola. At Pitt's command, the crew chief signalled to another crewman, standing high atop the mooring mast, to release the nose tether. In unison, the ground crew then tugged at the weightless airship, walking it to a safe launching point several dozen yards away from the mooring mast.

Pitt gave a thumbs-up signal to the crew chief, then reached over and pulled down a pair of levers protruding from the centre console, increasing the throttle to the twin engines. As the ground crew let go of their lines and moved clear, he gently pulled back on a yoke control, so tilting the churning motor-driven propellers to an angle that gave additional lift. *Icarus* began to rise. Giordino cheerfully waved out of an open side window to the ground crew, who shrank to the size of bugs as the airship gained altitude.

Pitt steered the airship directly offshore from Oxnard after leaving the airport, and soon levelled the blimp off at a height of 2,500 feet. The Pacific Ocean was a deep aqua colour under a bright sun, and the men easily spotted the northerly Channel Islands of Santa Cruz, Santa Rosa and San Miguel under the clear skies.

As they floated east, Pitt glanced at the helium pressure gauge, noting a slight rise as the helium expanded in the warming temperatures and at higher cruising altitude. An automatic venting system would release any excess gas if the pressure rose too high.

When they were thirty miles offshore, Pitt angled the airship south and began navigating a large, lazy arc off Los Angeles. On his laptop computer Giordino powered up the LASH optical system, which enabled him to spot the images of incoming surface vessels up to thirty-five miles away. A constant stream of freighters and container ships came chugging in towards the ports of Los Angeles and Long Beach. Giordino reported that he could see two large inbound vessels that he figured to be commercial ships of the size they were looking for.

'Let's go take a look,' Pitt said, turning the airship towards the approaching ships. Flicking a button on the Coast Guard radio set installed in the cockpit, he spoke into his headset. 'Coast Guard Cutter *Halibut*, this is airship *Icarus*. We are on station and preparing to survey two inbound vessels.'

'Roger, *Icarus*,' came a deep-voiced reply. 'Glad to have you and your eyes in the sky with us. We have three vessels deployed and engaged in interdiction actions. We'll await your surveillance reports on new inbound vessels as they approach. Out.'

AFTER RESOLVING the launch position dispute, Tongju had returned to the *Odyssey* and stolen a few more hours of sleep. Throughout the night, the launch platform continued to inch her way closer to the California coast. An hour before dawn the radio crackled with the voice of Captain Lee on the *Koguryo*. 'We are approaching the launch site. Prepare to halt engines, and we will take up position to the southeast of you. We will be standing by to initiate launch countdown at your direction.'

'Affirmative,' Tongju replied. 'We will set position and ballast the platform. Stand by for positioning.'

He turned and nodded to one of Kang's undercover crewmen, who was piloting the *Odyssey*. With skilled confidence, the man eased off the throttle, then activated a computer-controlled system of forward, side and rear thrusters, locking the *Odyssey* in a fixed position.

'Position control activated,' the helmsman barked in a crisp voice. 'Initiating ballast flooding,' he continued, pushing a series of buttons.

Two hundred feet below the pilothouse, a series of gate valves were automatically opened inside the twin pontoons, and half a dozen computer-controlled pumps began pumping salt water into the hollow steel hulls. In sixty minutes the platform had dropped forty-six feet, the bottom of its twin hulls now submerged to a stabilising depth seventy feet below the surface.

The helmsman stood back from the console. 'Flooding complete. Platform is stabilised for launch,' he reported.

Tongju entered a small elevator at the rear of the bridge, which he rode to the deck on which the hangar was housed. Inside the huge space, a dozen or so engineers were hovering around the horizontal rocket, examining an array of computer stations that were wired directly into the launch vehicle. Tongju approached a thick-haired man with round glasses named Ling, who headed up the launch operations team.

'Is the rocket ready to be transported to the launch tower?' he asked.

Ling nodded enthusiastically. 'We have been awaiting word.'

'Proceed at once. Notify me when you are ready to evacuate the platform.'

'Yes, of course,' Ling replied, then hurried over to speak to a group of engineers, who quickly scattered to their posts. Tongju stood and watched as the massive hangar doors opened, revealing a set of rails that led across the deck to the launch tower at the opposite end of the platform. A series of electrical motors were started, which reverberated loudly off the hangar's interior walls. Tongju walked over to the main console panel and peered over Ling's shoulder as the launch leader's hands danced over the controls.

The 200-foot horizontal rocket rocked sluggishly towards the hangar doors, its support cradle creeping forward on a mass of wheels that churned like the legs of a centipede. Tongju strolled alongside.

The launch vehicle ground to a halt as it reached the base of the launch tower. The transporter was locked in place and then the lifting mechanism engaged and the rocket slowly tilted upright, until it stood vertically against the launch tower. Workmen on the tower then plugged in a series of data cables that allowed the engineers on the *Koguryo* to monitor the dozens of electronic sensors embedded under the rocket's skin. Once the Zenit was upright, the support cradle was gently eased away and returned to the hangar.

Ling spoke by radio to the launch control centre on the *Koguryo* before dashing over to Tongju. 'The launch vehicle meets all major prelaunch parameters,' he reported.

Tongju looked up at the towering rocket with its deadly payload. He relished this moment of power. 'Very well,' he said. 'Begin the countdown.'

TWO THOUSAND feet above the Pacific, silver-skinned *Icarus* floated gracefully onwards across the sky at thirty-five miles per hour. The vessels that Pitt and Giordino had checked on from the air had turned out to be perfectly benign. Giordino now pointed at a turquoise ship in the distance. 'There's *Deep Endeavor*. I wonder what she's up to.

'Let's find out.' Pitt guided the airship towards the NUMA ship, calling it up on the radio. '*Icarus* to *Deep Endeavor*. How's the fishing down there?'

'Nary a nibble,' Captain Burch's voice replied. After two days of interdiction support duty, the crew of *Deep Endeavor* had been requested to board and search only one ship, a small freighter from the Philippines carrying timber. 'How are you gentlemen enjoying your sightseeing?'

'Delightful, except for Al's incessant crunching of caviar, which is interrupting my enjoyment of the in-flight movie. We'll see if we can't rustle you up some more business.'

'Roger, we'd be much obliged.'

Giordino examined the LASH screen on the laptop. 'Looks like we've got an inbound vessel in the main shipping channel about twenty-two miles to the northwest, and a couple of stationary targets eighteen miles to the west of us,' he said, pointing to some grey and white patches on the monitor.

Pitt looked at the laptop. 'Let's go see what's parked out there first,' he replied, aiming the airship towards the two large smudges on the screen that were sitting oddly still.

TONGJU STOOD near the base of the launch tower and gazed over at a large digital clock mounted on the roof line of the hangar. The red illuminated numbers read 03:32:17, with the digits clicking down a second at a time. Three hours and thirty-two minutes until lift off. There would be no halting the launch now.

But before the ignition button could be pushed, Ling and his engineers had to transfer to the *Koguryo*, where they would complete the launch from the *Koguryo*'s launch control centre. There was also the transfer of the *Odyssey*'s own command system to be made, which would allow the launch platform to be remotely controlled after all personnel were evacuated.

Once all the controls had been passed to the support ship, Ling approached Tongju on the deck. 'My work here is complete. My team and I must return to the *Koguryo*.'

Tongju glanced again at the countdown clock. 'My compliments. You are ahead of schedule. I will call for the *Koguryo*'s tender, and you may take your men off the platform at once.'

'THERE'S NOT supposed to be an oil platform located here.' Giordino's eyes shifted from the large square object on the water ahead of them to a chart on his lap. 'No man-made hazards are indicated in this region at all.'

'And that oil platform has a rocket aboard,' Pitt commented drily.

Giordino squinted out of the airship's windshield towards the platform. 'Well, I'll be . . . Give that man with the eagle eye a cookie.'

Pitt turned the airship in a loop around the platform and adjacent support ship, careful to avoid its airspace. Then he punched a switch on a marine band radio and hailed the platform. 'Airship *Icarus* to Sea Launch platform. Over.'

A pause ensued and then Pitt repeated the call. After another lull, an accented voice replied, 'This is Sea Launch platform *Odyssey*. Over.'

'*Odyssey*, what is your status? Do you require assistance? Over.'

Another long pause. 'Who is requesting information? Over.'

'This is airship *Icarus*, supporting Coast Guard border security. Please identify status. Over.'

'This is *Odyssey*. We are conducting satellite system tests. Please stay clear. Over and out.'

'Friendly sorts, aren't they?' said Giordino. 'D'you want to stick around?'

'I guess there's not much we can do from up here. We'd better just do our job and play tag with the next inbound vessel. But let's have one of the boys downstairs check this out.'

Giordino took the radio as Pitt turned the airship northwards. After a few minutes of calls to other vessels, Giordino reported: '*Deep Endeavor* and the Coast Guard cutter *Narwhal* are working this region. *Deep Endeavor* is still searching a Japanese freighter. The *Narwhal* is freed up at the moment, but he says the platform is outside their twelve-mile operating limit.'

'We're not asking for a boarding. Just request a visual survey and verification with Sea Launch authorities.'

Giordino spoke into the radio again, then turned to Pitt. '*Narwhal* is on her way.'

'Good,' Pitt replied, watching the platform fade into the distance. A nagging sensation told him they had missed something on their fly-past. Something important.

THREE MILES AWAY, Lieutenant Bruce Carr Smith braced himself against a bulkhead on the *Narwhal*'s cramped bridge as the Barracuda-class patrol boat lurched over a swell, her bow slapping the sea with a spray of foam. With their mission focused primarily on inspection and sea rescue, the boat's crew of ten was only lightly armed.

'Lieutenant, I've radioed command headquarters. They're going to contact the Sea Launch port office to determine what's up with that platform,' the *Narwhal*'s communications officer stated.

Smith nodded, then spoke to his helmsman. 'Steady as she goes,' he said.

The two dots on the horizon gradually grew larger, until the distinct shapes of an oil platform and a utility ship came into focus. Smith could see that the ship was in fact now moving away from the stationary platform. He took a quick glance over his shoulder and saw that in the distance *Deep Endeavor* appeared to be following his path.

'Bring us alongside the platform for starters, then we'll go take a look at the ship,' Smith told the helmsman as they drew nearer.

The small patrol boat slowed as it eased near the platform. Smith looked in awe at the huge Zenit rocket standing at its launch tower. Peering through binoculars, he studied the platform's deck but saw no signs of life. Surveying the forward section, however, he caught sight of the countdown clock, which now read 01:32:00.

'What the hell?' he muttered as he watched the digital numbers tick lower. Grabbing the marine transmitter, he called to the *Odyssey*.

'Sea Launch platform, this is Coast Guard cutter *Narwhal* Over.' After a pause, he tried again. But met only with silence.

'SEA LAUNCH Director of Information, how may I help you?' a feminine voice answered over the phone line.

'This is the Eleventh District US Coast Guard, Los Angeles, central dispatch. We're requesting mission and location status of Sea Launch vessels *Odyssey* and *Sea Launch Commander*, please.'

'One moment.' The information director shuffled through some papers on her desk. 'Here we are. The launch platform *Odyssey* is on route to her designated launch site in the western Pacific, near the equator. Her last reported position, as of eight a.m. this morning, was eighteen degrees north latitude, one hundred and thirty-two degrees west longitude, east-southeast of Honolulu, Hawaii. The command ship *Sea Launch Commander* is presently at port in Long Beach undergoing minor repairs. She is expected to depart port tomorrow morning to rendezvous with the *Odyssey* for the launch of the Koreasat 2 satellite in eight days.'

'Neither vessel is currently located off the Californian coast?'

'Why, no, of course not.'

'Thank you for the information, ma'am.'

'You're welcome,' the director replied before hanging up, wondering why the Coast Guard would think the platform was anywhere near California.

LIEUTENANT SMITH was too anxious to wait for a response from the Los Angeles Coast Guard Group's headquarters, and brought his vessel closer to the platform. Annoyed at the lack of response from the *Odyssey*, he turned his attention towards the support ship, which had now crept a quarter mile of a away. But repeated radio calls to the ship went unanswered.

'Sir, she's flying a Japanese flag,' the helmsman noted.

'No excuse for ignoring a marine radio call. Move alongside the vessel and I'll talk to them over the PA system,' Smith ordered.

As the *Narwhal* moved out from the shadow of the platform, pandemonium struck. Coast Guard headquarters broke over the *Narwhal*'s radio with word that the *Odyssey* was reported to be a thousand miles away from California and that her support ship was sitting docked in Long Beach. At the same moment, aboard the *Koguryo*, crewmen pushed aside a lower deck siding, revealing a row of torpedoes pointing at the *Narwhal*.

Smith was barking orders before he even realised the words were out of his lips. 'Hard to port! Apply full power! Prepare for evasive manoeuvres!'

But it was too late. The helmsman was just able to swing the *Narwhal* broadside to the *Koguryo* when a plume of white smoke suddenly billowed from the larger ship's lower deck and a bright flash burst forth. Out of the smoke, a surface-to-surface missile erupted from its launch tube, moving horizontally away from the ship. Smith had the distinct sensation of being shot between the eyes.

The small cutter stood no chance. The *Narwhal* exploded in a massive fireball, and fifteen minutes later slipped under the surface.

CHAPTER 9

'**M**y God, they've fired a missile at the *Narwhal*!' Captain Burch cried out as he watched the Coast Guard ship disappear in a cloud of smoke two miles ahead of the *Deep Endeavor*.

Summer grabbed a pair of binoculars, but there was little to be seen apart from a thick veil of smoke.

'There may be survivors in the water,' Aimes stuttered, stunned at the sudden demise of a boat and crew he knew well.

'I daren't move any closer,' Captain Burch replied. 'We're completely unarmed and they may well be aiming their next missile at us as we speak.' Burch ordered his helmsman to hold their present position.

Delgado spoke to Aimes. 'The captain is right. We can't endanger our crew. We don't know who or what we are up against.'

'It's Kang's men,' Summer said, handing the binoculars to Dirk.

'You're sure?' Aimes asked.

'She's right,' Dirk said slowly surveying the vessels. 'The support ship. I'll bet my next paycheque it's the same vessel that sank the *Sea Rover*. She's even flying a Japanese flag. But they've painted and reconfigured her.'

'Why are they standing off here with the platform?' Aimes asked.

'There can only be one reason. They are preparing to launch a strike with the Sea Launch rocket.'

Silence fell across the bridge as the gravity of the situation sunk in.

'Aimes, you need to get some help out here, and now,' Dirk said firmly. 'I'll go see if there are any survivors.'

Delgado looked at Dirk with a furrowed brow. 'But we don't dare bring *Deep Endeavor* any closer,' he cautioned.

'I don't intend to,' Dirk replied as he quickly exited the bridge.

TONGJU GAZED down from the *Odyssey*'s bridge at the smouldering debris of the Coast Guard vessel and silently cursed the Ukrainian engineers for moving the launch site closer to shore, conveniently forgetting that the final decision had been his.

A radio call from the *Koguryo* broke his thoughts.

'This is Lee. We destroyed the enemy vessel, as you directed. There is another vessel, believed to be a research ship, standing off two thousand metres. Do you wish us to destroy her also?'

'No. Save your armament, we may need it later.'

'As you wish. Ling reports that his launch team is securely aboard the *Koguryo*. Are you ready to evacuate the platform?'

'Yes. Send the tender back to the platform; my remaining team will be ready to evacuate shortly. Out.' Tongju hung up the radio transmitter, then turned to a commando standing at the rear of the bridge. 'Transfer the Sea Launch prisoners to the hangar and lock them in the storage bay. Then assemble the assault team for transport back to the *Koguryo*.'

The commando nodded, then slipped out of the rear of the bridge. Tongju slowly walked across the pilothouse to an array of marine electronics. Finding the panel that contained the manual override switches, he pulled out a combat knife and prised open the cover with its blade. Grasping a bundle of wires inside, he yanked the serrated edge of his knife through them, rendering the switches useless. Then he gathered up half a dozen keyboards attached to various navigational and positioning computers and tossed them through an open window. Tongju had disabled the computers in the pilothouse, destroying any possibility of last-minute intervention. With less than an hour to liftoff, all control of the platform and the rocket was now in the hands of the crew of the *Koguryo*.

'LET ME GO with you,' Summer said.

'It's just a two-seater, and Jack is the only one with experience in this thing. It's better that he and I go,' Dirk replied, nodding towards Dahlgren as he prepared the *Badger*, *Deep Endeavor*'s deep probe submersible, for launching. Grabbing his sister's hand, he looked deeply into her pearl-grey eyes. 'Get hold of Dad. Tell him we need help right away.'

'Be careful,' she said, giving Dirk a quick embrace.

Quickly he climbed into the ten-foot-long metallic red submersible, where Dahlgren was waiting in the copilot's seat with the motors fully powered up and ready to go.

On the stern of *Deep Endeavor*, a crane operator lifted the *Badger* off the ship's deck and over the side, dropping it into the ocean. The bullet-shaped vessel was dotted with a series of propulsion blades and from its nose a giant coring device protruded like a unicorn's horn. Luckily, the submersible was effectively blocked from the platform's view by *Deep Endeavor*'s super-structure and they were deployed without being seen.

'Let's see what she'll deliver,' Dirk said to Dahlgren, pushing the throt-tles to their stops as soon as the cable hook was released.

The submersible surged forward amid a whine of electric motors and rushing water. Dirk adjusted a pair of diving planes slightly until they were at a submerged depth of twenty feet, then followed a compass-directed path towards the wreck of the *Narwhal*.

A minute later he eased off the throttles, throwing the motors into idle as the *Badger*'s forward momentum waned. As they floated to the surface, Dahlgren adjusted the ballast tanks. Under his expert touch, the sub-mersible rose to show less than a foot of its topside above the water.

A few yards in front of them, they could see the floating debris that remained from the *Narwhal*, but there was no sign of life in the water. Dahlgren solemnly radioed Aimes on *Deep Endeavor* and told him.

'Captain Burch asks that we return to *Deep Endeavor* at once,' Dahlgren reported.

Dirk acted as if he didn't hear the comment, and guided the submersible closer to the platform. Suddenly he halted the *Badger* and pointed past the rocket to the launch tower. 'Look, up there.'

Dahlgren peered from their low vantage point and could see only the roof of the hangar and an empty helipad. Then he squinted harder and noticed the large digital launch clock—that now read 00:52:00, fifty-two minutes. 'That thing is going to fire off in less than an hour!' he exclaimed, watching the seconds tick down lower.

'We've got to stop it,' Dirk said, a note of anger in his voice.

'I don't know about you, pardner, but I don't know a thing about missiles or platform launches.'

'Can't be anything more than a little rocket science,' Dirk replied with a grimace, then jammed the submersible's throttles forward, making the *Badger* surge towards the platform.

They surfaced again near its stern, almost directly beneath the Zenit rocket, and peered up at a large set of panels that protruded from the under-side of the platform just below the base of the rocket. This was the flame deflector, designed to divert and dampen the rocket's fiery thrust, directing it through the platform to the ocean below. Thousands of gallons of fresh water were released seconds before launch to help cool the exposed portions of the platform during the rocket's slow rise off the pad.

'Remind me not to park here when that torch goes off,' Dahlgren said.

Their attention turned to the platform's thick support columns as they searched for a way up to the main deck. Dahlgren was the first to spot the *Koguryo*'s tender, tied up on the opposite side of the platform.

'I think I see a stairwell where the boat's tied up,' he said.

Dirk manoeuvred the *Badger* to the bow end of the platform, near the white tender. 'I don't think anyone is home,' he said, satisfied that the boat was empty. 'Care to tie us off?'

Before he could get an answer, Dahlgren had already opened the submersible's top hatch and was scrambling from the sub to the boat, then from the boat to the platform, tightly clutching a mooring line as he moved. Dirk shut down the submersible's power systems and climbed onto the platform as Dahlgren tied off the mooring line.

'This way to the penthouse,' Dahlgren said, motioning towards the stairwell.

The two men moved rapidly up the metal steps, careful to minimise the noise of their movements. At the top, they stopped to catch their breath, then stepped onto the exterior deck of the platform to come eye to eye with two enormous cigar-shaped fuel tanks, encased in a maze of pipes and tubing. Beyond the tanks they saw the Zenit itself, standing like a lonely monolith, and they paused for a moment, mesmerised by its size.

'I'm pretty sure the bridge sits above the hangar. That's where we need to get to,' said Dirk.

Dahlgren studied the structure. 'Looks like we'll have to go through the hangar to get there.'

The two men took off at a fast jog, wary of being observed as they dashed towards the open hangar doors. Dirk peered round the edge at the huge, empty cavern. Then, with Dahlgren on his heels, he slipped inside, moving quietly behind a large generator. Voices echoed across the empty chamber and the men froze in their tracks.

Midway down the length of the hangar on the opposite side, a door flew open and three men in Sea Launch jumpsuits staggered into the hangar, followed by two armed men in black commando outfits. The three men were marched to a storage room at the far end of the hangar and pushed inside, then the door was locked behind them. The two commandos stood guard outside.

'If we can get to the Sea Launch crew, they'll know how to stop the launch,' Dirk said in a low voice.

'Right. We ought to be able to take care of Mutt and Jeff,' Dahlgren replied, motioning towards the two guards.

Ducking and weaving through an array of electronic test racks and tool bins that lined the sides of the hangar, Dirk and Dahlgren crept towards the guarded storage room. They passed a rack of tools marked HYDRAULIC ENGINEER. Dirk grabbed a long-handled mallet while Dahlgren grabbed a wrench. Then, scrambling past the transporter/erector, they silently darted behind a work platform that sat a few yards from the storage room.

Dirk looked across at the two commandos. They were engaged in conversation and paying little attention to the rest of the darkened hangar. Dirk agreed a plan with Dahlgren, knowing that they would have only one chance to surprise and disable the two guards.

With his right arm extended above his head, Dahlgren lurched out from behind the work platform towards the nearest guard. The startled commandos hesitated for a second before levelling their guns. But Dahlgren had already swung the heavy wrench down towards the nearest man's head. It struck the guard square on the side of the jaw, and he crumpled to the floor.

Before the second guard could squeeze the trigger of his AK-74, Dirk had tossed the mallet like a long-handled axe, sending it spinning through the air until the business end struck the guard's head like a croquet ball, sending him tumbling to the ground. A burst of fire sprayed from his gun and struck the hangar ceiling.

The guard was only stunned by the blow, however, and dazedly rose to his knees, trying to retrain his gun. Dahlgren sprang towards the man and was making ready to swing the wrench again when a burst of gunfire split the air. Dahlgren froze as a neat row of bullet holes popped through the bulkhead just inches from his head. The sound of spent shell casings rattled across the floor as the echo of the gunfire gradually subsided.

'I would advise you not to move either, Mr Pitt,' spat the menacing voice of Tongju, who was standing in a doorway behind them, cradling a machine gun.

DIRK AND Dahlgren were held at gunpoint as Tongju and his team of commandos herded the remaining Sea Launch crew members into the storage room. Thirty crewmen were now crammed into the windowless box with no means of escape. Once the door was secured, Tongju walked over to the hangar wall, where Dirk and Dahlgren stood with a pair of gun muzzles aimed at their ribs. Tongju looked at Dirk with respect mixed with disdain.

'You have an annoying proclivity for survival, Mr Pitt, which is exceeded only by your irritating penchant for intrusion.'

'I'm just a bad penny,' Dirk replied.

'Since you have taken such a keen interest in our operation, perhaps you would enjoy a front-row viewing of the launch?' Tongju said, then nodded towards three of the guards.

Before Dirk could reply, the guards were prodding rifles into their backs, steering them in the direction of the open hangar doors. Tongju followed.

'You know, of course, that military units are on their way to the platform at this very moment,' Dirk said to the assassin, silently hoping that his words were true. 'The launch will be stopped and you and your men will be captured, or perhaps killed.'

Tongju smiled, his yellow teeth glistening. 'There is no way to stop the countdown now. The launch will proceed, Mr Pitt, and bring an end to the meddlesome activities of both you and your countrymen.'

Dirk and Dahlgren were led across the open platform to the base of the standing rocket. Tongju casually unholstered his Glock, aiming it at Dirk's throat as a guard tied his wrists and elbows behind his back and round a tower support beam. The guard then tied his ankles together and secured them to the beam before moving over to Dahlgren and roping him to the tower in the same fashion.

'Enjoy the launch, gentlemen,' Tongju hissed, then walked away.

'We shall, knowing that vermin like you won't have long to breathe,' Dirk cursed.

He and Dahlgren watched as Tongju and his men jogged across the platform and disappeared down the stairwell. A few minutes later, they observed the tender speeding away towards the *Koguryo*, which was now nearly two miles from the *Odyssey*. They also had a clear view of the launch clock as it ticked down to 00:26:00—twenty-six minutes to lift-off.

'Any chance you can slip your ropes?' Dirk asked hopefully of Dahlgren.

'Afraid not. This guy definitely earned his merit badge in knot tying.'

A loud clanging across the platform seized their attention, followed by a deep rumbling beneath their feet. The sound of liquid roared up behind them, rushing through a series of pipes built into the launch tower. Super-cooled liquid oxygen and kerosene were being pumped into the Zenit.

'They're fuelling the rocket,' Dirk observed. 'Too dangerous to do with the crew aboard, so they wait until they've been evacuated.'

'That makes me feel so much better.'

They both looked up at the rocket in apprehension, and heard a low hiss. As the chilled oxygen warmed in the daytime air, the expanding vapour was purged from the rocket, accumulating in wispy clouds above their heads. The sky seemed to darken as the vapour shadows obscured the rays of the sun. But Dirk's heart skipped a beat when he realised that the shadow cast over them was slowly creeping across the platform deck—it was *Icarus*.

TONGJU CLIMBED aboard the *Koguryo* and raced to the bridge, where Captain Lee and Kim stood surveying the *Odyssey*.

'You cut your departure a little thin,' Lee said soberly. 'They have already commenced fuelling the rocket.'

'A minor delay, due to an unexpected interruption,' Tongju replied. Scanning the horizon, he noted the airship drifting towards the platform. 'Have you detected any more approaching vessels?'

The captain shook his head. 'No. Besides the airship, there has just been the lone research ship that was following the Coast Guard vessel. She's remained in her present position, two miles northeast of the platform.'

'And no doubt has radioed for assistance. Those damn Ukrainians,' he spat. 'They have brought us too close to shore and placed the mission in peril. Captain, we must get under way immediately after liftoff. Adjust course due south at full power to Mexican waters.'

'What about the airship?' Kim asked. 'It must be destroyed as well, for it can track our escape.'

Tongju studied the silver airship which was now hovering over a large round helipad mounted above the *Odyssey*'s pilothouse. 'We cannot fire upon them while they are positioned near the platform. Besides, they can do no harm at this late stage. Come, let us enjoy the liftoff. We will dispense with them later.'

With Kim in tow, Tongju left the bridge and quickly made his way aft to the launch control centre. The brightly lit bay was packed with white-coated engineers sitting at workstations. On the front centre wall was a large flat screen that showed a full image of the Zenit rocket.

Tongju spotted Ling hunched over a monitor. 'Ling, what is the launch status?' he asked.

The engineer squinted at Tongju through his glasses. 'The fuelling will be complete in another two minutes. The launch will proceed as scheduled,' he said, 'in exactly twenty-three minutes and forty-seven seconds.'

AT TWENTY-THREE minutes and forty-six seconds, Jack Dahlgren looked up from the *Odyssey*'s ticking launch clock to *Icarus*. He knew it was a miracle that they'd been spotted by the high-flying gondola, and he still wondered if Pitt or Giordino might somehow find a way to stop the launch. He turned towards Dirk, expecting his friend to be looking at the airship with hopeful optimism. Instead, Dirk's attention was focused on trying to break free of his ropes. Jack started to offer words of encouragement but his lips froze when he saw movement inside the hangar. He blinked and took another hard look.

'Dirk, there's somebody running our way. Is it who I think it is?'

Dirk glanced towards the hangar while continuing to strain at his bound hands and feet. He squinted at the lone figure tearing across the platform, carrying what looked like a long stick. Suddenly he stopped struggling. '

I don't ever recall seeing my father move that fast before,' he said to Dahlgren, a broad grin spreading across his face.

As the head of NUMA drew closer, they could see that he was holding a fire axe in his hand. Sprinting up to the tower, the elder Pitt smiled in relief at seeing that the two men were uninjured.

'I thought I told you boys never to accept a ride with strangers,' he gasped, patting his son on the shoulder as he examined the ropes.

'Sorry, Dad, but they offered us the moon and the stars,' Dirk grinned, then added, 'Thanks for dropping by to get us.'

'I've got a taxi waiting. Let's get away before they ignite this thing.'

Eyeing the centre of the rope that secured Dirk's elbows, Pitt took a swing and laid the axe blade through it. With another swing, he cut the wrist binds. As Dirk worked to untie his ankles, Pitt attacked Dahlgren's ropes. The two men quickly scrambled to their feet as Pitt tossed the axe aside.

'Dad, the Sea Launch platform team is locked up inside the hangar. We need to get them out.'

Pitt nodded. 'I thought I heard some banging in there. Lead on.'

The three men dashed back across the open platform, knowing that every second counted. They bolted through the hangar doors and heard the sound of muffled voices and a metallic banging as the men inside the storage room fought to extricate themselves. Dirk, Dahlgren and Pitt hurried over and examined the padlocked door.

'That chain isn't going to give, but maybe we can prise the door off its hinges . . . if we can find a crowbar around here,' Dahlgren said, scanning the area for a potential tool.

Pitt glanced at a motorised work platform, which could be raised and lowered automatically using a control box. 'I think we've got our crowbar right here,' he said, pressing a button on the controls and lowering it a few feet, then rolling the device up to the front of the storage room. As Dirk and Dahlgren looked on, Pitt grabbed a loose end of the padlock chain attached to the door and wrapped it tightly round the platform's railing, then yelled at the men inside the shed: 'Stand back from the door.'

He hit the RAISE button and watched as the platform rose slowly, drawing the chain tight. The lifting mechanism groaned and strained and the wheels of the platform rocked off the floor. Then, with a loud crack, the storage-room door was ripped off its hinges. Pitt quickly backed the platform out of the way as the Sea Launch crew surged out.

'Are the captain and launch manager here?' Pitt shouted over the cries of thanks from the released crew.

A battered officer elbowed his way through the throng, followed by a thin, distinguished-looking man. 'I'm Captain Christiano of the *Odyssey*. This is Larry Ohlrogge, platform launch manager,' he added, nodding to the man beside him.

'Captain, the rocket is due to be launched in just eighteen minutes. Get your crew to the helipad now,' Pitt directed. 'There's an airship waiting that can evacuate everyone if we move quick.' Turning to Ohlrogge, Pitt asked, 'Is there any way we can stop the launch?'

'There is an override control in the bridge that would be our only hope at this late time,' the engineer replied.

'Then let's get moving.'

Quickly, the group shuffled to the rear of the hangar and crowded round a medium-sized elevator.

'There's not enough room for all,' Christiano said. 'We'll need three trips.'

'Jack, you come with the first group and help the crew onto *Icarus*. Let Al know there's more on the way,' Pitt said. 'Dirk, you bring up the last group, and make sure everyone makes it out of here. Captain, we need to visit the bridge now,' he said, turning to Christiano.

Christiano, Ohlrogge, Dahlgren and Pitt crowded into the elevator with eight other men and waited impatiently as the elevator rose to the bridge level above the hangar. Dahlgren quickly located the stairs off to one side that led to the helipad, and herded the crewmen up to where the silver airship was waiting, while Dirk led the others to the bridge.

Captain Christiano turned pale and shook his head silently when he saw the bullet-ridden computer stations, cut wires and smashed controls that littered the floor of the bridge. The last hope of halting the launch had gone.

'Here's your manual override control,' he spat, flinging a clump of wires and switches across the bridge.

Their attempt to prevent the launch had failed. Now they had no choice.

'I respectfully suggest we abandon the platform,' Pitt said, 'and *now*.'

As THE LAST four Sea Launch crewmen scrambled up the helipad steps to the waiting airship, Pitt grabbed his son by the shoulder. 'Get the captain aboard *Icarus* and tell Al to take off without me. Make sure he gets the airship well away from the platform before the rocket fires.'

'But they said there was no getting round the automated launch controls,' the younger Pitt protested.

'I may not be able to stop the rocket from launching, but I just might be able to change its destination.'

'Dad, you can't stay aboard the platform, it's too dangerous.'

'Don't worry about me.' Pitt gave his son a gentle shove. 'Now get going.'

Dirk looked his father in the eye. Once again he was placing the safety of others above his own. He opened his mouth to wish his father luck, but Pitt Senior had already vanished down the elevator.

Sprinting up the steps the younger Pitt leapt onto the helipad and looked in amazement at the waiting airship. The gondola looked like a can of sardines, with the many launch crew members packed inside.

Dirk ran over and wedged himself through the door, hearing Dahlgren's voice somewhere in the throng telling him that the copilot's seat was vacant. He squirmed his way through into the cockpit, taking the empty seat alongside Giordino.

'Where's your dad? We need to get off this barbecue grill, pronto.'

'He's staying put. Has one last trick up his sleeve, I guess. He said to get the airship away from of the platform, and that he'll meet you for a tequila on the rocks after the show.'

'I hope he's buying,' Giordino replied, then tilted the propeller ducts to a forty-degree angle and boosted the throttles. The gondola chugged forwards pulling the helium-filled envelope with it. But instead of rising gracefully into the air as before, the gondola clung to the deck, dragging across the helipad with a dull scraping sound.

'We've got too much weight,' Dirk stated.

'Get up, baby, get up,' Giordino urged the mammoth airship.

The gondola continued to skid across the pad. As they approached the forward edge, 200 feet above the sea, Giordino further adjusted the propellers and jammed the throttles to their stops, but the gondola continued to scrape along the deck.

Suddenly everyone was thrown forward as the airship's nose lurched down ten feet, then halted briefly before pulling the rest of the gondola with it and causing the entire airship to rush nose first towards the sea.

Giordino made a split-second decision. Instead of trying to pull the thrusters all the way back in the hope that reverse power would overcome the excess weight, he pushed down on the thrusters to try to increase the blimp's forward velocity, which would generate lift *if* he gained sufficient speed. He turned to Dirk in the copilot's seat. 'Above your head there's a water ballast release control. At my command, hit it.'

While Dirk located the button on the overhead console, Giordino focused his eyes on the altimeter. When it read sixty feet, he barked: 'Now!'

Giordino yanked back on the yoke while Dirk activated the water ballast system, which instantly dumped a thousand pounds of water stored in a compartment beneath the gondola. For an instant, Giordino thought he had acted too late. But then, even as the approaching ocean filled the view out of the cockpit windshield, the nose began to pull up with agonising slowness. As every man aboard held his breath, the base of the gondola slapped the surface of the sea for a second before slowly climbing a few feet above the water and holding steady.

The relieved passengers let out a cheer as Giordino gingerly coaxed the airship up to an altitude of 100 feet.

'I guess you showed us who's master of the airship,' Dirk lauded.

'Yeah, and almost commander of a submarine,' Giordino replied as he turned *Icarus* to the east, away from the platform.

Dirk scanned the horizon. To the northeast, he saw a tiny blue dot, which he knew to be *Deep Endeavor*. Then, just to the north of the NUMA ship, he noticed a small brown mass rising from the sea.

'That landmass up ahead. I recall from the navigation charts that it's a small channel island called Santa Barbara. Why don't we drop the crew there and have *Deep Endeavor* pick them up . . .'

'And get back to find your dad,' Giordino said, finishing Dirk's thought.

Dirk looked hesitantly back at the platform. 'Can't be much time left,' he muttered.

'About ten minutes,' Giordino replied, wondering, like Dirk, what Pitt could possibly pull off in so little time.

PHYSICALLY surviving a launch on board the *Odyssey* was not impossible. In fact, the deck, hangar, crew compartment and pilothouse were all built to withstand the fiery heat and exhaust generated from a powerful rocket launch. What a human being was not likely to survive, however, were the noxious fumes from the spent kerosene and liquid oxygen that engulfed the platform at blastoff.

But Pitt had no interest in hanging around the platform until the Zenit was lit. Instead, he was hell-bent on making it to the bright red NUMA submersible he had seen bobbing in the water from the pilothouse window. He ran, jumped and hurdled his way across the platform outside the bridge and sprinted down the stairwell to the water's edge.

Untying the *Badger*, Pitt jumped aboard and scrambled down the sub's top hatch, sealing it closed behind him. In seconds he had activated the power systems and proceeded along the underside of the platform before manoeuvring to a stop alongside the rear starboard support column. Directly above him was the recessed flame deflector, which would divert the blast of the Zenit's thrust towards the sea at liftoff.

Praying that his plan would work, Pitt turned the nose of the submersible until it was aimed at the column, then backed away and dived to a depth of fifteen feet. Using a set of manipulator controls, he lowered the *Badger*'s huge coring probe, designed to collect samples from the ocean bed, until it stretched horizontally in front of the submersible like a jousting lance.

Pitt braced his feet against the metal deck plate and muttered, 'OK, *Badger*, let's see your bite,' as he jammed the throttles to FULL FORWARD.

They shiny red submersible sped through the water and its full weight slammed into the side of the massive steel column, the coring probe ripping an eight-inch-diameter hole in it.

Pitt backed the *Badger* away, adjusted his depth slightly, then reversed the thrusters and charged into the column again. Once more, the probe tore through the column's outer wall, leaving a neat round hole for the seawater to pour into. Though crude, Pitt's mad ploy had an element of simple genius to it. He calculated that if there was no way to stop the rocket from lifting off, then perhaps there was a way to change its intended destination. By flooding the rear support columns, thereby creating an imbalance in the platform, he might at least angle the rocket off its intended flight path.

Pitt rammed the submersible into the column time and time again. Electronic equipment was jarred from its mounts, crashing and flying about his feet with each impact, and small rivulets of salt water began streaming into the interior through the damaged seams. But none of this mattered to Pitt. The risk to himself and the submersible was the last concern on his mind as the seconds to launch ticked down.

After more than a dozen strikes, he spun the leaking *Badger* around and raced towards the column on the port side. Glancing at his watch, he calculated there were less than two minutes left before liftoff.

ABOARD THE *Koguryo*, a red warning light began blinking in the launch control room. An engineer briskly stepped over to Ling.

'Mr Ling, we have a platform stabilisation warning,' he reported.

'What is the deviation,' Ling asked hurriedly.

'An aft list of three degrees.'

'That is inconsequential,' Ling replied, relieved. 'A list of five degrees or less is no cause for concern.'

'Do not halt the launch for any reason,' Tongju hissed at Ling.

The chief engineer gritted his teeth and nodded, staring nervously at the rocket shimmering before him on the video screen.

When, finally, he saw a row of green lights burst onto the screen at T-1 seconds, confirming the correct operation of all the rocket's systems, he allowed himself a sigh of relief. 'We have main engine thrust up!' he shouted aloud, as the display told him the computers were ramping up the rocket's engine to maximum launch thrust.

Every eye in the room turned to the video screen as the propellant floodgates were opened and the fuel burst through the rocket's engine in a torrent. For a long second, the rocket sat on the pad as the fiery exhaust burst from its nozzles, spraying a thick cloud of white smoke and flames across the platform. Then, with a burst of power, the Zenit surged up from the pad.

A cheer rang through the launch control centre as the engineers watched the Zenit rise. Tongju simply nodded in satisfaction.

The chief engineer was so mesmerised by the video image of the rocket climbing into the sky that he was oblivious to the fact that his computer showed that the platform stabilisation deviation had crept past fifteen degrees in the few seconds prior to launch.

FIFTEEN FEET beneath the water's surface, Pitt's ears were bleeding from the acoustic barrage. What had started as the sound of a distant freight train had increased to the bombardment of a thousand erupting volcanoes as the Zenit's engine reached full thrust.

Positioned almost directly beneath the launch pad, the *Badger* was pummelled like a small toy, surging twenty feet down in a blast of bubbles and vapour. The seams of the vessel groaned under the strain and the interior lights flickered. Bracing a hand against the bulkhead to steady himself, Pitt found that the bulkhead was searingly hot. He quickly pulled his hand away, cursing as he shook it in the air to cool it. A sickening thought fell upon him as he realised that the water sloshing at his feet was rapidly warming. The rocket's exhaust, having been deflected into the ocean, was creating a boiling cauldron around him that might poach him alive.

A second, more powerful surge struck the submersible as the rocket's full thrust came to bear, sending the *Badger* charging through the water like a raft down the Colorado River, until it collided head-on with the side of the *Odyssey*'s flooded port pontoon. Pitt was flung against the forward bulkhead amid a rain of electronic debris. A grinding noise told him that the *Badger* was sliding along the pontoon, then with another metallic clang the submersible tilted to one side and jerked to a stop. Pitt realised that the *Badger* was wedged against the hull, perhaps entangled in one of the pontoon's drive propellers. Because it was turned on its side, there was no way that Pitt could open the entry hatch, try to flood the interior and escape to the surface. With sickening awe, he realised that if he wasn't baked alive he would soon face death by drowning inside the leaking submersible.

FROM THE cockpit of *Icarus*, as they took off after setting down the Sea Launch team on Santa Barbara Island, Al, Dirk and Jack watched with dread as the first billows of smoke came from the *Odyssey*, indicating that the launch was initiated. For what seemed like minutes, the Zenit stood still at the launch tower, but finally the tall white rocket began to rise, its blinding exhaust glaring like a fireball.

Though it was a powerful, almost beautiful sight, Dirk felt sickened. The glistening white missile would cause the most savage terrorist attack the world had ever seen. And he had failed to stop it. As if that was not punishment enough, he knew that amid the noxious inferno of the rocket's blast off his father was somewhere fighting for survival.

INSIDE THE *Badger*, the temperature was unbearable. Pitt could feel himself on the verge of passing out as he clawed his way back to the pilot's seat. A handful of lights still blinked on the control panel, indicating that the emergency life-support system still had power, but the propulsion systems were long expired. He quickly calculated that he had one chance to break free from the grip of the pontoon. Through sweat-laden eyes, he reached for the button marked BALLAST PUMP. Then, grasping the control yoke, he flung himself backwards into the rising water, using his full weight to yank the sub's rudder against the current. The rudder blade protested at first, and for a second nothing happened. All Pitt could hear was the churning torrent of the water rushing against the sub. Then, almost imperceptibly, a grinding noise struck his ears. It grew louder, and a faint smile crossed Pitt's lips. Hang on, he told himself, gripping the yoke tightly. Just hang on.

ON BOARD the *Koguryo*, the excitement of the launch had yet to wane when a flight engineer turned to Ling and said, 'Sir, the Stage One engine indicates gimballing beyond nominal flight plan parameters.'

Once on its established flight plan the Zenit-3SL, like most modern rockets, was steered in flight by adjusting, or gimballing, the launch vehicle's engine, redirecting its thrust to govern the rocket's heading. As Ling was aware, the navigation system would only initiate steering adjustments in the first phase of the flight if there was an undetected imbalance at launch.

Ling walked over to the engineer's station and peered at the man's computer monitor. His mouth fell open as he saw that the rocket's engine was gimballed to the maximum degree. He watched in silence as, a second later, the engine adjusted back to its neutral position, then gimballed to the full extent in the opposite direction.

'Choi, what was the launch pad horizontal deviation at T-O?' he shouted to the platform engineer.

The engineer looked sheepishly at Ling and whispered, 'Thirteen degrees.'

'No!' Ling gasped, closing his eyes in panic and disbelief. Grasping the computer monitor to steady himself, he slowly opened his eyes and stared at the video screen display of the charging rocket, waiting for the inevitable.

PITT'S FRENETIC hole drilling had allowed a flood of seawater to quickly overpower the *Odyssey*'s ballast pumps. The water collected in the rear support columns and tugged the platform down at one end. The Zenit rocket was nearly fifteen degrees off vertical centre as it left the launch pad and the computer immediately tried to correct the deviation by shifting the engine's thrust. But at the relatively low speed of takeoff, the effect of initial command was diluted so the engine position was tweaked again—this time to maximum adjustment. As the rocket gained speed, the adjustment quickly became an overcorrection and so the computers gimballed the engine in the opposite direction to counterbalance the movement. The overtaxed stabilisation control system tried vainly to smooth the flight but, ultimately, exacerbated the situation. What started as a slight wobble at liftoff grew into a continuous waggle during ascent, until the entire rocket was shaking uncontrollably towards the clouds. Had Sea Launch been managing the flight, an automated safety control would have re-detonated the rocket. But the abort command had been deleted from the flight software by Kang's crew and the Zenit was left to struggle upwards in a tortuous dance of death.

To the disbelief of those who watched, the huge white rocket began literally snapping in two. The lower Stage 1 disintegrated in a massive fireball as the fuel tanks ignited, and chunks of rocket machinery rained down over a swath of empty sea, leaving a mushroom cloud hanging in the blue sky.

The nose cone and upper stage of the Zenit sailed free and continued speeding across the sky like a streaking bullet. Then, in a graceful parabolic arc, it gradually lost energy and nosed down into the Pacific. Stunned observers stared incredulously at the white rainbow of smoke that trailed the flight and arched from horizon to horizon.

KANG FLINCHED as the satellite feed of the Zenit disintegrated before his eyes. Silently he reached for the remote control and turned off the monitor.

'Though the strike has failed, the spectre of the attack will still represent a serious provocation to the American public,' Kwan assured his boss. 'Tempers will run high and the fallout against Japan will be significant.'

'Yes, our staged media leaks should ensure that,' Kang said, suppressing his anger. 'But the disappearance of the *Koguryo* and launch team remains a problem. Their capture will corrupt much of our hard work to date.'

'Tongju will fulfil his duties. He always has,' Kwan replied.

Kang slowly nodded.

THE MOOD in the *Koguryo*'s launch control centre had quickly turned from joy to shock to sullen disappointment. The assembled technicians and engineers sat silently at their computer stations, not knowing what to do next.

Tongju threw Ling a long, cold glare, then left the control centre without saying a word. As he made his way to the bridge, he called Kim on a portable radio and spoke briefly in a low voice.

On the bridge, he found Captain Lee staring out of the starboard window at the white strips of vapour.

'She shook herself apart,' Lee said with wonder, then looked into the blank eyes of Tongju.

'A problem with the platform,' Tongju replied. 'We must evacuate the area immediately. Can we get moving at once?'

Lee nodded. 'We just need to hoist in the tender.'

'There is no time,' Tongju hissed suddenly. 'The American Coast Guard and navy may already be looking for us. Proceed under full power at once, and I will personally cut the tender loose.'

Lee looked at Tongju warily. 'As you wish.'

Tongju took a step to exit the bridge, then stopped to gaze out of the forward window at the smoke-enshrouded Sea Launch platform. Approaching the platform was the silver airship. Tongju waved an arm in its direction. 'Take out that airship immediately,' he spat, then vanished out of the door.

As THE *Koguryo*'s twin propellers began churning the water beneath the ship's hull, Tongju made his way back to the ladder that ran down the vessel's port flank. At its base bobbed the tender, its mooring line tied to the rail. Quickly untying the line, Tongju hopped aboard and shuffled towards the cabin. Inside, he found Kim and two of his commandos beside the wheel.

'Everything aboard?' Tongju asked.

Kim nodded. 'During the excitement of the launch, we moved our arms and provisions on board, and even grabbed some extra fuel.' Kim tilted his head towards the rear where four drums of gasoline were tied to the gunwale.

'When will the changes detonate?'

Kim glanced at this watch. 'In twenty-five minutes.'

'Plenty of time for the missile crew to destroy the airship.'

The *Koguryo* quickly churned away from the small boat idling in the low swell. Kim waited until there was a good quarter of a mile of open water between the boats then he moved the throttles to SLOW and crept forward with the bow pointed southeast. In no time, he figured, they would look like another ordinary fishing charter heading home to San Diego.

EVER SO GENTLY, the light sea breeze began poking holes through the cloud of white smoke that still hung over the *Odyssey*, revealing glimpses of the launch platform to the three men on *Icarus*.

'I think that baby is sinking,' Dahlgren said from behind Dirk's shoulder as they glided around the aft end of the platform and could clearly see that the support columns there appeared shorter than the bow columns.

'She's definitely taking on water in the stern,' Dirk replied.

'Wonder if that's the handiwork of your old man? He may have just cost somebody a new rocket,' Giordino said.

'And maybe a new launch pad,' Dahlgren added.

'But where is he?' Dirk asked aloud.

'The smoke is starting to clear. Once the helipad opens up, I'll take us in for a closer look,' Giordino replied.

As they drifted towards the other end of the platform, Dahlgren looked down and grimaced. 'Damn. The *Badger*'s gone, too. Must have sunk during the launch.'

The threesome fell quiet, reflecting that the disappearance of the submersible was the least of their losses.

THREE MILES to the south, a crewman on the *Koguryo* was transferring the coordinates of the airship into a surface-to-air missile guidance system. The slow-moving craft was an easy target.

The man picked up a telephone that was connected directly to the bridge. 'Target acquired and missile armed,' he said to Captain Lee. 'Awaiting orders to fire.'

Lee looked out of a bridge side window towards the blimp hovering over the platform in the distance. The exploding airship would make for a spectacular display, he thought childishly. Perhaps they should also destroy the distant turquoise vessel that lingered on the edge of their radar screen, and then make a clean escape. But, first things first. He moved the receiver to his mouth to issue the command to fire when suddenly his lips froze. His eyes had detected a small pair of dark objects emerging from behind the airship. He stood frozen, and watched as the objects quickly materialised into a pair of low-flying aircraft.

The sleek grey F-16D fighter jets had been scrambled from an Air National Guard base in Fresno minutes after a NORAD satellite had detected the launch of the Zenit rocket. Flying low over the water, they burst over the *Koguryo* just a few hundred feet above her forebridge, rattling the windows.

Lee stood with a sickened look on his face. 'Stand down! Stand down and secure the battery,' he barked over the phone. As the missile was stowed away, Lee watched as the two jets began circling his ship.

'You!' he yelled at a crewman standing nearby. 'Find Tongju and bring him to the bridge at once.'

THE MEN in the airship beamed in relief at the sight of the jets circling above the *Koguryo*, having no idea how close they were to being blasted out of the sky by the ship's surface-to-air missile. They turned their attention back to the platform below.

'The haze is lifting off the helipad,' Giordino observed. 'I'll set her down if you boys want to jump off and take a look around.'

'Absolutely,' Dirk replied. 'Jack, we can start with the bridge, then move down to the hangar.'

'I'd start with the ship's lounge,' Giordino said, trying to ease the sombre mood. 'My money says he's mixing a martini and eating up the ship's store of pretzels.'

As Giordino lined up the airship over the helipad and began losing altitude, Dahlgren pointed out of the side window. 'Take a look over there.'

Several hundred feet away from the side of the platform, a surge of bubbles erupted from beneath the surface, followed a few seconds later by a mottled grey metallic object.

'Launch debris?' Dahlgren asked.

'No, it's the *Badger*!' Giordino exclaimed.

Guiding the airship towards the object, the three men could see that the underwater vessel's bright metallic paintwork had been cooked off in the launch blast, leaving its skin a dappled mix of primer and bare metal. The bow section was bent and mangled, as if it had been involved in a head-on traffic accident. How the thing still managed to float was anybody's guess, but there was no denying it was the same submersible that Dirk and Dahlgren had sailed to the platform.

As Giordino brought the airship down for a closer look, the three men were stunned to see the top hatch suddenly twist and pop open. A cloud of vapour streamed out, then, after several agonising seconds, a patch of dark hair appeared and Pitt hoisted himself out.

'It's Dad! He's OK!' Dirk exclaimed with relief.

Pitt climbed to his feet and swayed on the rocking submersible. He was a haggard mass of blood and sweat, and his clothes glued to his skin, but he looked skyward and threw a jaunty wave to the men in the gondola.

'Going down,' Giordino announced. He guided *Icarus* towards the sea, until the gondola was skimming inches above the waves, then deftly eased the airship alongside the submersible.

Pitt took a few steps and staggered through the open door of the gondola.

'I believe,' he said in a parched voice, 'I'll take that drink now.'

'WHY HAVEN'T they fired on the aircraft, or that infernal airship?' Tongju raged as he stared at the *Koguryo* through a pair of binoculars.

'The aircraft have intimidated Lee,' Kim said over his shoulder as he clutched the tender's steering wheel tightly. 'He will pay with his life in about two more minutes.'

The *Koguryo* was growing smaller on the horizon as the tender accelerated south. But when the planted explosives detonated, Tongju and Kim could clearly see puffs of water spray into the air along the ship's hull line.

STANDING on the bridge, Captain Lee at first thought that the F-16s had fired on him. But the warbirds were still circling lazily above, and there was no sign that they had fired any missiles. As the damage assessments came in reporting that the lower hull was compromised in several places, Lee suddenly realised the culprit. Minutes before, a crewman had reported observing Kim and Tongju board the tender, and the small boat was now seen running south at high speed. Lee felt sick at the betrayal.

As the captain of the vessel that launched the aborted missile attack against the United States, he would be the scapegoat if he was rescued and captured. If he somehow escaped, there would be no telling what sort of reception he'd receive from Kang. Lee excused himself from the bridge and retired to his cabin. Retrieving a Makarov 9mm pistol from a drawer, lay down on his bed, held the barrel to his ear, and pulled the trigger.

THE MEN in *Icarus* caught sight of the series of explosions that ripped along the hull of the *Koguryo*.

'Are those lunatics trying to scuttle her?' Dahlgren wondered.

For several minutes, they watched the ship as she began to list. Then Giordino glanced at the LASH system output on the laptop computer, spotting several grey shapes to the southeast approximately thirty miles away.

'Our navy pals are on the way,' he said, tapping the screen.

With a speed advantage of nearly twenty knots, the airship began to gain ground easily on the fleeing tender.

Pitt directed the surveillance camera at the boat's rear deck. 'Recognise anyone?' he asked, focusing the zoom lens of the camera on the men so that their faces could clearly be distinguished.

The younger Pitt studied the screen. 'The Fu Manchu character standing in the centre—he's Kang's master of ceremonies for torture and assassination. He was calling the shots aboard the *Odyssey* earlier.'

'For such a nice guy, it would be kind of a shame to ruin his Mexican vacation,' Giordino replied.

Closing the gap between the two vessels, he eased back on the throttles until he matched speeds with the bouncing tender. Above the din of the airship's motor-driven propellers, the men in *Icarus* detected an unwelcome staccato noise. Glancing at the tender, Pitt saw that Tongju and the two commandos had retrieved automatic weapons and were standing on the stern deck blasting away at the airship.

Before departing Oxnard, the crew of *Icarus* had been told that the airship could withstand a profusion of holes and gashes to the air bags, although the safety of the gondola was less assured.

'Everybody down!' Pitt yelled as a burst of fire shattered the side cockpit window, the bullets grazing just over his head. Giordino jammed the throttles forward and turned the yoke full to port, away from the tender.

'No,' Pitt yelled at him, 'Turn and fly over him.'

Giordino knew not to question Pitt's judgment and, without hesitation, threw the rudder over in the opposite direction, pushing *Icarus* back towards the tender. The blistering fire abruptly stopped as the gondola passed over the tender's cabin roof, temporarily obscuring the field of fire.

'Everyone all right?' Pitt asked.

'We're OK,' Dirk replied, 'but one of the engines isn't faring too well.'

Giordino shook his head. 'Oil pressure falling, temperature rising. Going to be tough to run away from these guys on one leg.'

Pitt peered down at the deck of the tender, spotting Tongju and the two gunmen moving to the stern of the boat, reloading their weapons. 'Al, hold your position,' he said. 'And lend me your cigar.'

Giordino handed Pitt the green stub. 'It's one of Sandecker's finest.'

'I'll buy you a box of 'em. Hold steady for ten seconds, then turn hard to port and get us the hell away from the boat.'

'You're not going to do what I think you are?' Giordino asked.

Pitt just flashed him a sly look, then reached up for an overhead ripcord with one hand while he turned a dial marked FUEL BALLAST to the open position. Pulling on the cord, he silently counted to eight, then released the line and returned the fuel ballast lever to its original position. At the stern of the gondola, an emergency dump valve had released seventy-five gallons of gasoline directly onto the deck of the tender. Tongju and the two gunmen sprinted into the cabin as the rain of liquid splattered down on them, but quickly returned after the deluge ended and raised their weapons to finish off the airship. Pitt watched as the pool of gasoline washed around their feet and the four drums tied to the side. Then, with calm nonchalance, he took a puff on the cigar and casually tossed it towards the tender.

As Tongju jerked the stock of the AK-74 assault rifle to his shoulder, he barely noticed the small green object that fluttered down and struck the deck beside him. His finger was just tightening on the trigger when the deck erupted in flames at his feet.

In seconds the whole of the boat was a wall of flame. A commando standing beside Tongju had been drenched in fuel and the flames shot up his legs and torso in a rush. The panicked man danced frantically about the deck, screaming in pain, then flung himself over the side.

Kim gazed at the blazing stern with a look of alarm in his eyes.

'Keep going,' Tongju shouted, 'the flames will burn themselves out.'

The sea spray from the charging boat had, in fact, extinguished some of the flames, but pools of burning gasoline still sloshed across the deck.

'The fuel barrels!' Kim cried, watching as the flames licked at the drums of gasoline.

Tongju had forgotten about the inflammable cargo tied to the rear deck. Spotting a fire extinguisher mounted to the bulkhead, he scooped it up, pulled out its lock-pin, and sprinted over to protect the fuel drums. But he was too late.

One of the drums exploded like a powder keg. In quick succession, the other three ignited with devastating effect. A huge fireball rolled into the sky as the stern of the boat rose into the air briefly, its propellers churning. The boat was quickly sucked under the waves, taking the bodies of Tongju, Kim and the third commando to the sea floor.

CHAPTER 10

The mere sight of the US navy frigate and destroyer was enough to make the captainless crew of the *Koguryo* throw in the towel. In minutes, a small boarding party arrived from the destroyer USS *Benfold* and took custody of the ship, which was sailed to San Diego.

A media frenzy erupted as word broke of the attempted rocket attack on Los Angeles. Scores of small boats packed with reporters and cameramen buzzed around the harbour trying to get a close-up of the terrorist ship and her crew. When the *Koguryo* docked at the San Diego Naval Station, teams of government security and intelligence officers whisked the crew away to a secure facility for interrogation.

The Japanese Red Army was behind the attack, newspapers and television reports screamed. Lost in the news was the issue of Korea and the pending vote in the National Assembly about the removal of US troops from the South Korean Peninsula.

The men from NUMA were lionised as heroes and every news organisation was on the hunt for them. But they were nowhere to be found. After setting the perforated airship down on an unused runway at Los Angeles airport, they had beaten it down to Long Beach, where they slipped quietly aboard *Deep Endeavor*, to be greeted by a relieved Summer and the ship's crew. Dahlgren was happy to see the mangled *Badger* sitting on the fantail deck.

'We've got another search ahead of us,' Pitt said to Burch. 'How soon can we be under way?'

'Just as soon as Dirk and Summer step ashore. Sorry, son,' he said, turning to the younger Pitt, 'but I'm afraid Rudi called. Says the top brass wants to talk to you and Summer, right away.'

'Some guys get all the luck,' Giordino said, grinning at Dirk's misfortune.

Dirk and Summer said a quick goodbye to their father and the other men on the bridge, then hopped off *Deep Endeavor* as the vessel backed away from the dock.

As they waved farewell to the ship, which would soon be on a mission to recover the Zenit's payload from the ocean bed, Dirk's mind was churning with anger. The deadly virus strike had been prevented, the *Koguryo* was captured, and even Tongju was dead. But on the other side of the world, Kang still breathed.

AT THEIR BRIEFING with FBI and Defense Department officials, Dirk and Summer learned that Vice President Sandecker had finally persuaded the President to authorise an operation to take out Kang, swiftly and silently, without informing the South Korean government. An assault plan had been formulated, targeting several of Kang's facilities, including the shipyard at Inchon. The mysterious magnate had not been seen for days, so his private residence was top of the list of targets. Because few Westerners had ever been invited inside it, Dirk and Summer's insights were critical.

'We'll be happy to provide you with a full layout of the site, identify entry points and passageways, even give you the security force positions and monitoring technology,' Dirk offered, to the delight of the intelligence agents. 'But I expect one thing in return, and that's a ticket to the show.'

After some grumbling and a few calls to Washington, he won out.

Summer thought he was crazy. 'Please be careful, Dirk,' she said with sisterly concern when the agents had left the room. 'Leave the assault work to the professionals. I nearly lost you and Dad today.'

'Not to worry. I'll keep to the rear with my head down,' he promised.

Two hours later, he was whisked away to Los Angeles airport and put on a government jet back to South Korea. After briefing the Special Operations forces, he joined a SEAL team tasked with broaching the mogul's residence on Kyodongdo Island. Their mission was to capture Kang alive.

The billionaire fled, however, in his white Benetti yacht. In the chase that followed, the speeding yacht collided with a river dredge.

Kang did not survive.

EPILOGUE

JULY 1, 2007

As Kang was obliterated, so his empire fell. The SEAL forces that swept through his residence captured his assistant Kwan alive, along with cache of incriminating documents that he was desperately trying to destroy in his employer's private office. To the south at Inchon, additional Special Forces teams sped through Kang's shipyard and neighbouring telecommunications facility. The secret biological research lab was soon discovered, as were the staff's ties to North Korea. Faced with mounting evidence and the death of his master, Kwan quickly folded under duress and fully confessed Kang's sins to save his own neck. The confession led to the release of Master Sergeant Keith Catana, the US serviceman convicted of murdering an underage prostitute, though Catana would never know that he had been set up as part of a concerted plot to influence public sentiment against the US military presence in Korea.

The remains of the rocket payload that Pitt and Giordino had managed to salvage were transferred under secrecy to Vandenberg Air Force Base, north of Los Angeles, where they were carefully disassembled. CDC epidemiologists found, to their shock, that the payload contained a lethal mix of smallpox and HIV organisms. Samples from the Inchon lab were quietly matched up and the horror confirmed. The chimera was destroyed.

With the *Koguryo* and her crew traced to Kang Enterprises and Kang's ties to North Korea firmly established, officials from the Homeland Security Department finally went public. A media firestorm broke out worldwide as details of the deadliest attempted terrorist attack on US soil were released. The failed rocket attack brought worldwide outrage against the North Korean totalitarian regime and the few trading partners that the country had cultivated before the incident retaliated by placing even tighter restrictions on imports and exports. Once again, the starving North Koreans began to quietly question the dictatorial rule of their nepotistic leader.

South Korean sentiment turned from shock and disbelief to anger and outrage at their country's duping by Kang. The fallout was rapid. A wave of resignations swept through the National Assembly, leading right up to the presidency. Revelations of close personal ties with Kang forced even the South Korean leader to resign from office.

Reunification remained a national goal, but it would have to be on South Korea's terms. When the South Korean National Assembly voted on a bill calling for the expulsion of US military forces, it was unanimously rejected.

IT WAS A CLEAR, crisp afternoon in Seattle. The declining sun was casting long shadows from the tall pines dotting Fircrest Campus when Sarah hobbled out of the front door of the Washington State Public Health Laboratories.

She winced slightly as she set her weight on a pair of aluminium crutches, her wrists and forearms sore from carrying the load of her broken leg for the past few weeks. The heavy plaster would finally be removed in just a few more days. Hobbling a few paces out of the doorway, she did not notice the car at the sidewalk entrance and nearly bumped into it. Looking up, her jaw dropped in amazement.

Parked in front of her was Dirk's 1958 Chrysler 300-D convertible. It looked to be in a state of partial restoration. The pockmarked leather seats had been temporarily taped over, while the bullet holes in the body had been sealed with Bondo. Scattered spots of grey primer across the turquoise body gave the car the look of a giant, camouflaged manta ray.

'I promise not to break the other leg,' said a deep voice behind her.

Sarah turned to find Dirk standing there with a bouquet of white lilies and a mischievous grin on his face.

Overcome with emotion, she dropped her crutches and threw her arms round him. 'I was worried. I hadn't heard from you since the rocket attack.'

'I was away on an all-expenses-paid trip to Korea.'

'The virus they concocted . . . it's mad,' she said, shaking her head.

'There's no need to worry any more. All the samples were retrieved and destroyed. That bug will never appear on earth again.'

'There's always some crazy working on the next biological Pandora's box for money or notoriety.'

'Speaking of crazies, how's Irv doing?'

Sarah laughed. 'He's going to be the only modern-day survivor of small-pox in the world. He's on his way to a full recovery.'

'Glad to hear it. He's a good man.'

'Looks like your car is on the road to recovery as well,' she said, nodding towards the Chrysler.

'She's a tough old beast. I had the mechanicals refurbished while I was away but haven't got to the body and interior yet.' Dirk looked at Sarah tenderly. 'I still owe you that crab dinner.'

Sarah looked deep into Dirk's green eyes and nodded.

He bent over, picked her up and placed her gently on the front seat of the car with the lilies, then kissed her lightly on the cheek. Tossing the crutches into the back seat, he jumped in behind the wheel and fired up the car.

'No ferries?' Sarah asked, snuggling close to Dirk.

'No ferries,' Dirk laughed, slipping an arm round her.

He tapped on the accelerator, and the old convertible rumbled deeply as he steered it across the lush grounds and into the pink-tinted dusk.

CLIVE & DIRK CUSSLER

Website: www.numa.net

The facts are remarkable. He has a readership of over 125 million avid fans; there is a society, The Cusslermen, devoted to him; his success has brought him homes in Colorado and Arizona, a fabulous collection of classic cars and the funds to run his very own shipwreck salvage company—the National Underwater and Marine Agency (NUMA)—named exactly as it is in his novels. So why, after all these years, isn't Clive Cussler as famous as other mega-selling authors?

'After thirty years, I guess it's kind of strange,' he remarks, 'but it's fine by me.' One reason for the low profile is that Cussler has been notoriously wary of Hollywood deals. All that's about to change, though, as the agent who has stuck by him, from the first string of rejection slips to today's multi-million-dollar contracts, is negotiating a deal with Crusader Entertainment for a film version of Cussler's 1992 novel, *Sahara*. It's due to be released in 2005, if the negotiations don't get mired in legal wranglings about the casting and the screenplay.

Like his fictional hero, Dirk Pitt, Cussler is starting to hand over the reins to a younger man. After twenty-eight books, he admits he's a little tired. And who better to take on the Cussler mantle than the son who was the inspiration for the books? Though he was only six at the time, Dirk Cussler still remembers falling asleep to the sound of his dad pounding away on the typewriter. Cussler Snr had a day job then, in advertising, but he'd decided to try his hand at writing and, like any good creative director, did research into what would appeal. He wanted to do something fresh, and was struck by the fact that no one was writing pure, old-fashioned adventures. It seemed to be a lost genre. Next came the matter of a hero. 'My son's name was Dirk,' Cussler remembers. 'I was looking for a good tough name and there it was.' But how could he differentiate 'Dirk' from all the secret agents and investigators already out there? 'It suddenly hit me: I'll put him in and around water. I'd been scuba-diving for years and thought it would be a great backdrop.'

He was right, of course. It now seems very fitting that Dirk Cussler should take on where his father leaves off, and Cussler is pleased with the handover that has begun with *Black Wind*. 'I think he does a very good job,' he says of his son's creative powers. 'I think he writes a tad better than I do, but I might have a better imagination. It was great working together.'

THE CUSSLERMEN

Denver-based Dave E. Hyatt, pictured (right) at a book signing with Clive Cussler, runs The Society of the Cusslermen (www.cusslermen.com), a web-based club dedicated to supplying fans with information about Cussler's work and original editions of his books.

By day Dave is vice-president of an insurance company; in his spare time he keeps in touch with 3,000 other Cussler devotees all over the world. During the last three months alone, he claims, his site has received two million visits.

Dave recalls coming across his first Dirk Pitt adventure in 1973 when he was searching for a novel to read in his lunch breaks and asked a bookstore owner for something that was 'adventure, and believable'. He was sold a copy of *The Mediterranean Caper*, which he quickly devoured, and from there his passion for Cussler-style adventure steadily grew. 'It's a lot of fun how he ties an event or story from the past into the present' is Dave's explanation of the special appeal of Cussler's stories.

Memories of a
Hong Kong Childhood

Gweilo

Martin Booth

If the truth be told, I have never really
left Hong Kong, its streets and hillsides,
wooded valleys, myriad islands and
deserted shores with which I was closely
acquainted as a curious, sometimes
devious, not unadventurous and streetwise
seven-year-old. My life there has been
forever repeating itself in the recesses of
my mind like films in wartime cartoon
cinemas, showing over and over again, as
if on an endless loop . . .
This is hardly surprising. Hong Kong was
my home . . . is where I grew up.
– Martin Booth, 2003

1

Fifty feet below, my grandparents stood side by side. It was a warm spring day, yet my paternal grandfather, Grampy, wore a grey trilby and an overcoat buttoned to his neck. From far off he looked like a retired Chicago mobster. His wife wore a broad-brimmed Edwardian hat decorated with faded feathers and wax flowers, which, even at that distance, gave the impression of being on the verge of melting. Her mound of white hair being insufficiently dense to retain her hatpin, every time she craned her neck to look up at me, the hat slid off backwards and Grampy deftly caught it.

It was late on the afternoon of Friday, May 2, 1952, and I was seven.

A deck steward in a white uniform approached me. He carried a silver salver bearing rolls of coloured paper streamers. 'Where're you going to, sunshine?' he asked as he handed me three rolls.

'Hong Kong,' I replied. 'My father's been posted,' I added, though I had not the faintest idea what this meant. As far as I knew, one only posted letters.

'You'll need to grow your hair, then,' he announced. 'Far too short . . .'

I asked why.

'Well, in China men wear their hair in pigtails. You're not going to be able to put a plait in that.' He winked at me and moved on down the deck.

Aghast at the thought of my hair being put in a braid, I asked my mother if this was true, but her response was obscured by the thunderous blare of the ship's horn, high up on the funnel, announcing our imminent departure.

Further along the rail, my father threw a streamer over the ship's side. I followed suit, hurling mine into the sky. It arched through the air, bounced off the corrugated iron roof of a dockside warehouse and rolled into a drain. It was then I realised that one was supposed to keep hold of one end of the ribbon. I threw another streamer. My grandfather caught it and held it until it tautened and tore as the ship edged away from the quayside.

The vessel upon which we were embarked was the SS *Corfu*. According to my father, she (not *it*, he impressed upon me) was a twenty-two-year-old liner operated by the Peninsula & Oriental Steam Navigation Company and accommodated 400 passengers.

At first the ship's movement was infinitesimal, yet quite suddenly, it seemed, my grandparents were minute figures on a dockside far away, indistinguishable from others in the waving crowd. I watched the land pivot round as the bow gradually turned to face the open sea.

My father disappeared to his cabin, but my mother and I stood at the ship's rail for over an hour. The wind ruffled her short blonde hair as we passed the Isle of Wight to head down the English Channel. Above us, the funnel pumped out a plume of smoke and the windows of the bridge glistened with the sunlight reflecting off the sea. My mother held my hand. It was not that she was afraid I might fall overboard but that she wanted to share her exhilaration.

At last, with England a thin line on the darkening horizon, she said, 'Let's go and sort out our cabin.'

Ahead was an ocean of sea water and endless possibilities.

My mother and I shared a twin-berth, second-class cabin while my father 'bunked up', as he put it, with another male passenger. Although attached to the Royal Navy, my father was no more than an Admiralty civil servant. Yet this did not prevent him from assuming naval ways and speech. He drank pink gin, called sausages 'bangers', never let a knocked glass chime (for fear it sounded a sailor's knell), referred to his superior as 'the Old Man' and used nautical expressions whenever possible.

The cabin I shared with my mother was fairly basic: two bunks, a wardrobe, a chest of drawers, a steel washbasin, the top of which folded down, two stools and a chair. I was allotted the top bunk. The ablutions (or, as my father would have it, 'the heads') were communal and a little way down the corridor. The cabin walls were cream-painted iron bulkheads lined with rivets, the ceiling traversed by girders and ventilation pipes.

What was strange was that everything continually quivered. It was like living in the entrails of a vast, benign beast, the corridors its bowels, the pipes its arteries and the various cabins its organs.

We unpacked our cases and then my mother ran me a bath. On returning to the cabin, I found a silver tray on the table bearing a plate of thin-cut sandwiches, a freshly sliced pear and a glass of milk.

'Supper,' my mother announced. She lifted one end of a sandwich and exclaimed, 'Roast chicken!'

This was opulence indeed. In England, still held in the grip of postwar austerity, chicken was a luxury. So was a pear.

As night settled upon the sea, I climbed into my bunk, pulled the blanket up to my neck and lay on my side. Pressing my forehead to the porthole, I looked down. The sea was speeding by, the white tops of the wake catching the light from other portholes and the promenade deck above. Now well down the French coast, the *Corfu* rolled gently in the Atlantic swell.

My mother leant up and kissed me. 'We're on our way now,' she whispered with hardly suppressed excitement. 'Aren't we the lucky ones?'

THE VOYAGE to Hong Kong took a month, with seven ports of call *en route*. My father, assiduously studying our course on a daily progress map pinned to a notice board in the lounge, announced what we might see each day. His first prediction was that we should see Gibraltar 'off the port beam', but it was hidden in mist. This upset him greatly.

'You've not lived until you've seen Gib,' he informed me.

'Why not?' I replied. 'It's just a big rock.'

'Just a rock! What did they teach you in that bloody school?'

We arrived at our first port of call, Algiers, three days out of Southampton. The city consisted of low buildings encircling a bay. A few minarets poked upwards into the sky. Almost every vehicle was of prewar vintage or ex-military. All the cars were black Citroëns. The air tasted of the desert.

My mother was eager to go ashore. This was the first time she had set foot outside Britain. I was just as eager to follow. My father, conversely, was not at all enthusiastic. A friend of his had been stabbed to death in Algiers during the war and he considered the place unsafe. That this friend had been in military intelligence, that Algiers had been under the influence of Vichy France and the war against Hitler had been in full flood at the time did not seem to occur to him. However, my mother prevailed and we set off in a small, decrepit bus with some other passengers from the ship. Our ride culminated in the kasbah, the sixteenth-century fortified part of the old Ottoman city. Here, we got out and wandered through the souk.

Every street and alley was an animated illustration from *The Thousand and One Nights*. Men wearing turbans and baggy trousers passed by, leading donkeys. Some of the women wore burkas, their eyes bright in the dark slits. Stalls under arcaded buildings sold vegetables I had never seen before, quaintly shaped copper jugs, vicious-looking daggers, leatherware and sand-coloured pottery. In coffee shops, men sat drinking from small cups or smoking hookahs. Away from the smokers, I found the air heavy with smells reminiscent of my grandmothers' spice cabinets, of minced pies and apple tart—and the odour of donkeys, camels and human sweat.

My mother purchased some fresh dates from a stall and set about eating them, much to my father's alarm.

'How can you tell where they've been?' he remonstrated with her.

'They've been up a date palm,' my mother replied.

'And they picked themselves, I suppose?'

'No,' she responded, 'I expect they were plucked by a scrofulous urchin and thrown down to his tubercular aunt who wrapped them in her phlegm-stiffened handkerchief.'

'Well, don't give one to Martin.'

I had no idea what I was being forbidden, but I was determined not to miss out on it. Surreptitiously my mother slipped me a date. Its taste and texture reminded me of solidified honey.

Once through the souk we climbed up to a battlement, where I sat on a large cannon. I could see camels below, their wooden-framed cargo saddles being laden with sacks. As we retraced our steps through the souk, my mother asked me what I thought of the city and was later to write to relatives that I compared Algiers favourably to the outer-London suburb of Woking.

My mother's first encounter with a camel was costly. It was sitting on the ground, fully laden, chewing the cud, its eyes shut. My mother, who had an in-built attraction to anything of fur or feather, approached the beast, hand outstretched, to stroke its muzzle. In an instant, it was wide awake and getting to its feet. Its neck arched forward, it sneezed and then it spat. A shower of bactrian spittle lodged in my mother's hair. She stepped back sharply. The camel lunged after her but its front feet were hobbled. The camel herder hurried over and struck the beast on its rump with a stout stick, shouting a spate of invective at it in Arabic. The camel lay down again. Its owner looked balefully expectant, so my father parted with all his loose change, no doubt hoping this would be sufficient for us not to be knifed in revenge.

When we stepped into the square where we had left the bus, it had gone. Panic entered my father's eyes. His friend had bled to death in a gutter hereabouts. At this point, my mother disappeared down an alley.

'Joyce!' my father called after her. 'Joyce!' His voice rose half an octave with anger, frustration and fear. 'Joyce! This isn't Piccadilly . . .'

Yet, in less than a minute, my mother returned, unscathed. Following her was an elderly bearded Arab in a flowing blue-and-gold striped robe leading a morose-looking donkey in the shafts of an ancient trap. My mother was ever a resourceful woman.

MY PARENTS, Joyce and Ken, were in many ways an incompatible pair. My mother was a very pretty strawberry blonde, petite and lithe; my father slim and handsomely dark. They looked the ideal couple, yet they were not. My mother was full of fun, with a quick wit, an ability to make friends from all walks of life and an intense intellectual curiosity. She was also as tenacious as a bull terrier. By contrast, my father was a stick-in-the-mud with little humour, an all-abiding pedantry and a chip on his shoulder that grew throughout his life. He came to hold all relationships at arm's length, considering himself a cut above most of his contemporaries.

My parents' coming together was perhaps unavoidable: born within five weeks of each other, they lived out their childhoods virtually next door to each other in Portsmouth. The marriage, however, greatly discommoded my paternal grandmother. Her husband had been a commissioned officer, but my mother was the daughter of a noncommissioned officer from the lower deck. What was worse, she was a Modern Woman, had a job as a General Post Office telephonist and smoked cigarettes. In my grandmother's eyes, she could not be more common unless she worked in Woolworths.

During the Second World War, my father spent a good deal of his time overseas in south and west Africa and the Middle East. When the hostilities ended, he was employed at the Admiralty in London. Although he made himself out to be an important man, he was in fact little more than a superior clerk. Indeed, my mother had an almost equivalent wartime job provisioning submarines for the Battle of the Atlantic.

After the war, we lived in a semidetached house in Brentwood, Essex. My mother was a housewife, my father a daily commuter into London. Then, one day, he came home to announce that he had been posted to Hong Kong, to serve upon a Royal Fleet Auxiliary naval supply ship plying between the British crown colony and the Japanese military dockyard of Sasebo. The Korean War was in full flood and he was, he claimed, to be a part of it.

My father was all for sending me to boarding school in England: I could spend my holidays with his parents. He and my mother, he pointed out, would only be gone three years. He would not have me educated in a local school or a school for children of military personnel.

'I'm not leaving him here,' my mother pronounced obdurately. 'He'll wind up like some poor child in a Kipling story.'

'Don't be ridiculous, Joyce! If he's in England, he'll be safe. The Far East isn't Farnham. There are tropical diseases, civil unrest, native—'

'It's a British colony, Ken. They have hospitals and a police force. I had a child to raise him, not foist him off on a gaggle of minor public school masters, half of them as interested in the contents of his underpants as his mind.'

'Don't be so bloody stupid, Joyce. The masters at Hilsea . . .'

Hilsea College, an insignificant private boys' school in Portsmouth, was my father's Alma Mater.

'Hilsea!' my mother echoed in a voice verging on the falsetto. 'You can have another think coming! Martin's going to be with us. Fix it!'

I overheard this conversation through a closed door and missed bits of it but the gist was clear and the outcome decided. I was going too.

LIFE ABOARD ship quickly settled into a routine. Mornings were spent reading in deck chairs, writing letters in the lounge or walking briskly round the promenade deck. Some passengers joined in physical exercise classes on the boat deck. At midmorning, a steward served beef tea in china cups. After luncheon, most passengers took to their cabins or lay in deck chairs. A few participated in deck sports, most of which seemed to involve quoits of tough rope that one threw over a net or shuttled across the deck.

As far as I was concerned, the voyage was a prolonged vacation, although, early on, a blot appeared on this landscape of bliss.

Passengers under the age of twelve were expected to attend lessons every morning in the ship's nursery, a room decorated with Disney characters, furnished with chairs and desks of Lilliputian dimensions and overseen by a crabby-faced woman in a nanny's uniform. The instruction offered bore no relation to any school syllabus and my mother, after visiting to find me shoehorned into a desk, excused me from all future attendance. Thereafter, she taught me geography and history herself for an hour a day.

The days at sea were euphoric, reading Enid Blyton or Arthur Ransome in a deck chair, playing with the children of similarly enlightened parents and painting watercolours of imaginary volcanic desert islands. A subtropical sun beat down from a cloudless sky, its heat deceptively cooled by a stiff sea breeze. I quickly acquired a tan.

To amuse the younger passengers, 'diversions' were arranged. The chief engineer conducted a trip to the engine room, a cathedral-sized cavern filled with mechanical noise, spinning flywheels, heaving piston rods, levers, taps and vast propeller shafts that turned incessantly.

Another excursion took us to the bridge, where we were permitted to steer the ship, keeping her on her bearing with the aid of a large gimbal-mounted compass and the officer of the watch, whose hand did not leave the wheel.

One morning I awoke to find the ship still and alongside a quay seething with activity. Men in white turbans mingled round the entrance to a warehouse, chivvied into order by a portly man in a bedraggled suit and red fez.

'Port Said,' my mother announced, entering the cabin. 'Egypt,' she added.

After breakfast, my father decreed we could safely go ashore. He had been here during the war, had lost no friends to enemy agents and purportedly knew his way around. A decaying landau pulled by a gaunt pony took us into the centre of town, where we entered a low, colonnaded building that seemed to be attracting passengers from the *Corfu* as a picnic did ants. This was the Simon Artz department store, almost as famous in Egypt as the Sphinx or the pyramids, alabaster replicas of both of which it sold in a variety of sizes. In addition, one could buy leather pouffes, copper water jugs, wooden boxes inlaid with brass or ivory, carved camels, red felt fezzes, alabaster ash trays and a working model of a water-raising system called a shadoof, which I coveted but was forbidden to purchase by my father in case it harboured woodworm. Without his knowing, my mother bought me a small wooden camel supposedly devoid of insect infestation.

That evening the *Corfu* left the dock to join a line of vessels waiting to sail through the Suez Canal; the following morning she started down it. Along the west bank ran a road and a railway line. It seemed bizarre to be travelling on a ship through a desert dotted with low, square houses and palm trees. Moving at only six or seven knots, it was not long before a train overtook the ship, and cars and trucks continually passed it on the road.

By late morning the dry heat was oppressive. My mother insisted I wore a white straw sunhat at all times. As it resembled a cross between a Mexican sombrero and a surrealist's lampshade, I contrived to forget it whenever possible, eventually managing to engineer for the detestable thing to blow over the side, only to discover the ship's shop had a seemingly inexhaustible supply of them.

Despite the blowers being on full blast and the porthole wide open, our cabin still reverberated with heat like the sides of a blast furnace. Luncheon consisted of a green salad in a bowl immersed in a tray of ice. Even the sliced roast beef was served to us on plates set in beds of ice.

My mother spent the afternoon wallowing in the ship's minuscule swimming pool or lounging in a deck chair wearing tight, brief shorts and a blouse with flounced sleeves. Meanwhile, my father busied himself with his binoculars, watching out for shipping coming the opposite way and dhows that looked as if they had recently set sail out of the child's illustrated edition of the Old Testament that Granny had given me the previous Christmas.

Gradually, the desert receded and the air cooled slightly. Around dusk, the lights of Port Suez twinkled in the hot night air and, shortly afterwards, we entered the Red Sea which, to my disappointment the following morning, was not in the least red.

Nevertheless, the ocean provided diversions. Dolphins cavorted ahead of the bow wave and we were permitted, under the supervision of a deck officer, to go for'ard to the fo'c's'le (as my father would have it) and look down on them. They were sleek and grey, the colour of torpedoes. On occasion, they swam on their sides, the better to look up at us. Flying fish scudded over the waves, their fins outspread like grotesque, ribbed wings. Off the Horn of Africa, a vast pod of at least fifty whales was sighted, blowing and diving.

At seven o'clock—or nineteen hundred hours, as my father preferred— my mother, having seen me into my bunk, would join my father for cocktails and dinner. Although, once in the tropics, the formal dress code for the dining room was waived, my father insisted on wearing a lounge suit when all that was demanded was a tie. This embarrassed my mother and, one afternoon between Aden and Bombay, it created an argument conducted *sotto voce* in my cabin. I only heard a part of it, eavesdropping at the door.

'. . . but it's unnecessary, Ken,' I heard my mother say. 'You stand out.'

'Just because the mercury touches eighty, Joyce, it doesn't mean we have to abandon all our bloody standards.'

'You know what they call you, don't you? Commodore Blimp.'

'I don't give a bloody damn,' my father answered. 'I'll wear what I bloody like, when I bloody like, where I bloody like. It's a free bloody country, thanks to the likes of me.'

'Here we go,' I heard my mother say. 'Tell me, Ken, I forget: which submarine did you serve on? Which landing craft did you command on D-Day?'

'Don't you ever speak like that to me again, Joyce, or . . .'

'Or? Or what, Ken? A divorce? My! That would look good on your record sheet, wouldn't it? A real blot. And what about Martin?'

'What about him?' my father answered.

I decided to make myself scarce, and scurried away down the corridor.

Every evening, shortly before eight o'clock and the sounding of the chimes for dinner, my mother would return to the cabin with two silver-plated bowls. One contained salted potato crisps, the other small pickled gherkins speared by cocktail sticks shaped like arrows and bearing the ship's name. I had never come across either delicacy in England and saw them as harbingers of a new and wondrously strange life to come.

MY MOTHER detested Bombay. The streets were dirty, the buildings decrepit, and the beggars persistent and frequently mutilated. The liberty with which cattle wandered about, dunging where they chose, also disturbed her.

I asked what cows were doing wandering in the city.

'They're considered holy,' my mother said. 'People here worship them.'

This struck me as too bizarre to be true. Yet, with each port of call, I was realising that the world was not as I had anticipated.

Later, I was shown—from a discreet distance—the Parsee death tower. My father explained that the Parsees did not bury their dead but left them for the vultures to eat. No sooner had I been told this than a flurry of plump crows took to the wing from the tower, several trailing ribbons of flesh from their beaks. They flew into a nearby park to squabble over their bounty. Meanwhile, the vultures, with their naked necks and hooked beaks, perched in the flame-of-the-forest trees, preening themselves and letting go pressurised streams of excrement onto the flowerbeds and monkeys below.

Yet the memory of Bombay that was to linger was of a scrawny cat on the dock. It came slinking out of the shadows each of the two evenings the *Corfu* was berthed alongside. Its ribs and shoulder blades protruded through its skin and it had a bloody, torn ear. I tossed it a gherkin, which it ignored, but it relished the potato crisps. The night before we were due to sail, I tried to persuade my mother that we should give it a good home, but she resolutely refused. Finally, she allowed me one concession. She led me down the gang-way and along the quay, where I placed two cocktail sausages and a pile of crisps on the quayside, to keep the cat going until its ear healed. I then climbed into my bunk just in time to watch through the porthole as an urchin ran to the food, crammed it into his mouth and fled.

In contrast, Colombo was paradisaical. We arrived in the early afternoon, tying up to a mooring about a mile out. In the distance were beaches of coral sand fringed with palms. No sooner were the ship's engines shut down than a plethora of small naked boys appeared in the sea off the starboard side. Bronzed and lithe, they must have swum out from the shore. Shouting up to the passengers, they invited us to throw money down to them. As each coin struck the surface, it quickly sank. The boys dived after them. As they were stark naked, I could not understand where they stored their booty.

'They put the coins in their mouths,' my mother said.

After half an hour, a canoe arrived on the scene, sculled by a wizened old man and a girl of about twelve. The boys clambered into the boat, arched themselves forward and either spat out or retched up—I was not sure which—a substantial amount of small change. The old man rowed back to shore, the boys following him like brown porpoises.

That evening, we went ashore in a motorboat to a wooden jetty. We were met by Auntie Cis and Uncle Bud, my father's cousin and her husband. They piled us into a vast black Humber saloon and drove us in the tropical twilight to their home at Mount Lavinia, on the coast south of Colombo.

Our destination was a rambling bungalow with a wide verandah. The pillars supporting the roof were ornately carved with snarling demons. Upon the verandah stood rattan furniture and a number of collapsible chairs. Oil lamps hung from hooks or stood on the table. Drinks were served by an almost black-skinned, barefoot man in a patterned sarong. My parents drank gin and tonic but I was given a tall glass filled with an opaque liquid in which were suspended small white flecks. I tentatively sipped it. It was exquisite, cooling and strangely sweet. I asked Uncle Bud what it was.

'Coconut juice,' he replied.

'Where do you buy it?' I enquired.

'We don't,' Uncle Bud answered. A ripple of night breeze teasing the lanterns was followed by a dense thud in the darkness. 'There's your answer.'

He called the manservant, who led me into the night to pick up a coconut the size of my head.

'Now you know why we don't park the cars under palm trees,' Uncle Bud declared.

Two DAYS out of Colombo, we skirted the northern tip of Sumatra and headed east across the Strait of Malacca, bound for Penang. A small British colony founded in 1786, it consisted of an island bearing the main settlement of Georgetown and a parcel of the Malayan mainland opposite. We went ashore to walk along an esplanade, drink lemonade and look at a number of squat colonial buildings. My parents then decided we should take the funicular railway to the summit of Flagstaff Hill, from which, my father declared, one was afforded a panoramic view of Georgetown.

The funicular took twenty minutes to arrive at its destination, passing over viaducts and through dense expanses of jungle. Halfway up the mountain the carriage slowed, and a troop of several dozen macaques materialised out of the undergrowth. They swung in through the carriage windows and grabbed what they could with proficiency. One seized on my father's binoculars and, finding them attached to him by a strap, proceeded to chew through the leather. My father batted it away, only to have a second monkey take its place. Another grabbed my sombrero lampshade hat.

'Let him have it!' my mother wailed. 'Let him have it!'

I willingly complied.

'Don't resist! Don't let them bite!' one of the other passengers from the *Corfu* yelled, a plump woman in a sundress. 'They'll be rabid!' She turned to my mother. 'I lost my first-born to rabies at a tin mine upcountry from Ipoh.'

As my mother hugged me to her bosom, in much the same fashion as one of the monkeys clutched its own infant, nimble fingers skilfully plucked a handkerchief from her blouse pocket not two inches from my eye.

In less than a minute, the raiding party retreated into the jungle, followed by a hail of pebbles hurled far too late by the funicular brakeman. Once in the cover, they chattered and screamed and howled. Victory was theirs.

On our way back down the mountain, I caught a brief glimpse of my detested sunhat hanging from a thorny creeper, shredded. There were, I subsequently discovered with ill-disguised glee, none left in the ship's shop.

IN SINGAPORE, our next port of call, we were greeted by a friend of my father's who whisked us off in a large black Cadillac at breakneck speed. I noticed a submachine gun propped against the front seat between the driver and my father. At intervals along the road were stationed Bren gun carriers or armoured scout cars with soldiers sitting in them.

After half an hour of driving we turned off down a gravelled drive, at the gates to which were posted several British soldiers in a sandbagged emplacement. They wore steel helmets covered in camouflage netting stuck through with leafy twigs, the muzzle of a heavy machine gun protruding through a gap in the sandbags. I asked why there were so many soldiers.

'It's the Emergency,' our host told me. 'A war between the British and the Malayan Communist Party.'

I wanted to ask why but my father cast me a keep-your-mouth-shut look.

We had arrived at an extensive bungalow surrounded by gardens of huge, fanlike travellers' palms, elephant-eared banana trees and cycads, a plant dating back to the time of the dinosaurs. By the verandah was a virtually leafless tree in full blossom, its perfume exquisite. Our host informed me it was a frangipani. The entire garden was enclosed by coils of barbed wire.

We had a hurried lunch, after which I was permitted to play in the garden—overseen by two Chinese men—and an equally hurried tea, and then we were driven once more at speed back to Singapore and the *Corfu*.

'Why did we have guns in the car?' I asked my mother that night as she brought me my gherkins and crisps.

'We could have been ambushed by terrorists,' she answered.

The following night, my parents attended a formal end-of-voyage dinner, my mother dressed in a long evening gown, my father in a tuxedo. They cut a dashing couple. The next day we spent packing. I realised that all I had to show for my voyage halfway round the world was a collection of cocktail sticks, the small wooden camel and a coconut. My mother persuaded me to abandon the last of these, but not until the cabin steward had drained the juice from it, which I sipped slowly, as if it were ambrosia.

I WOKE on the morning of June 2 to find the sea outside my porthole hardly moving by. I dressed quickly and went up on deck, where my mother was standing at the rail. The *Corfu* was sailing slowly into a narrow channel. On the starboard side were scrub-covered mountains descending to a treacherous rock-strewn shore. To port were more steep hillsides intersected by several bays containing sandy beaches. The summits of the mountains were lost in a thick fog. The air was warm and humid.

'That's Hong Kong,' my mother remarked.

The *Corfu* steamed slowly to port round a headland lined with warehouses. I crossed to the starboard rail. A peninsula of land culminating in some docks and a railway station jutted out towards the ship. Behind them was a city of low buildings. In the distance were undulating mountains, free of mist. Rejoining my mother at the port rail, I discovered that the *Corfu* was moving slowly past a city that extended up the slopes of the mountains behind. In the centre were two tall buildings and a Royal Naval dockyard, the basin and quays lined with grey-painted warships.

'That dockyard is HMS *Tamar*,' my father said. 'And that ship there,' he pointed to a grey vessel devoid of armaments, 'is a Royal Fleet Auxiliary. An RFA. I'll be on one of them. RFA *Fort Charlotte*.'

The *Corfu* eased round to moor alongside a jetty on the western side of the peninsula. Immigration officials came on board. Disembarkation formalities completed, my father met a naval officer dressed as he was in a tropical white uniform but with his rank in black and gold braid epaulettes on his shoulders. Our cabin baggage was collected from our cabins by two Chinese naval ratings. Neither, to my relief, had his hair in a pigtail.

At exactly noon, as signified by the dull boom of a cannon somewhere across the harbour, we walked down the gangway and into a large, dark blue saloon car with the letters *RN* painted on the side in white.

2

The drive to our lodgings, the Grand Hotel, took but minutes. My room was on the third floor next to my parents'. I stepped onto its narrow balcony the moment the door was opened, to look down upon a street lined with shops. Directly below me was a rickshaw stand, the coolies who pulled them squatting or lying between the shafts of their vehicles. Those not asleep smoked short pipes, the sweetly pungent fumes rising up to tease my nostrils.

Before I could begin to unpack my suitcase, my mother entered. She ran a damp flannel over my face and a wet comb through my hair, then hustled me down to the hotel lobby and out into the dark blue saloon once again.

'Where are we going?' I asked.

'Lunch,' my father replied sternly. 'And mind your p's and q's.'

The saloon drove through a gateway guarded by two army sentries and pulled up in front of a large, long Nissen hut. Inside was a large dining room with a bar at one end and rattan tables and chairs. We were joined by the officer who had met us on the *Corfu* and we sat at a table. A Chinese waiter dressed in loose black trousers, a white jacket and black felt slippers took our order for drinks. I requested lemonade, but the officer ordered me a brown-coloured drink in a green fluted bottle with a straw in it.

'What is it, sir?' I enquired, heedful of my father's instruction that I was to address all men as *sir* unless I knew them very well indeed.

'It's called Coca-Cola. If you don't like it,' the officer replied, 'you don't have to drink it and I'll get you that lemonade.'

He was not to know it, but that first day in Hong Kong he started me on a lifelong addiction. The same thing happened when we came to order our meal. To be on the safe side, I asked for an egg and cress salad. A salad appeared before me with, arranged around it, some bizarre, pink, curled objects with long feelers, a battery of legs and black shoe-button eyes.

'Prawns,' the officer said, leaning across the table to me in a conspiratorial fashion. He picked one up and deftly stripped off its carapace with his thumbnail, dipping it in a ramekin of mayonnaise and holding it out to me. I bit it in half and another addiction was given its first rush.

At the end of the meal, the officer shook my hand.

'A word of advice, my lad,' he said. 'So long as you are in Hong Kong, whenever someone offers you something to eat, accept it. That's being polite. If you don't find it to your fancy, don't have any more. But'—he looked me straight in the eye—'always try it. No matter what. Promise?'

I was never to break my promise.

As dusk fell, the street below my balcony at the Grand Hotel underwent a transformation. Hoardings and shop signs erupted in numerous shades of neon colour. The lights were thin neon tubes shaped into Chinese characters, English letters, watches, diamonds, jackets, cameras and even animals. Just down the road, a restaurant bore a red and yellow dragon ten feet high.

That evening, my parents were invited to a welcoming cocktail party and I was left in the care of the hotel child-minding service, a middle-aged Chinese woman with her black oiled hair scraped into a tight bun.

'This is Ah Choo,' my mother said.

I collapsed into paroxysms of laughter, which were promptly silenced by a stern maternal grimace.

'Ah Choo is the hotel baby amah,' my mother went on.

'What's an amah?' I enquired, ignoring the implication that I was a baby.

'A female servant,' my mother replied, 'and you'll do exactly as she tells you. Exactly!' She turned to the amah. 'Ah Choo, this is my son, Martin.'

'Huwwo, Mahtung,' the amah replied, then, looking at my mother, said, 'You can go, missee, I look-see Mahtung. He good boy for me.'

The first thing Ah Choo attempted to do after my parents had departed was undress me. I had not been undressed before by anyone save my mother and grandmothers and I wasn't going to let this diminutive, alien stranger called Sneeze be the first. As soon as she unfastened one button and turned to the next, I did the first up again. Finally, unable to undo more than three shirt buttons at a time, she gave up, informing me, 'You bafu w'eddy.' Going out of the room, she left me to disrobe and wash myself.

I gave her a few minutes, wet the bar of foul-scented hotel soap, pulled the bath plug and glanced outside the bathroom. She was not in my bedroom. The door to the corridor was open. Leaving the room, I headed nimbly down the stairs. The street called to me.

Buzzing with the frisson of an explorer stepping into unmapped territory, I made off down the street. The first shop I stopped at was a jeweller's. In the illuminated window, gold chains glistened enticingly. Inside the shop stood a sailor, his arm round the waist of a young Chinese woman wearing a very tight dress. The sides of the garment were slit to the top of her thigh. When she moved, her entire leg was visible. I had never seen anything like it.

The sailor's uniform was different from a British naval rating's. It was all white with blue edging and insignia, topped off with a pillbox hat that made me think of Popeye. His sleeves were rolled up to his armpits, showing the tattoo of an anchor. As I watched him, he slid his hand in one of the slits in the dress and squeezed the young woman's buttocks. She made no sign of complaint, and I wondered if this was how one greeted all Chinese women.

The shop door opened and the pair came out.

'Hey, kid!' the sailor addressed me. 'How yah doin'?'

'I'm not doing anything, sir,' I answered defensively.

'Where d'yah live, kid?' asked the sailor. I pointed down the street. 'Well, y' come along now, y' hear? Ain't right for yah to be out so late.'

They walked me back to the Grand Hotel, passing me into the custody of the desk clerk.

Back in my room, Ah Choo had run another bath. I undressed, washed and put on my pyjamas. I was tying the cord when Ah Choo came in, bending down to gather up my clothing. I seized the moment to test my rudimentary understanding of local etiquette and squeezed one of her buttocks.

She stood bolt upright as if a lightning shaft had run along her spine.

Turning sharply to face me, she exclaimed, 'You v'wy lautee boy, Mahtung!' Yet, behind her indignation there lingered a smile.

She put me to bed and left. I slid out of bed and went onto the balcony. The rickshaw coolies were sharing a saucepan of rice, on top of which was a complete boiled fish. I watched as they dissected it with their chopsticks. Opposite my balcony was a tenement building that housed a workshop over a tailor's establishment. Under the blaze of strip lights, a dozen men deftly cut and sewed suits. Next door, four men shuffled what looked to me to be cream-coloured dominoes, which rattled loudly on the metal table top.

I climbed into bed and fell asleep to the staccato rattle of the game tiles, the traffic, and the occasional raised voice or laugh from the rickshaw coolies.

The next morning, I woke with a nagging headache. So did my parents.

Sitting at breakfast, my mother remarked, 'I hope we're not all coming down with something.'

'You didn't sleep well, Joyce,' my father observed. 'Tossing and turning . . .'

'Well,' she answered, 'what with the whine of the fan, the clatter of that infernal mah-jong game opposite and the stench of the rickshaw coolies' pipes, is it any wonder? I really don't think, Ken, we can go on staying here.'

I was not a little dismayed. I wanted to explore more of the streets.

'I like it here,' I chipped in. Then, hoping to justify my statement, added, 'I like the smell of the coolies' pipes.'

For a long moment, my parents looked at each other.

'That does it!' my father agreed. 'We move as soon as we can. Another week here and we'll all be ruddy opium addicts.'

THE NEXT SEVEN DAYS were filled with activity. My father prepared to join his ship at the Sasebo naval base in Japan. I was enrolled in Kowloon Junior School, and kitted out with khaki shorts and white short-sleeved shirts.

During this time, we stayed with a colleague of my father's in a spacious bungalow halfway up a mountain on Hong Kong Island, which I was told was known as Hong Kong-side, the peninsula upon which we were to live being referred to as Kowloon-side. Many places were suffixed with -side: shop-side, beach-side, office-side, school-side and so on.

The air was much cooler at the bungalow. The only sounds were birdsong and, in the evenings, the metallic click of the geckos encircling the ceiling lights to pick off small moths, gnats and mosquitoes. We slept under mosquito nets: the bungalow was above the Wong Nei Chong valley, an infamously malarial area in the early days of the colony.

The verdant undergrowth of the hillsides coming right down to the edge of the bungalow garden encouraged more than insects into the house. On our third morning, the houseboy woke me with a gentle shake.

'Young master,' he addressed me in hushed tones. 'You come. Slowly, slowly. No makee noise.'

With that, he led me out on to the verandah, where everyone else in the house—servants and residents—were gathered.

The man who lived in the bungalow with his wife and a son six years my senior, muttered, 'Don't make a sound or move a muscle, old boy.'

In the sitting room, the gardener and another Chinese man seemed to be rearranging the furniture. Suddenly, one of them darted behind a rattan settee and scrabbled about on the parquet floor.

When he stood up, the Chinese muttered *Ayarh!* in unison. In his hand, held by its neck between thumb and index finger, was a cobra over four feet long, its hood expanding and contracting against the man's palm. He carried it onto the lawn and killed it by cracking it once, like a whip. The tenant of the bungalow gave the gardener and his companion a purple dollar bill each.

'That'll make a nice purse,' my mother remarked as the gardener walked off with the reptile's carcass.

'I doubt they'll take the snake to a tanner,' came the answer. 'They'll cook it. The Chinese'll eat anything that can move under its own locomotion.'

FIVE DAYS after arriving in Hong Kong, we booked into two adjacent rooms on the third floor of the Fourseas Hotel at 75 Waterloo Road, Kowloon. It was a modern three-storey block with modest gardens and a short, crescent-shaped driveway, built on one of the main thoroughfares running down the Kowloon peninsula. My parents' room had a balcony: mine did not. On either side of the hotel were low-rise apartment buildings, while opposite was the bare dome of a hillside rising about a hundred feet from the street.

'This is definitely a leg-up,' my mother declared as, for the third time in a week, she unpacked our cases. 'Now, if you ever get lost, this hotel is called *sei hoi jau dim* in Cantonese. You say that to a taxi driver and he'll bring you home safe and sound and the receptionist will pay him. Repeat it.'

These were my first words in Cantonese. I realised that, as many Chinese spoke no English, if I wanted to explore I would need a command of their language. In next to no time, I possessed a substantial vocabulary, ranging from a polite *Nei wui mui gong ying mun?* (Do you speak English?) to such commonly used colloquialisms as *Diu nei lo mo*, which implied anything from Well, I never did! to Don't bullshit me, you sonofabitch! And worse.

Early the following Monday, my father reported to Kai Tak airport to depart for Japan. My mother was very anxious, not because my father was in effect heading for a theatre of war—Korea—but because he was flying out of Hong Kong. According to my father, the wind direction was crucial to a successful take-off. If at all possible, aircraft took off towards the southeast, the runway aiming for the sea. However, rarely, aircraft had to take off facing inland. This meant that as soon as it was clear of the ground the aircraft had to veer sharp left to avoid crashing into the Kowloon hills. These rose to nearly 1,900 feet, two miles from the end of the runway.

Pilots regarded it as one of the most dangerous airports in the world.

Standing at the steps of an RAF twin-engined McDonnell Douglas 'Dakota' DC3, my parents atypically hugged each other for several minutes. My father then bent down, gave me a cursory embrace and shook my hand.

'While I'm away, look after your mother,' he ordered. 'You're the man of the family now.'

It was a pure Hollywood moment.

'Yes,' I replied. I was about to enquire how to do it but my father was already at the aircraft door. A moment of fear swept through me. I had been given a serious task, yet how could I, in my ignorance, hope to do it efficiently? Even before the DC3 took off, I was dreading my father's return.

The engines started and the plane taxied to the southeastern extremity of the runway. It was to be a take-off into the mountains.

The Dakota rumbled forwards. Its tail wheel lifted off the runway, the plane taking to the air. Its ascent seemed excruciatingly slow. For a moment, I was certain it was heading straight for the mountains.

'I can't watch,' my mother declared. Shaking, she studied her shoes.

At what seemed the last minute, the DC3 banked sharply to the left. It flew along the face of the hills, climbing slowly, levelled out and began its gradual ascent until it disappeared in the haze of the day.

'What's happened?' my mother asked, almost in tears.

'Nothing,' I said. 'It's flown so far away we can't see or hear it.'

A Royal Navy saloon car took us back to the Fourseas Hotel.

'When does Daddy come back?' I enquired.

'In about twelve weeks,' my mother replied. 'On his ship,' she added.

'What happens if I don't look after you very well?' I said anxiously.

'Don't you worry,' my mother answered. 'You'll do just fine.'

The Thursday after my father's departure, I started school.

Since the age of five, I had attended a small dame school in Brentwood. Operated by a kindly, elderly spinster called Miss Hutt, Rose Valley School provided a sound basic schooling from the huge, dark front room of a mid-Victorian terraced house, where a dozen pupils aged from five to twelve hunched round two old dining tables. At the back of the house, the garden had been covered with cinders to make a playground of sorts.

By contrast, Kowloon Junior was a long, two-storey building with verandah corridors, bright, airy classrooms with ceiling fans and individual desks. Everyone wore a uniform, which somehow gave the place an added appeal. Outside, the playground was beaten earth with patches of grass surrounded by a chain-link fence. In one place, the fence stopped at a vertical earth bank into which the boys had cut mountain roadways for Dinky cars.

The school was less than a mile from the Fourseas, so I walked there most days, my mother at first seeing me across Waterloo Road. If it was raining, I was sent in a scarlet-painted rickshaw with a green pram-like hood.

Riding in a rickshaw was a strange sensation. When one stepped between the shafts onto a footboard in front of a padded seat and sat down, the whole contraption was sloping forwards and downwards. I had to hold on to the sides to stop sliding off. When the coolie picked up the shafts, the rickshaw tipped back and the passenger fell to the rear of the seat.

The coolie set off at a walk, building to a steady trot. His bent arms acted like springs, reducing the shock of the road bumps for his body. The coolies were usually bare to the waist, except in winter, and one could see their muscles flexing across their shoulders. Most of them were sallow, with sunken chests and gaunt faces. They looked old enough to be Confucian sages, but were almost certainly no older than their late twenties. A rickshaw coolie seldom reached thirty-five. Virtually every one of them was an opium addict.

They wore small, domed rattan hats with numbers painted in scarlet on them: it was from these I learned to count and read numbers in Cantonese— *yat*, *yee*, *sam*, *sei*, *ng*, *lok*, and the coolies were called by their numbers. Of the half-dozen who lingered near the hotel, I always chose number three, hailing him by shouting, 'Ah Sam!' I never knew his real name.

In a letter to her mother, my mother wrote, *Ken gone to Japan. Lonely.* To counteract her solitude she turned to me, and I found myself exploring Kowloon with her.

We started after school one afternoon by going to the Peninsula Hotel for tea. Known locally as the Pen, the hotel was considered one of the best in the world. We sat in the grand entrance lobby, surrounded by gilded pillars and serenaded by a string quartet. Silver pots of tea were served with wafer-thin sandwiches and delicate little cakes. My mother was in seventh heaven. When the bill was discreetly presented, she blanched.

'Martin, go outside and wait round the back of the hotel. I'll be out in a moment,' she said abruptly.

I did as I was told. Five minutes later, my mother appeared, walking briskly along the street. Taking hold of my hand as if I were a baton in a relay race, she headed for the nearest bus stop.

Yet my mother was a woman of honour. Returning the following afternoon, she made straight for the head waiter's desk. Holding out the previous day's bill and payment, she blushingly explained the situation. He consulted the maître d'hôtel. I am sure my mother was anticipating the view from the nearest police lockup. The maître d'hôtel, a Frenchman, said, 'Madame, these accidents may happen.' He closed her fingers over the bill and money in her hand. 'Please, be our guest for tea this afternoon.'

Leaving the Pen, my mother made her way down Hankow Road, window-shopping. She paused outside the Hing Loon Curio and Jewellery Company. Something in the window caught her eye and we entered.

The interior of the shop was like a treasure cave. Glass cabinets contained cloisonné trinkets, ebony carvings, ivory figures and beads, trays of gold rings, displays of gold chains, pendants and brooches.

The proprietor, Mr Chan, approached my mother, smiling. 'You like a drink? Very hot today. You like a Coke, Green Spot, San Mig?'

My mother, feeling it impolite not to accept such a kind invitation, went for a San Mig. Mr Chan poured her an ice-cold beer. I, being adventurous, asked for a Green Spot and was passed a bottle of sickly orange juice.

The drink was a means of keeping a would-be customer in the shop. For twenty minutes, we sat on leather-topped stools in front of a glass-topped counter. My mother bought a curio or two to send 'home', which meant Britain. When she was done, Mr Chan asked me, 'What year you born?'

'Nineteen forty-four,' I replied.

'What mumf?'

'September.'

'You *mahlo*.' From a cabinet behind him, he produced a small, crudely carved ivory monkey. 'For you,' he said, handing it to me. 'I see you again.'

Mr Chan was to be my mother's jeweller for the rest of his life and his two sons thereafter until the end of her life. She never bought a single item of jewellery from any other Hong Kong shop.

Before long the wives of my father's colleagues began to invite my mother out during the day, and to dinner or cocktail parties in the evenings. When this social whirl began in earnest, she delegated the job of seeing me safely to and from school to one of the hotel room boys. Tall for a Chinese, he was handsome, in his late twenties and spoke English without the usual Cantonese pronunciation. His full name was Leung Chi-ching, but we called him Ching. Every morning he guided me across the traffic on Waterloo Road, Chinese-style. This meant crossing to the central white line and lingering there as vehicles zipped by, waiting for a gap in the traffic to complete the journey to the far pavement. He insisted on carrying my rattan school case—an oblong sort of picnic hamper-cum-briefcase known as a Hong Kong basket—containing my books and some sandwiches.

One day, I asked Ching where he lived. He was reluctant to inform me. However, over the next few days he told me his life story.

His father had been a wealthy landlord in Kwangtung province, in China. I asked how he came to speak such good English. He replied that his father had been rich enough to send him to a good Christian missionary school.

'Then, when I was seventeen years old, there was much fighting. It was Communist Chinese fighting Kuomintang Chinese.'

'What are Kuo—' I began.

'Nationalist Chinese,' Ching explained. 'The army of Generalissimo Chiang Kai-shek.'

'What happened?' I asked.

'They lost,' Ching said candidly. 'Then the Communist soldiers came, and the officers, and they took away my father's land and our house. Our belongings were taken, our farm animals killed.'

'What happened to you?'

'We were told to go, so we went. If we had not they would have killed us. They killed our friends who refused to go. I came to Hong Kong.'

'Why do you work as a hotel room boy?' I ventured.

'I have no money,' Ching answered. There was no regret in his voice. 'All I have are my clothes. When the Communists drove us away, we could only take what we could carry. There are many, many people like me in Hong Kong who have escaped from the Communists. At least half the room boys have. Some with their families, some, like me, alone.'

I felt a terrible sadness for Ching and took hold of his hand. 'You've got me and my mum,' I said comfortingly.

I never discovered where Ching laid his head.

A week or so later, my mother was invited out to a dinner party on Hong Kong Island. It was already dark before she left for the Star Ferry to cross the harbour. I waited a respectable time, got dressed and walked out of the hotel tradesmen's door. I turned left and headed for Soares Avenue.

The streets were warm, the air heavy with the scents of exotic food cooking in the tenements. Above the sound of passing cars was a trill of argumentative birdsong from the trees. Finches in bamboo cages, hung outside the tenement windows for an evening airing, joined in.

Walking along the streets was mildly hazardous. First, one was dripped on from laundry hanging out over the street on bamboo poles. Second, and less benign, one could be hit by a chicken bone or other detritus from a meal. Ching later explained to me that in China one threw waste food into the street and the local pigs or dogs ate it. That there were no pigs wandering the streets of Kowloon seemed immaterial to the residents.

In Soares Avenue there was a line of shops. They did not have front windows, being more like square caves. One sold kitchen utensils. Shallow cast-iron woks hung from hooks overhead; a shelf bore rice steamers. Packets of chopsticks, rice bowls, porcelain spoons tied together with string, soy sauce dispensers, teapots decorated with red and gold dragons and handle-less teacups stood or lay in profusion on a trestle table.

Moving on, I came to a fruit seller. He sold oranges, lemons, bananas and apples, but the remainder of his stock might well have been picked on another planet—waxy-looking star-shaped fruit reminiscent of my grandmother's hat flowers, huge grapefruit-like citrus fruits, knobbly custard apples, deep sea-green watermelons, spiky ovals I discovered to be durians, and what appeared to be short lengths of leafless tree branch.

The shopkeeper spoke to me, picking up the grapefruit-like pomelo and holding it out. I said, '*M'ho cheen*,' (no money) and patted my pockets. He laughed, took out a knife, sliced open the pomelo and offered me a segment.

I said, '*Dor jei*,' (thank you) and put it in my mouth. It was sweet and tart at the same time. '*Ho!*' I said and I meant it. It was very good.

The fruit seller smiled and picked up one of the lengths of branch. It was pale silvery-green and about an inch thick. He shaved the bark from all of its length but a few inches at one end, with which he handed it to me. I had no idea what to do with it. Seeing this he prepared another length, bit some off the end and chewed it. I followed suit. It was sugar cane, saturated with syrupy sap. When he had sucked the stringy cane dry, he spat it out on the pavement. I copied him. Then a fish head hit me on the shoulder. I was, I considered, now at one with the streets, duly initiated and baptised.

I MADE FRIENDS at school but rarely visited my friends' homes or spent time with them away from the classroom or playground. My life was centred on the Fourseas and the adjacent streets and alleyways.

In one fetid passageway, I came across a family of four who lived in a large packing crate. They had nailed a sheet of tin to their abode to protect it against the elements, put a plank across the entrance to stop rubbish drifting in and stood the crate on four short blocks to keep it clear of the rainwater that cascaded down the alley. When the hotel started to redecorate some of the public rooms, replacing the venetian blinds with curtains, the manager agreed to give me one of the blinds. I gave it to the family to hang over the crate entrance. They were delighted with it, but a week or so later they had vanished. So had the crate. I never saw them again.

My primary circle of acquaintances consisted of the shopkeepers to whom I was introduced by the fruit seller, whose name was Mr Tsang. Next door but two to Mr Tsang was a tiny shop squeezed into the sloping space under a staircase. It consisted of a display counter with a pigeonhole arrangement of shelves behind it. Owned by an elderly man, it sold note-books, Biros, rubbers, rulers, toy guns, playing cards, glass marbles and combs. It also sold something that at first bemused me. Packed into small cardboard boxes were what appeared to be clay marbles. I picked one up and put it between my thumb and forefinger as if to flick it marble fashion. The store owner shook his head. Then, taking the clay ball, he waited for a break in the traffic and tossed it into the road. It exploded loudly with a drift of clay dust. A passing rickshaw coolie volubly cursed. I returned in min-utes with a dollar and bought a boxful. They were confiscated the following morning by the teacher on playground duty, who informed me they were called cherry bombs and they were illegal. A letter was sent home to my mother and I was roundly chastised. At the same time, I felt that my mother did not entirely disapprove. From that moment, I knew she was not averse to my wandering the streets, and I began ranging more widely.

I traversed Nathan Road, the main artery running up the spine of Kowloon, to enter the district of Yau Ma Tei. Many of the three- or four-storey residential buildings were old, their balconies lined with green-glazed railings, patterned to look like bamboo. The roofs of some were covered in green-glazed tiles and curved up at the eaves. A few bore ceramic ridge tiles of dragons and lions in faded blue, red or gold.

The shops were more traditional than those in Soares Avenue. A bakery sold soft bread buns with red writing stamped on them. Dried fish shops displayed desiccated shrimps, squid, cuttlefish, scallops, mussels, sharks' fins and other unidentifiable seafood. Butchers offered raw meat hanging from hooks under 100-watt bulbs beneath red plastic shades. Poultry shops sold live chickens, ducks, quails, pheasants and geese, crammed into bamboo cages. No self-esteeming Chinese housewife bought fowl that was not still breathing and it was commonplace to see someone walking down a street with two trussed clucking hens.

One afternoon I wandered into a back-street butchery and was suddenly confronted by the corpse of a black chow dog hanging by a hook. Its black tongue hung down from its mouth. No sooner had I seen it than the butcher arrived, and, swearing volubly, turfed me out into the street. From subsequent questioning of Ching I ascertained that the Chinese ate dogs—black ones, preferably. Dog-eating was illegal in Hong Kong, however, because the *gweilos* liked dogs as pets.

Rice vendors were prevalent in Yau Ma Tei, displaying several dozen types of rice in open sacks or, if they were of special quality, in dark polished barrels with brass hoops. I was fascinated by the egg shops too, where fresh duck and chicken eggs were on offer alongside dried egg yolks and 100- (or 1,000-) year-old eggs. These preserved duck eggs were prepared by soaking them in strong tea then rolling them in a coating of wood ash, salt and lime. They were stored in a huge earthenware jar and surrounded by fine, rich soil, then left for just over three months, during which time the yolk hardened and turned grey-green, the white of the egg turning into a semi-transparent black jelly that looked like onyx. They were then stored in an airtight jar sealed with candle or beeswax. When consumed, they were usually taken raw as an hors d'oeuvre.

Several streets were lined by food stalls known as *dai pai dongs*, from which exotic and enticing aromas wafted. One evening, I hoisted myself onto a stool and asked for one of the preserved eggs. It was served sliced on a plate with pickled sweet vegetables and a dipping bowl of Chinese vinegar, rice wine, soy sauce and thinly sliced ginger. I picked up the chopsticks. A crowd gathered. The spectacle of a blond European boy sitting at a *dai pai dong* alone of an evening was more than most could resist.

Tentatively I picked up a piece of yolk, dipped it in the sauce and ate it. The taste was unique, savoury and rich and not at all egg-like. The stallholder put a bowl of steaming green tea before me. I held it up as if giving a toast. The crowd applauded, laughed and gradually dispersed, not a few of them touching my head in passing. When I was done, the stallholder refused payment. I tried to press him. He refused again. I then saw why. I had brought him good luck. He had not a vacant stool.

My excursions into what my mother referred to as Darkest Kowloon were, during term time, limited to the late afternoon and early evening. This was an exciting time. The *dai pai dongs* commenced a vibrant trade. Stalls appeared selling clothes, shoes, kitchenware and bolts of cloth. The streets filled with shoppers or those merely out for a stroll.

Just off Nathan Road stood a large temple dedicated to the deity Tin Hau, also known as the Queen of Heaven and the protectress of seafarers. Next to it were smaller temples to To Tai, the earth god, Shing Wong, the city god, and She Tan, a local god without, it seemed, a celestial portfolio.

Tin Hau was a major goddess of the first league, and her temple was ornate. The roof ridge was lined with glazed china figurines and the interior woodwork painted deep red. Tin Hau's effigy sat on her altar wearing a Ming dynasty headdress hung with pearls and a red cloak embroidered with gold dragons. Her face was expressionless, painted a garish pink. Before her were brass candlesticks, offerings of oranges and a brass bowl of sand for worshippers to stand their joss sticks in.

In the evenings, crowds flocked to the area in front of the temple to consult fortunetellers, necromancers and phrenologists. The fortunetellers would invite their customers to cast small elliptical pieces of wood or shake numbered bamboo splints out of a bamboo cup, which they would then interpret according to the way they fell. In their midst, an old man, a four-inch-long wisp of grey hair sprouting from a mole on his cheek, sat at a small lectern writing letters for illiterate coolies at five cents a time.

One man held my attention every time. He was seated on a stool, his client perched on another before him. He plucked their eyebrows with tweezers, then either pulled out or clipped their nasal and ear hair. The high point of his service came when he produced a tiny steel spatula and assiduously scraped out his customer's ear wax, which he put into a tiny bottle. What he did with this disgusting gunge was left to my vivid imagination.

On the western edge of Yau Ma Tei was the sea and a typhoon shelter, a large artificial basin surrounded by a sea wall of massive boulders, behind which small craft took shelter during storms. It was also where fishermen landed their catch. Some Saturday mornings, I would go to the shelter to watch the night's haul landed—green and blue-backed crabs and azure lobsters, gold and black mottled grouper, silver needlefish, octopuses, squid, sea cucumbers, long-spined sea urchins, eels, rays and sharks. Nothing, it seemed to me, had been thrown back: everything was up for sale as edible. Even the seaweed snagged in the nets sold for ten cents a bundle.

Three types of vessels predominated in the typhoon shelter. The smallest and most numerous were sampans, ranging from little more than skiffs to boats about fifteen feet long. Constructed of wood, they were propelled by a single stern oar, although some had a short mast with a square-rigged sail. Most had arched canvas awnings that ran their length, beneath which lived a complete family. The majority of sampan dwellers were fishing folk, who cast gill nets or fished with sleek, long-necked cormorants.

I was intrigued by cormorant fishing. When a sampan reached a shoal of fish, the fisherman would let the bird go. With its wings clipped, it could not fly off. It would dive into the sea and catch a fish. However, the bird could not fully swallow its prey because of a ring affixed round its neck. Once the cormorant returned to the sampan, it spat the fish out. When it had caught a few fish, the fisherman would remove the ring, let the bird have a fish as a reward, reaffix the ring and wait for another shoal.

The next boats up in size were the walla-wallas, motorboats that operated round the harbour as water taxis. They acquired their name from the puttering sound their exhaust pipes made when a wave covered them.

Most impressive of all were the ocean-going fishing or trading junks. Three-masters, they lay alongside the typhoon shelter quay like the remnants of the lost age of sail. Made of seasoned teak, some over eighty feet long and twenty wide, they were family enterprises. Infants to grandparents lived on them, as did chickens and ducks, dogs, cats and even pigs.

Not infrequently, I was invited aboard one of these wooden leviathans. My blond hair, considered by the Chinese to be the colour of gold and therefore likely to impart wealth or good fortune, was my passport to many a nook and cranny of Chinese life. It was also the reason why a passer-by would often briefly stroke my head. I was a walking talking talisman.

PERHAPS BECAUSE SHE was lonely, or because her love of animals was getting the better of her, my mother decided she wanted a pet. As we lived in a hotel, a cat or a dog would be impractical, but this did not deter her.

Lee Chun Kee and Company at 646 Nathan Road offered, according to their business card, to 'procure strange animals from all countries'. The walls of the shop were lined with cages containing songbirds, guinea pigs, terrapins, rabbits, sulphur-crested cockatoos, kittens with their eyes barely open, macaws, lovebirds, mynas, puppies with eager tails, budgerigars and canaries. My mother drooled longingly over the kittens and puppies.

We were approached by a man we assumed was Mr Lee. He smiled ingratiatingly. 'You wan' baby dog, missee?' he enquired, swiftly opening a cage door and depositing a puppy in my mother's arms, from where it proceeded to lick her face furiously. I could almost see her heart melting.

Reluctantly, my mother returned the dog and, after much soul-searching, she purchased a budgerigar, a bamboo cage, a porcelain water bowl, a tin seed bowl, a mirror, a bell and two pieces of cuttlefish.

'What shall we call him?' my mother questioned me, as we retraced our steps through the back streets. 'How about Sai Juk?' she suggested.

As this translated as Little Bird, I was not impressed. My mother's desire, which lasted the rest of her life, to give everything—dogs, cats, cars—a Cantonese name did not always show imagination.

In the end, we settled for Joey. He was happy in his cage, kissing his image in the mirror, ringing his bell, and hopping from perch to perch. My mother deemed this insufficient exercise, so every afternoon she closed all the windows and gave Joey the freedom of her hotel room. With a flutter of wings, he darted about the room depositing birdshit wherever he went. This continued for two months until the day my mother omitted to close the fanlight window. Joey was out of the window like a ballistic missile. My mother was devastated and we returned to Mr Lee.

Despite being fully equipped, my mother decided not to get another bird because, she said, 'It's cruel to keep them in cages.' So she bought a terrapin, a glass tank to keep it in and a stone for it to sit on.

About two inches in diameter, its carapace was grey on top with a yellowish-green underside. Its head was yellow and black striped with bright red flashes by the ears. My mother asked Mr Lee what it ate.

'He eat wice, missee. Plenty wice. An' dis one.' He reached under the counter to bring out a container of writhing bloodworms.

My mother recoiled, but it was too late. She had paid for the terrapin.

On the walk back, we determined to call it Timmy, my mother not knowing the Cantonese for terrapin.

Timmy and his tank were delivered an hour later. Convinced that terrapins did not exist on rice and bloodworms, my mother phoned the University of Hong Kong biology department to get the truth, which was that redeared terrapins ate fish. They could also grow to twelve inches in length. Our tank was fifteen inches by ten. Luckily for us, but unluckily for Timmy, he was dead in three months, despite a diet of boiled fish that stank out my mother's room, even when the tank was placed on the balcony so, as my mother put it, he could feel the warmth of the sun on his back. Her consideration may have been what put paid to him. In the wild, terrapins avoided the sun and took to deep water. Timmy's tank water was barely an inch deep.

Timmy's death did not, however, occur before my father's first return. On the second morning of his shore leave, my father stepped out onto the balcony to be confronted by Timmy the terrapin.

'Martin!'

I came running.

'What, for Pete's sake, is this ruddy thing?' He pointed at the noxious tank in which Timmy was perching on his rock.

'It's Timmy,' I replied. 'He's Mum's.'

At that moment, my mother entered the room. 'Joyce, get rid of this bloody thing. It smells to high heaven.'

'That's because his tank needs cleaning. I'm doing it later.' She reached into the tank, picked Timmy up and held him level to her face. His head came out from under his shell, his legs treading air. 'He means no harm,' she remarked and tickled his throat with her fingernail. 'Do you, Timmy?'

'I'm going back on board,' my father declared, bringing the argument to an abrupt conclusion. 'You've got the ship-to-shore number.'

With that, he left, not to return until nightfall.

Despite the escape of Joey and the demise of Timmy, my mother had still not learned her lesson. On another trip to Mr Lee, she purchased a cute lop-eared rabbit, naming it To Jai, which predictably meant Rabbit. This too succumbed in a matter of months. By then my mother had made a number of new friends among the members of the United Services Recreation Club and no longer felt lonely. The cavalcade of pets mercifully ceased.

I HAD BEEN at school only a matter of weeks when the summer holidays began, which posed my mother a problem. She was loath to take me everywhere with her, but just as loath to leave me to my own devices. A compromise was reached. I was given a crossing-the-road examination and restricted to the areas bounded by Nathan Road to the west, Prince Edward Road to the north and the far side of the hill opposite the hotel to the south. To the east, where there was no obvious boundary, I was told to use my discretion. From my mother's viewpoint, there was little risk involved. Muggings were unheard of in Hong Kong, and street violence usually restricted to a territorial fight among hawkers and stallholders. The nearest a European was likely to come to crime was when he had his pocket picked.

In exchange for this liberty, I was to accompany my mother at any time she requested without whining or whingeing. I consented with alacrity.

A day or two into the holidays, my mother tested my submissiveness. She was going to Tsim Sha Tsui that afternoon and I was going with her.

'Are we going to tea at the Pen?' I asked hopefully as we waited for a number seven bus at the stop opposite the hotel.

'No,' she replied. 'Somewhere far better.'

The bus pulled up and we boarded. The conductor rang the bell twice and we set off. We disembarked in Tsim Sha Tsui, an area at the tip of the Kowloon peninsula filled with watch and camera shops, restaurants and tailors. This was where the tourists from the big liners or staying in the better hotels unwittingly mingled with touts and pickpockets.

When we alighted, it was to head through the streets to a small baker's shop. Above a bow window was the establishment's name—Tkachenko's. Inside were a number of rattan chairs and tables. Along one wall ran a glass-fronted cool cabinet containing a cornucopia of sumptuous cakes and pastries: gateaux covered in flaked dark chocolate, fresh fruit tortes, puff pastry slices filled with fresh cream and cherries, and white chocolate éclairs with segments of glacé fruit and angelica embedded in them.

My mother and I sat opposite each other at a table. She ordered a pot of Assam tea, a tumbler of cold milk and four cakes.

'What is this place?' I asked in wonderment.

'A long time ago,' my mother began obtusely, 'there was an uprising in Russia called the Bolshevik Revolution. Many people were killed. Others lost their homes and businesses and had to flee. Some fled to France, a few to London even, but most came east. And where they went, they took their skills with them. And the Russians are famous for their cakes and pastries.'

An elderly European woman, her grey hair in a dishevelled and disintegrating bun at the back of her neck, approached our table with a tray.

'Herrre iss your orderrr, madame,' she announced.

The cakes were summed up by my mother, her upper lip moustachioed with cream. 'If God was a baker,' she said, 'this is what he'd bake.'

THE RESIDENTS of the Fourseas were a mixed bunch. There was a small contingent of British forces wives and children, their men either involved in the Korean War or waiting to be allocated permanent quarters. There was a fluid population of troops billeted in the hotel while in transit to the war. On the rear top storey of one wing, four rooms were occupied by Chinese whores. The rest of the floor was taken up by itinerant American salesmen.

Under my mother's leadership, the expatriate wives forced the hotel manager, a tall, inoffensive and highly educated Chinese man called Mr Peng, to place a large Kelvinator refrigerator in the third-floor lobby for their use: my mother kept New Zealand butter, jam and Tkachenko's cakes in it. She also tried to have the whores evicted, but in vain. They paid well over the going room rate, the troops in transit keeping them busy twenty hours a day at what I came to know as *jig-a-jig*, although I did not know exactly what this entailed. The owner probably regarded them as an asset, for they kept the troops in the hotel buying beers and eating food.

This disparate community was catered for by the room boys. By and large, they were happy young men despite the fact that many, like Ching, were refugees from Communism. They were efficient, thorough and paid a pittance. Yet they were grateful for a job, knowing that only a tweak of fate's tail lay between them and sleeping on the pavement.

My mother befriended them all. Over the years, as they improved their lot, she remained in touch with them, attending their weddings, giving them advice and loaning them money.

My special friend was Ah Kee, the bellboy. My mother called him Halfpint (abbreviated to Halfie) because he was short and wore a white uniform with a pillbox hat that made him look like a bottle of milk. From Halfie I learned how to roll aerodynamic pellets and fold paper planes out of Pan Am timetables, propelling them with rubber bands or flying them off the hotel roof to see if we could get one over the hill opposite. We never did succeed.

SOME WAY DOWN Waterloo Road from the hotel, a dirt track ran up behind the hill opposite. It was rutted from rainwater and unsuitable for motorised vehicles, but people always seemed to be going up and down it, laden with bundles. Curious, I followed the track one sweltering day in August.

For a few hundred yards it rose steeply before coming out on a mildly sloping plateau—an area of about fifteen acres crammed with shanties. Most were wooden with roofs made of flattened oil drums, while a few had scraps of tarpaulin patchworked over them. Doors fitted loosely and windows were shuttered without glass. Laundry was drying on poles and women attended to domestic chores with babies strapped to their backs.

At first, I thought they were residential shacks, but I soon found out at least half the shacks were thriving industrial units. Men and women toiled over paraffin or charcoal stoves. In one shack, a man was cooking up what smelt like Brylcreem. In another, a woman was stooping over a vat of bubbling sugar, making boiled sweets. In a third, another woman was steaming the flesh off fish to shape into fishballs.

These people were on the bottom rung of Hong Kong's social ladder, only the street-sleepers below them. All of them refugees, they were setting out to rebuild their lives and here was where they were starting.

The shanties had no water supply. Water had to be fetched in a bucket from a standpipe down near the school on Waterloo Road. That one tap had to cater for several thousand people. Sewage flowed away down the hill in a network of shallow ditches to soak into a stinking gully.

Over the summer, I frequently went up the hill and sat on a boulder on its summit. From there, I could see most of Kowloon, the Kowloon hills, Kowloon Bay, Hong Kong Island and the western harbour. It was a breathtaking panorama.

Early one afternoon as I was sitting on the boulder, I heard a faint droning coming from the direction of Lei Yue Mun, the narrow strait of water the *Corfu* had sailed through to enter Hong Kong harbour. As the sound grew in volume I could make out a dot in the sky, which became bigger until its shape was obvious: it was a Short Sunderland flying boat like the ones I had watched with Grampy, taking off from Poole harbour not thirty miles from my grandparents' homes.

It dropped slowly but surely to the water, a huge spray clouding out behind it as it touched down. It was, I thought, strange to think that just five days before it had been in England. For a moment, I felt homesick. I wanted to be back in my grandfather's garden shed with him, surrounded by rusty, obsolete tools. It soon passed. Here the sun shone, you could buy cherry bombs and go to Tkachenko's: no one made cakes like that in Portsmouth.

DISSATISFIED WITH the rudimentary hotel laundry service, which really only catered for bed linen, my mother decided to employ a wash amah.

The first applicant, a middle-aged Chinese woman, arrived. Her black hair was scraped into a bun and she wore a white tunic jacket and baggy black trousers. On her feet were black slippers.

'Me name Ah Choy,' she said softly. 'I good wash-sew amah for you, missee.' My mother introduced me. 'Ve'y han'sum boy,' Ah Choy replied, no doubt perceiving my blond hair. 'Be plentee luckee.' At that point she produced some sheets of paper bearing references from previous employers dating back to the late 1930s with a gap from 1941 to '45.

'Where did you go in the war?' my mother enquired.

'I go quick-quick China-side,' she replied. 'Master go soljer p'ison Kowloon-side. Missee and young missee go war p'ison Hong Kong-side. Japan man no good for Chinese pepul.'

She got the job, my mother paying her $100 (about £6) a month.

A gentle soul, Ah Choy arrived at nine in the morning, collected the laundry and took it onto the hotel roof where other wash amahs congregated round the tap, squatting at basins with their sleeves rolled up. When the laundry was done, they hung it to dry from lines strung across the roof. At midday, they vanished, returning at two o'clock to collect the laundry. This was taken away, I never knew where to, but it returned three hours later ironed, starched, as pristine as the day it was made. Missing buttons had been replaced and rents invisibly mended. My mother couldn't believe it.

Ah Choy was one of the *saw hei* amahs, a sorority of single Chinese women who had sworn a vow of celibacy; *saw hei* meant 'combed' and referred to the way they kept their hair in taut buns. Originally from Kwangtung province, in the thirties they had been displaced by the advancing Japanese forces during the Sino-Japanese War, most fleeing for British Hong Kong. During the Japanese occupation, many *saw hei* amahs remained in the colony, at great risk to themselves. It was not unknown for them to smuggle food to their former employers in prisoner-of-war camps. Others fled to China, crossed north of the Japanese lines and eked out an existence. When Japan capitulated in 1945, they returned to Hong Kong, sought out their former employers and took up where they had left off.

It was not long before Ah Choy started to assign herself other duties. She insisted on seeing me over the road to school, even though Ching had long since given up the task as I was now considered traffic-wise. At the end of the day, she would waylay me halfway from school to carry my Hong Kong basket for me. I found this agonisingly embarrassing. Should I not feel well, she would come into my room and curl up on the floor by my bed. If I woke in the night, she would fetch me a glass of milk or call my mother.

I came to love Ah Choy. She was kind, tolerant and loyal. Yet in three months she was gone, employed by someone with an apartment and servants' quarters. We could hardly blame her.

There followed a succession of interviews, culminating in the appointment of Ah Fong. She was the antithesis of Ah Choy. A young, smiling woman, she wore her hair in a perm and was determined to brook no nonsense from me. I consequently led her a merry chase. It was a matter of principle.

BENEATH THE MAIN hotel staircase was a snug hideaway in which Halfie and the luggage porter huddled while waiting for their services to be called upon. In this little den was a telephone, three stools and an electric ring.

Returning from school one September afternoon, I walked up the hotel drive to see Halfie twirling something round his head on the end of a length of cotton. When he stopped swinging it round, it flew of its own volition.

'I wan' one,' I said.

Halfie tantalisingly hid the object in his pocket and, pointing to the lobby clock, answered, 'You wan', you get. Light-time, I show you.'

At six thirty that evening, I met him and the porter and followed them out into Waterloo Road. We stood under one of the neon streetlights and waited. Twilight fell. The lights came on. In a few minutes, when they had reached full brilliance, something hard hit me on the head. Before I could react, Halfie ran his fingers through my hair and showed me a beetle nestling in his palm. The insect was the size and shape of a large plum stone, its glossy dark green carapace edged with a bright yellow stripe.

'What is it?' I enquired.

'Wartar bee-chew,' Halfie answered.

Suddenly, attracted to the streetlight, more water beetles flew into the bulb, knocked themselves senseless and fell to the pavement. Halfie and the porter collected them and put them in a saucepan. As soon as they gained consciousness, they took to the wing inside it, banging against the lid and sides.

The following morning, Halfie presented me with my beetle-on-a-line. He had tied a six-foot length of cotton to the insect's two hind legs.

I gently swung the beetle round my head. It flew above me like a miniaturised motor-powered kite. All the way to school, I was accompanied by its whirring flight as it kept ahead of me. It was a wonder to behold. Inevitably, however, it was confiscated the moment I entered the school premises. I was given a hundred lines to write on the topic of cruelty to animals.

Reaching the Fourseas that afternoon, I went straight to the niche under the stairs. Halfie and the porter were hunched over a pan on the electric ring.

'Bee-chew gone,' I said.

'Lo ploblum,' said Halfie. 'Can get wung more light-time.' He opened the lid on the pan. Inside, the water beetles were simmering. 'You wan?'

This was the severest test of my promise to the naval officer so far. Halfie removed a beetle with a spoon, blew on it to cool it then split the carapace open with his thumbnail, flicking the wings and legs into a rice bowl.

'You eat . . .' Halfie made a kissing-cum-sucking noise '. . . lo go down.' He pointed to his throat then mimed spitting the bits into the bowl.

I put the beetle in my mouth and chewed it. The flavour was like the smell of stagnant ponds mixed with smoked fish. I spat the bits out. Expecting to be violently sick, I went to my room and sat on the bed to await the regurgitated beetle, but it never came, so I went down to the hotel bar and ordered a cold Coke. In the cubbyhole, all the beetles had been consumed.

MY FATHER came back from Japan for Christmas, bearing gifts. I received a battery-powered wooden motorboat and a superb model of a Chinese junk with hand-sewn sails. The hotel did its best to become seasonally cheerful, with decorations in all the public rooms and Christmas dinner of American turkey and Australian roast potatoes and brussels sprouts. The kindly old odd-job man went around wishing everyone a 'Happee Kiss-Mee'.

My father's return was not the happy occasion it should have been. After delivering his largesse, he soon slipped into his old short-tempered ways.

The day before the ship sailed back to Japan, we were invited aboard the *Fort Charlotte* for lunch. I was shown my father's cabin, the wood and brass polished, his clothes neat in the drawers, his bunk immaculately made. Lunch was taken in the wardroom with the chief engineer and the captain, both of whom wore uniforms with gold braid. The meal was beef curry and rice. When it was over, we were given a tour of the ship, which did not impress me. I had seen bridges and engine rooms before.

Leaving the wheelhouse, my father muttered, 'Show some interest. The Old Man doesn't have to show you round.'

Returning to Kowloon on a naval launch, my father set upon me. 'You are a rude little ingrate,' he said irately.

'Well, Ken,' my mother replied, 'he did see it all on the *Corfu*. Let's face it, unless you're an engineer, one ship's boiler looks much like the next.'

'Neither the *Corfu* nor the *Fort Charlotte* has a boiler in the accepted sense,' my father retorted. 'They're diesel driven. That's what I mean. The two of you. Blind to life's opportunities. As inquisitive as a building brick.'

For the remainder of the day, my father sulked. That evening, I asked my mother—foolishly in my father's hearing—why the other men on the ship wore gold braid but my father did not.

'Go to your room!' he shouted at me. 'Put your pyjamas on.'

'I was only being curious,' I defended myself.

'Get out!'

Ten minutes later, he entered my room. I was bent over a chair and hit twice across the buttocks with the flat of my mother's silver hairbrush.

'That's for your bloody insolence,' my father said spitefully.

ONE AFTERNOON early in January, my mother took me to Tsim Sha Tsui. She was going to Hing Loon to collect a ruby and gold pendant she had ordered.

As usual, we boarded the number seven bus. As it slowed for the last stop before turning left down Nathan Road, a face surrounded by rats' tails of dishevelled, filthy grey hair appeared at the window next to me.

I instantly recognised it. It was that of an old European woman who lived in a cockloft—a sort of semipermanent shanty—on the flat roof of a tenement block in Liberty Avenue. I had often seen her wandering the back streets, scavenging from restaurants and buying (or stealing) fruit from stalls.

She ran along the side of the bus as it slowed, banging her hands on the panelling. I broke into a sweat. Whenever this old woman saw me, she would stagger after me, an animated pile of rags that stank of urine, sweat, rice wine, tobacco and opium, shouting, 'Alexei! Alexei!'

The bus stopped. She boarded it and headed straight for me and my mother. 'Gif me one thousan' dollaire!' she demanded.

My mother looked over my head and out of the window. 'Ignore her, dear,' she instructed me, *sotto voce*.

I was only too glad to obey.

'Gif me fife hundred dollaire,' the old woman urged, holding her filthy hand out close to my mother's chin.

'Would you mind going away?' my mother said through gritted teeth. We were becoming the object of much curiosity from the Chinese passengers.

'Gif me two hundred dollaire!' the crone insisted, her voice louder still.

My mother opened her handbag, unclipped her purse and removed some dollar bills. The old woman snatched at them and dropped something wrapped in pink lavatory tissue into the handbag. At the next bus stop, she got off and swiftly disappeared. We carried on to Tsim Sha Tsui and went into Tkachenko's. When it came time to settle the bill, my mother opened her purse. She took out the tissue paper, unwrapped it, studied the contents for several minutes, replaced it in her purse and paid the bill.

When we entered his emporium, Mr Chan welcomed my mother, poured us each a Coke and produced the ruby pendant set in rose gold my mother had commissioned from him.

As he put the pendant and matching chain into a small brocade bag, my mother took the pink tissue out of her purse and placed it on the counter.

'What is this, Mr Chan?' she asked, adding, 'It's probably paste.'

He unwrapped the tissue and tipped a colourless stone onto the counter, rolling it about on the glass top with his finger. He then picked it up with a pair of tweezers and held it against a bare light bulb in a desk lamp.

'Is a good quality diamung,' he said. 'Maybe two-half carat. Can recut, make maybe t'ree, four nice stone. For ring maybe for you?'

'How much is it worth?'

'Is little bit damage,' Mr Chan said, 'but maybe fife t'ousan' dollar.'

My mother stared at him. The sum approximated to £312.

For the next fortnight, my mother caught the same bus at the same time every day in the hope of coming across the woman again and returning the stone to her. She never saw her again. The diamond was duly recut and the resulting three stones set in a ring, as Mr Chan had suggested.

I, of course, could have told my mother exactly where to find the old woman, but I did not, for fear that, had she discovered the insalubrious haunts I frequented, my freedom to roam would have been curtailed.

The Chinese in the streets called the old crone the Queen of Kowloon. Bit by bit, I came to know her story. She was a White Russian, the wife of a high-ranking army officer of minor nobility. When he was killed in the Bolshevik Uprising, she headed east with the White Russian diaspora. Settling in Shanghai, she made her living as a courtesan and piano teacher. She became the mistress of a Chinese gangster and lived comfortably for a while. Then war intervened again and she moved on, drifting ashore in Hong Kong in the mid-thirties. She lived in a tenement apartment where, once again, she gave piano lessons. However, it was not long before she took to the bottle and pipe, which were the start of her decline into beggary.

From time to time, she appeared at pawn shops in Yau Ma Tei with pieces of jewellery. Her tenement was burgled several times and thoroughly turned over, but the thieves found nothing. Clearly, her stash was hidden elsewhere, so the thieves began to tail her, but she was as sly as a leopard.

In later years, as opium fumes befuddled her mind, she claimed to be Grand Duchess Anastasia, who had survived the assassination of the Russian Royal Family, but no one believed her.

One day, I was trapped by her in a dead-end alley. She advanced on me slowly, swathing me in her odour, and studied me closely.

'Why do you run, Alexei?' she asked in English.

'My name's not Alexei,' I replied.

She smiled at me. Her teeth were grey. For a moment, a shard of the beauty she must once have been shone through her decrepitude.

'One day, you will be the Tsar,' she prophesied.

I looked round her to see if I might make my escape.

She glanced over her shoulder. 'Are they coming?'

Terrified, I shook my head.

'If they come,' she went on, 'you will tell me. Yes?'

I nodded, having no idea who might be coming. Stepping forward, she stroked my hair. She then moved past me, her rags brushing against my face. I sprinted for the Fourseas and immediately ran myself a bath and shampooed my hair twice. It was one thing to have the Chinese touch my golden hair for luck. They were clean. She was a different matter altogether.

3

In 1952, Hong Kong was just beginning its metamorphosis into one of the financial powerhouses of Asia, but it was still essentially a very Chinese city with a non-interventionist British administration. Rickshaws were commonplace. Coolies carried extraordinarily heavy loads on bamboo poles over their shoulders. Conical rattan hats were widely used while the Hakka women wore hats with black cloth fringes hanging from the rim. People ran like hell across the street through fast-moving traffic to shake off the demons they believed were perpetually following them. Unlicensed street hawkers sold sweetmeats, sugar cane, melon seeds and *wah mui,* plums soaked for several days in sea water then dried in the sun. Others carried braziers on poles, selling roasted peanuts or chestnuts, slices of hot roast pork with the crackled skin still on it, cut from a whole pig.

These were everyday sights in the streets around the Fourseas. Much less frequent were itinerant street entertainers. Few had survived the war years and the advent of Radio Hong Kong, but one who did was the plink-plonk man.

My mother based his moniker upon the rosewood xylophone he played. His pitch was in Emma Avenue, behind the Fourseas, where he occasionally appeared to place his instrument on the pavement under the shade of the trees, squatting behind it. After striking a few keys to alert those in the buildings around to his arrival, he invariably launched into a Chinese classical arrangement of 'Tipperary'. Once this was over, he opened a wooden box he carried over his shoulder, from which pranced a small monkey dressed as a Ming dynasty mandarin, tethered to the box by a leather leash.

The plink-plonk man's second tune was usually a rendition of the Japanese song known in English as 'Rose, Rose, I love you' followed by an embellished version of 'Marching through Georgia'.

As he played, his monkey cavorted about in a haphazard jig, while people threw down ten-cent coins from windows and balconies. At the end of the performance, musician and monkey collected up the coins.

One day, halfway through 'Marching through Georgia', the monkey managed to bite through its leash. In a flash, it was up the nearest tree.

The music stopped abruptly. The plink-plonk man tried to sweet-talk the monkey down, holding up a piece of a bun. The monkey peered down through the branches, then slowly, striptease fashion, divested itself of its ludicrous costume, letting each piece drift to the ground, where the musician collected them up. His attention taken by this task, the plink-plonk man's eye was briefly off the monkey, which, holding on to its little cock, proceeded to urinate upon its erstwhile master.

The musician unwisely looked up to be hit in the face by the full stream. Driven into an irate frenzy, he cursed the monkey at the top of his voice and threw the clothing at it. The monkey headed off down the street, swinging from tree to tree, always keeping just out of reach of the musician, who ran below, jumping up to attempt to grab the dangling leash.

By now, a crowd had gathered far greater than any the plink-plonk man could ever have hoped to collect through his music. He ran behind the escaping monkey, pleading, cussing, cajoling and threatening the creature by turns, while his audience hooted with laughter.

At the junction of Emma Avenue and Soares Avenue, a network of electricity wires spanned out from a junction box. The monkey, blithely swinging through the foliage, was unaware of the danger. There was a violent blue flash accompanied by an equally brief high-pitched squeak. The monkey was instantly immolated. All that was left was a charred corpse stretched between two wires and the acrid smell of burnt hair.

The plink-plonk man sat on the kerb, his feet in the gutter, and broke into tears. The crowd, now subdued, dispersed.

I never saw him again.

In 1953, Chinese New Year fell over the end of January and the beginning of February. Dependent upon the lunar calendar, the date varied from year to year. Friends advised my mother to leave the Fourseas for the duration of the main festivities, but my mother wanted to be in the thick of it.

Over the weeks leading up to the festival, firecrackers had been on sale in practically every shop. They came in boxes the size of a paperback book, sealed with a label printed with images of laughing children letting them off. Always coloured red, they ranged in size from those not much fatter than a thick pencil lead and about an inch long—and named by us tom thumbers—to others three inches in length and thicker than a cigarette.

Although tiny, the tom thumbers packed a punch sufficient to blow a five-inch-wide, two-inch-deep crater in the earth of a pot of the chrysanthemums that decorated the hotel front lawn. If you held one by the base, gripping it between two fingernails, and kept your eyes closed, you could light it and let it explode with no danger. The first I held as it went off left a tingling feeling in my fingers. The second hurt, but machismo demanded I did not show it and lose face with the other expatriate children who lived in the hotel at the time. Thereafter, we embarked upon tom thumber fights, hurling them at each other. No one was hurt. It was good seasonal fun.

The first day of the fortnight-long festival was quiet. All the shops in Soares Avenue were shut. The hotel room boys gave me *lai see* and I returned the compliment. *Lai see* was a small red paper packet containing a small amount of money. It was not so much a gift as an omen of good luck and prosperity for the year ahead. I was warned by Ching not to swear, not to mention death, illness or bad luck even in passing. Our amah refused to take anything but Chinese New Year's Day off, despite my mother's protestations, yet she did accept a thirteenth month's salary, as was common practice.

On the second day, the celebrations started in earnest.

Across the road from the rear of the Fourseas was a pro-Communist secondary school. Every morning, the pupils gathered in the school yard behind twelve-foot-high stone walls and sang patriotic songs about labouring in the fields, striding ahead for liberty, equality and fraternity under the red flag and in the footsteps of Mao Tse-tung. The accompaniment was provided by a phonograph with a set of well-worn records.

Shortly after dawn, the school staff had hung strings of firecrackers over the high stone walls. There must have been two hundred of them, the walls looking as if they had been festooned with vermilion ribbons. These firecrackers were the size of a grown man's index finger. They were grouped in threes, and their fuses woven together round a core of hessian twine. The aim was not to provide a display but to create as much noise as possible to drive off devils, demons and other supernatural ne'er-do-wells.

A whistle was blown in the school yard. The teachers ignited the end of the first string of firecrackers, moving immediately on to the next. After a brief fizzle, the explosions began in the first string, then the second, then the third . . . The air went blue with smoke, and the acrid smell of gunpowder was inescapable. The reports echoed off the walls of the buildings for at least twenty minutes and a dense blizzard of paper blew along the street.

I re-entered the hotel with a blinding headache but a feeling of elation.

Over the next few days, Kowloon sounded as if it were a war zone. In some places the streets were inches deep in paper fragments. The traffic stopped to allow fifty-foot strings of firecrackers to explode down the front of the taller buildings. Gradually, a semblance of peace returned. On either side of many shops and doorways, new red scrolls with black writing upon them were pasted over the previous year's, presaging good fortune.

When I visited the temple to Kwun Yum, the goddess of mercy, it was doing brisk business. At the rear of the altar, in the half-light of red wax candle flames, the deity's effigy sat demurely, with attendant gods to either side. The altar was hung with an embroidered cloth in imperial yellow, red and gold. From the tarnished brass incense burner rose a column of smoke.

In front of the altar, women and children were making offerings, praying and casting fortune-telling sticks. Among the offerings, mostly of food, was money. I was amazed to see poor-looking women dropping fistfuls of banknotes into a cauldron of hot embers. When a scorched note escaped the fire I saw the currency. It was not dollars issued by the Hongkong and Shanghai Bank but Hell's Banknotes in vast denominations—$100,000, $1,000,000, $10,000,000. This was celestial not terrestrial cash.

Pushing through the crowd, I purchased a fifty-cent pack of joss sticks from an elderly man by the door, lit them all from a candle and stuck them in the urn full of sand provided. It was not that I was a devotee of Kwun Yum, but that I was bent on doing what everyone else was—hedging their bets for the coming twelvemonth by getting on the good side of the gods.

The lighting of firecrackers was not restricted to Chinese New Year. Whenever a new shop or business opened, long strings of firecrackers suspended from roof to pavement would be lit, the street soon filling with choking smoke and the continuous cacophony of explosions.

At only one event were firecrackers not let off—funerals.

When I saw my first Chinese funeral procession, I thought the circus had come to town. The initial indications of the approaching procession were the muted sounds of inharmonious music. I went out onto the communal balcony of the hotel to watch. Soon, a small truck appeared further down Waterloo Road. A bamboo frame had been fixed to the front of the truck and adorned with paper flowers, gold and scarlet bunting and, I presumed, the name of the departed in huge characters. In the centre of this was a large monochrome photograph of the deceased. This vehicle was followed by a 200-yard procession of delivery tricycles similarly decorated. Interspersed between these were men carrying tall poles topped by fringed umbrellas, a large paper orb with a ladder rising through it and a number of other ceremonial items. Then came the coffin, carried in a sort of palanquin between eight perspiring coolies. The sides were decorated with white and yellow flowers. To the rear of the coffin walked the relatives of the deceased, the foremost being a small boy of about my age wearing a white cloak.

'Who is he?' I asked a room boy standing beside me.

'He dead man son. Now he Number One man for family. Big job for him.'

Just behind the leading truck walked a small classical Chinese band of about eight musicians. The music they played was doleful, the woodwind instruments high-pitched and keening, the small gong cracked and discordant. Not far behind them came a band equipped with Western brass instruments. They played 'When the Saints Go Marching In'—badly. Three other bands played 'Doin' What Comes Naturally', 'Greensleeves' and, finally, Chinese classical music once again. Each band played in apparent ignorance of the others, so the whole musical contribution to the event was a raucous medley of disconnected tunes from three cultures.

My mother, who watched this procession with me, remarked that she preferred firecrackers to the assassination of music, but she had by then forgotten the five-day migraine that marked Chinese New Year.

MY FATHER returned for good from Japan in the early summer of 1953. The Korean War was winding down, and his job at the Sasebo naval base near Nagasaki was becoming redundant. Moves were put under way for us to leave the Fourseas. It was deemed an unsuitable billet for a family. There was, however, a shortage of quarters, so we were to move temporarily into a flat on the top floor of a building in Boundary Street, which, as the name implied, marked the periphery between British Kowloon and the hinterland of the New Territories, ceded to the British for ninety-nine years from 1898.

Two weeks before the move, I was walking back from school alone when I saw a thin wisp of smoke rising from over Ho Man Tin hill. As I reached the hotel, I saw that the wisp was now a column. People were running down the track and spilling out onto the main road, blocking the traffic. Then I heard the far-off bells of fire engines.

I dumped my Hong Kong basket in the hotel garage and headed for the hill. Hordes of squatters were pouring off it, every one carrying something. Even toddlers clumsily dragged a cooking pot or enamel basin. Adults piled high with bedding struggled down the gravel track. Laden rickshaws wove between them. The exodus was orderly but noisy. Everyone was shouting.

The police and the fire brigade turned up simultaneously. In minutes, hoses were snaking up the track and the police directed the flow of people.

I hurried to the bottom of the track. The squatter area was over a ridge, so I could not see the blaze. I joined the throng of people returning to save their belongings. Cresting the ridge, I was shocked by the scene before me. At least half the squatters' shacks had been reduced to piles of smouldering ashes. The conflagration was moving through the area like a forest fire. The noise was terrifying, with tin sheeting cracking as it warped, the incessant hiss and spit of burning wood, and the crash of shacks caving in.

Ahead of the fire, people were running in and out of their shacks, piling their belongings on the ground, on handcarts, on their children. I gathered up armfuls of clothing from a pile and folded them in a sheet, tying the corners together, using the clothes to pad out some rice bowls and other crockery. A young Chinese man appeared and added a framed sepia photo to the bundle. It showed a family group seated on upright chairs. In the centre sat an ancient woman with a baby on her knee.

The fire was moving nearer, and quickly. I could feel its intensity on my bare arms and legs. My eyes began to weep from the heat and smoke.

'*Wei!*' I shouted. '*Ché! Ché! Fide! Fide!*' (Hey! Go! Go! Quick! Quick!)

The man came out of the shack followed by a woman carrying a baby. He was laden down with a battered suitcase and a wooden box. I gathered up the bundle and started down the track. I could not see my feet and frequently stumbled. At the police line we were allowed through by an English inspector, and directed to Soares Avenue, which was now a sort of squatter holding-pen. There the young man gave his name to an official and we were guided into Emma Avenue, where the pavements were filling up with squatters.

There was a touch on my head. It was the young man. 'You luckee boy for me,' he said. 'T'ankee you plentee plentee.'

'Martin,' another voice remonstrated, 'you're filthy.'

My mother stood before me. I put the pile down and studied myself. My legs and arms were covered in ash; no doubt my face and hair were, too.

'What have you been doing?'

'Dis you littul boy?' the young man asked my mother. 'He plentee good littul boy. Plentee good for me. You no beatee, missee. No beatee.'

It came to my mother what I had done. She hugged me, ash and all. The young man touched my hair again, and his wife did likewise. I was sent in for a bath, and my mother offered her assistance to a Red Cross worker.

Lying in the warm water, I realised that everything one counted upon could come crashing down in less than the time it took for a double maths class. I also learned that while it was one thing to live in a large box, a cockloft or between the shafts of a rickshaw, it was quite another to lose everything.

NUMBER 133 Boundary Street had been built in the 1920s as a bijou residence on the edge of the countryside. By the time we moved in it had gone down in the world. The stonework was blotched with dead lichen and the flat roof leaked. The city had reached out to it and the countryside was no more, although the barren foothills of the Kowloon hills did come down to within a hundred yards of the garden of the ground-floor flat.

Moving to a flat necessitated more servants. As it was usual to employ a husband and wife, the wash amah who had replaced Ah Fong was let go.

After an in-depth culinary interview, my mother took on Wong and his wife, Ah Shun. With them came their four-year-old son, Chan-tuk, to whom my mother took an instant liking and nicknamed Tuppence.

Wong—whose references gave his name as Hwong Cheng-kwee—was a Shanghainese who was a refugee from Communism. He and Ah Shun had several other children whom they lodged in the New Territories or had left with relatives in China. A tall, round-faced man, Wong had apparently worked in a top-class hotel in Shanghai as a pastry chef. My mother gave him a month's probation. This ended after a day when he made his first sponge cake. It did not so much sit on the plate as float over it. He had a permanent job from my mother's first mouthful. Ah Shun became the wash-sew amah and the two of them shared the chores of keeping house.

Wong was a one-in-a-thousand cook-houseboy, with the attentiveness of a high-class butler, the culinary skills of Escoffier, the attention to detail of a watercolourist and the mien of a true gentleman's gentleman. He and Ah Shun wore the customary white jacket and black, loose-fitting trousers with felt slippers, in which they glided across the polished parquet floors.

When the monthly provisions bill came, my mother found Wong had used six dozen eggs, which accounted for the levitatory sponges. She asked him to cut down, then saw that he had used nine bottles of Heinz Salad Cream. Wong was called into my mother's presence. It was not long before I was summoned too.

'What is this?' my mother muttered, indicating an item on the invoice. 'And this. And this. Wong tells me this is your doing.'

I had no idea why she was cross but I admitted I ate salad cream.

'Eat it!' my mother replied. 'Wong tells me you put it on your breakfast!'

Every morning, I ate breakfast alone while my mother was still preening herself for a hard day at the canasta table. Wong always provided a fried egg on crisp fried bread, a fried tomato and brittle rashers of grilled bacon. I ate the bacon first then waded into the remainder, which I smothered with salad cream. I loved it. Indeed, I could go through a bottle in three days. That avenue of pleasure was promptly closed.

Wong lived with Ah Shun and Tuppence in the servants' quarters beyond the kitchen: a closed-in balcony and laundry sink, two small bedrooms and a shower room with a squat-down toilet. Wong and his family used our kitchen to prepare their food but they ate it squatting on the balcony until my mother found out. Thereafter, they ate at the kitchen table.

My mother found having servants somewhat disquieting. She was a humanist at heart who believed no man should lord it over another. Yet here she was with two people who were there at her beck and call. She suffixed every request with 'please' and 'thank you' and made sure I did, too. It was impressed upon me that I should never make unreasonable demands of Wong or Ah Shun.

The environs of the flat were very different from those of the Fourseas. To the northwest was the one-time garden suburb of Kowloon Tong, to the north were the barren lower slopes of the nine Kowloon hills. The name Kowloon derived from the Cantonese *gau lung*, meaning 'nine dragons'. To the south was a residential area and the Kowloon hospital. Only the foothills offered the slightest opportunity for exploration, and that was soon exhausted.

Not a mile to the east, however, was the most romantic and allegedly dangerous place in the colony. It was called Kowloon Walled City.

It was not and never had been a city. It covered not much more than 25,000 square yards and, although it had been surrounded by a crenellated wall, the defences had been demolished by British prisoners-of-war under Japanese command and used as hard core for an airport runway.

It had originally been established in the eighteenth century as a far-flung outpost of the Chinese empire. After the British gained control of Hong Kong and, later, Kowloon in the early 1840s, the Chinese insisted on maintaining a local presence, so the British turned a blind eye towards Kowloon Walled City. Behind its walls, a nominal Chinese garrison was maintained. When the New Territories were ceded to the British, Kowloon Walled City was to find itself completely surrounded by British territory. The cessation treaty was also ambiguous. Kowloon Walled City was now, in effect, cut off and ruled and possessed by neither—or both—countries.

It remained a backwater for fifty years, visited at the turn of the twentieth century by Europeans in Hong Kong for vicarious excitement, a fragment of the 'real' China on their doorsteps. Ruled by a mandarin from his *yamen* in the centre, it was, in effect, a minute city state all on its own.

When China fell to the Communists in 1949, many criminal refugees fled to Hong Kong, some of them gravitating to the walled city area, where they quickly established fresh enterprises. Thereafter, Kowloon Walled City remained an enclave governed by no one. It was more or less closed to outsiders. If the police entered the area, they went in armed patrols of three.

We had not been in Boundary Street a day when my mother took me aside. 'Martin,' she said, 'I know you like to roam and explore, and round here that's all right. But,' she continued, unfolding a map of Kowloon, 'you do *not* go even near here.' She pointed to Kowloon Walled City.

To utter such a dictum to a streetwise eight-year-old was tantamount to buying him an entrance ticket.

The following afternoon, homework hurriedly completed, I had a quick glance at the map and headed east down Boundary Street. In ten minutes, I was on the outskirts of Kowloon Walled City.

A number of new six-storey buildings were being erected, and a lot of shanties and older two-storey buildings were leaning precariously. It looked like a squatter area but with permanent structures in the middle in ill repair. Winding into the buildings and shacks was an alleyway. I set off down it.

Through the open doors I spied people sewing, assembling torches or painting lacquer boxes. In one shack a baker was placing trays of buns in a wood-fired oven; in another, two men were making noodles, swinging sheets of thin dough in the air around a wooden rolling-pin.

Arriving at one of the older stone buildings, I was about to peer in through an open door when a Chinese man rushed out. Stripped to the waist, he bore a coloured tattoo of a dragon on his back. He glowered at me.

'W'at you wan'?' he asked.

'Nothing,' I said. Then, hoping it might soften him a bit, I added, '*Ngo giu jo* Mah Tin.' I held my hand out. '*Nei giu mut ye meng*?'

He was taken aback by my introducing myself—especially in Cantonese—and it was at least thirty pensive seconds before he shook my hand.

'Mah Tin,' he said. '*Ngo giu jo* Ho. Why you come?'

'Just looking,' I answered, adding in pidgin English, 'Come look-see.'

'You no look-see,' he answered sternly. 'No good look-see for *gweilo* boy.'

I said, '*Choi kin*,' (goodbye) and turned to go.

'You look-see,' he declared, changing his mind. He opened the door, indicating I follow him.

What until now had seemed a harmless saunter immediately took on a sinister aspect. No one knew I was here. If I stepped over the threshold, I could vanish. For ever. On the other hand, I had seen nothing yet. And so, I threw caution to the wind and followed him into the building.

The ground floor consisted of one vast room, heavy beams holding up the ceiling and the floor above. It was furnished with rosewood chairs, low tables and several ornate mirrors. Halfway down the room stood a wooden screen, the top half pierced by intricate fretwork, the rest a painting depicting hills and lakes. There was an air of faded gentility about the place.

To the rear was a staircase beneath which a door opened and an old hunched woman entered, walking with the aid of a stick. She grinned toothlessly, hobbled to my side and, inevitably, stroked my hair. This put me at ease. No one would risk harming such a harbinger of good fortune.

'You come.' Ho beckoned me up the stairs.

I followed him into a room along three sides of which were wooden *kangs*—traditional Chinese sleeping platforms. On one of these a man lay supine on a woven bamboo mat, his head on a hard headrest, his legs drawn up, his hands twitching like a dog's paws in a dream of chasing rabbits.

'*Nga pin*,' Ho announced and beckoned me towards the fourth wall, which was shuttered. He unlatched one of the shutters and we stepped out onto the balcony, which sloped alarmingly down to a crumbling balustrade.

From here, I was afforded a panoramic view of the walled city. Tucked between the tightly packed shacks were a few larger buildings. One stood in a wide rectangular courtyard with a number of outbuildings close by; from another rose a faint cloud of bluish smoke, which meant it had to be a temple. In the distance was Kowloon Bay. Over to my left was Fei Ngo Shan, the most easterly of the Kowloon hills. To the southwest, indistinct in the haze, was Hong Kong Island.

Ho took me back inside. We passed the sleeping man and descended the stairs, which creaked loudly. Once outside, Ho bade me farewell and I set off the way I had come, feeling I had taken a terrible risk. I resolved not to be so foolhardy again. Yet I knew I had to return to Kowloon Walled City to investigate the temple and the building in the courtyard.

When I returned to our apartment, I asked Wong what *nga pin* meant. He looked quizzically at me and replied, 'Opium.'

ON HIS RETURN to Hong Kong, my father had taken delivery of a Ford Consul saloon. Never a man for a hobby, the car became the centre of his leisure activities. He mollycoddled it as he might have done a mistress. The interior was kept pristine; he checked the oil and tyres weekly and spent hours polishing the bodywork and vacuuming the carpets and seats. When he saw Wong knocking dead leaves off the bonnet with a feather duster, he hurtled downstairs to stop him: the feathers, he explained, might scratch the paint.

The first Sunday after the delivery of the car, my father announced that we were going for a drive around the New Territories. And so, after a hearty breakfast, we departed. My father decided to take a circular route without deviation, digression or diversion. My mother had hoped that we might have a look at a few places on the way.

We crossed the Kowloon hills by way of a pass on the Tai Po road and descended to Sha Tin, a small fishing village on the shores of a large inlet. The tide was out, leaving mud flats upon which sampans lay settled on their hulls. Across on the other shore, on the northern slopes of the Kowloon hills, was a rock outcrop that, if the imagination was stretched, looked in silhouette like a woman with a baby in a carrier on her back.

'Amah Rock,' my mother declared, reading from a notebook she was compiling in the hope that, one day, she might write a Hong Kong guide. She went on to relate a story about a fisherman lost at sea, his loyal wife who waited on the outcrop for his junk to return and the gods who changed her into stone so she could wait for ever. The story I had heard was that the stone was a childless amah who had stolen her mistress's baby and been frozen in stone by punishing gods, but I said nothing.

The road more or less followed the coast and the railway, grassy hills rising on the left with heavily wooded valleys. Just beyond the next town, another fishing community called Tai Po, we entered old China. The land became a patchwork of rice paddies separated by low dykes, the rice beginning to sprout above the water, bright green and pristine. The villages and farmhouses were ancient. Farmers walked along the side of the road wearing wide-brimmed conical hats, their trousers rolled up to the knee, leading docile-looking buffaloes. Hakka women with coolie poles over their shoulders carried heavy loads of fodder or bundles of pak choi.

Every now and then, my mother demanded that my father stop for her to take a photo. Each time, it was twenty yards before we came to a standstill so my father had to back up. Before long he was seething. When my mother suggested turning into a side road into the countryside, he lost it completely.

'Joyce!' he said through gritted teeth. 'We've come to drive round the New Territories. Not into them. I am *not* driving into the blithering hills. For all I know, we could wind up in Communist China.'

'That's not likely,' I injudiciously piped up. 'If we take a road on the left we'll stay in Hong Kong. China's to the right. Anyway, you can't drive into China because there's a border and a river to cross and—'

'Shut up!' my father exploded.

Several hundred yards further on, a duck farmer was moving about two hundred birds from one pond to another down the middle of the road. My father beeped his horn. The duck farmer turned. My father signalled with his hand for the man to get a move on. The farmer walked towards the car.

'*Mat yeh?*' he said, somewhat belligerently. This translated roughly as: What d'you want? The subtext was: Damn your eyes, foreign devil.

My father looked blank. 'Martin, what's he saying?'

'I don't know,' I lied.

The farmer shrugged and turned. Taking his time, he rounded the ducks up and made his steady way ahead of us. We edged forward in first gear.

At the next left junction, we turned up a narrow road towards a steep hill. The road petered out. We stopped and got out. While my father stood pondering how to do a three-point turn, my mother and I set off up the slope.

We came upon a narrow terrace cut into the hillside. It was overgrown with grass and held a row of large urns with lids. The view was spectacular, a vista of wetlands over which soared flights of ducks and, beyond, the sea.

My mother busying herself with her camera, I decided to look in one of the urns. I lifted one of the lids. Inside, neatly packed away so that it might all fit in, was a human skeleton, the skull on top. The bones were brown and looked as though they had been lightly varnished. I quickly replaced the lid.

'It's called a *kam taap*, or golden pagoda,' my mother said. 'When a Chinese dies, they bury the body for seven years then they exhume it, clean the bones and put them in an ossuary—that's one of those urns.'

We walked down to the car. My father had turned it round and was buffing off scuff marks—caused by his reversing into a bush—on the rear bumper with a soft cloth.

'The view's wonderful,' my mother said sweetly as we joined him.

'You're a bloody nuisance, Joyce,' my father snarled.

At about five o'clock we arrived back at Boundary Street. My mother strode into my parents' bedroom and locked the door. My father spent an hour rubbing imaginary scratches off the rear panelling of the Ford Consul.

OVER THE COMING WEEKS, I paid repeated clandestine visits to Kowloon Walled City. Whenever I arrived, Ho appeared before I had gone twenty yards, smiling expansively. It was as if some unseen sentry had been watching out for me. For as long as I was in the enclave, he would accompany me. Sometimes, we took a bowl of soup together in a shack done out as an eating-place. On many occasions, I offered to pay but Ho invariably pushed my money aside. On the other hand, he never paid either.

Apart from inviting me to drink tea or broth with him, Ho took me nowhere else. I had hoped he would show me the temple but any attempt to steer the conversation or our feet in its direction was futile.

After a while, Ho told me he was going 'long time Macau-side' and introduced me to his *ho pang yau* (his good friend). This man was in his mid-twenties, not tall but immensely handsome, and spoke good pidgin English.

'My name is Lau,' he introduced himself.

'I am Martin,' I replied.

'*Mah Tin*,' he repeated. 'In Cantonese, this mean *horse, electric*. You are electric horse.' He grinned at his interpretation.

We shook hands and drank tea to cement our new-found friendship.

'When you come Kowloon Walled City-side,' he went on, slurping at his bowl of tea, 'I show you this place. If I not here, you no come. Unner-stand?'

I agreed to these terms. After all, to have a personal guide to this maze of shanties and ancient buildings was more than I could have hoped for.

Our tea finished, I said goodbye to Ho and set off with Lau. Everyone greeted him and stepped aside to let him pass in the narrow alleys.

'I will show you some thing,' Lau said.

We arrived at the temple and entered. As my eyes adjusted to the gloom, I saw that this one was grander than any I had seen. It had three larger-than-life-size effigies completely covered in gold except for their tightly curled, black-painted hair—yet even that had a gold finial on top. All three were seated in front of intricately embroidered gold tapestries. The altar table was huge, made of black wood and carved with gold-painted leaves, dragons and curlicues. Upon it were not only the customary offerings but also exquisitely painted porcelain vases and two gold-leaf-coated lanterns.

'You like?' Lau enquired.

'Like plenty,' I replied. I took a joss stick and, lighting it, bowed to the effigies before sticking it in the sand of the incense bowl.

Lau watched me, bemused. 'You no *Gai duk toh*?' He made the sign of the Cross on the palm of his hand.

'Yes,' I answered. 'Church of England.'

'Why you . . . ?' He pointed to the altar and made a cursory bow.

'Respect,' I said, but Lau just smiled in his incomprehension.

We walked on. Lau said, 'Now I show you good place.'

Our destination was the balustraded building I had visited on my first excursion into the Walled City. We entered it, passed through the downstairs room, went behind the screen, out through a door into a courtyard and down some steps. At the bottom was an old wooden door secured by a large padlock. Lau produced the key and we entered.

There was a small table in the centre of the room. Upon the walls hung various pennants and banners in red with serrated black borders and black writing on them. Opposite the door was an altar bearing a small idol of a male god with a fierce-looking face, one candle alight before it.

'God Kwan Ti,' Lau explained. 'This my god.'

Something caught my eye. Hung between the banners were macabre, ferocious-looking weapons. One was a chain with a ball set with spikes at one end; another chain culminated in a spear-point blade. In a wooden rack were a number of metal six-pointed stars of varying diameters.

'What is this place?' I enquired.

Lau made no attempt to explain but said, '*Gweilo* no come here. You vewy lucky boy I show you.'

Taking the chain with the point on it, he gave it a quick flick. The blade flashed through the air and embedded itself in the rear of the door. It took both Lau's hands to dislodge it. Once the blade was hanging back on the wall, he took down one of the smallest stars. With a brief twist of his wrist, it spun through the air and also lodged itself in the door timbers.

Lau ushered me out. 'You no tell you see here,' he said as he locked the door. 'You tell, plenty trouble for me. Plenty more for you.' He made the sign of a knife slicing across his throat.

I nodded and we went back the way we had come. As we moved through the big room, a boy of about my age descended the stairs carrying a tray on which there was a small lamp, several minute bowls, a number of metal needles and the most bizarre pipe. A good fifteen inches long, the stem was made of bamboo, the mouthpiece of milky-coloured jade or soapstone. The bowl appeared to be a virtually sealed container, with a tiny hole in the top.

'*Nga pin*?' I asked tentatively.

Lau stared at me. 'How you know *nga pin*?'

'I know,' I shrugged, still not knowing exactly what it was.

He took me by the hand and led me up the stairs. 'No talk,' he whispered.

As my head rose above the first-floor level, I saw half a dozen men lying on the *kangs*. All but one were asleep on their sides. The air had a familiar perfume to it. I recognised it as the scent of the rickshaw coolies' pipes.

The man who was awake had by his head one of the little lamps, the flame contained within a glass funnel. The boy went to the man, impaled a small bead of something on one of the needles and revolved it in the lamp flame. Then, very adroitly, he placed it over the tiny hole in the pipe bowl, passing it to the man, who sucked evenly on the pipe. After doing this three times, the man lay down and closed his eyes. The boy removed the pipe.

Once we were outside, I asked, 'What was that man doing?'

'He smoke opium,' Lau answered. 'Get dream, go good time-side.'

'Can I smoke *nga pin*?' I asked.

'No,' Lau said emphatically. 'No good for *gweilo*.'

Whenever I visited Kowloon Walled City, Lau was always there, ready to guide me around, drink tea with me and talk. When, after a few months, the place started to lose its appeal and I stopped visiting, I never saw him again.

It was some years before I realised that he and Ho had been Triad members—Chinese *mafiosi*—infamous for their utter ruthlessness, whose secret fraternity ran the opium dens and brothels, and held Kowloon Walled City in its thrall. The semi-subterranean room had been their meeting place.

MY GROWING PENCHANT for reading gave me a reason to range further afield. My parents agreed that I should be permitted to go to Tsim Sha Tsui where, in the next street to Mr Chan's Curio and Jewellery Company, there stood the Swindon Bookshop.

Tsim Sha Tsui was camera-toting, rubber-necking tourist country, banker and briefcased businessman territory, completely different from the world of *dai pai dongs* and whole roast pigs. I had been there on occasion with my mother. However, I savoured discovering it on my own.

Apart from the tailors' window displays of lengths of cloth and suits hanging off mannequins, every shop window was a glittering tableau of expensive watches, jewellery, pens, cameras and binoculars.

I knew I could not just walk into one of these shops, so I worked the obvious ploy, waiting until a tourist couple entered and tagging along camouflaged as their child. It worked time and again and I got to study—close up—such marvels as Audemars Piguet, Longines and Vacheron et Constantin gold watches, emeralds as big as peas, and Rolleiflex and Leica cameras. At times, the palms of my hands itched with desire.

Yet the crimes of Tsim Sha Tsui were not conducted by me but by the wily shopkeepers and even more artful pickpockets. One of the shopkeepers' scams was brilliant in its simplicity. The first time I saw it happen was in a watch shop. I overheard a conversation that went something like this:

'OK, buddy, how much is this one?' (*American tourist*)

'V'wy good choice. Suit you good. Fi'e hund'ed dollar.' (*Shopkeeper*)

A few minutes of haggling followed, culminating in an agreed price of $450, the shopkeeper declaiming with a disarming smile, 'You too cleffer for me. Beat me down too much. Now my p'ofit only small.'

All the prices were shown in Hong Kong dollars and the price label on the item marked up by at least 100 per cent over the wholesale buy-in cost.

Then came the question bolstered by a belief in the universal power of the US greenback. 'Say, buddy, is that American or Hong Kong dollars?' *Hong Kong* was always spoken with a slight air of condescension.

The shopkeeper, after a brief pause as well timed as the best comic actor's, would always reply, 'Ame'ican dollars.'

Out would come the wallet of American Express traveller's cheques, the customer grinning broadly at his bargaining skill.

In 1953, when I first saw this trick pulled, the foreign exchange rate was approximately HK$6: US$1. Even my elementary school arithmetic told me the customer had paid over five times the original asking price.

The pickpockets operated in pairs, keeping in the crowds. Once a target had been spotted, they would move in, one bumping into the victim, knocking them slightly off balance. The other, with lightning speed, would slip their hand into bag or pocket, grab a wallet or purse and pass it to the barger, who would disappear in the crowd. If the victim found they had been pickpocketed, had a suspicion who had done it and accosted him, he could plead innocence. The proof would already be three streets away.

Although these kinds of street theft must have ruined many a holiday, I could not bring myself to condemn them. The perpetrators were often boys even younger than myself, street urchins, the children of squatter shack dwellers and pavement sleepers, doing the best they could to stay alive.

ONE SWELTERING DAY, the humidity over 90 per cent, my mother and I went shopping to buy a wedding anniversary gift for my paternal grandparents.

With a military methodology my mother went up and down the streets, but could find nothing suitable. It was either tourist tat or too fragile to post.

Having found nothing in an area catering for European taste, my mother turned into Shanghai Street, an area providing for the Chinese. We started with the shops selling crockery. One variety, known as rice-patterned ware, caught my mother's attention. Each dish, bowl or cup was made of white porcelain with a patterned blue border and base, between which the porcelain was speckled with what looked like rice grains fired in the matrix. If the bowl was held to the light, each grain appeared translucent.

'This is the one, don't you think?' my mother declared as she held up a large serving bowl to the light.

I agreed. It cost only a few dollars.

While the shopkeeper wrapped the bowl in wood straw and newspaper, my mother sauntered round the shop, picking up a piece here and there. I sat on a stool and sweated. The shopkeeper did not offer me a drink. We had parted with our money and he no longer needed to keep us in the place.

Finally, my mother said, 'Sod it!' and ordered a six-setting complete dinner service of the same sort, asking for it all to be delivered.

The shopkeeper beamed, shouted for an assistant, relieved my mother of $110 (about £6) and gave us each a chilled bottle of Watson's lemonade.

'I don't think,' my mother said as we walked at a leisurely speed towards Nathan Road, 'that we need to mention this to your father.'

The arcaded pavement ahead was obstructed by a row of barrels being off-loaded from a green lorry with a canvas awning. As we entered the restricted space, we were ambushed by a young Chinese woman. She was barefoot, her hair awry and her face, as my mother would put it, in need of a kiss from Mr Flannel. In her arms she carried a baby about a month old. There was no way we could avoid her without turning heel.

'Missee! Missee!' she said as she approached us.

My mother opened her handbag and took out a purple dollar bill.

The young woman refused it. 'No *kumshaw*, missee. No *kumshaw*!' She held the baby out. I could see it was a girl. 'You tek, missee, pleas.'

My mother stopped dead in her tracks.

'Pleas', missee! You tek.' She reached forward with the baby, pleading now. The pain in her soul tainted the only four English words she knew.

I looked at my mother. Tears ran down her cheeks. She shook her head. '*M'ho*,' my mother murmured. No.

At that, the woman turned and disappeared.

We walked on in silence. Once in the apartment, my mother poured herself a gin and tonic and sat heavily in a chair.

'What did that woman want?' I enquired.

'She wanted to give me her baby.'

'Why?' I replied, taken aback at this information.

'Perhaps she can't afford to feed it. Perhaps the father told her to get rid of it. It was a girl . . .'

'So what?' I came back.

'In China, boy children are precious. Girls are not. To the Chinese, nothing is more important than keeping the family name going. So sons are important and daughters, who will marry and take another name, aren't.'

'But what will happen to the baby girl?' I half-wondered aloud.

'She will die. Either her parents will smother her or they'll take her into the Kowloon foothills and leave her to die of exposure.'

'But that's murder!' I exclaimed. 'Can't we go back? I don't mind if . . .'

The appeal of an adopted Chinese sister was suddenly growing on me. And it was now of paramount importance to me that we did something.

'No,' my mother said, 'I'm afraid it doesn't work like that . . .' She patted the cushion on the settee beside her. I sat down and she put her arm round me. 'It is terrible, but it has been going on for centuries in China. There's nothing we can do about it. You cannot change a culture overnight.'

BY EARLY MAY 1953, Hong Kong was gripped by Coronation fever. A vast *pi lau*, a sort of Chinese triumphal arch, was erected across Nathan Road, made of bamboo poles lashed together by bamboo twine. By the week before the Coronation, it was festooned with gold and scarlet decorations, a row of lanterns, a picture of the new Queen and the letters *EIIR*. These also appeared on every lamppost on every major thoroughfare. Shops displayed framed pictures of the Queen, sometimes next to ones of Chiang Kai-shek.

On Coronation Day itself, there was a huge parade on Hong Kong-side. Keeping to Queen's Road, it wound its way through the city for six miles, the pavements jammed with tens of thousands of spectators. The queues for the Star Ferry on Kowloon-side stretched for well over a mile, but we avoided these by crossing the harbour on a Royal Navy launch from which we were ushered into a dockyard office building overlooking Queen's Road.

The parade was interminable. Soldiers, sailors, airmen, marching military bands, St John Ambulance volunteers, Boy Scouts and nurses marched by in dizzying, monotonous ranks. The tedium was relieved only by a drive-past of tanks, howitzers, scout cars and other military paraphernalia.

After the pageant of imperial militarism came the Chinese half of the parade. At the head were two stilt-walkers and a classical marching orches-tra. Other Chinese bands followed, instilling in me that day a lifelong love of Chinese classical music. Between them were flatbed trucks decked out as floats, with tableaux enacted on them by children dressed as characters out of Chinese mythology, wearing stark pancake make-up.

The highlights of the parade, however, were the lion and dragon dances.

The lion had a brightly coloured stylised head on a bamboo frame, with fur-lined jaws and bulbous eyes. It was held aloft by a dancer who swung it to and fro to the clashing of cymbals and striking of hand gongs, and gener-ally acted in a ferocious fashion. Behind him was the lion's body, a covering of less decorated cloth under which another dancer jostled and jived.

Stilt-walkers and jugglers followed, and then the dragon arrived. It was magnificent. Its head was at least nine feet high, excluding the horns on top. Its mouth—red-mawed and lined with white teeth—was operated by a man walking in front of the dragon with a pole connected to the lower lip, while the remainder of the head was held high by one man, who swung it to and fro. Several yards in front of the dragon pranced a man with a paper fish almost as big as himself on a pole, with which he teased the beast. Behind the head was a hundred-yard-long reptilian body constructed of coloured cloth painted in scales and stretched over a series of bamboo hoops. Under this danced several dozen men, giving the dragon's body the appearance of a multicoloured circus centipede. The crowds applauded, the cymbals clashed, the gongs clanged and then it was all suddenly over.

'What did you think of that?' my father asked as we lined up for the launch.

'Very impressive,' I replied noncommittally.

'Just think,' my father went on, 'all over the Empire, these celebrations will be going on today. All for one young woman, our new Queen.'

4

We drove onto the vehicular ferry at Yau Ma Tei, the ramp was raised and the vessel headed out across the harbour. My mother and I stood at the front, a light spume blowing over us. My father remained with the car at the back of the deck, wiping spray from the paintwork with a chamois leather.

'Where are we going?' I asked insistently and not for the first time.

'I've told you, I'm not telling you,' my mother retorted impishly.

Living in Kowloon, I rarely crossed the harbour to Hong Kong Island. My parents frequently visited friends there, and, of course, my father crossed the harbour daily to go to his office; but I accompanied them only on select occasions, such as an Open Day on an aircraft carrier or submarine.

On Hong Kong-side, we drove off the ferry and a short distance through the city streets before ascending a steep, wide road. Ahead was verdant mountainside with low apartment blocks on the gentler slopes and houses half hidden in trees as the mountain rose more precipitously. The car climbed through luxuriant forest. Lianas and aerial roots hung down like ropes while butterflies flitted through the dappled light. Through gaps in the trees I caught snatches of open sea: we had crossed to the island's south side.

Still we climbed. Edging the car into first gear, my father gunned the engine and we set off up a thirty-degree incline, then turned up another steep road that ran along a knife-edge ridge. At the end of this was a four-storey block of apartments. My father parked the car and we entered the building.

'Who lives here?' I asked my mother as we climbed the wide stairs.

'We do,' she replied. 'From the day after tomorrow.'

On the top floor, my father produced a key and we entered Apartment 8, Block A, Mount Austin Mansions.

'Close your eyes,' my mother said as we went in.

I did so. She led me through the apartment. I heard a door open then the gentle shush of a mountain breeze.

'Open them.'

I was on the verandah. At my feet lay Hong Kong.

The view left me speechless. Down below was the central business district, the Bank of China and the Hongkong and Shanghai Bank next door little more than a child's building bricks. The harbour was a pool with small boats moving across it. Beyond lay the peninsula of Kowloon. In the distance were the Kowloon hills and, further away still, a progression of hills disappearing towards China. The sun was now low and the riot of neon in the streets to the east and on Kowloon-side started to come alive. In fifteen minutes, it was night, the lights of the colony shimmering in the heat.

'So?' my mother asked.

'I don't know,' I replied.

'What do you mean, "I don't know"?' my father snapped. 'This is one of the most famous panoramas in the world. People sail halfway round the world to see this view for fifteen minutes and you're going to have it twenty-four hours—'

'Do stop harping on, Ken,' my mother muttered.

'Well, honestly . . .' my father replied, determined to have the last word.

In truth, I was fully appreciative of the view. It was just that the enormity, the grandeur of it did not match my eight-year-old vocabulary.

LIFE ON THE PEAK had as much in common with that in Kowloon as a bowl of fish soup at a *dai pai dong* had to a traditional English fried breakfast, with or without salad cream. There were no shops except for a small Dairy Farm general store. There were hardly any people about except around an observation point where tourists with cameras mingled with touts trying to sell them packs of photographs of what they were themselves about to photograph. There were no eating places except the Peak Café. The few buildings that did exist were either the houses of the rich taipans, secure behind walls topped with broken glass, or apartment blocks. From a busy urban existence, I was suddenly catapulted into a pacific rural one.

The morning of the move, we arrived at Mount Austin shortly after two dark blue Bedford lorries with RN painted in white upon the sides. Half a dozen Chinese ratings leapt out and began to carry all our belongings up to Apartment 8. To complement the general-issue furniture provided by the Navy, my parents had purchased a low Chinese coffee table with bow legs, reminiscent of an English bull terrier's, and a Chinese dining-room suite.

As soon as the unpacking commenced, it was diplomatically suggested that I might like to go outside and play. Hardly believing my good fortune, I left the building and set off towards the summit of the Peak.

The road was steep and passed a cleared bombsite: I had seen enough of those in Portsmouth to recognise it. Higher up, several rather fine houses stood to the right of the road. I walked on.

I found myself on a path that crossed a small tumbling stream filled with tiny fish, which seemed amazing not three hundred feet from the top of a mountain. I stepped over the water by a small stone bridge and walked on. The narrow path clung to the not-quite-sheer side of the hill. It was obvious few people came this way, for the undergrowth met over the path and my legs were soon scratched and bleeding. Yet it was worth it. The views were breathtaking. Below me was a pale azure reservoir, Lamma Island across a narrow channel and the South China Sea beyond it. To the west, beyond the next hill, were the islands of western Hong Kong and, beyond them, Lan

Tau Island, the biggest in the territory. I did not realise quite how high I was until a kite briefly hovered near me. It swivelled its head with avian wonderment at finding someone so close on the normally deserted mountainside.

The next morning, I opened the curtains to discover we were in the clouds.

At breakfast, my mother announced, 'You're going to go to the Peak School now. We've an appointment with the headmistress at eleven.'

The school was about twenty minutes' walk away down the very steep hill. Later that morning, my mother, wearing high-heeled shoes, attempted the descent, stopped after a few yards and removed her shoes. We arrived at the school hot and harried. I was taken to a classroom and obliged to stand in front of my future classmates, declare my name and then sit down at a desk next to another *gweilo* with breath that smelt as if he had breakfasted on hundred-year-old eggs. It did not bode well.

The pupils were predominantly British with a few Chinese, Americans and others of European extraction. Many of them seemed distant and snooty. I preferred to keep myself to myself, get on with my work, and head for the door at the first chime of the bell. I rebuffed most approaches of friendship. When the school play was being cast, I was given a lead part, perhaps to bring me out of my shell. The play was *Toad of Toad Hall*. I was Mole.

One memorable facet of my thespian adventure remains—the costume.

Each parent was asked to provide their child's outfit. My mother, not being adept with a needle and thread, summoned her tailor.

Mr Chuk, a soft-spoken, elderly Chinese gentleman, came to the apartment. He could make a midnight-blue silk cocktail dress in five days, a lady's two-piece suit in seven. A mole costume was another matter.

My mother—no artist—produced her drawing of a mole.

The tailor studied it and shrugged. 'I no look-see dis an'm'l,' he said. 'Maybe dis no an'm'l China-side.' The tailor noticed that the sketch had no eyes. 'He no can look-see?'

'No can look-see,' my mother confirmed. 'Live underground. You make?'

'Can do,' came the optimistic reply.

It was deemed that I did not require a fitting and so, two days before opening night, the tailor arrived at the apartment carrying a bundle containing a dark chocolate-brown, one-piece boiler suit. I tried it on. It was as loose and shapeless as a maternity smock. My mother stifled a laugh.

The tailor had sewn whiskers (made of thin bamboo strips taken from a broom) on the top of the head. My face peered out through the mouth, which was lined by white serrated cloth teeth. The tailor had clearly taken pity on the mole's disability and given it two shiny glass eyes, as well as a pair of catlike ears. On opening night, Rat (grey hairy costume, tail, beady eyes, bowler hat, waistcoat), Toad (mottled green rubber attire made from a frogman's wet suit, a pair of cut-down plus fours and a deerstalker), Badger (tweed jacket and cut-down tartan golfing trousers with a realistic black and white papier mâché head) appeared on stage alongside a mutant creature of indeterminate species. At curtain call, I received resounding applause. It was not, I was certain, due to my acting abilities.

ONCE A MONTH, a cylindrical package wrapped in brown paper arrived for me by sea mail. It had been mailed by my grandfather. The rolled-up contents were the previous month's issues of the *Eagle*, *Dandy* and *Beano*. Tucked somewhere in them would always be a ten-shilling postal order. This package was, to me, the height of love and I promptly wrote back by blue airmail lettergram to thank Grampy and give him my news.

I held no information back, telling him of all my escapades, in the certain knowledge that he would not report them to my grandmother and, through her, to my father. Not once did he betray my confidence and he always replied, although my questions were not always answered. He did not tell me what *jig-a-jig* meant, so I assumed he did not know.

All expatriates referred to the country of their origin as 'home', even the old China Hands, who had lived 'in-country' since the 1920s. At first, my mother followed suit. However, by the winter of 1953, her outlook had changed. She started to write to her mother that she wanted to remain in Hong Kong after my father's three-year-long tour of duty ended. In addition to learning Cantonese, she attended classes in Chinese history and culture.

Of the old China Hands, I was to come to know two.

The first was a friend of my mother's, an Englishwoman called Peggy who had married a Dutchman in the 1930s. When war broke out in 1939, her husband may have returned to Holland to fight for his homeland or he may have stayed in Hong Kong and been killed when the Japanese invaded in 1941. Certainly, Peggy was rounded up and thrown into the civilian camp— the high-security prison at Stanley. I think they had no children. She employed a traditional *saw hei* amah, who risked her life smuggling food and herbal medicines into the camp for her missee. Her clandestine activities saved Peggy's life. After the Japanese surrender, Peggy remained in Hong Kong and the amah returned to work for her, but now they were no longer missee and amah but two spinsters living together and looking out for each other. Peggy obtained employment with the Hongkong and Shanghai Bank. The amah kept home for both of them in a small flat on Robinson Road, which they shared with two dozen rescued stray cats. She and the amah were to die in their late seventies within days of each other.

The other China Hand was Sammy Shields, my dentist. His surgery was in Star House, a two-storey building facing the Kowloon Star Ferry pier. Sammy was not a qualified dentist. Before the war, he had been a dental technician. When he, too, was incarcerated in Stanley, he was the only person in the camp with any real dental know-how, so he became the camp dentist by default. After the war, he set up in practice, his reputation growing, as it were, by word of mouth.

Sammy had a special technique with small boys such as myself, whose mothers he refused to allow into his chamber of tortures. Whenever my mother left the room I felt terrified, but Sammy would put me at my ease: 'Right now, open wide. Let's see . . . a filling needed here, I'm afraid . . . just a little prick for the cocaine . . .' ('*Aarhh! Ah hurhs!*') 'All done . . . wait for it to put your jaw to sleep. Did I ever tell you about my time as a guest of his Imperial Japanese Majesty?'

From then on, the sound of his drill and the jab of pain as he hit the nerve were mere momentary interruptions in a narrative of roasting rats on shovels over a fire of dried cow dung collected on Stanley beach, of face slappings and rifle buttings, of men dying of disease or being shot on the beach, of the Americans' bombing of two prison buildings, killing the occupants.

'Bloody fools, Americans,' Sammy would end this story.

I heard these stories every six months. They never lost their potency and never failed to take the edge off what I was undergoing. It was, I thought, nothing compared to what he must have endured for four years.

A FORTNIGHT before my ninth birthday, Wong asked me, 'What shape you likee you burfday cake, young master?'

As far as I was concerned, cakes were round and that was an end to it.

'Maybe you likee house?' he suggested, seeing my bewilderment.

Without really thinking about it, I answered, 'I'd like a battleship.'

Several days later, I went to the kitchen to find my way barred.

'You lo can come kitchen-side now,' Wong declared with authority.

'I only want a Coke,' I said.

He handed one to me through a crack in the door, adding, 'Two week, you lo go kitchen-side. You go, Wong v'wy ang'wee.'

I complained to my mother. Her reply was that I was to obey Wong.

On my birthday, I arrived home from school in eager anticipation, as it had been decided that I should not receive my presents until teatime.

'Tea first, prezzies second,' my mother announced.

My father was home two hours before normal. I was led into the dining room where Wong had laid out tea . . . Yet the moment I saw the table all thought of gifts and food evaporated.

In the centre of the table was a two-and-a-half-foot-long model of a Royal Navy destroyer, exact in every detail. It was painted battleship grey with its identification letter and numbers on the hull. At the bow hung the Union Jack, at the stern the White Ensign. On the bridge were the Aldiss lamp and searchlights, the wheel and a brass compass and engine room telegraph. On deck, the guns pointed fore and aft.

I was speechless. Wong stood by my side.

'Dis you cake, young master. Happy burfday for you.'

I just hugged him.

The cake had taken Wong a fortnight. He had worked every spare moment he could afford. The hull and superstructure were a rich fruit cake covered in hard royal icing, the lifeboats were made of marzipan and icing, the main armament and gun turrets of solid icing, the rigging of spun sugar. The cake had been hidden in the windowless room off my parents' bedroom where clothes and shoes were kept to avoid them going mouldy in the tropical air. A charcoal burner was kept alight, absorbing any humidity that got in.

I did not want to cut into it. At the end of the table was a smaller ordinary cake with candles on it. We ate that instead, but the following day we started on the destroyer. I forget what presents I received.

The destroyer was not Wong's only artistic culinary masterpiece. He could carve chrysanthemum blooms out of raw carrots and decorative leaves out of cucumbers. For cocktail parties he prepared what was known as *small chow*: mushrooms stuffed with anchovies, cheese and soy sauce sticks, thinly sliced fresh pineapple and shrimps on toast with homemade mayonnaise and a scattering of sesame seeds—his repertoire seemed inexhaustible.

At drinks parties, Wong being occupied in the kitchen, my father delegated me to help him wait on the guests. At first I regarded this as an onerous chore, but I came to look forward to it. My father taught me how to mix drinks and I was able to consume Wong's delicacies on the sly. Such parties also had their lighter side. On Christmas Eve morning, 1953, I went into my parents' bathroom only to discover a Royal Navy commander asleep on his back in the bath, gently snoring. I tiptoed out and never saw him again.

That same winter, my father returned home in the early hours from a mess night with the Royal Air Force at Kai Tak airport. He was well-oiled and his dinner suit was caked in congealed blood.

I stood by as my mother, simultaneously concerned and furious, stripped my father to his vest and Y-fronts, sat him in the bath and washed him down. He had a nasty gash on the inside of his arm. When he was clean, my mother sent him into the spare room.

In the morning, she held a breakfast inquisition.

'What the hell were you doing last night, Ken?'

'Fan cricket,' my father admitted.

After the formal dinner, the RAF officers' mess members had decided on a game of fan cricket, mess versus guests, which involved everyone present forming a circle round a ceiling fan. This was set at maximum speed and an empty beer can tossed into it. Wherever it flew out from the spinning propeller, it had to be caught. Of course, after the first toss, the metal was mangled into pieces as sharp as razor blades.

'Your trousers are torn and the remnants of your jacket smell of petrol.'

My father confessed how the evening's jollity had ended. The mess piano had been carried outside and placed at the rear of a Hawker Hunter jet fighter parked on the apron. The engine was fired up and the piano incinerated.

As time went by, my father's increasing delight in and reliance upon the company of Johnnie Walker, Messrs Justerini and Brooks, and his namesake Mr Booth—not to mention his friend, Mr Gordon—grew. When he arrived home from the office, his first visit was to the drinks cabinet. His favourite snifter was pink gin. It consisted of gin diluted with water, with a dash of Angostura bitters. My father took it without the water.

My father never got truly, staggeringly drunk. Furthermore, he never suffered from a hangover. Consequently, he never felt himself to be sozzled, as my mother termed it, trying to make light of the situation for her own sanity and self-respect. Worse still, he would never admit to being under the influence. No matter how much alcohol slid down his gullet, my father remained vertical and comparatively lucid. The only obvious sign of intoxication was his attitude towards my mother and me. He was psychologically abusive, skilfully criticising or belittling us in front of our friends. His attacks were calculated to undermine his subject's spirit and, as his drinking increased, they melded together into a continuous animosity that drove people away in disgust. As a result, my father became a lonely, disenchanted and bitter man.

ALTHOUGH WE NOW LIVED across the harbour from all my mother's Chinese friends, she remained in touch with them, meeting the room boys from the Fourseas on their days off, going to teahouses with them, sometimes spending an afternoon with them at the beach. At other times, she went on picnics with them. When these occurred at a weekend or in the school holidays, I was invited along.

My father took a dim view of these outings.

'If you ask me, Joyce, you should stay home at the weekends. All this gallivanting about will get you a reputation. Tongues'll wag.'

'I don't care if they flap in the wind like flags,' my mother rejoined.

One Saturday we met up with Ching, Halfie and some of the other Fourseas staff at the Outlying Islands ferry pier. A Hongkong Yaumatei Ferry Company vessel pulled alongside and we boarded it with a throng of boisterous Chinese weekend picnickers, all carrying rattan baskets or bags.

After an hour the ferry turned into the harbour of Cheung Chau, a dumb-bell-shaped island with an ancient village in the centre. Deep-water fishing junks rode at anchor, sampans weaving between them like agile aquatic insects. A drift of joss-stick smoke indicated the location of a large temple.

I wanted to visit it but it was not on our itinerary. Instead, we went south along the *praya*, passing fishermen mending nets or baiting lines and houses with their windows shuttered against the fierce sunlight. At the periphery of the village, we struck out along a path through a tunnel of trees and rocks. It was alive with tawny Rajah and delicate cream-and-black dragontail butterflies supping on fallen fruit. Birds flitted through the branches of a sacred banyan tree, upon which pictures of the gods had been pinned. Here and there were groves of yellow-and-green striped bamboo. All the while, the sea glinted away to my right through sparsely needled pine trees.

My mother walked with a jaunty step. 'Isn't this fun?' she asked.

I agreed that it was but, after a short distance, posed a question that had long been bothering me. 'Why doesn't Dad come to places with us?'

She looked down at me. 'He's a stick-in-the-mud,' she responded.

'Was he always a stick-in-the-mud?' I enquired.

'No! We used to go for walks and cycle rides in the country or go to the pictures . . .' She paused. I sensed she was sad but then she perked up. 'What the hell! It was all a long time ago.'

The path descended a hillside towards the sea. Up ahead, our companions were singing a Chinese song. My mother joined in.

We halted by a group of boulders. Someone lit a small Primus and boiled water for tea. A cloth was spread over a flat rock and weighted down with stones. With the others, my mother set about laying out our picnic.

I settled myself on a granite slab, the sunlight dancing on the mica fragments. To my left was a cove surrounded by low cliffs, gentle waves sucking at the rocks. My mother approached with Ah Tang, one of the room boys.

'Martin, come and see this!'

We followed Ah Tang along a cliffside path and down to the shore, where there was a tumble of huge boulders. Several had formed a sort of cave.

Ah Tang gestured us in. 'This place for Cheung Po Tsai. He live here.'

'Who is Cheung Po Tsai?' I enquired.

'Long time before, more four hund'ed year, Cheung Po Tsai big time py-rat. Got many junk, many men work for him. Also got *gweipor* wife. Catch her on one ship one time. She love Cheung Po Tsai, no wan' go back Inglun'-side. Stay here.'

'Just imagine,' my mother said, 'living here with a pirate chief, thousands of miles from home and knowing you could never return.'

The romantic in her was working double-speed.

When the picnic was over, some of the room boys' girlfriends started to dance. It was a Chinese dance that involved tiny steps, moving in a circle, singing a song and, with arms raised, making a twisting motion with the hand, as if one were screwing in a light bulb. My mother was invited to join in, being taught the words and motions. I watched as she danced. She was, as she would have put it, as happy as a sand boy.

We sailed back to Hong Kong, and took a taxi home. My father was sitting with a gin and tonic listening to the BBC World News on the radio. I went out on to the verandah and looked down on the city. The first neon lights were coming on, bright as coloured stars.

'Have a good time?' my mother asked.

I nodded.

'It's days like this you never forget, no matter how old you get,' she advised me. 'It's what life's all about. Warm sun, friendship and music.'

CHRISTMAS DAY 1953 dawned bright. The sky was cloudless and blue, the air chill. At nine o'clock, we embarked upon the ritual of present giving.

In the lounge, we had a tinsel-hung, glass-ball-strewn, fairy-lights-lit Christmas tree, imported from California. We gathered before it, shortly to be joined by Wong and his family. Tuppence was seated on an armchair and showered with small presents, which included clothing as well as Chinese sweets and toys. Wong and Ah Shun received their presents, and then we got on with opening ours.

Lunch that day could have graced a monarch's table. The turkey, a gift from the Asia Provision Company, was stuffed with cranberry, sage and thyme and the flesh fell apart like fish. The pudding was traditionally round and the size of a football, with a sprig of holly on top. We wondered where Wong had got it: holly was not indigenous to southern China. Then we found out. It was made of icing sugar. As for the pudding, it was so big we were still eating it fried in butter in the first week of January.

Christmas afternoon was spent playing Dover Patrol on the lounge carpet and listening to the Queen's Speech. Late in the afternoon, I walked down to a block of 1920s apartments near the Peak Café to visit a friend. We messed around a bit and I set off for home just before dark.

My parents were playing canasta at the bull terrier coffee table when I arrived home. My mother had a gin and tonic at her side, my father a tumbler of neat whisky. I settled down in an armchair to read the latest *Eagle* album, a Christmas present from Grampy.

After a while, my father put a 78 record on the phonograph: the Original Dixieland Jazz Band playing 'Tiger Rag'. It was tentatively suggested that I might go to bed, but I pleaded Christmas night and the subject was dropped.

At about half past ten, my mother went out onto the verandah to take in the view. This was a nightly ritual.

'Ken,' she called, her voice tight with urgency, 'get your binoculars.'

'What is it?' I enquired, joining my mother on the verandah.

'I don't know,' she replied, pointing across to the northwestern end of Kowloon. 'What do you make of it?'

A dull ruddy blush glowed behind some low hills. My father arrived and put his binoculars to his eyes, turning the focusing ring.

'Oh my God!' he murmured.

My mother snatched them from his face.

'Can I see?' I insisted. I had to ask several times before she would relinquish them.

I adjusted the focus. It seemed as if a whole hillside was ablaze. It was the Shek Kip Mei squatter area going up in flames. Even from a distance of five miles, individual flames could clearly be seen licking into the air. I thought of my experience at Ho Man Tin, of the young man with only the photo of his family to link him to his former life back in China.

My mother turned into the lounge, calling for Wong, and set to work.

'Wong, get all the blankets out of the camphor wood chest. Martin, you—'

'What are you doing, Joyce?' my father asked.

'What do you think I'm doing?' she snapped back. 'Go and get the car.'

'Get the car?' my father repeated. 'It's after eleven, Joyce!'

'I know! Get the bloody car, cloth ears!' It was a derogatory expression my father often used on her.

In thirty minutes, all the bedding in the house was tied into individual bundles of one blanket and two sheets. My school Hong Kong basket was full of turkey sandwiches and there were two cardboard boxes of tonic and soda water. This was loaded into the car and we set off.

We drove down the Peak and onto the vehicular ferry. There were only two other private vehicles on board. The remainder of the deck was occupied by several fire engines and ambulances.

Once we landed at Yau Ma Tei it was only a mile or so to Shek Kip Mei, but we were halted by a road block at Prince Edward Road. My father parked in the forecourt of an apartment block and my mother got out, piled me high with blanket and sheet bundles and, with as many as she could carry herself, set off in the direction of the fire. I followed.

We had not gone three hundred yards when a British police officer stopped us. 'You can't go beyond here,' he told my mother.

'St John Ambulance,' she replied.

Her bluff worked. He let us through. The side streets were thronged with hordes of people sitting down. What was unnerving was that they were virtually silent. My mother handed out bundles to the first families she came across. They took them, smiling at her. One man touched my hair.

The air was contaminated with the smell of burning rubber and cloth. Ash blew past us, some of the flakes still alight. A fire engine pumped water from a street hydrant but it could not have had much effect. The sky was alight with sparks and flames, a thick column of smoke rising upwards.

Next, we distributed the turkey sandwiches, but carrying the boxes of bottles was beyond us so we returned home with them.

The following day, the full extent of the fire was broadcast on the radio: 10,000 huts had been destroyed; 60,000 people had been made homeless. Incredibly, no one was killed. This prompted the conjecture that the fire had been set deliberately to force the government into speeding up the squatter rehousing and rehabilitation programme. If this were the case, it worked. Within a year, the site of the blaze was a brand-new refugee housing estate.

IN WEEKS I HAD become more or less au fait with the geography of the Peak. The path I had taken that first day was called Governor's Walk. The neighbouring hill was called Sai Ko Shan (or, in English, High West), *shan* meaning mountain. At its base was a rifle range where I collected deformed .303 bullets, digging them out of the butts with my penknife.

To reach the rifle range, I had to take what must be one of the most spectacular walks on earth. It began—and ended—at the foot of Mount Austin Road and circumnavigated the Peak.

I would always set off clockwise, walking beneath overhanging trees alive with butterflies and the birds that ate them. A short distance further on, the road narrowed and became unsuitable for vehicles. Holding more or less to the same contour, it continued round the mountain, sometimes as a viaduct, at others cut into the rock. Bit by bit, an incredible vista unfolded, of the western harbour approaches, Kowloon peninsula, the central business district and the eastern suburbs, and beyond, the nine dragon hills.

Yet it was not the view that captivated me. I took that for granted. Halfway down the western flank of the Peak, on a promontory 1,100 feet above sea level, was a large gun emplacement known as Pinewood Battery. During the war, it had been equipped with two three-inch antiaircraft guns but had been destroyed on December 15, 1941, during the battle for Hong Kong. The gun platforms still existed, as did the subterranean block houses, the command post, ammunition bunkers and sleeping quarters.

The ruins were an adventure playground in which friends and I could enact the Japanese storming it and the British defending it, the latter always winning in strict contradiction of history. When I went there alone I would hunt for wartime relics. I wanted a British cap badge or uniform button, a Japanese shell from a Zero fighter, machine-gun cartridge cases and a shell case from one of the AA guns. What I actually found outdid the lot.

I was working through the low, dense scrub below the battery when I came upon a piece of khaki material sticking up from the ground. Hoping it might be a fragment of discarded uniform with a button on it, I grabbed it and tugged. It would not shift. I set to work excavating it with my penknife. In less than a minute, I discovered the edge of a collar. Just beneath it was the smooth side of a skull, an eye socket filled with earth staring up at me.

I jumped back as if it had been a reared cobra. Scrambling through the undergrowth, I ran to the Peak Café, where I asked someone to telephone the police for me.

An hour later, I was back at Pinewood with a dozen police officers and some coolies. As they dug up the skeleton, I was asked questions by a British police officer, who then took me home in a police car.

We were informed that the skeleton was that of a Japanese soldier. He had not, I was told, died in the war but afterwards, captured by local Chinese who had probably murdered him in retribution for what the Japanese had done to the local population.

'What's going to happen to him?' I asked.

'His remains will be handed over to the Japanese authorities for return to Japan,' the police officer answered, 'where he can rest in peace.'

AT THE BOTTOM of the valley that dropped away to the south of Mount Austin was Pokfulam reservoir. As 1953 had been the driest year on record, by December the reservoir was very low indeed. This implied two things to me: first, that whatever lived in the valley would probably have to visit it to drink, and second, that whatever lived in the reservoir was now restricted to shallow water and therefore easily seen.

With a picnic lunch supplied by Wong, I set off one Saturday morning and settled myself down on the dam wall. The water lay below me, as still and transparent as green bottle glass. Schools of tiny fish occasionally darted by. A frog swam along. Suddenly, there was a large flurry of mud. As the water cleared, I noticed an oval outline in the mud about the size of a large meat-serving dish. Very slowly, it detached itself from the bottom and rose towards the surface. From one end, a white-and-grey mottled head appeared, stretching out on a long neck that curved up towards me. It culminated in a prehensile nose, which broke the surface for a moment before the head was retracted and the turtle drifted back down to the mud.

Other encounters were not quite so benign. Walking to and from school, I daily passed along Plunketts Road, at the side of which ran an open drain, or *nullah*, designed to shed heavy rainfall off the mountain to prevent landslides. One afternoon, taking the path beside it, I heard what sounded like a hissing water leak. I went to investigate.

In the *nullah* was a common rat snake, a fangless constrictor approximately three feet long, dark brown with no pattern. This snake must have fallen into the smooth-sided *nullah* and could not get out. If it continued downhill it would reach a storm culvert and escape. If it headed uphill it would arrive at several blocks of apartments and, I was certain, a place on the supper table in one of the servants' quarters. It was facing uphill.

I found a stick in the undergrowth and attempted to force the snake's head round to face the way to safety. I had given it a few prods when it reared up, spread its hood and spat at me.

This was no common rat snake. It was a cobra.

I recoiled, a smear of slimy venom on my shirt. Very carefully, I removed the garment and dropped it on the path. At that moment, two boys from my class arrived on the scene. We debated what to do. The primitive and illogical fear of snakes welled up in us. We would stone it to death.

We gathered as many large stones as we could find and hurled them at the snake. Some found their mark, most did not. All the while, the snake raised its head, the hood spread to show the black-and-white ghostlike pattern of a face on its surface.

We had been at this endeavour for five minutes or so when two coolies carrying poles over their shoulders came trotting down the hill. They looked over the edge of the *nullah*. The cobra seemed slightly wounded. One coolie, signalling us to stand back, reached down, grabbed the cobra by its tail, swung it up in the air and slammed it down on the concrete path. It was dead. They coiled it up, tied it with twine, hung it from one of their poles and set off down the hill. I walked home, ashamed that I had taken part in this assassination and vowing never to kill a snake again. Except in self defence.

My only other dangerous encounter occurred one evening on the Old Peak Road, a very steep footpath that wound down the mountain to the city below. I had descended as far as Barker Road when I heard a noise behind me that sounded like someone rattling several half-empty boxes of matches. Turning, I found a fully grown porcupine coming at me in reverse, its quills upright and a-quiver. I clapped my hands and shouted—to no avail. I fled. The porcupine kept pace. The angle of ascent soon told on me. I slowed. The porcupine continued its attack. I reached the observation point. The porcupine stopped at the roadside and faced me. It was three feet long and bulky, its nose blunt like a beaver's, its quills black and white. It shivered. The quills rattled. Then it was off, running clumsily down Harlech Road and into the twilight. It was only later that a Chinese friend of my mother's told me that porcupines could kill a leopard cat with their quills.

THERE WERE only two ways to reach the top of the Peak, discounting walking up the Old Peak Road, which would test the stamina of a marine. One was by car or bus, the other by the Peak Tram.

Built in 1888, this was the world's steepest funicular railway, operating on the simplest of systems. A long, well-greased steel cable was wrapped round a massive drum in the engine house at the top. On each end was a tram car. As one travelled down the mountain, the other rose up it. At the halfway point, the track divided so that the cars might pass each other.

The tram car was constructed of varnished wood on a steel frame and chassis. The uphill portion was an enclosed cabin, where Europeans or wealthy Chinese travelled. Other Chinese passengers were obliged to ride in the rear half, which, although roofed, was otherwise open to the elements.

Whenever I could, I chose the rear portion. There were no restraining ropes, no safety bars. The only thing to hold on to was an armrest. Just before leaving the lower terminus, a tinny bell rang three times and the car edged forwards. The single track climbed steeply. To request it to stop, one pressed a button; for boarding, one just put one's hand out to hail the brakeman.

All the while, the angle of ascent increased. Above Bowen Road it was at least forty-five degrees. The May Road station, just below the halfway passing place, was at the steepest point. Here, when the car stopped, it yo-yoed alarmingly as the long steel cable flexed. Of necessity, it was elastic. This bouncing always set tourists and American sailors chattering. From here the tram car trundled steadily upwards, entering a cutting and turning a long bend in the middle of what was essentially subtropical jungle. This is where it would sometimes stop to accommodate the other car in a lower station.

I grew blasé about the Peak Tram, for I took it as commonly as most people might a bus. The view, with everything apparently leaning at a bizarre angle, was an everyday phenomenon.

The comments made by the tourists and American sailors were as predictable as sunrise. At a mid-jungle halt: 'OK! Y'all out 'n' push!' At the elastic stage: 'How many times you reckon this baby's snapped?' To the brakeman leaning on a dead man's handle, who spoke not a word of even pidgin English: 'Ya hold that baby real tight now, y'hear?'

One day in 1954, my mother met me after school at the Peak Tram terminus to take me down to the city. As we waited for the next tram, a notice declared that Barker Road station was temporarily closed.

The tram set off. Barker Road station approached. It was thronged with people. A bright light switched on as we drew near. The car stopped in the station. Someone appeared briefly with a clapperboard. Another called, 'Action!' A man in a light-coloured suit detached himself from the crowd, walked down the platform and entered the cabin. The tram set off. The powerful light switched off. My mother put her hand on mine. It was quivering.

'That's Clark Gable!' she whispered.

And it was. He was shooting a film called *Soldier of Fortune*.

She scrabbled in my school bag, took out an exercise book, tore a page from it, fumbled in her handbag for a pen. 'Martin, get his autograph.'

'You tore a page out of my exercise book,' I complained. 'I'll get into trouble for that.'

'I'll square it with your teacher. Now get his autograph. He's one of the biggest film stars in the world.'

I remained unmoved. She grabbed my arm.

'Get his bloody autograph,' she threatened *sotto voce*. 'If you don't . . .'

'What if I do?' It seemed I might as well take advantage of the situation.

The Peak Tram reached May Road station and bounced on its cable for a minute. Clark Gable stood up, disembarked and walked off into a crowd of film people. The tram carried on down the mountain.

'Just for that,' my mother said peevishly, 'we're not going to Tkachenko's.'

ALTHOUGH THERE WAS both the local and BBC World Service radio, and the cinema, I tended to make my own entertainment. My imagination was sharp and I had the whole of the Peak on which to ramble.

Public entertainment was limited, because most people were too busy earning a living. Yet every Chinese New Year, temporary stages were erected on waste ground around Hong Kong for the presentation of Chinese operas.

The stages were marvels of oriental ingenuity. Made of thousands of bamboo poles lashed together with strips of the same material, they could be a hundred feet wide, forty deep, fully roofed with panels of canvas or *atap*—woven bamboo and/or rice-straw matting—and equipped with electric lights. The audience remained in the open. The clientele talked, drank, ate (even cooked) during the performance, which could last six hours. The actors dressed in flamboyant classical Chinese costumes and wore heavy, stylised make-up. They sang in high-pitched voices, their movements exaggerated and carefully choreographed.

I enjoyed these spectacles, but the falsetto singing prompted a headache in fifteen minutes. What I really enjoyed were the fights. Swords, pikestaffs and other weapons were flashed and swung, the combatants whirling and ducking, thrusting and slicing, cymbals clashing as swords met, gongs booming when the protagonists struck each other a mortal blow.

My favourite entertainment venue was the China Fleet Club in Wanchai, an infamous area of cheap hotels, tattoo parlours, Triad gangsters, bars and bordellos. The China Fleet Club was a social club operated by Royal Navy sailors for their comrades and incorporated several bars, a restaurant, sleeping accommodation, a barber's shop, billiards room and a cinema. I was permitted to go to the club cinema for Saturday matinées.

The main feature seldom interested me. What I went for were the cartoon preliminaries, and one in particular—*Tom and Jerry*. I was not alone. Sailors crammed into the seats, jostling and ribbing each other. As soon as the lights went down, the National Anthem was played. They all stood up. It ended. They sat down again. The screen came alive with the Pathé news. For this, the audience fell silent. Then the screen went black.

Someone would shout out, 'Where's Fred?' Other voices would join in. 'We want Fred! We want Fred!' Feet would start to stamp and hands clap.

If the screen lit up with a Donald Duck or Woody Woodpecker cartoon, all hell would break loose, the air growing thick with whistles and indignation. If, however, the cartoon was *Tom and Jerry*, the sailors would fall silent until the captions gave the name of the producer, then they all yelled 'Good old Fred!' in unison. The producer's name was Fred Quimby.

After the matinée ended, I sometimes strolled through Wanchai, passing the bars with their bamboo bead curtains, young women standing in the doorways smoking. Once or twice, I tried to enter one of these bars but was rebuffed by the girls at the door, never mind the barmen within. Either they were brusque and ordered me out, or they accepted my presence, asking me if I wanted *jig-a-jig*, which sent everyone but myself into paroxysms of hilarity. I meant no harm and only wanted a drink and a bit of conversation.

Wanchai did not appeal to me. The streets were sombre and lacked the vivacity of the rest of Hong Kong. Certainly, they were usually crowded, but there were few *dai pai dongs*, the newer buildings were characterless concrete blocks. There were no dried prawn or fish shops, no vendors of preserved eggs or rice, no little temples tucked away in back streets.

I mentioned to my mother that Wanchai seemed to lack soul.

'Maybe it's because it's on reclaimed land,' she remarked.

'Reclaimed land?'

'They knock a mountain down, pour it into the sea, then build on it. Hong Kong hasn't got much land space, so they make more of it in this way.'

I could only wonder how they knocked down a mountain.

FROM THE TIME my mother's mother was widowed in 1947, she had not left Portsmouth and was living on a state pension. To give her a holiday, my parents arranged for her to visit us, 'indulging' on an RFA vessel.

'Indulgence' was a quaint military arrangement, whereby a spare cabin on a ship could be rented to a close relative of a serving officer for a nominal sum. The passenger had to take pot luck: departure and arrival dates were speculative. If the vessel was diverted *en route*, the passenger went with it.

My grandmother was found a berth upon the RFA *Bacchus*, a tiny, shallow-draft ship used as a freighter carrying naval stores. My grandmother was listed on the ship's manifest as supercargo.

The *Bacchus* arrived alongside HMS *Tamar* on March 14, 1954. My grandmother walked unsteadily down the gangplank, holding on to both side ropes. She looked a lot older and frailer than when I had seen her last. She was wearing a dark blue dress, an overcoat and heavy, flat shoes. All the elderly women I had met in Hong Kong dressed in bright colours.

'Nanny's not sick, is she?' I enquired of my father.

'No,' replied my father, who disliked his mother-in-law. 'She's as fit as an old fiddle.'

'But she looks so old and ill,' I said.

'That's what England does to you,' he retorted bitterly.

For all his imperial, monarchist jingoism, my father loathed Britain—'the lousy benighted weather . . . the bloody taxes . . . the bloody strikes . . .'— and yet he never felt really at home in Hong Kong.

My grandmother stayed for just under three weeks. Her time was filled with cocktail parties, Chinese banquets, shopping outings (which bedazzled her, coming from utilitarian Britain) and a drive round the New Territories. My mother took her in a rickshaw to Hing Loon, where Mr Chan gave her a beer and she bought a string of pearls; to tea in the Pen; to Mr Chuk's establishment for new clothes; to the dockyard mess for dinner. It was a social whirl the likes of which my grandmother had never known.

My mother greatly enjoyed sharing her colonial life with her mother. She wanted to share her new existence, in which she felt so at ease, with someone she loved. For my father, Hong Kong was just another place in which to work: he might as well have been posted to a supplies office in Chatham.

I too revelled in showing my grandmother the Hong Kong I knew. Walking round Harlech and Lugard roads, I was quick to point out a butterfly, a blue-tailed skink, a giant snail. I took her to the rifle range and dug out a bullet for her. It had been my intention to take her to Pinewood Battery, but the walk was too much for her. I also took her on the Peak Tram, sitting in the open section. To my surprise, this frightened her.

My grandmother's brief visit made me aware of how much I had changed. Sitting beside her on a bench one afternoon, I recalled my life 'back home' in England, the cinder playground at Rose Valley School, the compost heap at the bottom of our garden that was my castle, the incessantly grey skies and that damp-dog smell of drizzle-sodden pullovers. When a coolie trotted by and I returned his greeting in Cantonese, and my grandmother commented that I was now 'a proper little Chinese boy', I felt strangely proud. This was, I now understood, where I wanted to be.

When the time came for my grandmother to depart, I imagine she realised that she would rarely see her only child and grandchild again. She knew she was condemned to a lonely widowhood, looking out for the postman delivering a blue airmail lettergram or an envelope with exotic stamps on it.

THE PEAK CAFÉ was a single-storey stone building with a tiled roof, opposite the Peak Tram terminus. Erected in 1901 as a shelter for the sedan chair and rickshaw coolies, it was an unpretentious place consisting of one large dining room under a roof crisscrossed with wooden beams. The menu offered toast, sandwiches and eggs and bacon as well as Chinese food, soft drinks, sundaes, beer, tea and coffee, ice creams and Popsicles. The last could also be purchased from itinerant Dairy Farm ice-cream sellers riding bicycles with cold boxes mounted over the front wheel. The Popsicles were made in fruit flavours as well as milk, soya milk and red bean paste, which looked enticing but were an acquired taste I never acquired.

Every day during term time my mother gave me a dollar to buy a drink on my way back from school. When the temperature was in the eighties, I often forewent a Coke and had two ten-cent 'popsies' instead, saving eighty cents a day. However, I was frequently able to save the money completely.

Although the Korean War was all but over, Hong Kong was still experiencing a large throughput of military personnel, especially Americans. Like all tourists, they would head up the Peak Tram to marvel at the view.

The Peak Café did a roaring trade when the US fleet was in. The sailors seemed programmed to need a beer and there was only one place to go. Yet before they could order, I would ambush them, leaning on the wall by the entrance to the café and panting with thirst. Within a few minutes, an American sailor would say something like, 'Hey, kid! How ya doin'?'

'Tuckered,' I would reply, wiping my brow with my forearm.

'Sure is hot! Ya wanna Coke, kid?'

And I was in, seated at a table with a bottle of Coke and the dollar bill still secure in my pocket. They wanted to know where I came from, where I

lived, what my father did for a job and had I any big sisters. These preliminaries over, they would embark upon their own life stories. I listened avidly.
A black sailor told me how his grandfather had been a slave. A lieutenant—
he pronounced it *lootenant*—from New York made me believe he was the
son of a gangster. Many may have told me tall stories, but I came to appreciate that a man may tell a stranger far more than he could his best friend.

My sojourns at the Peak Café came to an abrupt end one day when the
proprietor came out and shooed me away. 'You no good boy,' she criticised
me. 'You always hanging round to get something from the sailor.' She
shook her finger at me. 'But you come here again, I tell your mother.'

I apologised to her in Cantonese and thereafter took to buying a drink or
a ten-cent popsy, if I needed one, from one of the bicycle vendors. She lost
out on my custom, yet I had saved over forty dollars in two terms.

MY FATHER's principal hobby was sleeping. He would return from the office
at noon on Saturday and then, except for meals, the BBC World News and
to replenish his glass of whisky or pink gin, he would essentially stay in bed
until Monday morning. At first, my mother tried hard to get him to take an
interest in life outside his work, but without success. On only a few occasions did he surrender to my mother's sense of adventure.

One winter Sunday, a naval launch was requisitioned by a party of my
father's dockyard colleagues to visit Sunshine Island, or Chow Kung Chau.
A hilly island about three-quarters of a mile long by a third wide, it had been
settled by a few farmers, fishermen and, in the nineteenth century, pirates,
but abandoned since 1941. It was now home to two European families.

My father was enticed along by the prospect of being on a boat, which
brought out the sailor in him. He persuaded the Chinese coxswain to relinquish the wheel to him once we were out of the harbour. The coxswain agreed,
assuming a naval *gweilo* would be familiar with manoeuvring a launch, but
soon regretted it when he noticed my father was heading for the wrong
island. Not having the courage to admonish him, the coxswain mentioned it
to Alec Borrie, my father's divisional superior—his Old Man.

'I think we need to go a few degrees to port, Ken,' he said quietly. 'You're
on a heading for Peng Chau.'

My father looked extremely sheepish and altered course. A few minutes
later, he surrendered the wheel and busied himself with his binoculars.

I noticed on these occasions that my father was often left out of the conversation and he seldom sought to join in. Sometimes, I felt sorry for him

and wanted to go over and talk to him, but at the last moment I would decide against it, knowing that I would be put down, dismissed or derided.

An hour out, we swung in to a small beach on a windswept, treeless island. Boxes were unloaded and placed at the top of the beach. We all then went ashore and the launch reversed away.

Carrying our boxes, we set off along a footpath across the island, coming first to an *atap* hut, the home of Jack Shepherd, aka Jonathan Sly. Formerly manager of the Kowloon YMCA, he now lived with his wife in this hovel, making a meagre living writing short stories for the local press. As we drew near, he appeared at the door. Skinny, barefoot, with short hair and a trim beard, he was wearing an ordinary shirt with a blue Chinese padded silk jacket and a multihued Malay sarong.

My father looked disparagingly at the figure. 'He's certainly letting the side down,' he remarked to no one in particular.

We walked on, descending into a valley between two hills where more huts stood amid some newly tilled plots. This, my mother informed me, was the home and dream-child of a Quaker activist called Gus Borgeest.

Borgeest, his Chinese wife and their small daughter had arrived in 1951 as refugees from Hangzhou. He had worked for the Hong Kong government social services department and came to appreciate at first-hand the plight of the thousands of squatters and street-sleepers. It dawned on him that many had been farmers in China. In them, he reasoned, was a work force that merely required a chance to rise up above poverty and contribute to society.

Agricultural land being at a premium in Hong Kong, Borgeest turned his attention to the outlying islands. Chow Kung Chau provided what he required. He took out a lease upon it from the government, moving there and renaming it Sunshine Island. By the time we walked into the valley, the embryonic community consisted of the Borgeests, two Chinese associates and several families of impoverished Chinese farmers.

We were all introduced to Borgeest and given a short talk on his aims and ambitions. This over, we were taken on a quick tour of the centre of the island, interrupted by such expressions as 'Here will be the piggery' or 'This is the site of the fish ponds'. All I could see was a bleak, rock-strewn, grassy hillside with, here and there, plots marked out with stakes.

Then Mr Borrie divided us into work parties. I realised that my mother had brought me to the island under false pretences. I spent the remainder of the day helping to dig a ditch, carting the soil away in a bucket. The only relief from this toil was a sparse supply of sandwiches and a bottle of lukewarm Coke. We left the island at five o'clock. My back ached, my arms and legs were sore and I had a blister on my palm.

My mother rubbed the base of her spine as we waited for my father to bring the car. 'The strain of honest toil. Doesn't it make you feel good?'

'No,' I replied pointedly.

'But think of the good you've done. You've helped those far less fortunate than yourself to start rebuilding their lives. A hundred and something years ago, we stole this land from the Chinese. We owe an obligation to the people who live here. Many of them are refugees from Communism. We must help them. In a tiny way, that's what you've done today.'

Put that way, it made me feel smugly self-righteous.

THE OLDEST PART of the city was Western District, which clung to the lower slopes of the Peak beneath an almost sheer rock face that glistened with water in all but the hottest and driest of summers. I decided to see what the district had to offer. For two hours, I sauntered through the streets where Hong Kong had first begun, at least as far as the *gweilo* population was concerned. Most of the streets were narrow, built for coolie rather than car traffic, while many of those that ran north to south up the mountainside consisted of steps. The vehicular roads that ran parallel to them were very steep with sharp corners. The buildings were ancient and dilapidated, their plaster cracked by the sun and eroded by typhoons. From their ornate balconies projected the ubiquitous bamboo poles of dripping clothes.

What made this Chinese street scene different were the shops and businesses. Whereas Yau Ma Tei had its pavement *dai pai dongs*, Tai Ping Shan (as the Chinese called the area) had little cafés and restaurants inside the shop spaces under the buildings. They mostly sold noodles, *won ton*, soups and *dim sum*, the ingredients of some of which I could not identify, despite having graduated from the Yau Ma Tei school of street-eating.

The ladder streets, as the stepped thoroughfares were called, contained stalls balanced on the steps or constructed on platforms. These precarious entrepreneurial adventures sold buttons, thread and zips, cut keys, sharpened knives, or repaired wok handles. One stall sold ancient Imperial Chinese dynastic bronze coins with square holes in the middle. People bought them to ensure fiscal good fortune.

As I walked along, a faint herbal smell reached me. The source was a store with a shop-front window and a glass door bearing vermilion Chinese characters. A neon sign of a snake coiling itself round a bamboo stake hung over the street. The window display included bowls of seeds, bits of dry twig and bark, dried leaves, dehydrated roots, shrivelled fungi and flowers. Behind them were a dozen or so ground-glass stoppered bottles containing preserved frogs, lizards, snakes and other less easily recognised pieces of flesh. Beside them were trays of what looked like black dried turds.

Going in, I found there was only one other customer, a woman. Behind the counter a man was busy writing on sheets of plain paper and opening drawers in a cabinet that ran the length of the shop. From each he took a pinch or a handful of the contents, putting them into the sheets of paper. Every so often, he studied an old book. This done, he skilfully folded each sheet into a parcel and placed it in the woman's rattan basket. When she had paid and left, the man turned his attention to me.

'Wha' you wan'?' he asked in pidgin English.

'What dis shop?' I replied.

'Dis Chilese med'sin shop,' he replied. 'You sick by 'n' by, you come. I see you lo more sick. You lo sick now?' he enquired optimistically.

'I lo sick.'

'You wan' see med'sin? Lo all same like *gweilo* med'sin.'

Never one to turn down an opportunity, I said I did, and he showed me round the shop. In addition to a vast array of plant and fungal material, there were velvet-covered deers' antlers, tiny birds' nests, powdered pearls like grey talc shot through with stardust, the ghostly pale exoskeletons of sea horses, dried bears' spleens (the 'turds' in the window), an assortment of dried insects, and his pièce de résistance, a rhino's horn. When I asked what these were cures for, he reeled off a list of ailments, most of which I was ignorant of. When he was unable to give the English name, he mimed the symptoms.

Before I could leave, he mixed up a packet of dried plant matter for me.

'Good gen'ral med'sin for you. Like tonic. You put water, boiloo wung hour. Drink wung cup wung day. Make you st'ong.'

When I got home, I gave the packet to my mother, it being Wong's day off. She tipped the contents into a saucepan and boiled it for an hour. The apartment filled with a noxious odour.

My mother and I let the liquid cool then poured a cup. It tasted execrable. We left the remainder for Wong.

THE MAIN mercantile district of Hong Kong, Central District, held little interest for me. Most of the buildings were the offices of banks, shipping lines, lawyers, insurance companies and import/export firms. Only one place in Central held me in awe and I visited it over and over again. It was the main banking hall of the Hongkong and Shanghai Bank headquarters.

I had gone there first with my mother. On either side of the entrance was a life-size bronze lion. The left-hand one was growling.

'They're called Stephen and Stitt,' my mother said.

'Which is which?'

'Stephen's growling,' was her reply.

'What's a stitt?'

'They're named after two bank managers, Mr Stephen and Mr Stitt.'

The lions had bullet holes in them from the war and Stephen had a lump of shrapnel embedded in him. Both were covered in a dark brown patina except that Stitt's front paw shone like gold. I soon saw why. People walking by touched it. For luck.

'This,' my mother announced as we entered the bank, 'is actually the back door. The front door, and the address, are on the other side.'

This seemed nonsensical and I said so.

'It's to do with the laws of necromancy,' my mother replied. 'The main door has to face the hills, away from the harbour, to keep the sea dragon out and to stop the money flowing out into the ocean.'

The banking hall was vast. The sound of voices was muffled by its immensity. Huge, dark brown marble pillars held up the ceiling—and what a ceiling it was: barrel vaulted and covered in a gargantuan mosaic. In the centre was an elaborate golden starburst set against an azure backdrop, around the sides was a multicoloured frieze of figures engaged in all manner of oriental and occidental craftwork and industry. The ceiling never failed to stun me. I would often take a detour through the bank on my way from the Peak Tram to the Star Ferry just to pass under the glow of the mosaic.

NOT LONG after the forced-labour day on Chow Kung Chau, another trip was arranged to the adjacent island of Hei Ling Chau. It was sparsely populated and consequently the location of a leper colony. It was this we were to visit.

My mother heard of the trip from a naval newsletter and immediately announced we were going. My father was reluctant in the extreme.

'What's a leper colony?' I asked.

'It's where they lock away the poor buggers who've caught leprosy,' my father replied, hoping this would deter me from joining my mother.

I asked what leprosy was.

'Leprosy,' my mother answered, 'is a disease caused by bacteria. There are two kinds—dry leprosy and wet leprosy. If you have the dry sort, your nerves die off bit by bit and you become paralysed. Or, because they have no nerves in them, parts of your body wither and drop off. Most common is you lose your nose and fingers and toes. If you have wet leprosy, your entire body is covered in running sores and ulcers. That kind is dangerously contagious, meaning you can get it just by touching someone with it, but the dry is very hard to catch indeed—'

'And your mother wants to take you to meet some people who've got it,' my father butted in. 'Really, Joyce, sometimes you take the bloody biscuit. I'm not having our son exposed—'

'Don't talk such bloody bosh. We'll be perfectly safe. You think the people who run the leprosarium will put visitors at risk?'

'Why do you think they lock the poor bastards away on a ruddy island?'

'They don't lock them away. They look after them and cure them.'

'And they just become beggars,' my father retorted. 'Better to let them die.'

My mother pursed her lips, 'Sometimes, Ken, I wonder what I saw in you.'

A fortnight later, on a Sunday of bright sun and high scudding clouds, we were all three of us cutting through a choppy sea aboard a naval launch heading for Hei Ling Chau. On arrival at a short jetty, we were met by a Chinese man who helped us disembark under an archway of gold and scarlet bunting. A dozen other private launches rode at anchor.

'Welcome to our fête!' the Chinese man said as we stepped onto dry land.

'This really is bloody madness, Joyce,' my father muttered.

Ahead of us were some low buildings surrounded by stalls. Everything was decorated with strips and banners of gold and scarlet crêpe paper. Several hundred people milled about, trying their luck at a coconut shy, a roll-a-ten-cent-coin table and other attractions.

We joined the crowd, tried the lucky dip and visited the tombola stall. My father hung back, smoking his pipe, his teeth clenched in anger on the stem. After a short time, we saw him strolling off southwards.

It was then I saw my first leper. He was sitting behind a trestle table upon which were arranged a number of homemade wooden objects such as book ends and paperweights shaped like the outline of the island, its name burnt into the surface with a hot poker. From the front of the table hung a sign in English and Chinese stating *Woodworks made by inmats. Please by. Garuntee very clean.*

The leper had no nose, only a ragged hole surrounded by flaps of skin. He had also lost several fingers and an ear. Apart from this, he looked quite healthy, certainly in better shape than many of the beggars on the streets.

Walking up to the stall, I studied the wares on offer. They were simple items but very well made. The leper smiled at me but did not speak.

'We get our wood from a timber yard,' a voice said over my shoulder. 'They're leftovers. Mahogany, teak, sandalwood.'

I turned. A European man stood behind me dressed in slacks and an open-neck cotton shirt. A stethoscope hung round his neck.

Seizing the moment, I asked him a question that had been bothering me for days. 'Is it true you only cure the lepers so they can become beggars?'

'Who told you that nonsense?' he exclaimed. 'We don't just cure them. We train them to do jobs. This man here's going to be a carpenter. Once he has a job, which we'll find for him, he'll get his dignity and his life back.'

I pointed to the book ends and asked, '*Gai doh cheen*?'

The leper sort-of chortled and raised five assorted digits. I gave him five dollar notes and he handed me the book ends.

'*Dor jei*,' I thanked him.

He chortled again, and I saw that he had only half a tongue.

As I was about to go, he reached out with one hand, his eyes pleading for something. Fleetingly, so that I hardly felt it, he touched my hair.

On the return trip, I took my mother aside, out of my father's earshot. 'I let a leper touch my hair,' I admitted, hurriedly adding, 'but he was a dry one.'

'Well, then,' my mother replied with a smile, 'let's hope to God it brings the poor man luck, shall we?'

When we got home, however, I accidentally mentioned my encounter with the leper to my father. He went apoplectic.

'You did what?' he bellowed. 'Joyce! Do you know what this stupid little sod has done? He allowed a bloody leper to stroke his hair . . .' His face was red with anger. 'Go into your bedroom and stay there.'

I did as I was told. There were raised voices in the sitting room followed by a slammed door. My father entered my room carrying a red leather slipper.

'Bend over the side of the bed.'

'Why? I haven't done anything wrong.'

I was amazed at my defiance. Always in the past, I had meekly succumbed to a beating. Yet now, I thought, I would not. I had not been disobedient or insolent; a paddling now would be an injustice.

'Bend over, damn you—'

'No.'

He swung the slipper at my buttocks. I sidestepped.

'And they don't cure them to be beggars. You were wrong. They find them proper jobs so they get their dignity back. The doctor told me.'

I had no idea what dignity was but it had to be a good thing.

'I'll give you bloody dignity, you little sod!'

Grabbing me by the back of the neck, my father forced me to bend over, then, with all his might, he hit me four times in quick succession on the buttocks. I did not cry: I would not give him the satisfaction.

'Now get into bloody bed.' He was grinding his teeth with rage.

From that moment I hated my father, truly abhorred him with a loathing that deepened as time went by and was to sour the rest of both our lives.

5

My mother and I had planned to go swimming at Repulse Bay on the afternoon of Sunday, August 27, 1954. My father reluctantly said that he would drive us there. As Wong set the table for lunch, my father stood on the verandah surveying the harbour through his binoculars.

'Lunch 'edy, missee, master,' Wong announced.

My father stepped into the lounge and announced, 'Beach is off, Joyce. Number One signal's up.' By this, he meant that he had seen a storm warning on the signal mast at the Hong Kong Observatory.

My mother, not to be done out of an afternoon's swimming, replied, 'Are you sure? It's a lovely day and One is only a stand-by . . .'

'Tropical storms can gather very quickly,' my father opined.

'Surely not between now and five o'clock,' my mother came back.

To win the argument, my father telephoned HMS *Tamar*. The meteorological officer on duty confirmed it: they expected to raise the Number Five some time in the early evening. We sat down for lunch.

'What do the signals actually mean?' I asked.

My father replied, 'Number One is a standby signal, Numbers Five to Eight predict winds up to sixty miles per hour and designate the direction they will come from, Number Nine is winds up to gale or storm force and Number Ten hurricane force, with gusts up to a hundred and thirty.'

'What's this one going to be?'

'*Tamar* says a near hit, so Nine, possibly Ten.'

After lunch, we removed ornaments from windowsills and put old towels along them and along external doorsills. My father parked the car well under the adjacent block of apartments. In her bedroom, my mother stored away all her make-up jars. In my bedroom, I removed my ornaments from the windowsill—a pile of High West bullets, my carved wooden camel and a detailed model of a junk—placing them in my cupboard.

I had experienced several tropical storms and one typhoon before, but we had been living in the Fourseas or Boundary Street at the time and only suffered a few leaking windows. Now we were positioned on the pinnacle of a summit secondary only to the Peak, about 1,500 feet above sea level.

'What's this typhoon called?' I enquired.

Every typhoon was allotted a girl's name, for a reason I could not fathom. This one was called Ida. We had a spinster relative of the same name, a mousy, quiet woman who lived in a rural shire town, and spent her life baking scones. Perhaps we were not in for a bad typhoon after all, I thought.

I was wrong.

By the time I went to bed, the sky was covered with dense cloud. I read my comics, recently arrived, and went to sleep to be woken just after dawn by the booming gusts of wind. Each time one hit the building, I could feel the pressure on my ears. It was like living inside a bass drum.

I crossed to the window. The cloud base had dropped to not much above the roof of our building and the metallic sky seemed to glower with rage. I could still see the city below, but Kowloon was invisible. Intermittent squalls of heavy rain blew by, spraying off the corner of the stonework as if it were the bow of a ship. What was most frightening was my reflection in the window. When a gust hit the glass, it distorted like a circus Hall of Mirrors, the distortion lasting only seconds.

'Martin, get away from the window!' It was my mother in her nightie and dressing gown. 'Now!'

'Why? I was only looking—'

'The glass is bending. If we get a really hard knock, it'll implode and you'll be cut to shreds. Go to the front door.'

Suddenly, I felt vulnerable.

In the entrance hall to the apartment were piled suitcases filled with everything moveable and of value.

'Are we going away?' I asked.

'Don't be so bloody stupid!' my father retorted. He was dressed and ready for action. 'How the hell do you think we'll get down the bloody drive?'

I had to admit that he had a point. The curving driveway up to the building was completely exposed. We were marooned.

Over the morning the wind increased. Water seeped in through the allegedly typhoon-proof window frames, keeping Wong busy soaking it up with a mop. All Hong Kong business was suspended, the ferries were in the typhoon shelters and radio messages warned everyone to stay inside. Live electricity cables were lying in urban roads, a number of landslides blocked major roads and flooding was reported in the New Territories.

My father still thought he should be at work. The Royal Navy, he insisted, counted on people like him to keep things going. That there was not a single warship in the harbour, all of them having put to sea to ride out the storm, was neither here nor there. Consequently, he spent two hours on the telephone trying to organise supplies for a destroyer that had sailed to safety in international waters. Then the line went dead. He slammed the receiver down and cracked it.

'Intelligent,' my mother remarked bluntly. 'We're stranded on a mountain top in a typhoon and you break the bloody phone.'

'The line's down,' he replied sourly. 'Fat lot of use the phone is.'

'Yes,' my mother agreed, 'but they'll soon fix the line. It'll take days to get a replacement phone.'

'I'm an essential user,' my father said. 'They'll bring us a new one PDQ.'

The telephone line was operational by late the following morning. The telephone, which my mother fixed with Elastoplast strips, worked. A new telephone arrived four weeks later, when my mother remarked caustically it was a good job China had not invaded since Ida.

The Number Nine signal was raised at half past eleven. By now, the wind was terrifying. The building creaked like a galleon under sail. The rain turned squally, lashing the windows. The verandah become an inch-deep pool.

Suddenly, over the space of fifteen minutes, the wind died to less than a summer zephyr and the rain let up.

'Eye of the storm,' my father announced. 'You come with me.'

He and I left the building and made our way down the drive. Leaves and branches were everywhere. We turned left and went beneath the next block of apartments. There, at the back, was my father's car, littered with leaves.

'Get the leaves off the paintwork,' my father ordered. 'They'll discolour it.'

I started at the boot. It seemed a pointless exercise. I knew that all tropical cyclones—we had done the topic in geography—were circular and that, in the middle, was the eye, a place of calm around which the storm revolved. Once that passed by, the winds would blow again, from the opposite quarter. The leaves we removed would soon be replaced.

'Not the bloody windows, cloth ears!' my father said, breaking into my thoughts. 'The glass won't discolour, will it? We haven't got all bloody day.'

Indeed, the wind was already beginning to pick up again, so we made our way back. I could feel the gusts tugging at my lungs. By the time we reached our apartment block my father could physically lean on the wind.

In the early evening, the Number Eight signal was raised and remained in force through the night. By noon the following day, the typhoon was gone, leaving behind squally showers and a gunmetal sky, and the clear-up began. My father revisited his car. The back was heavily bestrewn with leaves, but the front was devoid of them. A downpipe had broken free and sprayed rainwater over the car for hours. My father unlocked the door, got in and attempted to start the engine. The starter motor turned over asthmatically but nothing else happened. He opened the bonnet. The engine was sodden, a deep puddle beneath it covered a rainbow film of oil.

'Buggeration!' my father exclaimed and slammed the bonnet down. A piece of trim fell off.

We had got off comparatively unscathed. An apartment at the top of the adjacent building had lost a window, setting off a chain reaction with three or four others. The wind sucked out anything lighter and smaller than a coffee table, splintering them to pieces as they struck the window frames.

The wind having died down, I walked up the road to the police post. All the hibiscus bushes had lost their blooms, and these lay in the road like sodden purple scraps of tissue paper. And yet the birds were singing, and when the sun came out between squalls the tarmac was alive with butterflies drying their wings in the warmth. I wondered where they had weathered the storm.

MY MOTHER and I went to the Peak School for an interview with the headmistress. I had been playing hooky from games lessons and she wanted to know why. So did my mother. Education was important to her because her own had been so minimal. I declared that team sports destroyed one's individuality. This left both women momentarily flabbergasted. I was told to join in more, in lessons, in sports, in the extracurricular life of the school.

On the walk back, my mother was silent. Several times, she started to speak then thought better of it. I guessed she felt torn. On the one hand, she had to back the school. On the other, she would rather have had an independently minded Sinophile than a soccer player for a son.

We entered the apartment to find Ah Shun sitting on the settee and Tuppence disconsolately perched by her side. This was unusual.

'Are you all right, Ah Shun?' my mother enquired in English. It was no use speaking Cantonese to her; she spoke only Shanghainese.

'Lo, missee,' Ah Shun replied.

'Go and get Wong,' my mother ordered me.

'Wong go,' Ah Shun said.

Wong was not in the kitchen or the servants' quarter.

'Oh my God!' my mother exclaimed. 'He's left her.'

My mother sat next to Ah Shun and put her arm round her. A short time later, we heard a movement in the kitchen. My mother rushed out to find Wong depositing the shopping bags on the floor.

'Thank God!' she said. 'Wong, Ah Shun is sick.'

'Lo sick, missee,' he answered calmly. 'Ah Shun got baby come.'

My mother stared at him for a long moment. I looked at Ah Shun. By now, I knew a fair amount about the birds, the bees and babies. She certainly did not look fat but then her uniform was hardly close fitting.

'When?' my mother asked.

'Lo long time,' Wong replied. 'Maybe wung week.'

'One week!' my mother exclaimed. 'Wong, you cannot let Ah Shun carry on cleaning, doing the laundry.'

'Lo p'oblum, missee. Ah Shun can do. Dis her job. Mus' work for money.'

'Ah Shun cannot do!' my mother replied. 'You help Ah Shun to her bed. I'll call a doctor. You find another amah to help you.'

Later, a naval midwife in attendance, Ah Shun gave birth to a little girl whom they named Su Yin. My mother was appointed 'godmother'.

My father, who never broke any law, by-law, rule or regulation, read his tenancy agreement and informed the naval quartering officer of the event. A month or so later, a letter came to the effect that babies were not allowed in the servants' quarters as their crying might *discommode other residents*. It was firmly stated that either the servants be dismissed or the amah be let go, or the infant be sent to live with relatives.

'Put them out on the streets!' my mother raged. 'With a newborn baby! Remember, Ken, they've already got children lodging elsewhere.'

'Wong shouldn't be so fecund,' my father answered.

'What does fecund mean?' I enquired.

'You keep your bloody nose out of this.'

'They're not going, Ken.'

My mother went into the bedroom and slammed the door. The key turned in the lock. My father poured himself a pink gin.

An hour later, my mother reappeared, poured herself a gin and tonic, sat down and announced, 'Ken, get me an interview with the commodore.'

'Under no circumstance whatever,' he answered.

'Either I have an interview or I have a ticket for myself and Martin on the next P and O liner to come into port.'

I knew this was a bluff—my mother would pull her own teeth out rather than leave Hong Kong before she had to—but my father begrudgingly said he would see what he could do. The outcome was that it was not a naval matter but a civilian one.

'In that case,' my mother declared, 'I'm going to see the Governor.'

An exchange of letters with Government House followed, culminating in my mother being granted an audience with His Excellency, Sir Alexander Grantham, KCMG. She demanded that I accompany her, perhaps to demonstrate that she was also a mother who would not be parted from her offspring.

My father refused to drive us so we went to Government House by taxi. We were met by the Governor's aide-de-camp and guided into a large lobby. The Governor appeared, shook our hands, then led us into a room furnished like an English country house. We sat down. A steward came in with a tray of Chinese tea. The tea was poured into cups, then my mother and the Governor got down to business. I minded my own and sipped the tea.

In less than ten minutes, the matter was settled. So long as the landlord did not object and the fire escapes were acceptable, servants' families would no longer be arbitrarily split up. The matter would take some months to go through Legislative Council. In the meantime Wong, Ah Shun, Tuppence and Su Yin were to remain where they were.

Several months later, the law was changed and the Wong family's tenure was secure. My mother felt she had struck a blow for Chinese rights. And, as I heard her say to a friend, 'We'll still have Wong's marvellous sponges.'

TYPHOONS WERE NOT the only natural force with which Hong Kong had to contend. Heavy rain frequently caused landslides in which people were buried alive or crushed to death, and hundreds made homeless.

Droughts were not uncommon either. The wind, when it blew, was hot and dry. In such times, restrictions were enforced, the mains water being switched on for only a few hours a day. Then, every receptacle in the house would be filled—baths, basins, saucepans, woks, empty bottles. Gordon's gin bottles, being flat on one side, were ideal drinking-water containers that fitted in the fridge on their sides.

With the baths being used for water storage, many people went to the beach in the evening to wash. Sweetmeat vendors caught on to the exodus from the city, and soon the beaches were lined with purveyors of everything from sweet pickled turnip to Dairy Farm popsies. There would be a party atmosphere at the bigger beaches, especially at Repulse Bay, where the Chinese occupied the strand while the Europeans, once they had bathed, dressed in smart casual clothes and decamped to the bar of the Repulse Bay Hotel.

My parents chose to drive further afield, to a wide sandy beach at the eastern extremity of Hong Kong Island called Shek O. The bay, facing straight out into the South China Sea, was frequently visited by deep-water-dwelling sharks, and although they very rarely came close into shore, a lifeguard seated on a tall bamboo lookout tower kept watch for them.

Shek O was my mother's favourite beach. The water in the bay was usually calm, there was no undertow and the sea floor shelved gently. My father hardly ever went in the water. His excuse was that someone had to guard the tent containing our clothes, watches and so on.

Late one afternoon, we drove to Shek O armed with swimming costumes, towels, shampoo and soap. By the time we arrived, the beach was occupied by no more than a dozen parties. We rented a tent, and, wading in up to our waists, my mother and I washed ourselves. We then returned to the tent and sat in deck chairs while my father washed.

By now, it was dusk. The tent boy brought round two oil lanterns and placed them on the sand in front of the tent. The air was warm, the sea black and the world seemingly at peace. From the café on the beach came the distant clatter of mah-jong tiles, the only sound other than the lap of waters.

'It's time we were going, Joyce,' my father suggested.

'Not quite yet, Ken. It's a wonderful evening. I'm going to have another quick dip before we go.'

'Don't be ridiculous, Joyce,' my father said. 'It's dangerous in the dark.'

'Rubbish!' she retorted.

'You'd never see an attacking shark,' my father continued. 'Or a jelly fish.'

'I'd never see an attacking shark in broad daylight,' my mother rejoined.

It was truly dark by now. My mother set off for the water's edge. My father, abandoning his sentry post, followed her.

'Joyce! I forbid you to go in the water.'

'Forbid all you want, Ken,' she replied and stepped into the sea.

My father returned to the tent, sat down next to me and said, 'Do you know, the stings from a jelly fish can give you a heart seizure.' He squinted into the sea. 'I can't see her,' he murmured. 'If the tide's going out . . .'

To my surprise, he appeared to be genuinely concerned.

Then a voice called out urgently, 'Martin! Come here!'

'I forbid you to go,' my father said.

I got out of my deck chair.

'If you go down there, you'll get no pocket money for a month.'

I headed for the water's edge. My mother was standing up to her waist in the sea, not ten yards from the beach. I went and stood next to my mother.

'Watch!' she said. She splashed the water.

Suddenly, all around her radiated with a ghostly, pale green light.

'You do it!'

I brought my hands down on the sea. A fire of pale light spread out from my hands, dancing on the surface. I was entranced. Every movement I made produced an eruption of luminosity.

'It's called phosphorescence,' my mother said. 'Isn't it marvellous? It's made by millions of microscopic organisms called plankton. When the air touches them, a chemical called phosphorus in their body glows.'

We splashed around for a few more minutes, then rejoined my father.

'That was one of the bloody stupidest things I've ever known you to do, Joyce. As for taking Martin with you . . .'

'Tell me, Ken,' my mother asked as we reached the car, 'have you ever, in your entire bloody life, done anything out of the norm, on the spur of the moment, because you suddenly felt the urge?'

My father did not answer. He got in the car and waited for us to get in. We drove the length of Hong Kong Island in silence. Later, my mother came into my room to tuck me up. She leant over and kissed me.

'Good night, Martin. That was fun, wasn't it?'

'Yes,' I confirmed. 'It was.'

'Don't ever tell,' she whispered, 'but if it weren't for you, I'd leave him . . .'

I did not at the time understand what she was talking about.

ON HONG KONG-SIDE, in addition to rickshaws, taxis and buses, there was a double-decker tram system that ran from Kennedy Town in the west to Shau Kei Wan at the eastern extremity of the city. The trams were slow and noisy as they rattled along tracks set in the metalled surface of the streets, yet they were almost romantic, a means of locomotion from another age. Furthermore, they were cheap. The fare was ten cents, no matter how far one travelled.

My father had a fierce hatred of the trams, based upon the facts that they had no brake lights, they caused traffic jams at tram stops where vehicular traffic had to give way to alighting or embarking passengers, and they had a right of way over the traffic lights. Worse, however, was their inability to stop as quickly as a car.

The first incident happened on Yee Wo Street. My father wished to turn right into Kai Chiu Road. Disregarding a tram coming up behind, he pulled smartly into the centre of the road—where the tram tracks lay—and waited for a break in the traffic. There was the sound of tearing metal. The tram slid into the back of the Ford at an impact speed of about three miles an hour. I was mildly jolted in the back seat. My father got out to survey the damage. The rear offside lights of the Ford were smashed, the bumper and rear wing dented and deformed.

The tram driver alighted, surveyed the situation then gesticulated for my father to get his car out of the way. My father refused to move. My mother and I joined him. A crowd began to gather on the pavement.

'Move the car towards the kerb, Ken,' my mother suggested.

'No, Joyce! Not until the police have seen it. The law states that the driver of any vehicle that goes up the back of another vehicle is liable. He's culpable,' my father said, pointing an accusatory finger at the tram driver.

The driver took umbrage at being pointed at and let off a stream of invective in Cantonese.

'Don't you speak to me like that!' my father retorted.

'Ken, this isn't helping matters,' my mother observed. 'Just let it go.'

'I'm damned if I will!' my father exclaimed. 'I'm not in the wrong here.'

The passengers in the tram started to egg the tram driver on. He commenced bouncing about on his heels like a boxer warming up.

Suddenly, the tram driver lunged at my father, who blocked the blow. The tram driver took another swing. My father blocked it once more and managed to land a clout round his opponent's ear. The audience gave vent to a loud *Whoa!* intermingled with an undertone of *Ayarhs!*

Needless to say, this enraged the driver further. He had lost face in front of at least two hundred onlookers.

Feeling I should do something, I stepped forward and yelled at him, '*Wei! Lei! Heui la! Diu nei lo mo!*' (Hey, you! Get lost! Go fuck your mother!). At the time I was ignorant of the exact meaning of the phrase but knew it was pretty expressive.

The crowd on the pavement broke out into hoots of hilarity. So did the passengers. The driver just stared at me, taken aback by this little *gweilo*.

The Ford, askew across both the east- and westbound tramlines, was now causing a backlog to build up in both directions. A traffic patrol arrived to see what was creating gridlock half a mile down the road.

'This bloody fool—' my father began.

'I can see what's happened, sir,' a European police inspector interrupted him. 'Now, with your permission . . .'

A Chinese constable drove the Ford to the kerb while four others directed the traffic. The westbound trams started moving again. After a few words from a Chinese police corporal, the tram driver returned to his place and the tram went on its way.

The tram company paid for the damage. They also accepted liability for the next two, identical accidents. On the fourth, they sued for remuneration of income lost due to delayed services. They did not win the case. As a result, however, my father—like my mother before him—was the cause of a change in the law. It was henceforth illegal to stop a vehicle on the tramlines.

FOR AS LONG as we lived in Hong Kong, my mother had attempted to get me to swim. At least once a week throughout my school holidays and often at a weekend during term, my mother and I would go to the beach together, sometimes in the company of friends. Her favourite spot when we lived in Kowloon was 11 Mile Beach. It lacked any amenities whatsoever and the only shelter was three or four ruined beach houses and a row of trees. However, a Dairy Farm Popsicle seller was usually to be found in the vicinity. Transport was provided by the Navy, which ran a daily families' bus service to Kadoorie Beach, seven miles further on. Whereas the latter was frequently crowded, 11 Mile Beach rarely had two dozen people on it.

As soon as her foot touched the sand, my mother would strip down to her swimming costume. I took longer, but I would reluctantly wade out to join her. The sea was always warm and lapped at my stomach.

My mother would take my hands and, towing me as she walked backwards, attempt to get me to kick my legs. I watched as the water rose up her body and knew that once her bosom was submerged I was out of my depth. At this point, she would let go of one hand and tell me to move it breaststroke fashion. I would obey but grip her other hand tightly, breathing hard in panic and begging her not to let me go. She promised she would not and she never did. As a consequence she didn't teach me to swim.

After our move to the Peak we frequented Tweed Bay, a secluded sandy beach for the exclusive use of the members of the Prison Officers' Club at Stanley, of which my parents were, curiously, members. It lay in a tiny bay under the walls of Hong Kong's top security jail and was reached by passing through several guarded gates. It was here I finally learned to swim.

Philip and Ray Bryant were close friends of my mother's. A handsome and jovial man, Philip was a Royal Navy commander, Ray a vivacious and pretty woman with black hair and the refined movement of a ballet dancer. They were both good fun and, as they had no children of their own, I became a surrogate son whenever we were together. One Saturday afternoon, my mother and I drove to Tweed Bay with the Bryants as our club guests, riding in their Jaguar.

There were no changing facilities but, as usual, we wore our swimming costumes in lieu of underwear. In next to no time, the adults were in the sea and I was paddling in the shallows. Eventually tiring of this, I sat on the beach, unsuccessfully digging for the small opaque crabs that lived in holes in the sand. After a while, Philip left the sea and walked up to me.

'I think it's time,' he said.

'Time for what?' I asked.

'To swim. Before we go home, I'll have you frolicking like a porpoise.'

This I very much doubted, but I trusted Philip. He and I walked out until the water was up to my chest. He then held his arms out and I lay across his hands, face down.

'Now,' Philip said, 'kick your legs like frogs do.'

I did as he suggested.

'Now, don't stop kicking and move your arms, fingers closed, as if you were pushing the water behind you.'

Again, I complied. Suddenly, I sensed his hands were no longer touching my stomach. Indeed, he was at least ten feet away and treading water. I panicked, stopped kicking, tried to stand up and sank vertically. I was going to drown. I knew it. I opened my mouth to scream. At that moment, my head broke the surface, strong hands under my armpits.

'I want to get out!' I spluttered, clinging to his neck.

'If you want to get out,' he answered calmly, 'you'll have to swim to the beach. I'll come with you.'

'I can't swim,' I pleaded.

'Yes, you can,' he declared, smiling at me. 'The human body floats. Look at your mother and Ray.' Sure enough, they were floating on their backs. 'Now, let's try again.'

Philip held me horizontal in the water again and off we went. He removed his hands and, with much splashing and gasping, I made it to the beach.

My mother and Ray kissed me; Philip shook my hand, man to man.

'You see,' he said when the clamour of female congratulation had died down, 'in life we can do anything within our physical power if only we have the courage. You could climb Mount Everest if you genuinely wanted to.'

That hot Saturday in the South China Sea, I learned more than how to swim. Philip had shown me that much more was possible if one pushed the limits a bit and, from then on, I did.

MY MOTHER'S HEALTH had begun to deteriorate. She started to suffer pains in her joints, periods of weakness and migraine headaches. There seemed to be no apparent cause for this but the diagnosis was the onset of rheumatoid arthritis, the prognosis (which fortunately turned out to be erroneous) being that she would be crippled by the age of fifty and probably dead by fifty-five. She was then thirty-four. It was noticed that she felt worse when our apartment was in the mist, which it was quite frequently, particularly during the hot season. My mother's doctors suggested we leave the Peak and move back down below the cloud line. But there were no available quarters.

Throughout the summer term, I hurried home from school every day to be with my mother. Those few friends I had were obliged to come to my home to play. She liked meeting them but there were times when our bois-terousness tired her quickly and we had to leave. She and I would also go for walks, my mother strolling rather than striding out as she was wont. I shared my places with her—the rifle range where she dug for bullets with me, Governor's Walk where she marvelled as had I at the fact that tiny fish lived at the top of a mountain, and Pinewood Battery.

It was when we were sitting on the wall of one of the gun emplacements at Pinewood late one afternoon that she first broached the subject with me that had clearly been in her mind for a while.

'Martin, you know that in less than six months we have to go back to England, don't you?'

I had not really given this much thought.

'Your father's tour of overseas duty ends and he's being posted to a naval stores depot at Corsham, near Bath. I don't want to go back,' my mother said emphatically. 'England is dreary, down-in-the-mouth, lifeless.' She turned and faced distant Lan Tau, the rays of the setting sun fingering between the mountains. 'How can I live in Romford or Woking after this?'

'Or Bath?' I suggested.

She laughed and stood up, suggesting, 'Let's go back via Lugard Road.'

As we walked slowly round the mountain, my mother said, 'I want to stay here. In Hong Kong. And I've been thinking. Your father will have to resign from the Admiralty and get a job here. In the government, perhaps. Tax is much lower here than in Britain and the salaries are a good deal higher.'

'Will he change jobs?' I wondered aloud.

'Oh, yes!' my mother replied with a cast-iron confidence. 'Maybe not this week, maybe not next month, but he will. You mark my words.'

After six weeks of intermittent mist and continuous painkillers, with no quarters becoming available, my parents decided there was only one thing they could do. Just in time for the beginning of the new academic year in September, we packed up the apartment, put our furniture in store, reluctantly dismissed Wong and Ah Shun with much shedding of tears (but with glowing references) and took up residency once more in the Fourseas Hotel.

THINGS HAD CHANGED inside the Fourseas Hotel during my Peak-side sojourn. Mr Peng was still the manager, but Ching had left, along with at least half the other room boys I had known. The whores had been moved out, the clientele now predominantly tourists or expatriates waiting for housing.

Little had changed, however, in the streets around the Fourseas. Mr Tsang, the fruit seller, remembered me and greeted me with a stroke of my hair. The Queen of Kowloon still lived in her cockloft. The rickshaw coolies still slept with their machines in Soares Avenue at night. But Ah Sam was not among them. I was told he had died of a weak heart, weakened no doubt by the *nga pin*. His number three hat was being worn by another now.

The Communist Chinese school still held its patriotic morning assembly, but with the stirring music now blaring from loud speakers rather than the scratchy phonograph.

Politics did not usually enter into the lives of the Hong Kong Chinese. They had no vote: members of the Legislative Council, Hong Kong's parliament, were appointed by the Governor. Once a year, however, the population could display their political allegiances.

October 10 was known as the Double Tenth, a public holiday celebrating the anniversary of the Wuhan uprising, which sparked the 1911 Chinese

Revolution and was the foundation of modern China. Strings of firecrackers were exploded. Buildings were decked out with red and gold bunting, huge portraits of Generalissimo Chiang Kai-shek and the Chinese Nationalist Kuomintang flag. The flag also fluttered in squatter areas and from tenement rooftops, washing poles, trees and even bicycle handlebars.

Not every building was so decked out. Some carried defiant Communist Chinese flags and a picture of Chairman Mao. This sometimes resulted in scuffles and street fights, broken up by the riot squad, which arrived armed with truncheons and rattan shields.

The fact that anyone could support the Communist cause seemed beyond me. They had butchered, dispossessed and robbed millions. Not a single squatter had avoided Communist brutality and yet even some of the squatter shacks flew the scarlet flag of mainland China with its five gold stars.

One of the hotel staff, though not a Communist sympathiser, had fought as a partisan with them during the Japanese occupation. His name was Ah Lam. When I discovered his past, I sought him out and asked him why.

'Japanese more bad Communist,' was his pragmatic response.

'But why do people support the Communists now?'

'They wan' China one country. Wan' China be one place for all Chinese.'

'But the Communists were very bad to the people.'

'All pepul bad to all pepul in war,' Ah Lam stated bluntly. 'Me ve'y bad in war. One day, I show you.'

A few days later, there came a knock at my parents' door. It was Ah Lam.

'Master and Missee Bo Fu,' Ah Lam began, 'I wan' ask you for me take Martin New Te'ito'ies-side, show him some t'ing from the wartime. In wartime, I fighting Japanese for English. I East 'iffer B'igade man. Not Communist. Fight for England.' He fumbled in his pocket and took out a medal. Cast in silver and attached to a red, white and blue ribbon, one side showed a lion standing on a dragon while on the other was the head of King George VI. 'Governor give me,' he continued, 'for fight Japanese. If Martin can come, I look-see him ve'y good. No p'oblem.'

My mother immediately acceded to the request. That Saturday afternoon, Ah Lam and I set off in the hotel Studebaker bound for Sai Kung, a fishing village at the far eastern end of the New Territories famous for its seafood and the distinctly Communist leanings of its populace.

Sai Kung was quiet. Fishing junks lay three deep at the quayside. Nets hung from the masts, drying in the sun. Outside the quayside buildings stood buckets of sea water containing live fish, lobsters or crabs.

Ah Lam parked the Studebaker and we walked through the village to a tea house, sitting at an outside table under an awning. He entered into a long conversation with the proprietor, whom he obviously knew well. At length, Ah Lam introduced me.

'How do you do?' he said, shaking my hand.

'*Ho! Ho! Nei ho ma?*' I replied. (Good! Good! How are you?)

He laughed. 'You don't need to speak Cantonese with me. I speak English. So,' he went on, 'you are going with Lam here to see what Lam and I did in the war. It is a long walk. Maybe two miles. And it is a hot day.'

He put four bottles of Coke in a small string bag. Thus provisioned, Lam and I set off along a wide path across paddy fields of waving green rice, the pale white grain hanging down like cascades of tiny opals, ready to ripen.

'Who was that man?' I enquired.

'He my boss in war,' Ah Lam replied. 'He East 'iffer B'igade off'cer.'

'What is the East River Brigade?'

'In war,' Ah Lam explained, 'many Chinese pepul wan' fight Japanese but he no can do. Got no gun. But Communist got gun. They make small-small army, liff in mountungs . . .' He pointed to the east where the land was mountainous with narrow wooded valleys between grass-covered ridges. 'He call East 'iffer B'igade. He fighter, not sol-jer. Sometime Communist, sometime just man no like Japanese.'

'But what did you do?'

'Make trubbul for Japanese.'

After about half a mile the path left the paddy fields and started up a hill-side carved into terraces upon which a variety of vegetables grew.

'What sort of trouble did you make?' I asked.

'Big trubbul. You know Watah-loo Road, near hotel, is a b'idge for t'ain. One time, we blow up. Put plenty plas-tic ex-plo-sif under b'idge. *Phoom!* No t'ain can go China-side long time.'

We carried on up the hill to where the path ran horizontally along the hillside, following the lie of the land. It was easier going now, and in twenty minutes we reached a steep-sided wooded valley. We crossed a dry water-course in the centre of the valley then followed the diminishing path through the trees. Halfway to the edge of the woodland, Al Lam sat down on a huge boulder. He gave me one of the bottles of Coca-Cola.

When he had drained his bottle Ah Lam slithered down the boulder, crossed the path, squatted down and started to clear away the leaf litter with his hands. 'You come see,' he said.

I joined him. A few steps from the path, he had uncovered six dull white stones in a line about three feet apart. Each was about the size of a small watermelon and decorated by a similar series of thin, jagged cracks.

'You know dis one?' he asked.

'No,' I answered.

'Japanese sol-jer head,' he declared matter-of-factly. 'Six piece. We kill him here. Hide behind rock, jump on him. Very quick! No noise.'

My toes curled involuntarily as I looked down on the tops of the soldiers' skulls. Then it occurred to me. Why could I see the tops of their heads?

'Why are they . . . ?' I mimed upright as opposed to supine.

Ah Lam grinned as he replied, 'Japanese man no like die up. If no lie down no can go to heaven.'

MY FATHER did not like having to return to the hotel. In part, I sympathised with him. He could no longer live as he had done in an apartment, with servants, entertaining in style, enjoying a prestigious address. There was another reason for his dislike. My mother was back in close contact with her Chinese friends among the staff. In my father's eyes, it was beneath her to befriend what were in effect her servants.

Bit by bit, my parents grew even further apart. My mother maintained her gradually increasing coterie of Chinese friends, seldom inviting my father into this circle but, whenever she could, including me in her excursions. I particularly loved going with her to festival celebrations.

Some, such as the Moon Festival, involved little more than a slap-up meal takcn *al fresco* with the moon high in the sky and the children carrying lanterns shaped like rabbits, birds, butterflies, dragons and fish. If clouds threatened to obscure the moon, everyone made a loud noise by banging saucepans together or letting off firecrackers to drive the clouds away. The only aspect of the festival I just could not abide was the moon cakes. They came in a variety of sizes and looked vaguely like English pork pies. The dough was made of flour, syrup or honey, rice wine and eggs, which was then rolled out and a filling made of lotus-seed paste and whole duck-egg yolks, care being taken not to break them. Once filled and shaped in a ball, they were glazed and baked. The Chinese adored them but most *gweilos* found them inedible.

Other festivals, like Ch'ing Ming (or the Hungry Ghosts' Festival), were more exclusive and it was a sign of the regard in which my mother was held that we were invited to attend this most personal of ceremonies.

On the morning of the appointed day in early April, we rendezvoused with a noisily joyful gaggle of thirty Chinese at the railway station in Tsim Sha Tsui. Everyone was weighed down by a parcel, wicker basket or string bag. After twenty minutes, we were herded aboard a train that set off for Fanling. It trundled through Kowloon and entered a tunnel in the hills. When it emerged in the Sha Tin valley, it was if I were riding a time machine. At one end of the tunnel was a mid-twentieth-century city, at the other a timeless landscape of tiny villages, paddy fields, salt pans and fishing junks.

Following the coast to Tai Po, the train headed north to Fanling, where we disembarked. The party then headed into the low hills to the south, along a path through brush and scattered trees. Finally, we arrived at our destination: three graves and a dozen golden pagodas. The women swept the semicircular platforms before the graves. A man with a tin of red paint touched up the characters on the grave doors. This done, joss sticks were burned, with everyone, including my mother and me, kowtowing to the ancestors.

After this, food was produced, including, incredibly, a whole suckling pig. Bowls of hot rice ladled from a vacuum flask were placed before the entrance to each grave with a piece of the pig, some steamed vegetables and a little bowl of rice wine. On the top of the graves, thick wads of Hell's Banknotes were weighted down with a stone. Next to them was placed a car made out of tissue paper stretched over a bamboo frame. This was set alight.

'The money is to pay the ancestors' bills in heaven,' my mother whispered.

'And the car?'

'They haven't got one in heaven, so . . .'

Two of the men approached with armfuls of human bones. Behind them, one of the golden pagodas was open. The bones were placed on the ground, where several women set about buffing them up with light tan Cherry Blossom shoe polish. I watched, utterly mesmerised.

While the contents of all the nearby ossuaries were cleaned, a picnic was laid out. The human bones were then arranged around the picnic cloth. Every skeleton was set a place. I found myself sitting between my mother and a skull carefully balanced on a heap of its associated bones.

'What happens to their food?' I asked my mother.

'The ancestors in heaven soak up the essence of the food in the bowls, then it's thrown away,' my mother informed me. 'We eat the rest.'

When the picnic was eaten, we indeed threw the ancestors' food into the bushes for the ants and birds. With the bones returned to their golden pagodas, we set off for the railway station.

6

As 1955 advanced, the weather heating up and the humidity rising, my parents' life became increasingly frenetic and fraught. At his office, my father was preparing to hand over to his successor. This caused him frequently to return to the Fourseas in a flaming temper.

'I don't know how they do it!' he would mutter, pouring himself a pink gin. 'The oldest bloody civilisation on earth and they can't file. I've put a chart up. What goes where. Anchor butter is not the same as anchor chains. Dear God! My life is blessed with blithering idiots.'

My mother spent much of her time packing for the voyage 'home', which she no longer considered her home. Our larger possessions—furniture and the Ford—had been sent ahead by cargo ship. When she was not packing or visiting friends, my mother wept. She did this in private, but I heard her through the door between our rooms. On one occasion, my father found her wiping her eyes.

'What's the matter, Joyce?' he enquired as he poured himself a gin and tonic, the hotel being temporarily out of Angostura bitters.

'Nothing.'

He sat down in one of the armchairs. 'Must be something.'

'I got some dust in my eye.'

'Right,' he said and sipped his drink.

My mother was invited by her Chinese friends to a number of farewell banquets as the date of our departure drew nearer. I accompanied her to a few of these banquets, the best of which was given by the hotel room boys. We met at a restaurant in Tsim Sha Tsui just as night fell.

The banquet went on well past midnight, the dishes appearing with a mouth-watering regularity: sharks' fin soup, abalone, quails' eggs and hundred-year-old duck eggs, chickens' feet, braised duck, soft-shelled hairy crabs, chicken wrapped in pickled cabbage and baked in clay, various fish, pork and beef with chillies and garlic . . . We were showered with farewell gifts. They were simple things, like sets of chopsticks and decorated porcelain bowls, but to my mother they were as precious as gems.

After the banquet my mother elected to walk back to the hotel. I walked at her side, holding her hand despite the fact that I considered myself too mature now to do such a thing. In the circumstances, it just seemed right.

The air was warm. From the windows of the tenements came the sounds of everyday Chinese life—the song of caged birds, the clack of mah-jong tiles, the raucous chorus of a Cantonese opera on the radio. My mother and I did not speak; we were letting Hong Kong impinge itself upon us.

'Will you be sad to leave?' she asked, finally breaking our silence as we turned into Waterloo Road.

'Yes,' I admitted. 'Very.'

'Would you like to come back?'

'For a holiday? Yes!'

'No. For good.'

I thought about it. I had been happy in Hong Kong. It had been an exciting place in which to live and I was sure it had much to offer that I had yet to uncover. However, there was more to it than that. I felt I had grown up in Hong Kong. I could recall little of my life prior to the *Corfu*. It was as if my existence had begun the minute my foot had touched the dock in Algiers. England was as strange a place to me now as Hong Kong had been on that June morning in 1952. In short, I felt I belonged there.

'Yes,' I said at last. 'Definitely.'

HALFWAY DOWN Nathan Road, my mother said, 'Ken . . . ! Stop the car!'

My father, sitting in the front passenger seat, ordered the driver to pull into the kerb.

'Give me the boarding passes, will you, Ken? Mine and Martin's.'

For the briefest of moments, I saw intense fear pass over my father's face. If my mother really were going to leave him, and I assumed it was possible, this would be the supremely appropriate moment. And he knew it. Yet he reached into his jacket pocket and handed her two pieces of paper.

'How long will you be?' he asked.

'How long is a piece of string?' she replied evasively.

'Well don't be long, that's all.'

We stepped out of the car and it drove away.

Without any haste, my mother and I walked down Nathan Road. Ahead of us, between the buildings, rose the Peak, hazy in the midafternoon sun. It was hot and humid. Rickshaws passed us, carrying people, boxes and bales of cloth. Red and cream Kowloon buses sped by, washing hot air over us.

At the southern end of the barracks, we crossed Nathan Road, entered Haiphong Road and took the second left into Hankow Road. Hing Loon

Curio and Jewellery Company was open but we did not go in for a chat or a free drink. We had already said our goodbyes.

My mother asked, 'Well, what do you say?'

I made no answer. We both had the same thought in mind.

We entered the Pen and were shown to a table. My mother ordered Chinese tea for two. It arrived at our table in a bone-china teapot accompanied by wafer-thin sandwiches and a silver stand of dainty cakes. On a balcony above, a string quartet started playing tunes from recent hit musicals.

'This is living,' my mother said. 'Haven't we been the lucky ones!'

'Yes,' I said, 'we certainly have. And,' I added, 'we will be again.'

My mother reached across the table and took my hand in both of hers. 'Too bloody right!' she said defiantly. 'You can bet your bottom dollar on it.'

She looked at her watch and paid the bill, smiling at me with the memory of our first tea here. We left through the grand front entrance as if we were minor royalty, a Chinese boy in the hotel livery holding the door open for us, another asking if we required a rickshaw or taxi.

Beside the Tsim Sha Tsui fire station, as usual, an old man was seated on a folding stool, a rattan basket of bamboo splints and leaves by his side. With them, he skilfully wove grasshoppers, arranging them around his feet. As we approached, he held one out.

'You wan' g'asshoppah? B'ing you plenty good luck. Only one dollar.'

I bought two and gave my mother one.

'You good boy for you muvver,' the old man said, and stroked my hair.

We walked on into the Kowloon Docks. Alongside the first pier was the P&O liner *Carthage*, the sister ship of the *Corfu*. Her white hull towered over us, gleaming in the sunlight. Smoke drifted from her funnel. The Blue Peter announced she was soon to sail. The dock was crowded with baggage coolies, rickshaw pullers, cars, trucks and well-wishers.

I glanced at the Peak across the shimmering water. Block A, Mount Austin Mansions stood out, silhouetted against the subtropical sky, and I thought that, no matter what, I could always claim I once lived there.

Plank by plank, hand in hand, clutching our lucky grasshoppers, we slowly climbed the gangway. My mother was crying.

It was the afternoon of Monday, May 2, 1955, and I was ten.

Four years later, exactly as my mother had predicted, my father was a colonial civil servant and we were back. For good.

MARTIN BOOTH

Place of birth: Ribchester, Lancashire
Date of birth: September 7, 1944
Died: February 12, 2004

When Martin Booth started work on *Gweilo*, at the request of his two children, who didn't want precious memories of his Hong Kong childhood to be lost for ever, he knew that he was dying. He had been diagnosed with a particularly malignant brain tumour and, while convalescing from surgery, set to worked on the manuscript, which he completed a short time before his death.

Gweilo opens with the young Martin arriving with his parents, in May 1952, in the crown colony of Hong Kong—a place that would be his home for twelve years and to which he would often return, finding it a source of inspiration throughout his life. 'Britain is where I work,' he said once in an interview, 'but Hong Kong is where I come to live.' As well as *Gweilo*, the colony inspired an acclaimed nonfiction book about Hong Kong, part travelogue, part history, part memoir, titled *The Dragon and the Pearl*; a children's novel, *Music on the Bamboo Radio*; a history of opium, and a novel about a POW, *Hiroshima Joe*, that has been deemed a masterpiece.

'I'd find it incredibly boring to have to do the same thing every time . . . You don't find vets who say, "Sorry, we only do cats."'

When Martin Booth was twenty, he returned to England and, for a while, took a variety of jobs—insurance clerk, lorry driver, wine waiter—before settling on a career in teaching as being the best way to support his ambition to write. A meeting with the famous First World War poet, Edmund Blunden, arranged through one of Blunden's daughters with whom Booth was friends, had already fired in him a passion for poetry that was to shape his future. In time, many of Booth's own poems were published and, for thirteen years, he ran his own publishing house, Sceptre Press, which produced more than 400 poetry collections.

In 1968, Booth took his first job as an English teacher, and he continued in the profession until 1985, when the success of *Hiroshima Joe* enabled him to devote himself full-time to writing. His output was extraordinarily diverse and included five books for children and biographies of Jim Corbett the big-game hunter, Aleister Crowley, who was well known for his interest in the occult, and Sir Arthur Conan Doyle. 'I'd find it incredibly boring,' he once remarked, 'to have to do the same thing every time. I think of writing as a profession like any other. You don't find vets who say, "Sorry, we only do cats . . ."'

Martin Booth has been described as 'a natural raconteur' and a keen observer of place. He loved to travel and made some extraordinary journeys, visiting the Yao tribes in Guangxi, walking across the Serengeti and making a pioneering raft trip down the Athi River in Kenya. His Devon home was filled with a large library of books and an eclectic mix of souvenirs, including a hippo tusk, a snakeskin and a hinge from a 13th-century church door. The boundless curiosity that took him to every corner of Hong Kong as a boy clearly never left him—towards the end of his life he was still discovering new interests, one being a passion for the southwestern United States, its cowboy hats and remarkable Texan-style boots.

HONG KONG UNDER BRITISH RULE

When the British colony of Hong Kong was returned to China at midnight on June 30, 1997, it was yet another exciting moment in its colourful history.

Hong Kong Island and Kowloon were ceded to Britain after the Opium Wars that took place between Britain and China during the 19th century. The Nanking Treaty of 1842, negotiated by the colony's then governor, Sir Henry Pottinger, consigned the island to British rule in perpetuity. In 1860, the Convention of Peking granted Britain a further swathe of territory: the area now known as Kowloon plus Stonecutter's Island, and in 1898 the British negotiated a 99-year lease of ownership of the New Territories. Together, these regions were to

develop into one of the wealthiest and most dynamic territories in the world.

On July 1, 1997, Hong Kong became a Special Administrative Region of China, finally ending the island's existence as 'a borrowed place living on borrowed time'.

THE
BLOOD-DIMMED
TIDE

RENNIE AIRTH

John Madden has put his former life as
a Scotland Yard detective behind him
and now treasures what he has—a
peaceful existence as a farmer in the
beautiful Surrey countryside, with
his wife and two children.

But, when the body of a young girl is
found in the nearby village of Brookham,
he cannot resist the impulse to get
involved in just one more case . . .

PART ONE
1

O nly chance brought the Maddens to Brookham that day.

Earlier, they had driven over to Reigate to attend a luncheon party and in the normal course of events would have returned directly by the main road to Guildford. But the fine weather had tempted them to break their journey in order to climb a narrow bridlepath that led up the steep slopes of Colley Hill to the top of the North Downs.

It was a walk they had made many times before—the view from the crest was justly famous—and for more than an hour they had strolled arm in arm in the late-summer sunshine, pausing now and then to gaze out over a wide sweep of southern England, a patchwork of fields and hedgerows and woods.

A land at peace in that year of 1932.

By the time they returned to their car, however, the afternoon was well advanced and finding the main road clogged with Sunday drivers out for a spin, they had decided to return home by quiet back lanes.

Madden had driven with one eye on the road ahead and the other on the darkening sky. A bank of clouds had been massing in the west for some time, and although the harvest was over and the haymaking done, a hail-storm now would do costly damage to crops of vegetables still ripening in the fields.

Glancing up through the windscreen, he might have driven past the line of cottages without noticing anything amiss if Helen hadn't touched his arm.

'John! Look—'

They were passing through a small hamlet called Brookham, still a few miles from home. A group of men had gathered in front of one of the cottages in the row. An air of anxious expectancy hung over them.

Madden stopped the car.

'What is it, do you think?' Helen was a doctor and her first thought had been that her services might be needed.

Madden made no reply. The scene struck a chord in his memory. It had a grim familiarity, albeit one he hadn't encountered for many years.

At that moment the door of the cottage opened and the tall, uniformed figure of a police constable emerged from within.

'Good Lord!' Helen gasped in astonishment. 'It's *Will*!'

Will Stackpole was the village bobby at Highfield, where they lived.

THE CHILD'S NAME was Alice Bridger, Will Stackpole told them. She and a friend had set out shortly before midday to walk to Craydon, little more than a mile away, along a path bordering the road that linked the two villages.

'They were going to have lunch with a friend there, and then all three of them were going to a birthday party later.'

Catching sight of Madden and Helen as they got out of their car, the constable had left the group of men and crossed the road to speak to them.

It seemed that Alice, recently turned twelve, and her friend, a girl named Sally Drake, had got halfway to their destination when Sally realised she'd forgotten to bring her birthday present and had dashed back to fetch it, leaving Alice at a point on the path where it ran alongside Capel Wood.

Alice said that she would wait for her there, but when Sally got back—after not more than ten minutes—there was no sign of her friend. Thinking she must have decided to continue without her, Sally had gone on to Craydon herself, only to discover that Alice had not arrived.

'The family rang the Bridgers and Fred walked over to Craydon himself, looking for his daughter,' Stackpole told the Maddens. 'He's the dairy manager on a big farm hereabouts. Anyway, they were going to ring the local bobby when they remembered he was away on leave, so they got in touch with me, since I was next nearest. That was three hours ago.'

As he spoke, thunder rumbled in the distance. Helen saw that the men gathered across the road were glancing at her husband. Before their marriage Madden had been a policeman himself—a Scotland Yard inspector—and his name and reputation were widely known in the area.

'There's been no shortage of volunteers wanting to help,' Stackpole said. 'We've been up and down the road, searching the fields on either side, and the wood as well, but there's no sign of the lass. All we found was the present she was taking. A pair of mittens wrapped in coloured paper. It was lying in a ditch by the path, near to where the other girl left her.'

'Where are the Bridgers?' Helen asked.

'Fred helped with the search, but he's gone to join his wife now. Some of the women have been keeping her company. That's their cottage.' The constable gestured behind him.

'Has her doctor been notified, Will?'

'Dr Rowley turned up half an hour ago and gave her a sedative. Then he announced he'd be on the golf course, if needed.' Stackpole's lip twitched.

'He won't be there much longer,' Helen remarked as lightning streaked the advancing clouds, followed by another rolling boom of thunder.

'Is there anything I can do, Will?' Madden spoke for the first time.

'Thank you, sir, but I've rung Guildford and they're sending reinforcements. It looks as though we'll have to widen the search area.'

'What about detectives?' Madden's scowl signalled his concern.

'I've asked for them, and a couple of plain-clothes men are coming.'

Distressed though she felt, Helen was relieved to hear that her husband wouldn't be needed. She pressed his arm. 'I'll go and see how Mrs Bridger's doing,' she said, but just then her attention was caught by something she saw on the other side of the road, and she paused. The front door of a cottage near the end of the row had opened and a sandy-haired man had come outside.

'Isn't that Dick Henshaw?' she asked. 'He and Molly used to live in Highfield. She was a patient of mine.'

Stackpole glanced round, and as he did so the man caught sight of him and hastened in their direction. 'That's Dick, all right.' The constable frowned. 'Now what's this about, I wonder?'

He moved away and the two met in the middle of the road. Taller by a head, Stackpole had to bend to listen to the other man. They stood like that for perhaps two minutes while Madden and his wife watched from beside their car.

Abruptly, the constable wheeled and came striding back to them.

'It seems I'm going to need your help after all, sir.' He spoke to Madden in a low voice, but there was no disguising the urgency of his manner.

'What is it, Will?' Helen's fingers tightened on her husband's arm.

'There's an old friend of yours sitting in Molly Henshaw's kitchen and he's acting strange. It's Topper.'

Helen's eyebrows rose at the name. 'I didn't know he was back. We've been expecting him for weeks. I was starting to get worried.'

'Has he seen the girl?' Madden asked urgently.

'That's just it, sir. I don't know . . .' Stackpole's face was grim. 'There's some business about a shoe. Molly'll tell us more. But the thing is, he's gone silent. She can't get a word out of him. Now you know old Topper. One sniff of a police uniform and he'll close up tighter than a clam. So what I was wondering, sir, is would *you* try? See if you can get him to open up.'

'I'll try if you want me to, Will,' Madden said, after a pause. He sounded dubious. 'But you've got the wrong person.' Smiling, he glanced at his wife. 'Helen's the one to ask. If he'll talk to anyone he'll talk to her.'

Accompanied by Henshaw, they walked to the end of the line of cottages and followed the path that went round the back of the houses.

'Thank goodness you've come, Will.' Molly Henshaw's plump, motherly features were flushed with distress. Before Stackpole had even unlatched the back gate she was hurrying across the yard to meet them. 'I can't keep Topper sitting still any longer. He's all for running off. Dr Madden . . .!' Her face lit up when she saw Helen and she bobbed her head in greeting.

'Molly, dear! How are you? What a dreadful business this is.' Helen took her hand. 'Have you met my husband?'

Molly Henshaw's reply was drowned in a clap of thunder.

Stackpole glanced anxiously at the heavens. 'Quick now, love, before we go inside—tell us about this shoe.'

'Well, Topper knocked on the door—it must have been half an hour ago—and I asked him in. We know Topper, Dick and I.' She nodded to her husband beside her. 'He's been coming to these parts for years, usually in the summer. If there's something needs doing in the garden he'll lend a hand, otherwise I'll just give him a meal and a cup of tea. He never says much, but he likes to sit here with us. I reckon he knows he's welcome.'

'The shoe, Molly,' Stackpole urged her.

Mrs Henshaw wiped her hands nervously on her apron. 'I could see he was bothered about something as soon as I opened the door, but I wasn't surprised, not with all the fuss going on. I brought him inside and right away he went and sat down in the corner. Then I noticed he was carrying something in his hands, and when he held them out to me I saw what it was . . .'

'A child's shoe?'

Molly Henshaw gave the barest nod.

'Do you know that it belongs to Alice?'

'Oh, no, not for sure.' She swallowed. 'But Jenny Bridger bought her a new pair only the other day. Alice came and showed them to me. They were shiny black with pearl buttons on the straps, just like the one Topper brought.'

'But he wouldn't say where he'd found it?'

'No, nor anything else.' Molly Henshaw dabbed at a teary eye. 'So I gave him a cup of tea to keep him occupied and ran outside to look for Dick.'

'We'd just come back from the fields, Will, and I saw Molly waving to me.' Her husband took up the story. 'She told me what had happened and I came to fetch you directly.'

Stackpole caught Helen's eye, his glance bright with urgency.

'Molly, dear, could we go inside now?' Helen took Molly's hand again. 'I need to see Topper myself.'

THE ROOM lay in shadow, the only illumination coming from a shaft of dull light entering through the back window. It fell on the kitchen table, where a child's shoe, black and shiny, showed starkly against the scrubbed wood.

Helen crossed to the far corner of the room to where Topper was sitting in a straight-backed chair.

Well into middle age—his white-stubbled cheeks were deeply grooved—Topper sat with his chin resting on his chest, seemingly oblivious of his surroundings. Like others who'd encountered the old tramp in the past, Helen knew him only as Topper, a name that derived from the hat that he always wore, a battered piece of evening headgear that was given a jaunty air by the addition of a cock pheasant's tail feather stuck in a red velvet band. He was dressed in a black cloth jacket over striped trousers, and his feet were shod in heavy boots, tied with a combination of string and broken shoelaces.

'Hello, Topper,' she said softly. 'How have you been? Are you well?'

At the sound of her voice he lifted his head and a smile came to his lips. She drew up a chair.

'We missed you at harvest time. Why haven't you come to see us?'

'Was coming . . .' The words brought a gasp from the doorway behind Helen where Molly Henshaw had appeared. 'Had to meet Beezy first . . .'

'Who's Beezy? Where were you meeting him?'

Topper's grey eyes lost focus. He looked away.

Helen took his left hand in hers. 'You were right to bring the shoe, Topper. But we need very badly to know where you found it.'

The fingers she was holding stiffened and she saw the fear in his eyes. His glance went past her shoulder. She looked round. Madden had come quietly into the room with Molly Henshaw. Stackpole hovered in the doorway, and when Topper caught sight of him he slumped lower in the chair.

Helen turned back. 'The shoe,' she said in a low voice. 'Where did you find it? You *must* tell me, Topper. Please . . .' After a moment she felt renewed pressure on her fingers. When she bent closer he whispered in her ear.

She struggled to hear his husky murmur. 'Did you say Capel Wood?'

Behind her, Stackpole tensed in the doorway. 'We've already looked there,' he muttered to Madden. 'Is he sure?' he asked Helen.

'*Capel Wood?*' She repeated the name clearly and looked into the tramp's eyes for confirmation. He nodded. 'Would you take us there?' she asked. 'Would you show us where you found it?'

A tremor went through his body and he shook his head violently.

Helen leaned close again. 'Whereabouts in the wood, Topper?'

Drawn by her steady gaze, he bent forward and whispered once more.

Helen glanced behind her. 'By the stream, he says . . .'

'By the stream . . .' A scowl crossed Stackpole's features. 'There's a path that runs alongside it. It goes through the wood. I took some men and we walked the length of it, calling her name. Once you get off it you can't see three feet in front of you.' He glanced at his wristwatch, as a flash of lightning lit the dim passageway for an instant. 'Well, those detectives from Guildford will be here soon. Better wait for them, I suppose . . .'

His glance seemed to suggest another course of action, however, and Madden responded to it. Despite the formality of address which the constable insisted on maintaining towards him, they were friends of long standing.

'No, we can't do that, Will. We must get out there right away. I think Topper found more than a shoe.'

THE FIRST fat drops of rain splattered the windscreen of Madden's car as he turned off the road onto a rough track that ran round the flank of Capel Wood. Black, swollen clouds were racing in from the west.

'Won't be long now,' Stackpole predicted, squinting up through the glass. He glanced behind him at the roll of canvas lying on the back seat. It was Madden who'd suggested they bring it with them.

'I don't know what we'll find, Will, but you may need to cover the area.'

The tarpaulin was Dick Henshaw's. While he was fetching it from the garden shed Helen had come out of the kitchen to talk to Madden.

'I *must* go and see Jenny Bridger.' She eyed her husband unhappily, upset to see him becoming involved. Madden's life as a policeman lay in the past, and it was one she did not wish to recall. To the constable she added, 'You'd better keep an eye on Topper, Will. He'll slip off if he gets the chance.'

Stackpole had charged both Henshaws with this duty, and cautioned them to say nothing to their neighbours until the Guildford police arrived.

'We'll take the same route Topper took, will we?' Madden's low voice was barely audible over the sound of the car as they ground along in bottom gear.

'Yes, sir. If he was heading for Brookham he'd have come into the wood from the other side and walked through it on the path.'

They'd driven along the road to Craydon for half a mile before turning onto a track close to the point where Alice Bridger had last been seen. The track circled the wood until it petered out in a patch of dried mud beside a pair of haystacks shaped like beehives.

As Madden brought the car to a halt he glanced at the dashboard and saw they had covered just over two miles since leaving Brookham. He got out and briefly inspected the ground around them. It showed only the deeply engraved ruts made by cartwheels at some earlier date.

'Are you thinking someone might have brought her here?' Stackpole asked, as he climbed out of the car.

'It's possible.' Madden shrugged. 'But we'd only be guessing.'

The constable donned his helmet and cape, then retrieved the roll of tarpaulin from the back seat of the car, tucking it under his arm. He pointed ahead of them to a line of willows and low bushes that wound across an open field towards the tree line. 'There's our stream, sir. It runs clear through the wood and comes out on the other side not far from Brookham.'

The two men set off, with the constable leading the way round the outskirts of the wood until they came to the stream. A pathway was visible running alongside it on the far bank and they crossed to it by means of a fallen log. Thunder crashed all around them and they hurried to the shelter of the forest. When they got there, Stackpole stepped aside off the path.

'You lead the way, sir. Your eyes are better than mine.'

Madden went ahead and soon found himself in a zone of twilight cast by the dense canopy of foliage. Rain pattered on the leaves overhead, but did not reach the ground, which remained dry. The path continued to run parallel to the stream, which was visible most of the time, disappearing only briefly behind tree trunks or overhanging branches.

'How big is the wood, Will?' Madden spoke over his shoulder. 'How long will it take us to walk through it?'

'Twenty minutes, at least. It's a fair size.'

Half that time had elapsed, and so far they had seen nothing of note, apart from a set of steppingstones in the stream. Stackpole explained that they connected with a secondary path that ran back to the road to Craydon.

'So Alice Bridger could have walked into the wood?'

Stackpole nodded. 'Or been brought.'

Not far beyond this point the path changed direction, crossing the stream by a second set of steppingstones and then apparently taking a course away from the brook into the depths of the forest. Madden halted.

'Topper said *by* the stream . . .'

The constable came up to his shoulder. 'They only separate for a short distance, sir. The path and the stream. They join up again a little further on.'

'No, I want to stay by the water.' As the rain increased in volume Madden peered downstream, but his view was impeded by undergrowth and overhanging trees. Suddenly something caught his eye and he switched his attention to the brush lining the path, studying the ferns and low, stunted bushes that filled the spaces between the tree trunks.

'Look—!' He went down on his haunches. The constable peered over his shoulder. 'Someone left the path here, or rejoined it.' Madden indicated a fern that had been broken and, near it, a slender oak sapling bent askew.

Madden bent lower to scan the ground, hoping to find some trace of a footprint, but the damp leaf mould was too loose to hold an impression. He stood up. 'Will, I'm going to carry on down the stream on this side. You stay on the path. If what you say is right, we should meet up further on.' Without realising it, Madden had reverted to his old role, taking charge, behaving like the police inspector he had once been.

'I'll do that, sir.' Stackpole replied. 'Call out if you see anything.'

The constable crossed the stream on the steppingstones and followed the course of the footway, which left the brook but then bent back so that it was running parallel to it again, only further from the bank than before.

'Will?'

'I'm here, sir.' Stackpole halted. Madden's voice had reached him clearly from the other side of the stream. He wasn't far off.

'Someone's come this way, all right . . . there's a trail of sorts . . .'

Stackpole walked on, but after only a few paces heard Madden again.

'What kind of clothes was she wearing, Will? What colour were they?'

The constable thought. 'She had a blue skirt on, sir. White blouse.'

'I can see a bit of thread caught on a bramble. It might be blue . . . it's difficult to see in this light . . . No, wait! There's something else! Will?'

'Sir!'

'You'd better get over here!'

The sharpened note in Madden's voice caused the hairs on the back of the constable's neck to rise. 'What is it, sir? Have you found her, then . . .?'

'Yes, I've found her, Will.'

He said no more. But his voice told all.

IT WAS ONLY by chance that Madden had spotted the body.

Earlier, picking his way through the brush and clinging brambles, his attention had been focused on the abundant signs that one or more people had come by this route: snapped twigs and ferns bent back and flattened marked the rough passage that had been forced through the undergrowth.

He had carried on downstream until his attention was caught by the thread, which was snagged on a bramble at waist height.

All this time his glimpses of the stream were hampered by the thick brush that clung to the banks. But a few steps further on there was a break in the bushes that opened onto a small rectangle of turf bordering the stream. The opposite bank was hidden by the overhanging branches of a willow tree.

Sheltered from the rain and sun by the spreading branch of an oak tree, it struck Madden as a tranquil spot and he was surveying an irregular ring of stones that lay at one end of the rectangle, when his eye was caught by another object on the ground, closer to where he was standing.

What he was looking at was nothing more than an oak leaf, and it had taken him several moments to realise why his gaze had become fixed on it.

The colour, dark brown in the dreary light, was starting to run.

He'd bent down and picked it up by its stem. The patina coating the leaf's surface had been smeared by raindrops; the dry crust was reverting to its liquid form. There was no doubt in Madden's mind as to what it was.

Looking round then, he saw other bloodstains; other leaves bearing the telltale marks. The grass, too, was spattered with tiny rust-coloured flecks.

Backing into the bushes, Madden went down on his hands and knees so he could examine the ground minutely, and it was then that he saw, protruding from beneath the willow branches across the stream, a sock-clad foot.

Madden scrambled to his feet and waded through the cold, ankle-deep current to the opposite bank. Parting the trailing willow fronds he found the body of a young girl lying on its side on a narrow ledge. Without hope he bent down and felt for a pulse in the thin white wrist that rested on her hip. There was none. She was dead. He had called out then to Stackpole.

During their shouted exchange, Madden's eyes remained busy. The position of the body, wedged beneath an overhang in the bank and screened by the drooping branches, indicated that the killer had meant to conceal it.

Judging by her blood-soaked hair, which covered her face as she lay, she appeared to have been struck about the head, and the evidence pointed to the assault having taken place on the bloodstained grass behind him . . .

Coolly, Madden continued to compile his mental notes, aware that he was acting from habit, doing something he had once been trained to do, keeping his emotions separate from the process of observation. His poise deserted him, however, when he drew aside the matted hair to look at the girl's face.

'Dear God!' A gasp of horror escaped his lips.

He'd seen more than one murder victim cruelly battered, and during two years spent in the trenches had been witness to unspeakable injuries. But nothing in his experience had prepared him for the sight of Alice Bridger's face, beaten flat to a red pulp on which no trace of a human feature remained.

'Ah, Christ . . . no!' It was Stackpole's voice.

Madden looked behind him. Will Stackpole's tall figure had appeared through the bushes on the far bank. Unable to penetrate the wall of holly bushes that surrounded the willow tree, he had retraced his steps and followed Madden's route to the small clearing.

'There's blood on the grass over there, Will.' Madden gestured. 'You'd better keep off it. That's probably where she was killed. And raped, by the look of it. We can either protect that patch, or cover the body. But we can't do both.' He looked up at the sky. Although the rain was increasing steadily, the full force of the storm was yet to break. 'Let's cover the grass,' he decided. 'The stream's bound to rise, so we may have to move the body anyway.'

While Stackpole unrolled the canvas, Madden recrossed the stream, pausing to collect an armful of stones from the riverbed; the two men then laid them at the corners of the spread tarpaulin, on which the rain now drummed.

The storm now broke in earnest. As he was caught in the downpour, Madden's eye fell again on the ring of stones he'd noticed earlier. In the last few minutes an answer had occurred to him to a question he'd been asking himself since entering the wood, and he looked around now for other indications that might confirm it. His inspection of the rain-blurred scene had hardly begun, however, when he was interrupted by a yell from Stackpole. Madden glanced up to see the constable plunge into the stream. The level of the water had risen with alarming speed and Stackpole was already knee-deep in the frothing torrent, struggling to keep his footing.

'Hand her to me, Will!'

The constable tugged aside the screen of willows and lifted the body of Alice Bridger from the lapping water, wrapping her slight form in his cape and turning unsteadily to hand the bundle to Madden.

Madden laid her on the ground beside the tarpaulin.

Stackpole clambered out of the stream and the two men looked at the rushing water, which had now flooded the ledge where the body had lain and was close to overflowing onto the bank where they stood.

'Looks like we may lose the lot, sir.'

'No, I don't think so, Will. It's passing. See!' Madden pointed up at the sky, which was clearing fast. The rain, too, was diminishing noticeably, and without warning it stopped.

Madden's mind returned to the problem he'd been wrestling with earlier. His eye lit on a birch tree that stood outside the ring of bushes, its pale trunk partly screened by undergrowth. He gestured towards it. 'I just want to go and have a look at that.'

Mystified, the constable followed him round the rectangle of grass until they reached the birch. 'Yes! There . . . Look, Will!'

Stackpole saw that Madden was examining the trunk, which had been scored by strange runic designs carved with a knife.

'Those were made by tramps. This is one of their campsites. *That's* why Topper left the path. He was coming here . . .' Madden gestured with his thumb behind him. 'That circle of stones on the ground over there—that's where they light their fires. You can't see it now because the grass has grown over. But look at these marks . . . that one's Topper's.'

Squinting, the constable made out the shape of a cross carved into the trunk surrounded by a crude circle.

'It's a calling card. A sign he was here. Just like those others.'

Stackpole ran his fingers over the faint, spidery furrows. 'But they're old, sir, not one of them done this summer, I'd say . . .'

'Except this one!' Madden indicated a design cut into the trunk somewhat lower than the rest. It showed a triangle with a line drawn through it.

'That's fresh, all right,' Stackpole acknowledged. 'The bark's only just been stripped. The wood's still white. Why, it could have been done today . . .'

'It probably was.' Madden turned to the constable. 'Topper told Helen he was due to meet someone hereabouts, a man called Beezy, another tramp, by the sound of it. That could be *his* mark.'

2

C alled out before dawn the next morning on a maternity case, Helen did not get back to the house until after nine. Twenty minutes earlier Will Stackpole had rung with news he'd obtained by telephone from the police in Guildford, which Madden recounted to his wife while they ate a late breakfast.

'They haven't had the pathologist's report yet, but there seems no doubt she was raped and strangled. What the pathologist will make of the damage to her face I don't know. It looked deliberate to me.'

'*Deliberate?*'

'Systematic. It seemed to me he'd set out to destroy her features.'

They'd been late getting back from Brookham the previous night. Darkness had fallen before Madden returned from Capel Wood and Helen had spent the intervening hours in the Henshaws' kitchen, keeping Topper company, but had twice visited the Bridgers' cottage, where the missing girl's mother had fallen into a restless sleep from the sedative she'd been given earlier. Mr Bridger had refused similar relief. She'd discovered him sitting in the parlour with neighbours, a short, stocky man with thinning hair, his pale features racked by unspoken fears. Alice was an only child, she'd learned.

Catching Madden's eye now, she smiled, hoping to dispel his dark mood. 'What's happened to Topper?' she asked. 'Are the police still holding him?'

'He spent the night in the cells at Guildford. By invitation, mind, but it seems to have loosened his tongue. He told them all he knew and they let him go this morning. He's been ordered to appear at the inquest on Friday.'

'Will he do that?' Helen looked sceptical.

'He'll be in the next county by then. Unless he drops in to see you.'

'I'll be hurt if he doesn't.'

Her words brought a smile to Madden's lips, just as she'd hope they might, and they laughed together. Topper had come into their lives several years before, knocking on the back door one summer afternoon, another in the legion of homeless: tramps, vagrants, men whose numbers had swelled with the Depression. The Maddens' cook, Mrs Beck, had standing orders to offer food and drink to these wanderers. Whether or not she admitted them to her kitchen was up to her, but Helen had returned that afternoon from her rounds to find Topper seated at the table, busily plying knife and fork under Cook's approving eye. He had risen to his feet when she entered and made a courtly bow.

'A proper gentleman, this one, ma'am.' Mrs Beck had purred her approval.

Helen had asked for her own tea to be served in the kitchen and had sat with the old man, finding herself drawn to the dusty, travel-stained figure with his absurd attire. Although he told her nothing of himself—either then, or later—she'd been moved by the sound of his soft voice and by his gentle manner. His grey eyes, seeking hers across the table in timid glances, had spoken of pain and loss; of some past to which he could never return.

His meal done, she had given him directions to their farm, with a note to her husband. Topper had stayed for a week, helping with the harvest and sleeping in the barn. On the morning of his departure Mrs Beck had found a jam jar on the step outside the kitchen filled with pink campion and the yellow buds of St John's wort, picked from the hedgerows. Tucked beneath it was a scrap of paper bearing a roughly pencilled message: *For the lady*.

'What did Topper tell them?' Helen asked Madden now.

'He said he came into the wood from the side we did and left the path to get to that campsite. Most of these old tramps have hidden spots tucked away, places where they can lie up for a while. Topper told the police he'd been using the site for years. When he got there yesterday he spotted the shoe lying on the bank across the stream. Then he saw the girl's foot.'

'It's a wonder he didn't run off at once.'

Madden agreed. 'Instead he collected it and brought it to Brookham. It was a brave thing to do.' He smiled at his wife.

'How have the police reacted? Do they believe him?'

'Oh, I think so. But they wanted to know more about this man Beezy. According to Topper they met at a dosshouse in London last winter. Beezy's usual summer base is Kent—he finds hop-picking work there. But this year for some reason he decided to join up with Topper and come down to Surrey instead. However, Beezy caught bronchitis while they were doing some odd jobs on a farm near Dorking and was laid up for a week. Topper moved on but they agreed to meet up again this weekend at the campsite.'

'But he never got there, did he? Beezy, I mean?'

'Ah, but he did,' he said. 'A lot of these tramps have marks. They carve them on trees at meeting spots. I noticed several cut into the trunk of a birch tree by the campsite, but only one was fresh: a triangle with a line drawn through it. According to Topper, that's Beezy's mark.'

'So if Beezy was there *before* Topper found the girl's shoe, that must mean he's a suspect,' Helen said.

'He's bound to be, I'm afraid.' Madden scowled. 'Topper's in the clear, you'll be glad to hear. He got a lift in a lorry from Coldharbour to Shamley Green yesterday afternoon—the police have already spoken to the driver—and couldn't have reached Capel Wood before three o'clock, which was hours after Alice Bridger disappeared.' His glance shifted to the open window behind her. 'Look—there's Rob. Has he been up in the woods?'

Turning in her chair, Helen followed the direction of her husband's gaze across the sunlit terrace to the orchard at the foot of the lawn, where their ten-year-old son, clad in shorts, was emerging from the trees. 'He told me young Ted Stackpole was going to show him a badger's sett he'd discovered. The boys thought if they got there before dawn they might see the cubs.'

Madden watched as the small figure made its plodding way up the lawn. 'They'll have to stop doing that for the time being. We can't have them wandering off into the woods alone. Not for the moment.' He caught Helen's eye. 'I'll tell Rob about the murder when he comes in. And Lucy, too. There's bound to be talk in the village. Better they hear it first from me.'

ALTHOUGH BROOKHAM was only five miles distant, the drive along country lanes busy with farm traffic was a slow one and it took Madden twenty minutes to reach his destination. An unmarked police car parked on the verge by the cottages signalled the presence of detectives in the hamlet.

His own return to Brookham was unplanned. Although he had talked only briefly with the CID men sent from Guildford the day before, he had promised them a statement, and already that morning, before breakfast, had written out a full account of all he had seen and done in Capel Wood.

But enough of the old policeman still dwelt in John Madden to ensure that he wouldn't rest satisfied. A nagging sense of duty, the feeling of a job half done, had dogged him since leaving Brookham the night before.

Morning had brought no relief and he'd risen with a feeling of guilt that initially he'd put down to his failure to make proper sense of the evidence that had been presented to him at first hand. Some instinct told him there was more to be learned from the murder site than he had so far deduced.

Still, he'd had no plan to involve himself further in what was now a police matter. It was only after Helen had left to go to her surgery and he was setting out for the farm that a sudden impulse had prompted him to change direction.

WATCHED BY Madden, Galloway fished up a stone from the stream bed and examined it closely. Portly and red-faced, he stood shin-deep in the fast-moving current, wearing waders.

'I thought myself he might have used a stone,' Madden remarked from the bank above. 'But then I wondered . . .'

'Wondered what, John?' Peter Galloway glanced up quizzically. He was the senior pathologist attached to the hospital in Guildford. Madden knew him socially through Helen.

'He did such a thorough job on her face I thought he might have used a tool of some kind. A hammer, perhaps?' It was the first time Madden had put into words the thought that had tormented him during the long night: the barely believable notion that the killer might actually have brought with him the means for demolishing a human face.

'As it happens, I think you may be right.' Galloway tossed aside the stone he was carrying. 'I was up half the night trying to decide that very point, based on the available evidence, the pulped flesh, I mean. I could come to no conclusion. When I return I mean to examine the bone structure, or what's left of it, to see if I can reach a more precise verdict. Would you mind?' He reached out a hand and, with Madden's help, hauled his heavy bulk onto the bank. 'I might add, it's the worst case of its kind I've ever come across. Thank God, *those* injuries were post-mortem.'

Madden had arrived back at Capel Wood to find Topper's secluded camp site a scene of activity, with four plain-clothes men scouring the small rectangle of sodden grass that he and Stackpole had attempted to cover the evening before and examining the far bank where the body had been concealed. Their labours were overseen by a fifth detective, the senior CID man in charge of the case, who had hailed his arrival.

'Mr Madden, sir! Wright's the name. Detective Inspector.'

The two shook hands. They hadn't met before, but Madden's name and face were well known to members of the Surrey force.

'There are some details I need to go over with you, sir.' Wright had a confident, bustling air. He was in his early forties, a thin, wiry man.

By way of reply Madden had handed him the written statement. 'It's all in there, Inspector. It'll save time if you read it first.'

'Thank you, sir. I'll do that now, if I may.'

Leaving him to read the statement, Madden turned his attention to the scene around him. He still felt there was more to be learned from this spot. His gaze came to rest on a leather case that lay open on the ground near his feet. It was half filled with labelled glass jars, the fruits of the detectives' efforts that morning, he supposed.

Galloway, catching the direction of his glance, gestured. 'You and the bobby did a good job with that piece of canvas, John. Thanks to you both, we can say for certain the assault was carried out here, on this very spot.'

Madden's thoughts had been moving on a parallel course. 'He'd have needed a spot like this, wouldn't he? Secluded, I mean?' For a moment he was distracted by the sudden appearance of a kingfisher that shot by like a blue streak, close to the water.

'I was thinking the same thing, sir,' Wright said, glancing up from the statement he was reading. 'He already *knew* about this spot, didn't he?'

Madden looked at him enquiringly.

'That tramp, sir,' he continued. 'Beezy. We can place him here earlier, before the other one found the body. What's his name . . . Topper? That mark on the tree . . .' He gestured towards the birch.

Madden frowned. 'You're treating Beezy as a suspect, then, are you?'

'Well, yes. We've had no word of other strangers seen in the area. And though we can't *exclude* the fact that it was someone local, I think you'll find that, being a Sunday, most were at home, and able to prove it.'

'So if there *were* any strangers about, it's unlikely they would have been seen.' Galloway made the point. Wright shrugged, but Galloway persisted. 'Don't you find it peculiar that he'd try to conceal a body at a spot where he'd already left his mark?'

'Yes, I do, sir.' Wright turned to him. 'And, what's more, a place where he was expecting to meet another tramp later. But that's looking at it rationally, and this sort of crime doesn't happen that way.' His eyes returned to Madden's face. He seemed to be hoping for some response.

'I can tell you how it *might* have come about,' he went on. 'This Beezy turns up yesterday to meet Topper, finds he has time on his hands, cuts that mark to show he's been here, then goes off exploring. Remember, he hadn't been to these parts before. Now you can get to the Craydon road from here easy. There's a way off the main path that runs through the wood to the road and it comes out not far from where Alice Bridger was last seen. He *could* have come on her there, lost his head maybe and knocked her out or choked her and then brought her back up here. There's evidence she was carried—'

'Evidence?' Madden asked.

'Yes, sir, that bit of thread you noticed caught on a bramble. It came from her skirt. We matched it. Now, if you recall, it was about waist high on the bush, and that suggests to me she was being carried at that point.'

Madden nodded his agreement, but made no further comment.

'Now, as I was saying, he could have brought her back here from the road, this Beezy—back to where he knew they wouldn't be seen. And if that's what happened, then I don't reckon he would have been thinking of any mark he'd made on a tree earlier. That would have been the last thing on his mind. Like I said, you can't expect rational behaviour with a crime of this type. Isn't that so, sir?' The confidence had begun to seep out of the inspector's manner as he spoke and there was a hint of desperation about the appeal he flung out to Madden, who had resumed his former attitude and was standing with arms folded, eyes fixed to the ground.

'And something else you can't ignore, sir, he took off in a hurry—'

'*Did* he?' Madden's head jerked up again. 'How do you know that?'

'Well, from that old clasp knife of his we found—'

'Clasp knife?'

'Yes. We picked it up last evening by the stream, not far from here. It was lying on the ground, wrapped in an old bandanna. Must have fallen out of his bundle, or his pocket. Now I can't see that happening unless he was in a hurry and not taking proper care. We showed them both to Topper this morning, the knife and the bandanna, and he confirmed they belonged to Beezy.'

'On the ground, you say? I wonder how I missed them?'

'Oh, it wasn't the way you and the constable came.' Wright was eager to explain. 'It was the other direction.' He pointed downstream.

'To Brookham? That's strange.'

'Well, if you ask me, he was in a panic by then and could easily have been confused. But all he had to do was get back to the path, and you can do that either way, upstream or down. Once he'd reached it he could have doubled back and left the wood the same way he came in, by the fields.'

'Yes, that's so,' Madden conceded. 'He must have done that.'

'But what's really suspicious, sir, is he's disappeared. We've been searching the neighbourhood since last evening and no one's seen hide or hair of him. He's made himself scarce, and you have to ask yourself *why*.'

Madden nodded. 'Yes, why? That's the question, Inspector. He *must* be found. And the sooner the better.'

DRIVING TO THE FARM later that morning, Madden had called in at the house long enough for him to acquire a passenger before he departed again: his six-year-old daughter, Lucy. She had been left in the sole charge of

Mrs Beck since breakfast and the Maddens' cook was in sore need of relief.

Lucy Madden's hair matched her mother's honey-coloured shade. A tireless child, her fair skin had been golden brown all summer from hours spent playing in the open air.

'Can we go and see the waggle-taggle Gypsies?'

'Raggle-taggle. And don't call them that. They're Mr and Mrs Goram to you.' Her eyes, blue as sapphires, challenged his in the rearview mirror. 'Yes, we can,' he said, after a moment. 'They're leaving soon, and I want to talk to Mr Goram before they go.'

The dirt road to the farm sparkled with muddy puddles. As they drove past the farmhouse, May Burrows, wife of Madden's farm manager, waved to them from the kitchen doorway. The land on which the farm lay was little more than a mile from the Maddens' house and less than three miles from Highfield itself. Madden and Helen had bought it soon after their marriage, when Madden had quit his job at Scotland Yard to return to the life he had known as a boy.

Madden parked his car at the stableyard. He saddled the old mare he used for getting about the farm and rode down to the Gypsies' camp with Lucy perched in front of him.

'Mr Madden, sir! I was hoping to see you today,' Joe Goram called out from the steps of one of his caravans as they rode into the encampment. He was a burly, dark-haired man with unshaven cheeks and a scowl that seemed permanently fixed until he caught sight of Lucy.

'Good morning to you, young missy.' Waving to her, he came down the steps. His broad grin showed he had several teeth missing.

'Hello, Mr Goram. May I see the puppies, please?'

'Of course, m'dear. They're tied up over there, behind the caravan.'

The little girl slid to the ground and ran off.

Dismounting, Madden shook hands with the Gypsy and noted the signs of activity in the encampment. The various members of Joe Goram's family—his wife and two sons, his daughter and son-in-law—were busy stowing items in the trio of caravans. A grandson was picking up rubbish.

'You were hoping to see me, you said?'

'Yes, Mr Madden, sir. We'll be pulling out first thing tomorrow and I wanted to thank you again for letting us stay.'

The Gypsies had first appeared four summers before. Joe Goram had presented himself to Madden, cap in hand, and asked for permission to park his caravans on a patch of tree-shaded land by the stream and to graze his horses in the lower paddock, which he must have seen was empty. Over strong objections from George Burrows, the farm manager— Gypsies had a reputation for being light-fingered, he'd argued—Madden had agreed. In spite of his policeman's conditioning, he clung to the belief he'd grown up with: that people, by and large, behaved according to how they were treated.

The Goram family had returned every year since, accepting the hospitality that was offered and in return doing odd jobs about the farm.

'There's something you ought to know, Joe. A young girl was murdered over at Brookham yesterday.'

'I heard about it, sir. Mr Burrows told us this morning. Poor lass . . .'

'I understand you were at the farm all day yesterday?'

'That's right. I took my boys up to say goodbye to Mrs Burrows. She gave us a cup of tea.'

'There's something else, Joe . . . Have you ever come across a man called Beezy? He's a tramp, a friend of Topper's.'

Goram shook his head. 'I've not heard the name, sir. *Beezy*, you say?'

'It's a nickname, I expect. He was in the Brookham area yesterday, near where the child's body was found.'

'Are the police looking for him, then?' Goram's face was expressionless.

'Yes, they are. They think he might have done it.' Madden paused. 'You might hear of his whereabouts,' he suggested.

The Gypsy's swarthy features darkened still further. He stared at his feet.

'No need to go to the police,' Madden said. 'Just get word to me.'

Goram's face cleared. He looked up. 'Oh, I'll do that, if you want, sir.' Vastly relieved, he offered his hand to Madden, who took it at once. 'Anything I hear, you'll hear. You have my word on it.'

THE CORONER'S inquest into the death of Alice Bridger, held at Guildford the following Friday, was quickly concluded. As officer in charge of the case, Inspector Wright baldly described the murder scene and outlined the measures taken by the Surrey constabulary at the start of their investigation.

'I am authorised to inform the court that we are looking for one man in particular,' Wright stated.

Silver-haired and in his sixties, Chief Superintendent Boyce, head of the Guildford CID, buttonholed Madden in the street outside afterwards. They were old acquaintances. 'Six months to my pension and we're landed with a case like this! Mind you, at least it's straightforward.' He waited for a response, but none was forthcoming. 'You don't agree?' Boyce cocked an eyebrow, then turned aside to doff his hat and bow. 'Dr Madden!'

'Mr Boyce . . . how are you?' Helen shook his hand. She had come from talking to Mrs Bridger, the murdered girl's mother, who was standing by the steps to the courthouse in a circle of Brookham villagers, clinging to her husband as though she required his support to remain upright. Bridger himself was hardly more steady on his feet.

'This man you're searching for,' she asked. 'Is he the mysterious Beezy?'

'He is, and I don't know why we haven't laid hands on him yet.'

Madden had seen the description circulated by the Surrey police. It had been sent not only to village bobbies in the district but to farmers and gamekeepers as well, and Will Stackpole had brought him a copy of the poster.

Beezy was described as being of middle age, bearded and dressed in rough clothes—words that could be applied to a good many vagrants. However, he had one distinguishing feature noted by the farmer he'd worked for recently at Dorking: the lobe of his right ear was missing.

'And we haven't seen any sign of Topper either since we let him go,' Boyce complained. 'But to get back to what I was saying, John—the girl's injuries aside, *do* you think there's something unusual about this killing?'

Listening to the Surrey policeman, Helen felt a twinge of unease. Well aware of the regard in which her husband had once been held by his colleagues, she knew that his views would be eagerly sought, and it filled her with misgivings.

'Oh, it's shocking, I grant you,' Boyce went on. 'But ten to one this Beezy will turn out to be the man we want. Or someone very like him.'

'A tramp, you mean?' Madden sounded surprised.

Boyce nodded. 'Look, living the life they do . . . tramps . . . vagrants . . . they lack so much . . . they've no opportunity . . .' He directed an embarrassed glance at Helen, who'd divined the source of his discomfiture.

'You're implying they're sexually deprived,' she said.

'Well, yes. Since you put it that way.' Boyce sought refuge in his handkerchief. He blew his nose loudly. 'And that sort of feeling can build up, can it not? And when the dam breaks, well, it can be sudden and savage. That's what happened here, I think.'

'Are you certain of that?' Madden's interjection took Boyce by surprise.

'What are you saying, John?' he asked. 'What are you suggesting?'

'I'm not sure, exactly.' Scowling, Madden seemed suddenly a prey to doubts himself.

Boyce frowned. 'Are you saying I should call in the Yard?'

'I don't see how you can,' Madden said. 'Not yet. You could be right about the tramp. And in any case he has to be found. But I'd make sure the Yard was *informed* about this. And I wouldn't waste any time, either, Jim, if I were you.'

THE DRIVE back to Highfield was a silent one. Madden's habit of withdrawing into himself when preoccupied was deeply ingrained, and Helen had learned from experience to be patient with him.

It had taken many weeks when they'd first met to learn the details of his past. To draw from him the story of his descent into the hell of the trenches, an experience from which he'd emerged so injured in spirit that, until fate cast him into her arms, he had ceased to have any hope in the future.

Long dispelled, these shadows no longer troubled their lives. What concerned Helen now was the irrational fear she had felt at the sight of her husband being drawn once more into a police investigation after so long an absence from the profession. His decision to quit his job and start a new life with her had not been taken lightly. Nor was it one he had ever regretted. If he was allowing himself to become involved now, it could only be in response to some deep anxiety, and this realisation kept the pulse of uneasiness throbbing inside her.

The happy years they had spent together had been born out of tragedy, something she could never forget. Indeed, the thought was fresh in her mind as they drove through the village, past the green and the moss-walled churchyard and along the straggling line of cottages that led to the high brick wall surrounding Melling Lodge. Leased by a succession of tenants in recent years, it was empty at present and the locked gates and dark, elm-lined drive lent it a mournful air.

Time had dulled the pain of that summer morning more than a decade past, when an urgent summons from Will Stackpole had brought her, the village doctor, speeding through those same gates to confront the unimaginable reality of a household brutally slain; her dearest friend among the victims. When she drove by now it was of her husband she was thinking.

Yet the two were inextricably linked. It was the subsequent police investigation that had brought them together, and although the love that had flowered between them had drawn a line under Madden's tortured past, their future together had been dearly purchased.

The case, one of the bloodiest in the Yard's annals, had come close to costing him his life.

3

Chief Inspector Angus Sinclair paused at the edge of the village green to take in the scene before him. Close to where he stood a cloth banner erected on poles bore the words HIGHFIELD FLOWER AND VEGETABLE SHOW in bold capitals, and beyond it, the broad stretch of grass ringed with cottages was filled with stalls, where the fruits of a long summer were on display.

Searching the crowd, the chief inspector's eye lit on a tall, elegant figure wearing a cream-coloured linen dress and a wide-brimmed straw hat standing beside a table stacked with preserves. A widower now for several years, Angus Sinclair considered Helen Madden to be the best-looking woman of his acquaintance, and it always gave him particular pleasure to see her.

Aware of his approach, Helen put down the jar of honey she was holding.

'I was wondering when you'd appear, Angus.'

Taken by surprise—he'd expected a friendly greeting at the very least— Sinclair stood abashed.

'It's that poor child's murder, isn't it? That's why you're here.'

Planting a firm kiss on her cheek, he said, 'I'll admit I've been at Guildford all morning, talking to Jim Boyce about it.'

'And now you want to see John. Angus, you're not to drag him into this. I won't allow it.' Her dark blue eyes offered no concession.

'*Drag* him in! It was John who found the child's body, for heaven's sake.' Sinclair broke off. The subject was a delicate one between them. He continued in a different tone. 'My dear, I *must* speak to him. Surely you see that.'

The smile he tendered her was conciliatory. But in truth it was no more than a gesture. Though he had never doubted the strength of Helen's feelings for her husband, he had equally never forgiven her for the part she had played in persuading such a talented officer to quit the force.

'Oh, very well. I see I've no choice in the matter. He's here somewhere. Probably in that tent.' She pointed to a tan-coloured marquee near the back of the green. 'John's chairman of the prize-giving committee.' She paused. 'You may think I'm making too much of this, but I know John. He won't turn his back on it now. He feels involved, and that worries me. I know you have to speak to him, but don't let it go further than that, I beg you.'

SINCLAIR CAME on his quarry outside the marquee standing beside a table laden with silver cups, dressed in serviceable tweeds and deep in conversation with a party of similarly tweed-clad worthies of both sexes. Catching Madden's eye, he winked.

'I've just spotted a pumpkin of outstanding merit,' he confided as they shook hands. 'Would you like me to point it out to you?'

'What are you doing here, Angus?' Grinning, Madden declined the bait. 'Is it the Brookham murder? Has the Yard been called in?'

'No, we're not involved. Not as yet. Surrey are handling it. But there are one or two points I'd like to discuss with you. You must have put a bee in Jim Boyce's bonnet. He rang me on Friday in a lather, right after the inquest. I couldn't get down to Guildford till today, but he came into the office to show me the file. On a Sunday, too!'

'I felt they'd made up their minds too quickly about the tramp. I wanted him to think again,' Madden said. 'But how can I help you, Angus? You say you've seen the file?' Madden drew Sinclair aside, out of earshot of the crowd milling about.

'I've studied the various reports and read the interviews taken. Based on what I know so far, I'd have to say the tramp's the most likely suspect.'

'So he is,' Madden agreed. 'And they have to find him, in any case. He may turn out in the end to be their key witness.'

'What makes you think that?'

'Why, the evidence, of course.' Madden frowned. 'It all depends how you read it, Angus. Wright reckons the tramp brought her back to the wood and after he'd killed her and hidden her body he ran off down the stream, dropping his knife and bandanna in the confusion.'

'And?' Sinclair was listening intently.

'It holds water, as a theory, up to a point. But there's another way of interpreting the facts. You see, Beezy ran off in the wrong direction, *towards* Brookham, not the way he came, and that doesn't make sense, unless you take Wright's view that he was in a panic, and didn't know which way he was heading.'

'Could there be another explanation?'

'Yes. It's possible he heard someone moving towards him through the bushes. From the same direction he'd come himself, from the fields. Since he was expecting Topper to arrive, that shouldn't have alarmed him. So if he did run off then—and in the other direction—it could well have been because he saw something that frightened him.'

Sinclair let out a sigh. 'Yes, but you can't overlook the fact he's disappeared. That's not the behaviour of an innocent man.'

'It's the behaviour of a tramp, Angus. An outcast. These men have no faith in the courts. It's possible he's afraid of going to the police in case he's charged with the crime himself. And he wouldn't be far wrong.'

'Very well. But either way the Surrey police must find this man. That's not a job for the Yard. Why did you suggest that Boyce get in touch with us?'

'You saw the photographs of the girl's face?'

'What remained of it. I can only imagine the killer was in a frenzy.'

'Perhaps. But it looked to me like he actually set out to obliterate her features. This wasn't simple abuse of a victim's body. It was something more. Has it been determined yet what was used in the way of a weapon? The pathologist seemed to think it might have been a hammer.'

'That's confirmed now.' Sinclair nodded. 'There's no reason why the tramp shouldn't have had one in his bundle.'

'Agreed. Whereas, if the killer was someone else, someone who picked her up off the road in his car, then the implication becomes quite different.'

'You're wondering—if it *was* someone else—why he should have had a hammer with him at all. What does it signify to you?'

'That the assault on her face was planned.' Madden spoke quietly.

'I want to be clear about this. Are you suggesting he was following a pattern? That he's done this sort of thing before?'

Madden nodded mutely.

'But surely, if that's the case, it would have come to our notice. A crime of that kind?' The chief inspector scowled. His companion shrugged.

'I can't explain that. But don't forget, he tried to hide Alice Bridger's body. If it hadn't been for the accident of him choosing a tramps' hide-out to commit the murder in, we might be searching for her still.'

'So you think he might have killed elsewhere without our knowing it . . .' Sinclair brooded on the thought. 'Children do go missing, it's true.'

Madden pressed harder. 'The Surrey police can't pursue a theory of this kind. The tramp's the obvious suspect; they have to keep looking for him. But it's different with the Yard. They can afford to take a broader view.'

'Which is why you urged Boyce to ring us? Yes, I see now. I won't say I'm persuaded. Not yet. But I'll certainly look into the matter. Rest assured.'

The smile of relief on Madden's face was testimony to a burden shed, and the chief inspector warmed to it. Among the many reasons he had for regretting the departure of his old colleague had been the depth of commitment

Madden had brought to his work, an impulse born of the sense of obligation he seemed to feel towards others; those whose lives touched his.

It was a rare quality among policemen; a rare quality anywhere.

AT TEN O'CLOCK on the Friday following, Sinclair presented himself at the Scotland Yard office of Sir Wilfred Bennett, assistant commissioner, crime. Burdened as he was with questions of policy and administration, Bennett would not normally have dealt with the matter Sinclair wished to raise had it not been for the absence of his deputy owing to a brush with peritonitis.

'I've asked Chief Superintendent Holly to join us, Chief Inspector.'

The assistant commissioner directed Sinclair to the oak table by the windows where he was in the habit of conducting his conferences. As they sat down facing each other, Sir Wilfred observed, not without a pang, his visitor's clear grey eyes and air of alertness. Despite having turned sixty, Angus Sinclair looked like a man who still had an appetite for his work.

There was a knock on the door and the chief superintendent entered. He was a heavyset man in his mid-fifties, blunt-featured and sporting a suntan.

'Good morning, Holly. Welcome back.' Bennett rose and shook his hand. 'I trust you had a good holiday.'

'Thank you, sir. The weather was excellent. I always say there's no place like the Scilly Isles at this time of year.' The chief super's soft burr betrayed his West Country origins.

'My word, Arthur, you've put on weight.' Sinclair eyed his colleague askance. 'I shall have to speak to Ethel. We must get you on a diet.'

Holly blushed. He was now the senior superintendent on the force and nominally Sinclair's superior. But he could never forget that he had once worked under the chief inspector; had felt the sting of his sometimes acid tongue and striven to earn the approval of the man who had since declined any further promotion, letting it be known that he was satisfied with the rank of chief inspector.

'So you went down to Guildford last Sunday, did you?' Bennett had waited until they were all settled before speaking. Pale of face, with dark, thinning hair, he had a quick, decisive manner that mirrored the mind behind it. 'I hope you trod carefully, Chief Inspector.'

'Jim Boyce is an old friend. We agreed to treat my visit as unofficial.'

'Guildford?' Arthur Holly frowned. 'That rings a bell. Wasn't there a child murdered there recently? I read something about it in the papers.'

'Yes, a young girl.' Bennett settled himself in his chair. 'She was raped and strangled. It happened while you were away. The chief inspector drew my attention to it. There are aspects of the murder that he feels can't be ignored.' He gestured to Sinclair, inviting him to continue.

'The injuries inflicted on the child's body after death were unusually severe. Her face was destroyed. The pathologist determined that the killer used a hammer for this purpose.'

'My God!' The shock showed on Holly's face.

'Among the various conclusions one might draw from such an act, the most disturbing to me is that the assault appears to have been planned in advance. It's one of the reasons why I believe this crime merits our attention. There may be more to it than meets the eye. For the present, all I can tell you is that the Surrey police are searching for a tramp in connection with the assault, a man whose travelling name is Beezy. He was known to have been in the wood where the girl's body was found round about the time she was killed.'

'What do we know about him?' Holly asked.

Sinclair drew a page from the file in front of him. 'His real name is Harold Beal. Twelve years ago his wife died suddenly. He began to drink heavily, lost his job as an insurance clerk and took to the road. He's been a tramp ever since, spending his summers in Kent, working on farms there, then returning to London for the winter. He's been found drunk and disorderly a number of times and has one conviction for indecent exposure on his record.'

'Has he, now?' Holly sat up. 'It's a pointer, isn't it?'

'It could be. But I'm not sure.' The chief inspector eased a muscle in his back. 'Between unbuttoning your flies in public and what was done to that poor girl, there's a vast distance. An enormous leap.'

'What does Boyce think? Does he believe this tramp is their man?'

'Not as strongly as he did before hearing John Madden's views on the subject.'

'Madden?' Holly's eyebrows shot up. 'How is he involved?'

'He happened to be the one who found the body. He was helping the local bobby search the wood. I had a word with him in Highfield on Sunday.'

'I take it Madden doesn't hold with the tramp theory?' Bennett asked.

Sinclair shook his head. 'Madden thought the damage inflicted on the girl's features was deliberate, the work of a man who might have done that sort of thing before, rather than the aberration of some old tramp who's come across an unsupervised child and suddenly taken leave of his senses.'

Holly scowled. 'I'm not aware of any recent crime that fits this pattern, Angus. Have you found something in the files?'

'No, nothing.' The chief inspector shook his head. 'But something has come to my attention, quite by chance, which I'd like to share with you.'

'Please do,' the assistant commissioner said drily.

'Three years ago—in July of 1929—a twelve-year-old girl by the name of Susan Barlow went missing in Henley. Her body wasn't discovered until this year: six weeks ago, in fact. She'd been presumed drowned in the river and her body was recovered from the water. It had got trapped in an inlet under a log which was wedged into the bank. Needless to say, the girl's corpse was in an advanced state of decomposition.'

'You're not telling us she'd been raped.' Holly frowned. 'Surely they couldn't know that.'

'Indeed not. Nor whether she'd been strangled, if we're going to compare it with the Brookham crime. But her nose and one of the cheekbones had been fractured and the skull cracked.'

'Yes, but a body lying in the water that long . . . there might be any number of ways injuries like that could be caused,' Holly growled.

'It's a mystery, certainly,' Sinclair acknowledged. 'One which is exercising the minds of the Oxfordshire police as we speak. I should tell you, too, that no murder inquiry has been instituted yet. I heard of it by chance. I bumped into George Ransom, a pathologist at St Mary's in Paddington, this week and he told me about the body taken from the river at Henley. He offered it more as a curiosity than anything else, but with the Brookham case fresh in my mind, I pricked up my ears. Ransom happened to be sitting next to the doctor who'd performed the autopsy—an Oxford medico named Stanley—at some annual medical get-together, so he got the whole story. Stanley said he was convinced the injuries were caused by blows struck to the face—he marked half a dozen at least from the bone evidence. He told Ransom the Oxfordshire police were holding back for the moment, looking for another explanation. But it's hard to see how they'll find one in this case.'

'River traffic?' Bennett shifted in his chair.

'Stanley feels the marks on the bones aren't consistent with the shape of propeller blades.'

'Even so, we can't be sure it's murder,' Holly muttered.

'No, but we can't ignore the common factors in these cases: I mean the ages of the girls involved and the damage inflicted to their faces.' He paused. 'Mind you, there's a problem with the time-lag. A gap of three years between crimes of this type is most unusual. I'm having a check made of prison records on the off chance that he may have been inside during this period—that's assuming it's the same man—but I'm not optimistic. I'm sure if he'd been arrested for a serious sexual offence we would have heard about it.'

Rising, Bennett went to the window and stood there, gazing out. 'The tramp's still the key, isn't he? Beezy? We must wait till they find him. Until we know whether he's responsible for the Brookham murder. The Surrey police are quite capable of handling a straightforward inquiry. I don't want the Yard butting in and seeming to steal their thunder. All the same, I want to be kept informed of the progress of the investigation. They've no objection to the interest we're showing, I take it?'

'Quite the contrary,' Sinclair assured him. He closed his file. 'After listening to Madden, Jim Boyce is as nervous as a cat.'

'Still, you seem unsatisfied, Chief Inspector.'

Sinclair shed the frown his superior had noticed. 'By all means let them search for Beezy. What's more, if he can be shown to have been the killer, I'd let the whole matter drop, at least as far as the Yard is concerned.'

'You don't think he could have been involved in the Henley business?'

'Hardly. Beal's known to have spent these past ten summers in Kent.'

'What, then? What's troubling you?'

Sinclair sighed. 'It's what Madden thinks that worries me. He feels we've only touched the surface of this case: worse is to come. And if past experience is anything to go by, his instincts are usually right.'

THE MADDENS' HOUSE stood at the end of a drive shaded by lime trees. Alerted by the sound of the approaching car, Helen was waiting in the portico to greet Sinclair when he drew up in front.

'Angus . . . how lovely to see you. Come inside. I've got a surprise for you. Franz Weiss is here. He's spending a few days with us.'

'Is he really?' Sinclair's face brightened at the name. A psychoanalyst of note, Weiss had been a friend of Helen's late father. Born in Vienna, but now living in Berlin, he was a man for whom the chief inspector felt not only affection, but uncommon respect. 'I had no idea. How is the good doctor?'

'Well enough, but worried. The situation in Germany's so unsettled.'

She drew him into the house and they passed through the hall to the drawing room. 'Come outside. He's waiting to see you on the terrace.'

As they stepped outside again, a figure emerged from the shade of the vine-covered arbour that stood at one end of it. White-haired, and some-what stooped now—he was in his early seventies—Franz Weiss bowed with old-world courtesy. 'Chief Inspector! This is an unexpected pleasure.'

'So it is, sir.' Smiling, Sinclair came forward to shake his hand. 'But the pleasure is mine, I insist.'

Though fully two years had passed since their last meeting—the occa-sion had been a dinner given by the Maddens when Weiss had been in London for a conference on psychoanalysis—he was pleased to see that the doctor had lost none of his alertness; that his eyes, dark, and crinkled at the corners, shone with the same mixture of intelligence and wry humour that Sinclair remembered with such delight from past encounters.

'Are you staying in England long, sir?' he asked. 'I was hoping we might lunch in London next week.'

'Alas, I leave tomorrow to return to Berlin.' Weiss's English, though fluent, was marked by a strong accent. 'But we have the whole day ahead of us. I've no doubt we will find an opportunity to talk.' He turned to Helen. 'And now, my dear, would you excuse me? I must return to my labours. We will meet again at lunch . . . yes?'

With a bow to them both, he left the terrace. Helen's eyes followed his departing figure. 'Franz has been up to London twice to talk to old col-leagues of his,' she informed Sinclair. 'Men who gave up their practices in Germany to settle over here. He wants to do the same himself, but Mina is unwell and he's not sure she's strong enough to travel.'

'Are things so bad in Berlin, then?'

'Bad enough. And likely to get worse, if you happen to be Jewish, or so Franz says. He thinks the Nazis will soon be in power. Who knows what will happen then? I do worry about them all.'

Her concern came as no surprise to the chief inspector, who knew that as a young woman she had spent six months with Weiss and his wife in Vienna, learning German, and that they had treated her like a daughter.

He was still seeking for some words of reassurance when she turned away to look out over the garden. 'John's down in the orchard,' she said. 'He's waiting for you. You and he can have your talk. But don't be long, please, and remember what I said.'

'I HAD A CUP of tea with Jim Boyce in Guildford on the way down. Not only haven't they laid hands on Beezy yet, they've not had a single report of his whereabouts.'

Sinclair had come on his host sawing up an old plum tree. He had seated himself on the low stone wall bordering the garden, taking out his pipe and tobacco, and waited until Madden spoke.

'Well, Angus . . . What can you tell me about the Brookham case?'

The chief inspector, puffing on his pipe, revealed what little his own enquiries had produced. 'There's nothing in the files; only this business at Henley, which has yet to be established as a murder case. The facial assault points to a connection with Brookham. But there are still difficulties in linking the two cases, not least the three-year interval separating them. If it was the same man, what's he been doing all this while? He wasn't inside.'

'Mightn't he have gone abroad?'

'That's a possibility. But not one I can pursue at present: not until the case is officially in my hands.'

Madden stood brooding, testing the jagged edge of the saw with his fingertips. Plainly he'd hoped to hear better news, and Sinclair sighed.

'I'm sorry, John. But without some fresh development, it's hard to see how this matter can be taken any further. All we can do now is wait while the hunt for this missing tramp goes on.'

THE FEELING that he had let his old colleague down haunted the chief inspector during the day and was still in the back of his mind when, with the clock on the mantel striking five o'clock and the shadows in the drawing room deepening, he looked up and saw Franz Weiss standing in the doorway.

'Ah, there you are, Mr Sinclair! I was hoping to find you here. We have not yet had a chance to talk.'

Smiling, the analyst crossed to where his fellow guest was seated by the fireplace. 'Is it true our hosts have abandoned us?'

'I'm afraid so, sir.' Sinclair rose to his feet to receive the older man. 'John's gone to collect Robert. He took Lucy with him.' The Maddens' son had been playing that day in a school cricket match. 'Then Helen was called out to see a patient. So you find me holding the fort.'

It was the first time the two men had been alone. The doctor had remained in his room all afternoon, working on a paper that he was due to present at a symposium on his return to Berlin.

'The subject to be discussed is certain aspects of psychopathology, in particular the treatment of patients who indulge in abnormally aggressive and irresponsible behaviour, a difficult question on which to air one's views these days when so many of one's fellow citizens display little else.'

He'd accompanied the remark with a characteristic wry smile, but his words had struck a chord with the chief inspector, echoing as they did a discussion that had taken place earlier, at lunch, when Weiss had spoken at some length about the situation in Germany and his fears for the future.

Sinclair's first impulse now was to return to the theme of their lunchtime conversation, to question the analyst further. But after he had poured him a drink and seen to it that he was settled comfortably by the fire before resuming his own seat, it was Weiss who broke the silence between them.

'Tell me, Chief Inspector, this case you are dealing with, the one to do with the murdered girl, is it causing you much anxiety?'

Sinclair realised that Madden must have discussed the assault with the doctor, something Weiss himself confirmed the next moment.

'I ask because John seemed so concerned when he told me about it the other evening. Clearly it has disturbed him a great deal. We did not discuss it at length. Helen was there, and I sensed she was upset by the subject.'

'She thinks he's too caught up with the case,' Sinclair grunted. 'She's never forgotten how close he came to death all those years ago. She doesn't want him involved in anything like it again. But John won't let go of this.'

Weiss nodded. 'Our friend is like the Good Samaritan: he cannot pass by on the other side. It is one of the reasons Helen loves him, of course.'

The shadows in the room had been deepening while they talked and Sinclair rose to switch on a pair of table lamps. 'There's something you don't know, sir,' he said as he returned to his seat. 'I only told John about it this morning. We've come across a case that involves a young girl who went missing three years ago in Henley. Recently her body was recovered from the river and it was found that her face had been damaged. In the opinion of the pathologist who examined the remains, the injuries were caused by blows. It's too late to tell whether she was raped, of course, or how she died.'

'But you think these two cases might be linked?'

'It's a possibility, certainly. But since there's no other indication a killer of this kind has been active in the past, no trace of him in our files, the odds are against it. The Brookham investigation isn't mine as yet, not officially, it's still in the hands of the Surrey police. However, I expect it to arrive on my desk before long, and when it does I'm going to have to decide how to proceed with the inquiry.' Sinclair paused. His eyes met the analyst's.

'What is it, Chief Inspector? Is there something you wish to ask me?'

Sinclair grimaced. 'You may find it an odd request, but I'm looking for advice of a kind which only someone in your profession could offer.'

'And what might that be, I wonder?' Weiss smiled. 'I'm curious to learn.'

The chief inspector cocked an eye at his companion. 'Let's assume John's right—this is a man who has killed before, who may have been active for some time without our being aware of it. Let's go further and say the Henley girl was one of his victims. Now, as a rule, sexual offenders tend to draw attention to themselves. They become solitaries. Pariahs. So what I want to ask you is this—how likely is it that such a man could have managed to disguise his true nature and somehow escaped notice? Is it even possible?'

Sinclair waited for Weiss to reply. The analyst had been gazing into the fire as he listened and it was some time before he responded.

'In most instances, the answer to your question would be "no". But I must qualify my reply. If this individual exists as you imagine him, then we are dealing with an exceptional case, not simply a compulsive rapist and killer, but a man with sufficient self-awareness to have avoided capture over a relatively long period. To call him a psychopath is only to touch on the problem that such people present to my profession, which in spite of our best efforts has yet to achieve any great understanding of them. For my part, I have come to believe that there are those born with a predisposition to commit acts appalling to the rest of us and with natures from which all trace of conscience is excluded. Indeed, if one were seeking proof of the existence of evil then one need look no further than these monsters who by rights should not exist outside the realm of our nightmares.'

Weiss paused for a few moments, his gaze returning to the fire. Then he continued. 'But we are straying from your question—how could such a man have eluded discovery for so long? There is no question in my mind that if this man exists, he has sought to disguise himself and to adopt, if not a way of life, then at least habits that would tend to mask his true nature. But even so, it's hard to imagine how he could have escaped detection for so long. The long interval between these two crimes may provide us with a clue. Have you considered the possibility that he might have spent time abroad? That he moves about?'

The chief inspector nodded. 'The trouble is, it's not an avenue I can readily explore. Not until the case is officially in my hands.'

'That is unfortunate.' Weiss gnawed at his lip. 'But there are other areas worth investigating. The question of his background, for example.'

'His background—?'

'His class, if you will.' He shrugged. 'Correct me if I am wrong, but in this country more than any other, a man's social position is thought to define him. Peculiarities of manner or behaviour are often overlooked, particularly among the upper classes, where distinction of rank can sometimes render a man above suspicion. But perhaps I exaggerate . . .'

He paused at the sound of footsteps in the hall. They heard Helen's voice as she spoke to Mary, the Maddens' maid. The two men caught each other's eye.

'We must conclude, yes?' Weiss spoke in a murmur. 'I have only one more suggestion—a murderer of this type might have found protection, or rather anonymity, in some unorthodox way of life, outside the law.'

'You mean he might be a criminal . . . a professional?' Sinclair was momentarily arrested by the notion. But then he shook his head. 'No . . . no, I don't think so. We have sources in that world. If a killer like this had been at large, we would have heard of it. More than that: he'd have been given up.'

'No doubt you are right.' But the doctor seemed unconvinced. 'Nevertheless, he has managed to survive somehow, and it might be as well if you considered the possibility that he has found some form of employment suited to his nature, one that has served as a disguise and has prevented him from coming to your notice.' Weiss leaned closer. 'The savagery of his crimes tells us that this is a creature devoid of all moral restraints: one surely capable of other, equally ruthless acts. Other crimes.'

Hearing the sound of approaching steps, Sinclair leaned forward in turn. 'But what place could he possibly have found for himself?'

'That I cannot tell you.' The doctor shook his head. 'All I can do is urge you not to dismiss the notion.' Dropping his voice still further, he peered at the chief inspector through the deepening shadows. 'We may wish it were otherwise, but the world has a use for such men. It has always been so.'

PART TWO

4

Assistant Commissioner Bennett ushered Chief Inspector Sinclair to a chair in front of his desk. 'You've spoken to your colleagues in Surrey and Sussex, I take it? They're happy about us moving in?'

'Quietly ecstatic would be closer to the mark, sir. This case is going to be the devil to crack. Nobody seems sure what to do next.'

Before Sinclair could say more the door opened and the reassuring bulk and rubicund features of Arthur Holly appeared.

'Come in, Chief Superintendent.' Bennett gestured to a second chair. 'You've heard the news, I imagine?'

'Angus rang me a moment ago, sir.' Holly nodded to the chief inspector. 'So they've found another one? Near Bognor Regis, I understand?'

'That's right. The Sussex police uncovered the body two days ago. This is now officially a Yard case and Mr Sinclair will be in charge from our end. Where do we stand now, Chief Inspector? Briefly, if you would. There's no doubt, is there, that it's linked to the Brookham business?'

'None at all, sir. Both girls were raped and strangled, faces destroyed in the same manner. However, there was *one* difference. The Bognor Regis body showed traces of chloroform in the lungs. Presumably used to immobilise her.'

'There was no mention of that in the Brookham report.' Bennett frowned.

'No, but I've had a word with Dr Galloway—the pathologist who dealt with the body—and he points out that as well as being strangled, there was a large amount of water found in the girl's lungs and so it's possible that any traces of chloroform in her lungs could have been washed away.'

Bennett grunted. 'Go on, Chief Inspector.'

'Now, as regards the weapon employed for the facial assaults, Galloway has plumped for a hammer, and I gather the Sussex doctor's of the same opinion. Mind you, *his* cadaver is in rather worse condition.'

'Why's that?' Holly intervened.

Sinclair turned to his colleague. 'The murder in Sussex *predates* the Brookham killing, by a month. That's according to medical opinion, and it's confirmed by the time of her disappearance, which was late July. Her body was found in a shallow grave on an empty stretch of the coast near Bognor Regis—the girl's name was Marigold Hammond, by the way.' The chief inspector's face darkened. 'I only wish we'd used the time better. The Surrey police have spent the past month looking for that blasted tramp. What's more they *still* have to find him. The more I think about John's reading of the case, the more convinced I am that he was right. It's odds on this Beezy actually caught sight of the killer. That's why he ran for it.

'All we can say for sure about our killer at this stage is that he's *not* Beezy—who was in Surrey for all of July, moving about within a relatively small area—and that in all likelihood he owns a car. In hindsight, it seems probable that both girls were picked up on the road.'

Holly interrupted. 'You say she vanished in July, the girl at Bognor Regis. Have the police been searching for her since then?'

'No, the child wasn't even reported missing until a week ago. Her parents are circus people. They travel all over the south coast during the summer months and they happened to be at Bognor Regis when the child went missing. Except it wasn't recognised as such at the time. She'd had a row with her mother and the man they were living with—the girl's father had gone off some time before—and announced that she was leaving to go and spend some time with an aunt of hers who worked in another circus that was performing in Eastbourne at the time.'

The chief superintendent was incredulous. 'And how old was this girl?'

'Marigold Hammond was fourteen, but she looked younger. This killer seems drawn to girls before they reach puberty.' Sinclair caught Holly's look. 'Yes, I know, Arthur, even fourteen seems too young, but all I can tell you is it doesn't seem to have bothered her mother when she packed a suitcase and announced she was off to catch the bus to Eastbourne.'

'But when she didn't hear from her . . . ?'

Sinclair shook his head. 'These people live their lives differently from you and me. They've no telephone, and I doubt they correspond by letter. Mrs Hammond only discovered six weeks later that her daughter had never appeared in Eastbourne, at which point she reported her missing. The circus she was with had moved on to Devon by then, but she came back to Bognor Regis to help the police. A week later the girl's body was found.'

'What next, Chief Inspector?' Bennett asked. 'Where do we go from here? I take it you don't plan to interfere with the Sussex investigation?'

'Oh, no, sir. Nor the one in Surrey. As I said, they still have to find the tramp. We may yet have a witness to the Brookham killing. For the time being our best role would be one of coordination. I plan to go down to Sussex tomorrow to talk to the officers conducting that investigation.'

'What about the Henley angle? The girl whose body was found in the Thames? Do you mean to take any action over that?'

'Yes, I do, sir. I'm sending a man down there tomorrow.'

THE TRAFFIC that morning was light, and Billy Styles was glad of it. The old Morris he'd been allocated from the Yard's car pool had tired gears and a tendency to stall. Not that he was complaining, mind you. Still clear in his memory were the days when motor cars provided for the use of detectives had been rarer than unicorns.

The summons to report to Chief Inspector Sinclair's office had come out of the blue, and Billy had responded to it with alacrity. After a dozen years with the Met he had been involved in a wide range of investigations. None, however, had approached the drama of the Melling Lodge case, and Billy had never forgotten the nerve-racked weeks he had spent in the company of the then Inspector Madden as they'd searched for a savage murderer.

The inquiry had been conducted under Sinclair's leadership, and his greeting when he'd arrived in Sinclair's office the previous day had been warm.

'Sergeant! It's been a while. How are you?' Sinclair had risen from behind his desk to shake Billy's hand. 'I spent last weekend with the Maddens. John was asking after you. I trust you keep in touch.'

'Oh, yes, sir.' Billy had taken the chair indicated. 'I go down and see them quite often.'

When he was settled the chief inspector's expression changed. 'You've heard about Madden finding that child's body, I take it?'

'Yes, sir. And now there's been another killing, I see. Down Bognor Regis way.'

'Quite right. The cases are clearly linked and the Yard's been called in. But there's more to it than that. It's possible the murderer has killed before. At Henley, three years ago. That's where you'll be going tomorrow.'

HENLEY POLICE STATION was situated in the middle of the town, a few minutes' walk from the riverside. Detective Sergeant Deacon was expecting Billy, and showed him to an office upstairs.

'You'll want to see this, I suppose.' The sour-faced detective tossed a file across the desk. Grey-haired and in his fifties, Deacon seemed put out to discover that they were the same rank, both detective sergeants. 'So they're calling it murder now . . .' His shrug was defiant.

'You don't agree?' Billy held out his packet of cigarettes to Deacon, who shook his head. Noticing there was no ashtray on the desk between them, the younger man pocketed his fags. He wanted to keep this friendly.

'I've got no opinion one way or the other.' Deacon's pale brown eyes were expressionless. 'But I'd like to see anyone prove it was murder.'

'The injuries to her face, though? Is there any way those could have been accidental?' Leafing through the file, Billy saw that he was familiar with much of its contents. Sinclair had obtained a summary from Oxford.

'Yes, since you ask.' Deacon sat forward, elbows on the desk. 'She disappeared originally during the month of July. You probably don't know what the river's like in summer. Let me tell you, son. It's chock-a-block with boats. After she drowned, the body wouldn't have surfaced for several hours. She could have got knocked about, been hit over and over.'

And every time in the face? *Come on!* thought Billy, but he continued looking at Deacon with the same friendly, slightly puzzled air.

'I noticed her body was found half a mile upstream from the town. Was that a surprise?' he asked.

'Not to me, son. You've got to start from the premise that she fell into the water, but it happens all the time, particularly with kids. The bank can be unstable . . . treacherous. You stray too close to it, and next thing you know you've tumbled in and the current's got you.'

'Yes, but that *far* upstream . . .' Billy wanted to make his point. 'The Barlow house was, what, less than a mile from the centre of Henley? Even supposing she walked back along the river and fell in somehow, wouldn't her body have been swept down closer to the town itself, or even past it?'

Having gone through the file in London, Billy had concluded there was little *mystery* about Susan Barlow's movements that July day. Her mother had asked her to slip into Henley and buy some oranges just after eleven o'clock. The house where the two of them lived Mrs Barlow was a widow whose husband had been killed in the war—lay on a lane that followed the course of the Thames upstream, running close to it for a few miles before linking up with the road to Reading. The walk to the shops would have taken the girl about fifteen minutes.

When midday came and went with no sign of her daughter, Mrs Barlow had walked into Henley and spoken to the greengrocer. She had then wandered about the town, asking various friends and acquaintances if they had seen Susan, before returning home in the hope that her daughter had reappeared. Finding she had not, the distracted mother had finally rung the police and the wheels of an organised search had ground into motion.

It was at that point that the question of *how* Susan had gone home, which route she might have taken, had become crucial. The quickest road back would have been the way she had come, along the lane, but she could also have walked further upstream along the river bank for anything up to a mile and then taken one of several footpaths that connected with the lane.

'She could easily have walked a mile up the river and then cut across the fields to her mum's house,' Deacon answered Billy's question. 'At least, that's what she had in mind, only somewhere along the way she went into the river.'

'She was spotted on that riverside path, was she?' Billy still wasn't clear on this point, despite having read Chief Inspector Sinclair's file carefully.

'Yes and no. There were witnesses who thought they'd seen her, or some-one like her.' Deacon shrugged. 'It was before my time here, but I know we had a description of what she was wearing from her mother. It was a pink dress. But have you any idea of how many young girls are on that path in the summer? And how many of them might be wearing pink dresses?'

Billy considered what he'd just heard. It made a difference.

'I'll hang on to this for a little while if I may.' He tapped the folder. 'But I'd like to go and have a look at the general area now. Care to come along?'

'Couldn't possibly, son. I'm due at the Magistrates' Court in ten minutes.'

'Never mind,' Billy said, taking care to disguise his relief at the news, 'I'll manage on my own.'

'Oh, we can't have that. I've got a PC waiting to show you around. Name of Crawley.' Deacon produced a thin smile. It was his first of the morning.

'Is THAT IT, then, Sarge? Are we done?' PC Crawley stood beside Billy, his eyes busy beneath his helmet as a trio of young girls dressed in light rayon frocks, their arms and legs bare, went strolling by. Downy about the cheeks, he hardly looked old enough to be wearing a policeman's uniform.

'Not yet, Constable.' Billy didn't need to recall Deacon's smile to realise that even by the standards of the Henley plod this young copper was dim.

He let his gaze wander along the river bank. Close by, on their left, was the terrace of a pub, its tables overlooking the Thames. Just beyond it a bridge spanned the river, and past that, further downstream, lay the straight patch of water where the famous regatta was held each summer.

Most of the holiday activity was centred there, he noted. There were a few campers in the fields lower down, their tents easy to pick out against the green meadow grass, while the river, though no longer 'chock-a-block', remained busy with pleasure craft and other waterborne traffic.

Upstream, the view was different. They were close to the outskirts of the town, standing on a footpath that followed the tree-clad river bank. For sev-eral miles, according to PC Crawley. Billy had already got the constable to show him the spot where Susan Barlow's body had been taken from the water. He'd been able to do that, though not much more.

'I only got posted here six months ago, Sarge,' Crawley had explained defensively when Billy asked him about the original search. He'd had to turn to the file for more, and discovered that the searchers had concentrated their efforts on the stretch of river below the bridge, which made sense. That was the direction a floating object would take, after all. It was pure chance that Susan Barlow's body had come to light on the bank upstream.

Billy had spent some time studying the site, a small cove on an outer bend of the river. The log beneath which the remains of Susan's body had been found was drawn up on the bank now, a piece of rotting tree trunk. It was possible to imagine how the current, swinging round at that point, might have carried the body into this shallow inlet. Trapped beneath the log, half-buried in the mud, it would have remained unaffected by the subsequent rise and fall of the river. A belt of undergrowth, separating the cove from the path, screened it from sight on the landward side, and its presence there had not been noted until some weeks ago when a couple in a rowing boat had pulled in to the bank and seen the girl's arm protruding from the mud.

Assuming it was a case of murder, how had she got there?

Not by walking beside the river and encountering some stranger bent on rape and murder. Having examined the route carefully, Billy was certain of that now. Though hidden from the water by brush and overhanging branches, the path was mostly visible to the open fields it skirted on its inward side, and these all showed signs of having been used as campsites during the summer. What was more, it was clearly a well-used footway. Billy simply couldn't picture the man—this careful killer—seizing hold of the girl in broad daylight, overpowering her and dragging her off to some secluded spot.

No, it couldn't have happened that way.

'Come on, Crawley.'

Billy turned his back on the river and led the constable to the lane where he'd left his car. This was the same road Susan Barlow had taken when she'd walked into Henley to buy her packet of oranges; and the one she'd used to get home, too. Or so he believed now. Only she'd never got there.

He paused on the pavement, looking up and down the narrow lane. A picture was forming in his mind, and the image wasn't pleasant. He saw the girl in her pink dress, with her brown paper packet clutched in her hand, walking along the verge. He saw the car drawing up quietly behind her . . .

What words had he got prepared, the smooth-tongued stranger? What invitation had proved so irresistible to Susan Barlow?

'Are we going back to the station now?' Crawley asked hopefully. 'It's getting on for lunchtime.'

AN HOUR LATER the constable's stomach was rumbling with hunger and Billy, too, was unsatisfied. He was beginning to agree that there was no way of proving that Susan Barlow's death had resulted from murder.

Sinclair had warned him of the likelihood that his journey would be wasted. 'These old cases have gone cold. We'll be lucky if we find anything new. But keep an eye open for any similarities to the Brookham murder.'

Billy had started from the supposition that Susan Barlow had been a victim of opportunity. There was no way the murderer could have known she would be walking into town that morning. But he must have been hunting, all the same, Billy felt, on the lookout for prey, and that argued he'd had somewhere in mind to take any child who fell into his hands.

Billy had returned to his car and spent the next sixty minutes with an increasingly unhappy Crawley exploring the winding, tree-shaded road that led to what the constable assured him had been Mrs Barlow's cottage. He already knew that the bereaved mother had moved away, unable to bear the associations the place held for her. He'd continued driving along the lane, noting several spots where a car might have been parked under cover of trees and bushes, but none seemed to offer the kind of privacy that the killer would surely have wanted.

Billy took it for granted that the girl must have been rendered unconscious, chloroformed perhaps, soon after she'd got into the killer's car. Her abductor could hardly have driven her past her own house without provoking some reaction on her part. But *where* had he taken his captive?

As he pondered this question, Billy's eyes kept flicking towards the mileage indicator. They had already covered two and a half miles since leaving the town centre.

Not back to Henley, certainly. So it must have been beyond the Barlow cottage. But while this fitted the facts, such as they were, Billy just couldn't picture the killer taking her any great distance.

Apart from the urgency of his desire, he must have been aware of the danger she represented. It didn't matter whether she was conscious or not, every moment she spent in his car placed him in peril and he would have wanted to do what he had to do as quickly as possible, so as to be rid of her.

Billy's glance went back to the dashboard. *Three* miles now. According to the map, they would shortly be linking up with the main road to Reading. It was far enough.

He looked for a place to turn and noticed a signboard on the road ahead. It bore a name—Waltham Manor—in gold against a green background, and below that, in smaller letters, the words 'Members Only'.

'What's this, then?' he asked, braking to turn onto a strip of dirt road. Ahead of him he saw a pair of gates standing open in a high stone wall.

Constable Crawley sniggered. 'It's a sort of club, Sarge.' He let out a hoot of laughter. 'They take their clothes off . . .'

'You mean it's a nudists' club?' Billy demanded.

The constable nodded, wordless now. His cheeks had turned bright red.

Billy stopped the car and stared at him. He shook his head, then started to reverse, intending to back onto the paved road, but at once felt a heavy drag on the steering wheel. 'Bloody hell!' he muttered under his breath.

They got out. As Billy suspected, the front near-side tyre had punctured on a sharp stone. Having opened the boot, they made a further discovery.

'There's no jack,' Crawley announced.

'Brilliant deduction, Holmes.' Billy kicked the flat tyre in frustration. He was thinking of the long drive he still had back to London. 'Come on . . .'

Beyond the gates of Waltham Manor, where a sign warned them this was private property and trespassers would be prosecuted, an elm-lined drive led to an imposing stone mansion with a handsome portico. A further sign, marked 'Reception', directed them to a gravelled parking area at the side of the house from which point a long white paling fence was visible.

'Is that where they take their clothes off?' Billy asked. There were only a dozen or so cars in the car park. Business must be slack, Billy thought.

The constable nodded. 'When they started up they used the whole garden, I was told. But then the local lads began shinning up the wall to peep over, so they had to build that fence.' He emitted his peculiar hooting laugh again. 'Now everything goes on inside there and they've let the rest go.' He nodded towards the parkland further off, where the bushes had grown into tangled thickets and the grass, uncut, was knee high.

A brick path led to a door in the side of the house. Billy opened it and was startled to see a young man, apparently wearing nothing, sitting at a table reading a magazine. He glanced up as they entered, his bored expression changing to one of consternation at the sight of Crawley's uniform.

'My name's Styles. Detective Sergeant Styles.' Billy showed him his warrant card. 'We've had a puncture outside your gates and we've got no jack. I was wondering if someone here could help.'

'I'll have to ask Dorrie,' the young man said, getting to his feet; he was, after all, wearing bathing trunks. 'Just a mo . . .'

He disappeared through a door at the back of the room, and a few moments later a young woman appeared at the door, wearing a white linen robe, belted at the waist and reaching to her knees. She had short brown hair and a quick, birdlike glance.

'Sergeant, is it?' Smiling, she eyed Billy with interest.

'Yes . . . Styles. And this is Constable Crawley.'

'My name's Doris . . . Doris Jenner.' She held out her hand to Billy and as she did so her gown fell open and one of her breasts was revealed. Unflustered, she covered it swiftly. 'Sorry about that . . . you get careless working here.' She remained smiling. 'It's a jack you need, then? Mr Rainey would have one—he's the manager—but he's out at present. Tell you what, I'll see if one of the members can help. Wait here.' She turned and went out.

A minute later Doris Jenner returned with a set of keys and they went outside into the parking area where she retrieved a jack from the boot of one of the parked cars. Billy handed it to the constable.

'Off you go, Crawley. Change the tyre, then bring the car up here.' Billy watched him stride off, then turned to find Doris Jenner observing them with a crooked grin. 'You wouldn't have such a thing as a cup of tea, would you?'

'Of course, Sergeant. Come inside.'

She led him to an office furnished with a desk and some easy chairs grouped around a low table. The walls were hung with paintings of men and women as God made them dancing in the open air or stretched out on the grass in decorative poses. 'Nymphs and shepherds,' Miss Jenner said drily, cocking an eye at them. 'Make yourself at home. I'll be back in a minute.'

'Is THIS your first time in a nudists' club?' Doris Jenner had returned with a tea tray and a plate of biscuits.

'Yes, but I've read about them. I thought the fad was dying out.'

'It is.' She seated herself opposite him, modestly drawing the robe tightly around her, but tucking her bare feet up on the chair so that Billy found himself gazing at a pair of rosy knees. There was a teasing look in her eye. 'A couple of years ago the car park would have been packed. We were turning people away. I give them another year at most.'

'Have you been here since it opened?' Billy lit a cigarette.

She nodded. 'It's not a bad job, if you don't mind taking off your clothes.' Her crooked grin displayed the tips of her small, pointed teeth. 'Well, most of them. Only the members strip down completely.'

'I didn't know that.' Billy returned her grin.

'So what brings the law up this way?' She put down her cup.

'A girl disappeared in Henley a while back, and her body's only recently been recovered from the river. We're trying to establish her movements. It's no easy job. She went missing three years ago.'

Doris Jenner's eyes grew misty. 'Poor kid . . . I remember when it happened . . . Susan . . . Wasn't that her name?'

'You've got a good memory.' Billy was impressed.

'Not really . . . it was something else, something that happened to me that day . . . or rather it *didn't* . . .' She smiled mischievously.

'Go on,' Billy prompted.

'You don't want to hear about it.'

'Maybe I do.' He was half flirting himself, but his words held a germ of truth. One of the reasons he was a good detective was a basic curiosity in his nature. He was interested in people—why they were who they were.

Doris Jenner's brown eyes twinkled. 'All right, then.' Her glance was provocative. 'It all has to do with a boyfriend I had then—his name was Jimmy. He was a member here. That's how we met. Jimmy lived in Birmingham, but he used to drive down every Saturday in a big fancy car.' She smiled, her eyes hazy with reminiscence.

'We never let on, of course,' she continued. 'The staff's not allowed to fraternise with members. But I always had Sundays off and when I'd finished work on Saturdays I'd leave on my bike as usual and after a few minutes Jimmy would roll up behind me in his big car and we'd load my bike into the back and off we'd go!' She laughed. 'I thought he was going to marry me, I really did . . .' She sighed. 'Well, anyway, that particular Saturday I sat there at reception all morning waiting for him to turn up and he never did. Once I thought I'd spotted his car, but it wasn't his, it was someone else's that was just like it. I almost burst into tears. I couldn't believe he'd let me down.' She lifted an eyebrow and shrugged. 'I can laugh about it now, but I'd never been so miserable in my life. Anyway, that's the day I heard about the girl . . . Susan . . . When I got back to my lodgings my landlady told me the police had been knocking on doors, asking if anyone had seen her. That's why I remember that day.'

'So what happened to Jimmy?' Billy asked.

'He wrote me a letter full of excuses and said he didn't know when he'd be able to get down again. I never saw him again.'

'You mentioned a car, not Jimmy's, someone else's . . . Can you tell me more about that?'

'What?' Her glance hardened. 'Are you being a copper now?'

'Yes, I'm being a copper.' He met her gaze.

'Is this about Jimmy? Is he in trouble?'

Billy shook his head. 'No, it's about the *car*. That's all I'm interested in.'

Flushing, she stared out of the window. Her lips had thinned to a hard line. 'If you came here to ask questions, you should have said so. I thought we were just being friendly.'

'Let me tell you what this is about, Doris.' Billy leaned forward. 'It's to do with that young girl, Susan Barlow.'

She turned to face him then, with a glance that was less hostile. 'I don't see how,' she said.

'I need to know if a stranger came and parked his car here that day. Please, try and think back. Tell me exactly what you saw.'

Doris Jenner shrugged. 'I was sitting at reception, as I said, and I saw what I thought was Jimmy's car drive into the parking area, so I waited, expecting him to come in, but he never did. I couldn't understand why—it's the only way into the club—so I went outside and looked for his car and saw what I thought was it parked away down the other end under a tree. I still thought it was Jimmy's. I have never seen another like it.'

'What make of car was it?'

'Don't know. Can't help you there. It was foreign, that's all I remember.'

'*Foreign?* Are you sure of that?'

She nodded. 'Jimmy was proud as punch of it.'

'To go back, you saw this car parked at the far end of the car park . . .?'

'Yes, but there was no sign of Jimmy. I wondered if he'd gone into the gardens, so I walked down to have a closer look.'

Billy shifted slightly in his chair.

'Well, when I got closer I saw that it wasn't Jimmy's car at all. I'd made a mistake. It looked just like Jimmy's. Dark blue. But Jimmy's upholstery was light brown. This one's was blue. Dark blue, like the chassis.'

'Did you wonder about the driver? Why he never came through reception?'

She shook her head. 'No, I never gave it a thought. I only had one thing on my mind . . . Jimmy!' She rolled her eyes.

'So you looked inside the car?'

'Did I?' Her good humour had returned, along with her crooked grin.

'You saw the upholstery. You must have noticed if there was anything lying on the seats.'

'Give me a break, Officer. It was three years ago.'

'Come on, Doris. You can't fool me. What did you see?'

She laughed. 'A man's hat lying on the passenger seat.'

'How about the back seat?'

She put her head on one side, inspecting him through lowered lashes.

'What if I told you there was a body lying there?'

'I'd say you had a good imagination as well as a good memory.'

She laughed. 'Well, it wasn't a body. Just a packet of fruit.'

'Fruit?' Billy went very still. She hadn't noticed.

'Yes, in a brown paper packet. I can see it there now.' She was smiling.

'What sort of fruit?' Billy asked casually. 'Can you see *that*?'

'Of course I can.' Her eyes sparkled. 'They were oranges. Lovely oranges . . .'

5

B ut would he really have chosen such a public place to leave his car? In a *nudists'* club?' Chief Superintendent Holly clung to his doubts. 'Surely he would have been spotted there?'

'No, that's just the point, Arthur.' In effervescent mood, Angus Sinclair was inclined to be forgiving towards his plodding superior. 'The area the club uses is fenced off. You can't see in *or* out. The killer could easily have driven into the parking area with the child, left his car there with the other vehicles and taken her down to the lower part of the gardens, near the river, without being seen. That part of the garden is overgrown and untended, Styles says.' The chief inspector switched his gaze to Bennett, who was sitting behind his desk.

'So where do we stand now?' Bennett drummed his fingertips on the desktop impatiently. Much as he wished to keep in touch with the investigation, he was beginning to realise that this piece of self-indulgence meant time stolen from other labours; ones better suited to his lofty station, furthermore. 'Obviously this car is a crucial lead. A Mercedes-Benz, you say?'

'Yes, and since it's foreign-made, there won't be many of them on the road in this country. What's more, we know the model!'

'What?' Holly asked. 'I can't believe this girl told Styles *that*.'

'No, but she gave him the name of her old boyfriend,' Sinclair countered cheerfully. 'A Mr James Stoddart, of Birmingham, and he's already been interviewed by the police up there, at my request. He no longer has his car. He had to sell it when his wife threw him out a year ago. But, my goodness, does he cherish the memory of it!

'Now, it turns out that particular model, the one Stoddart owned, was offered for sale in this country for the first time in 1929. I have a photograph of it, too.' He slid a glossy print across the desk to Bennett. 'I'm having that reproduced and circulated in the Brookham area in case anyone remembers seeing it. It's unusual enough to have been noticed.'

Sir Wilfred had been studying the picture of the sleek, long-bonneted saloon. 'It certainly looks a rather fancy piece of machinery,' he conceded. 'Not something for the average motorist, would you say?'

'Not at the asking price!' Sinclair smiled wolfishly. 'It sells for a little over two thousand pounds.'

Holly's gloom lifted momentarily and he whistled. 'You're right, Angus. There can't be many of them around.'

'No, and the advantage for us, of course, is that we only have to check purchases made between the spring of 1929, when the car came on the market here, and that summer, when the Barlow child was murdered. The Mercedes people are sending me a list of them this afternoon. It's not a long one.'

'Yes, I see. This really is quite extraordinary.' Bennett was recovering his enthusiasm. 'How will you approach these men?'

'All I'll want to know initially is where they were and what they were doing on those dates in July and September when the girls were murdered at Bognor Regis and Brookham. If any of them says he can't remember, well, we'll have a special word with *him*.'

Glancing at his watch, Bennett drew a pile of documents towards him. 'Will that be all, Chief Inspector?' He looked down.

'Not quite, sir. There's one further step I'd like to take. But I'll need your authorisation.'

Bennett looked up sharply. 'What is it?' he demanded.

'I want to send a telegram to the International Criminal Police Commission in Vienna. I'd like them to check their records for us.'

'Now, wait a minute!' Sir Wilfred put down his pencil. 'The International Commission! What the devil have they got to do with this?'

'Perhaps nothing, sir. But we are still faced with the problem of what this man, this killer, was doing between the summer of 1929 and the end of last July. It's almost unknown for a sex criminal of this type to remain inactive for so long. We've checked prison records of known offenders and come up empty-handed. One other possibility is that this man was abroad during that time. If so, he may well have killed one or more children in some other country. If that is the case, we *must* obtain that information.'

'Come now, Chief Inspector . . .' Bennett said. 'You know as well as I do what our government's policy towards the Commission is. We have as little to do with it as possible.'

'Nevertheless, we are members of the organisation, are we not? It seems a shame not to take advantage of the connection.'

Holly cleared his throat. 'Normally speaking, if it was a question of turning to a pack of foreigners for help, I'd be the first to vote against it. But in this instance, I think Angus might have a point. As far as we know this man has killed three girls: one in Oxfordshire, and two down south, but in different counties. So whatever else, he moves around. What's more he owns a car—we know that, too—and a damned great tourer by the sound of it.' He turned to Bennett. 'Sir, until we can positively identify him, I feel we should cast our net as widely as we can.'

Bennett glanced at his watch again and groaned, 'My God! Look at the time!' He rose. 'Very well. You may draft a telegram to Vienna. You may *not* send it before it's been shown to me.' He strode to the door.

Holly waited until he had heard it slam behind them, then he too rose. 'What are you doing with Styles now? Are you keeping him on the case?'

'Yes, I am.' Sinclair got to his feet as well, and they went to the door. 'In fact, I've sent him down to Guildford and told him to nose around. It's true, this lead with the car may crack the case for us, but you never can tell. And between you and me, Arthur, I've told Styles he needn't feel shy about picking John Madden's brains if the opportunity presents itself. John's got a rare instinct for this kind of case and I want to know what he thinks.'

'I see nothing wrong with that.' The chief super looked puzzled.

'Perhaps not. But I'm doing it in a rather underhand way. I can't involve John directly. Helen would have my hide if she found out. But Styles's position is different. His tie with Madden goes back to the time he worked under him, and he's a friend of the family; what's more, Helen has a soft spot for him. I'm hoping she'll allow him some latitude when he comes to call.' Sinclair scowled. 'But I've a nasty feeling I'm walking on eggshells.'

DRIVING CAUTIOUSLY over the bumps and ruts, Billy drew up outside the farmhouse and got out of the car. He had hardly set foot on the path leading up to the house, however, when he was stopped in his tracks.

'Don't bring your muddy shoes into my kitchen, Sergeant Styles.' May Burrows stood with folded arms in the doorway ahead of him.

'Hello, May.' Grinning, Billy came to a halt. 'I'm looking for Mr Madden.'

'He's over in the stableyard with the others. They're loading the hogs. You'll find Belle and Lucy there, too. You can tell them their tea'll be ready in five minutes. Come in and have a cup yourself, if you like.'

'Thanks, May. I will.'

Making a smart about-turn, Billy set off for the stableyard. On reaching its arched entrance he found a scene of bustling activity within. Two farm hands were prodding a young porker across the cobbles towards an open lorry, which was already half-filled with squealing pigs. Neither of them had noticed his arrival, and nor had George Burrows, who was standing by the gate to the sties, controlling the flow. Someone else had, however. A small figure with hair that shone gold in the sunlight came flying across the cobbles.

'*Billy!*'

The little girl flung herself without fear into his arms, and he whirled her around in the air before putting her firmly back down. 'Hello, Lucy!'

Their friendship had been sealed on one of Billy's weekend visits to Highfield when Lucy Madden had discovered, in the course of a walk they had taken in the woods together, that not only was the sergeant unaware of the existence of chiffchaffs, he didn't even know the difference between a shrike and a shrew. Never having encountered such ignorance in an adult before, she had made him the object of her special attention ever since.

'Come and see the hogs.' She dragged him by the hand over to the lorry.

George Burrows, apple-cheeked and sturdy, waved a welcome. His dark-haired daughter Belle stuck shyly to his side.

'Is Mr Madden about?' Billy called out to him.

'Yes, he is . . .' Madden's voice came from beyond the gate where George was standing. He emerged from the darkness within. 'Billy, how nice to see you. I heard you were in the neighbourhood.'

They shook hands—or tried to. Lucy was unwilling to relinquish the one she was holding, so Billy was forced to offer his left to Madden's grip.

'I've been stuck in Guildford, sir, catching up on all the details of the case. But I thought I'd stop in on my way back. I'm hoping to see Will, too.'

Madden caught the younger man's eye, then glanced at his daughter.

'Lucy, Mrs Burrows said to say your tea's ready in the kitchen,' Billy told her. 'Yours and Belle's.'

'Run along now, darling,' Madden said. 'Both of you.'

They waited until the two little girls had left the yard, hand in hand. Then Madden spoke again, 'I understand you've got a lead at last. Mr Sinclair rang me earlier this week. He also said it was a feather in *your* cap.'

Madden's grin of congratulation made Billy flush with pleasure. 'I had a piece of luck, sir. The chief inspector sent me down to Henley last week. Did you know a girl's body had been taken from the river there?'

'Mr Sinclair told me that some time ago. But I'd like to hear the whole story.' Madden looked at his watch and clicked his tongue with impatience. 'It'll have to wait till later, though. I'm just off to pick up Rob from a friend's house in Godalming. You'll stay for dinner, won't you?' Taking the sergeant's pleased smile of acceptance for granted, he went on, 'That'll give us time to talk. But walk me to my car now. Tell me briefly how things stand.'

Happy to oblige, Billy gave a swift summary of his visit to Henley.

'So he picked her up by chance. He couldn't have known she'd be walking along that road. But he knew where to take her, all right.' They had paused at the entrance to the yard. 'I can't make up my mind about this man. At first I thought he must have seen the girl at Brookham and come back looking for her. But I doubt that now.' With a sigh, Madden glanced at his watch again. 'Billy, I have to go. What was that you said about seeing Will Stackpole?'

'I rang him and told him I'd be looking in here. He said he'd come by.'

'Good! Stay and have a cup of tea with May. You can talk to Will when he arrives.' He smiled. 'And you could do me a favour and bring Lucy when you come over to the house. She'll count it a treat to have a ride with *you*.'

ONCE DINNER was over, with the excuse of a heavy day ahead of her, Helen had bade Madden and Billy good night, saving her last words for their guest.

'I won't ask what you and John are going to talk about, though I can guess. And welcome as you always are, Billy dear, I sense a hidden hand behind your visit today. You can tell Angus Sinclair I'm not deceived.'

On which note, she had left them by the fire.

Billy stifled a yawn. He still had to drive back to his lodgings in Guildford but there was a question he wanted to put to his host before leaving. 'You said earlier, sir, how you thought at first the killer might have seen the Bridger girl before—marked her out, as it were. I know you changed your mind, but what made you think that in the first place?'

'At first I thought it a strange coincidence when I found Alice Bridger's body that the murderer had hit on a tramps' campsite to commit the crime. It only occurred to me later it was much more likely he knew about the spot in advance. That's what made me think he might have had her in mind as prey, that he'd already scouted out a place nearby where he could take her.

'But later I discarded the idea. It implied he must have been hanging around Brookham for some time before, waiting for his opportunity, and there was simply no evidence to support that. No reports of strangers lurking in the neighbourhood that day, or the days preceding. But that left the first question unanswered . . . how did he find his way to the tramps' site?

'Do you see what I'm saying? He's not a pure hunter of opportunity, this man. He only acts when he's prepared.' Madden scowled. 'From what you've told me, I'd guess that at Henley he'd already inspected the manor grounds, perhaps that same day, and knew he could take any victim he picked up there. As for Bognor Regis, I'm familiar with that piece of coastline where the girl was abducted. There are long stretches of reeds and scrubland along the shore. No shortage of cover, I mean, and I'll wager he knew it.'

'And it must have been the same at Brookham—that's what you're saying,' Billy broke in. 'He only picked her up because he knew there was a place nearby he could take her. That spot by the stream.'

'If his behaviour's consistent, that seems to be the case,' Madden agreed. 'But it means he must have been in Capel Wood earlier, for some other reason, and I've been racking my brains, trying to think what it might be.'

'He could be a hiker, sir. The countryside's full of ramblers.'

'Yes, I'd thought of that.' Madden shook his head. 'But he'd have had to leave the path to have found that clearing, for one thing, and that's no easy matter. The undergrowth's dense. No, he'd have needed a *reason*, as I said, a particular purpose.' Madden's scowl deepened. 'That's what's been puzzling me. How *did* he find it? What took him there in the first place?'

IT WAS NEARLY two o'clock before Sam Watkin got to Coyne's Farm that Friday. Earlier, he'd been delayed in Midhurst making his weekly report to Mr Cuthbertson, who'd been held up himself by a talkative client.

While he waited, he'd used the time to write out a report of the work that would have to be done at Hobday's Farm, over Rogate way, where he'd been earlier that morning. One of the chimneys on the farmhouse had come down since his last visit, smashing the roof tiles beneath it and leaving a hole which went straight down to the room below.

The repairs would have to be done before the next rains came, which might be any day now—the spell of fine October weather they'd been enjoying the past few days couldn't last.

Such, at any rate, was the news that Sam eventually gave to Mr Cuthbertson after he was shown into his office.

Mr Cuthbertson had rubbed his chin. 'Oh, they won't be pleased to hear this. They do so hate paying out money.'

The banks, he meant. The ones that owned so much property hereabouts now. The terrible slump in prices in 1929 had led to foreclosures left and right. Sam himself had been among the victims. He'd owned a small farm just the other side of Easeborne, bought when he'd come back from the war. With the help of a loan from the bank, of course. Well, that had gone.

But he'd been luckier than most. It had been Mr Cuthbertson, of Tally and Cuthbertson, a firm of estate agents in Midhurst specialising in farming land, who'd been charged with handling the business and in spite of the painful circumstances, which had ended with Sam and his family having to move out, they'd somehow managed to hit it off and Sam had departed with Mr Cuthbertson's offer of a job in his pocket.

What he was paid to do now was keep an eye on the farms in the district that the firm had on its books. Farms that were for sale, but attracting no buyers, not in present conditions. The Depression had bitten deep into the country and farmers had suffered along with everyone else.

The business of the roof had been quickly settled. Mr Cuthbertson had told Sam to get hold of a workman if he needed one, but to see to the repairs himself. A firm of contractors would only charge the earth.

There being little else for them to talk about that day, Sam had soon been on the move again, returning to his van, which was parked in the square below. Sally, his old labrador, had thumped her tail on the van's floor in greeting as he'd climbed in behind the wheel. Sal liked to lie in the back, curled up on her blanket, snoozing; waiting till it was time for a walk. Or, better still, a snack.

'We'll run over to Coyne's Farm now,' he'd told her, as they set off.

But another delay had been in the offing.

Soon after he'd turned off the Petersfield road, he'd run into some road-works. A gang of men was engaged in widening a stretch of the paved surface and one of their number was controlling the flow from both directions, using red and green flags to warn approaching traffic.

Sam had eyed him with some interest, and given the signal to proceed, had drawn up beside the shabby figure. 'What ho, Eddie!' he'd exclaimed.

'Crikey!' A bristly face had peered in at him through the opened window. 'Is that you, Sam?'

Eddie Noyes was the chap's name and the last time Sam had seen him he'd been lying face up on a stretcher with the front of his tunic soaked with blood and his eyes wide with shock. At Wipers, it had been. Eddie had got his ticket home that day. He hadn't returned to the battalion.

'What are you doing over this way?' The reason Sam had asked was because he knew Eddie came from another part of Sussex—from Hove— but as soon as he spoke he'd wished he hadn't. It was obvious, after all, he was taking any job he could find. Things were that hard still.

But Eddie hadn't been ashamed to talk about it. (This was after Sam had pulled to the side of the road and sat down with him on the bank, one of Eddie's mates having volunteered to direct the traffic.) He'd lost his position as a salesman for a paper-manufacturing company the previous year—the firm had gone bust—and hadn't been able to find another. Just odd jobs from time to time, this stint with the road gang being one of them.

He was still living in Hove, he said, taking care of his mum and his sister, who had lost her husband in the war. Money was short but they managed. His only problem with this job was that it was too far to get home at night so he was having to bunk with the other men in the shed they'd put up to house their equipment. 'I've known shellholes more salubrious, Sam,' he said.

Sam's first impulse had been to put his hand in his pocket, but you couldn't offer money to a chap who'd won a military medal.

'You must come and have a meal with us, Eddie. Just let me warn my Ada first. She'll want to put a spread on for you.'

He'd wished he could have offered him a bed, too, but for one thing they were living over on the other side of Midhurst, and for another there wasn't room in their cottage, what with the kids growing up.

But the image of Eddie lying wedged with the other men like sardines on the floor of a builder's shed bothered him—it didn't seem right—and even before he'd reached Coyne's Farm he'd come up with a solution.

'SEE WHAT I mean, Sal? This would suit Eddie down to the ground. It'd be warm and dry and there's plenty of hay to make a bed with.'

Standing in the barn, Sam held forth to an audience of one. A sociable chap by nature, he found the solitude of his working days something of a burden and had fallen into the habit of treating Sally as his confidante.

'No problem with fresh water, either. There's that tap in the yard outside.'

It was Coyne's Farm being so near to where Eddie and his mates were working that had put the idea into his head. The turnoff to the farm was only half a mile further on, though in fact Sam never went that way himself, the muddy track having fallen into disrepair since the place was abandoned. No, he would stop some way short of the turning, where the road was crossed by an ancient footpath that led over a low saddle in the wooded ridge behind Coyne's Farm into the valley where it was situated.

This path—called Wood Way—marked the boundary of Coyne's Farm, and to get there all you had to do was walk down the path until you came to a gap in the hedgerow beside it, slip through that, cross an apple orchard and a kitchen garden, and—hey presto—there you were in the cobbled yard behind the house, with the barn not thirty paces away at the other end of it.

Coyne's Farm was on the market. Mr Cuthbertson expected to get a good price for it once things had picked up again, and Sam knew the opportunity of having a reliable man on the spot, in residence so to speak, would not be one he would turn down. He made up his mind to speak to Mr Cuthbertson on Eddie's behalf.

The barn stood at one end of the yard and at right angles to the house. A lofty wooden structure, it had been used as a storeroom when the farm was abandoned and its doors were kept padlocked as a deterrent against intruders. Sam had a key to the padlock, and having drawn the bolt, he'd flung both doors wide, flooding the dark interior with light, displaying the stacks of hurdles used for temporary fencing, which lined both sides of the building. Where they ended, towards the rear of the barn, the empty space was filled with a variety of objects, including furniture from the house, an old pony trap and an assortment of farm implements.

It was to the opposite corner that Sam had made his way and where he'd spent some minutes clearing an area of the earth floor. Seizing hold now of a pitchfork, he began raking together the old hay into a mound.

'See, this'll be his bed,' he told Sal, who'd accompanied him into the barn and was watching his activities. 'Eddie's bound to have a bedroll with him if he's sleeping rough, and this'll do for a mattress underneath.'

During the months of his stewardship he'd explored the stored treasures of the barn and remembered having seen one or two articles that might come in handy now. He went in search of them and returned dragging an old Victorian washstand with an enamel jug and basin balanced precariously on its marble top. A second expedition netted a pair of oil lamps and a mirror that he found in a wardrobe standing nearby, draped in canvas. Formerly attached to the inside of one of the doors, the mirror now stood loose inside. Sam hauled it out and leaned it against the wall beside the washstand.

'THERE, NOW. That's better.' Sam sat back with a sigh. The cheese sandwiches Ada had packed for him that day had gone down a treat, while the bit of cold sausage he'd set aside for Sal had been equally well received.

Even when he'd finished with the barn, he'd still had his regular tour of inspection of the house and outbuildings to make and it had been close to three o'clock before they'd quit the yard and walked up the hillside to the wooded ridge behind the farm to have their meal.

This was a favourite spot of his. From here he could see the whole valley spread out before him backed by the deep folds of the Downs, whose grassy crests still glowed with the fading light of afternoon.

It wasn't only the farm buildings he had to watch out for. Mr Cuthbertson wanted him to keep an eye on the land as well and from where he was sitting he was able to cast his gaze over a wide area, westwards in the direction of Elsted and east as far as the red roofs of Oak Green, a little hamlet a few minutes' walk across the fields.

That day the valley seemed deserted. The only figure he spotted was that of a lone man and he was some distance off, on the bare crest of the ridge opposite, gazing up at the sky through a pair of binoculars.

Sam shifted his gaze to the stream that ran down the centre of the valley, searching for telltale wisps of smoke. Not surprisingly, the empty farms had become a magnet for tramps and Mr Cuthbertson had told him to make sure they didn't try to take up residence in any of the buildings.

Sam glanced at his watch. It was a quarter to four.

'Come on, Sal. Time we were off.'

They were soon back on the path, where Sam paused for a moment to cast his gaze down the length of it toward the farm. He was thinking how easy it would be for Eddie to walk over here after work.

'*Sally!*'

The high-pitched cry came from behind them and he looked round. A young girl dressed in a gym-slip and carrying a school satchel was hurrying up the path towards them from the direction of the road. Sam waved to her.

'Look, Sal—there's your friend.'

Sally, whose eyesight wasn't all it had once been, seemed unconvinced. She let out a speculative bark. Then her tail began to wag.

'Oh, Sally! Didn't you recognise me?' The girl came up to them. Shedding her satchel and her white straw hat, she threw her arms round Sal's neck.

Sam grinned. 'I thought we'd missed you today,' he said.

Nell was her name. Nell Ramsay. She lived in Oak Green, but went to school in Midhurst, returning on the bus every afternoon. It had been early spring when they'd first bumped into her on Wood Way and since then she and Sal had become bosom pals.

'I'm sorry, Mr Watkin. I should have said good afternoon to you first.' Smiling, she looked up, brushing the dark hair from her eyes.

'How've you been, love?'

'Very well, thank you.' Though she talked posh, she had no airs at all and during the course of the summer Sam had found himself beguiled by her simple manner and the openness with which she talked to him whenever they met. Truth to tell, she reminded him of his own Rosie, who was a year younger, and fair to Nell's dark, but had the same eager expression in her eyes. The look young girls got when they were on the brink of womanhood.

Thanks to her lack of shyness, he already knew all about her—and her family. They had moved from Midhurst to Oak Green three years before, Nell had told him, but her father continued to work in the town as a chartered accountant and drove her to school every morning. Up until this year her mother had always fetched her in the afternoons. But since turning thirteen she'd been deemed old enough to make the journey on her own.

'I was saving up a biscuit in case I met, Sally. But I'm not sure I ought to give it to you now. You're getting so *fat*.'

At the word 'biscuit' Sal's ears had pricked, and Nell reached blindly into her satchel and brought out a gingersnap, which was quickly disposed of.

'I'm sorry, I've got to dash today. Aunt Edith's coming to tea and Mummy doesn't want me to be late.' She planted a kiss on the silky head beside hers and stood up. 'Goodbye, Mr Watkin. Goodbye, Sally.'

Grinning, Sam waved a farewell to her and then watched as she went hurrying off down the path towards the fork that would take her to Oak Green. As he turned to leave, he noticed something that made him stop in his tracks. The bloke he'd spotted earlier, on the ridge opposite, across the valley. The one with the field glasses. He was still there.

Sam had taken him for a birdwatcher. There were plenty of them around, particularly in the summer. But whatever this bloke was looking at now, it wasn't a bird. He had his binoculars trained on the valley below him, which was strange, Sam thought, since there was nothing there to see. Nothing of interest. Unless it was the sight of Nell's figure hurrying across the open field away from the path towards the red roofs of Oak Green, her white straw hat bobbing up and down like a flower carried on a stream.

6

'Vane? *Philip* Vane?' Bennett stared at the chief inspector with incredulity. 'Are you serious?'

'Perfectly, sir. Do you know him?' The photograph that Sinclair had just withdrawn from his file remained in his hand.

Bennett gestured impatiently for it and he handed him a studio portrait of a man in his forties with narrow, well-bred features. Elegant in evening dress, he wore the ribbon of some decoration about his neck. The assistant commissioner stared at the picture, then nodded.

'That's Vane,' he acknowledged. 'We've met several times.' He looked at the chief inspector, then glanced at Holly, who was sitting beside him. 'Have either of you any idea who he is?' he asked in a neutral tone.

'Never heard of him, sir.'

While Holly's reply had been prompt, Sinclair chose his words carefully. 'I'm aware that he works at the Foreign Office,' he said, although he was a good deal better informed about the individual in question than he let on.

'Oh, there's a little more to him than that, you know.' Bennett's tone was silky, but the chief inspector did not fail to catch the warning note in it. 'Vane's a specialist in European affairs, quite a senior figure.'

Sinclair contrived to look impressed.

'He lunches at the palace, what's more. Did you know that?'

'I did not, sir.' In the circumstances, the lie seemed permissible.

'My word!' Holly whistled. 'Is this the chappie with the car, then?'

Bennett kept his gaze on Sinclair's face. The chief inspector had come to this meeting in a state of some tension. Now he spoke bluntly.

'With respect, sir, the question here is not whether Philip Vane is well regarded at the Foreign Office—I'm sure he is—nor even if he's on the palace's guest list. The issue's a simple one. Is he or is he not a murderer?'

Bennett drew in his breath sharply and the chief inspector braced himself for the explosion he could see was coming. He knew only too well what effect even a whiff of scandal could have on those in high office.

Bennett spoke in a controlled tone. 'Apart from the fact that he owns a motor car of this make, have you any reason to think he might be?'

'Sir, all I have at the moment is information—'

The assistant commissioner interrupted him, staring. 'Can you really think a man like Philip Vane guilty of such bestial crimes? In all honesty?'

'Why, I have no *opinion* one way or the other.' Sinclair took care to appear scandalised by the suggestion. He saw he'd stumbled into a minefield. 'What I *must* emphasise, though, is there's every likelihood the man we're seeking has an unusual background. Otherwise we'd have caught him by now. And no one can be excluded simply because of his position, his class.'

Franz Weiss's words on the subject had returned to the chief inspector's mind while he was speaking. 'That said, I'm only interested in facts,' he continued. 'Let me tell you what I've learned.' He opened the file on his knee. 'Vane purchased the Mercedes-Benz in June 1929—you'll recall the Henley child disappeared in July of that year. In October he was posted to the British Embassy in Berlin where he remained until July of this year, when he was recalled to London.' Sinclair looked up. 'We've been puzzled by the long gap between the earlier case and the Bognor Regis murder, which occurred in late July, and we've discussed the possibility that the killer might have been abroad during that time.' He lowered his eyes again. 'Oh, by the way, he bought the Mercedes because he thought it would be easier to get the vehicle serviced when he was in Germany.'

The assistant commissioner blanched. 'Have you been making enquiries about Vane among his colleagues and friends, Chief Inspector?'

'Good heavens, no. He's a public servant. This is all a matter of record.'

'And his reasons, his *personal* reasons, for buying a German-made machine? Were those on the record?'

'Gossip, sir. Common knowledge.' Sinclair retained his composure. 'His name was on the list the Mercedes people sent us. It's the only one we haven't checked. If he hadn't been out of the country, in the normal course of events I would have spoken to him already. But I'm assured he'll be back shortly.'

'It's as well for you that you didn't,' Bennett said quietly. 'I'm warning you now, Chief Inspector. *Take care.* You are treading on very thin ice.'

'Am I, sir?' Angered himself, Sinclair met his superior's heated gaze coolly. 'Well, so be it. As of this moment Philip Vane is a suspect. He must be asked to give a detailed account of his movements on the relevant days in July and September and to provide supporting evidence, if possible.'

'And what explanation do you propose to offer him for this intrusion into his private life?'

'None, unless he asks for one, in which case I'll tell him the truth.'

Bennett breathed deeply. His pallor had receded, but in its place twin red spots had appeared in his cheeks. He stared at the chief inspector.

Sinclair refused to let the issue rest. 'I'm requesting your authorisation to speak to Philip Vane, and at the earliest possible moment. If he's in the clear, so much the better. We can strike his name from our files.'

The assistant commissioner's lips were drawn together in a thin line. 'Do you understand what you're proposing? It's not simply a question of Vane's position at the Foreign Office. He has powerful friends in other quarters.'

'I'm sure you're not suggesting those are reasons why we shouldn't interview him, sir.'

Bennett's lips whitened in anger. 'I want to think this matter over. I'll see you both at five o'clock. That will be all.'

Sinclair and Holly rose and left the office in silence.

THEY DIDN'T have to wait till five o'clock. Fully an hour before the time set, Sinclair received a summons to return to the assistant commissioner's office. Hurrying down the stairs to the corridor below, he prepared himself psychologically to resume the struggle—but he saw at a glance as he and Holly entered Bennett's office that the situation had changed. The assistant commissioner, paler than usual, was seated at his desk. The unnatural brightness of his gaze, as he looked up, hinted at some recent shock undergone.

'Sit down, gentlemen, please.'

Obeying, Sinclair noticed a stack of telegram forms lying on the desk blotter. Bennett had been looking at them when they came in, and now he turned his attention back to the shallow pile.

'Since we met, I've received a message in response to the request we sent to the International Criminal Police Commission asking them for information they might have relating to crimes similar to the ones we're investigating.'

'Have they a record of such cases in Vienna?' Sinclair asked eagerly.

'Yes . . . I imagine so . . . now.' Bennett hesitated. 'But this telegram comes from Berlin. It was sent by Arthur Nebe, head of Berlin CID. Nebe was informed of our request by the Commission. He asked them to let him respond to it directly, citing "special circumstances" . . . It appears the German police have a number of cases similar to ours under investigation, covering a two-year period starting in late 1929 . . .' He caught Sinclair's glance. 'Yes. Quite. That fits the period of Vane's posting to Germany.

'Nebe suggests that our two police forces cooperate in this "exceptional matter"—that's a quote—and says he's dispatched an officer to London "to inform you fully on the investigation being carried out in Germany and to offer any assistance" he can. This man will arrive in London tomorrow.'

He laid the telegrams aside. 'I owe you an apology, Chief Inspector.'

'Not at all, sir. I'm as shocked as you are.' Even as he made the required response, Sinclair was aware of how closely Philip Vane fitted at least one of the imagined portraits sketched for him by Dr Weiss during their discussion at Highfield. A man protected by his position, able to cover his tracks.

The assistant commissioner straightened in his chair. 'Let's turn to practical matters. You say Vane's abroad?'

'He is away on government business. He'll be back next week.'

'Good. By then we'll have heard what our German colleague has to tell us. But we'd better brace ourselves for the worst. It may be that responsibility for these crimes lies at the door of a senior government official, and that among his victims are nationals of a country to which he was accredited.'

'*KRIM . . . Krimin . . . ?*'

Arthur Holly squinted at the piece of white card Sinclair had just handed him. Although it was only a little past two o'clock, the lights in Bennett's office were all switched on. Outside, the blanketing fog pressed up against the windowpanes.

'*Krim-in-al . . . ?*' Holly scowled. The word he was struggling with—*Kriminalinspektor*—was one he had not encountered before.

'He's a police inspector, Arthur.' Sinclair came to his rescue.

The card had arrived a few minutes before, dispatched from the reception desk with the news that its owner was waiting in the lobby below. Bennett had ordered him to be shown upstairs to his office immediately.

There was a light tap on the door. Bennett's secretary put her head in. 'The German gentleman's here, sir.'

'Show him in, please, Miss Baxter.' Bennett rose, and the other two followed suit. As their visitor entered, the assistant commissioner came round his desk and offered him his hand. 'Inspector Probst?'

'Sir Wilfred!' They shook hands, Probst accompanying the action with a stiff bow. Hans-Joachim Probst was in his late thirties, with fair, curling hair that receded from a high forehead. Slight of build, he wore a suit of an old-fashioned cut and a shirt with a high, stiff collar. His manner struck Sinclair as being fussy and schoolmasterly until the two men were introduced, when the chief inspector found himself looking into eyes as cool and watchful as his own, yet not without a trace of humour in their blue depths.

Bennett ushered their visitor to the conference table. While the others seated themselves around him Probst undid the straps of his briefcase and took out a thick file, which he laid on the table before him.

'Before we begin, Inspector—may I offer you some refreshment? Coffee? Tea? Something to eat, perhaps?' Bennett had taken the head of the narrow oak table and placed Holly and Sinclair on one side of him, facing Probst.

'Thank you, Sir Wilfred. Water will suffice.' With a nod Probst reached for the carafe that stood on the table and poured himself a tumblerful.

'May I say at the start how relieved I am to find that you speak our language so fluently.' The assistant commissioner continued to prevaricate. No policeman could contemplate the arrest of a senior government official without trepidation, and Sinclair wondered what kind of night Sir Wilfred had passed. His own had been far from tranquil.

'You are kind to compliment me on my English, Sir Wilfred. The credit must go to a lady in Berlin, a Miss Adamson, from Durham. But I first learned the language in a prisoner-of-war camp. In 1915—I was blown sky-high . . . that is the correct term, is it not, "sky-high"?' His blue eyes twinkled. 'I awoke to find myself in a British field hospital and spent the rest of the war in a camp near Carlisle, learning not only English but bricklaying as well. Rarely have I spent my time more *usefully*, before or since.'

This calm discourse seemed to have put Bennett at ease, Sinclair observed. The assistant commissioner sat with his chin cupped in his hand, listening attentively. A glance at Holly revealed a different picture. Apparently the sight of a foreigner—and a hun, as the chief super preferred to put it, at that—spouting the King's English with such aplomb had taken the chief super unawares. Sheer disbelief was stamped on his blunt features.

Bennett resettled himself in his chair. 'To business, then.' He turned to Probst. 'Herr Nebe informed us that you have been investigating a series of murders in Germany that may well be linked to similar crimes under inquiry here. We should be very interested to hear about those.'

Probst dipped his head in acknowledgment. 'I have come armed with all the relevant information. The murders I'm about to describe have a distinct "signature", one you may find familiar. Should that be the case, we are ready to offer any assistance we can in bringing this man to justice. I speak not only for my superiors in Berlin, but for the Bavarian police as well.'

'The *Bavarian* police?' Bennett was taken aback.

'Yes, two of the murders I'm talking about were committed there. The other four were in Prussia. They took place in a period of a little over two years, between December 1929 and April of this year.'

'So there have been *six* in all?' The assistant commissioner was still coming to terms with the grim figure.

'Yes . . . though there may have been more.' Probst met their eyes.

'Why do you say that?' Holly spoke up.

'For two reasons. Firstly, this murderer hides the bodies of his victims. So it may be there are other corpses awaiting discovery.' Probst shrugged. 'Are there young girls missing, then, you ask me? Sadly, the answer is yes, but for reasons not necessarily connected to this case.' Probst paused, frowning. 'I'm sure you're all aware that my country has been through difficult times since the war ended. First, there was the collapse of our currency, next the Depression. Reparations to pay. All this is reflected in our political situation. German society has been disrupted, and one effect has been the breaking-up of families . . . young people cast out on the streets to beg. If this man was seeking victims unlikely to be missed he could hardly have chosen a better hunting-ground.'

'Quite, Inspector . . .' Bennett stirred uneasily beneath the Berlin policeman's cool, unaccusing gaze. 'But could you not give us some *details* about these murders? We need to decide whether they resemble our own cases.'

'From what we gleaned from your enquiry to Vienna, it seems certain we are dealing with the same killer.' The inspector had produced a pince-nez from his breast pocket, which he donned as he consulted his file.

'The victims in Germany have all been young girls, aged between ten and thirteen. Rape and strangulation occurred in each case and were followed by an assault on the victim's face in which, according to our pathologists' findings, the same weapon, or an identical one, was used.'

'A hammer, would that be?' Sinclair put the question in a low voice.

'Yes.' Probst looked up. 'It is the same with the victims here?'

Before Sinclair could respond, Bennett intervened. 'Our conclusions are very similar to yours. I think we can say there's every likelihood we're looking for the same man. We have two cases under investigation here. More of those later. Continue, if you would . . .' He caught the chief inspector's eye.

Probst bent to his file again. 'Our evidence leads us to believe the children were picked up, usually on a road, and taken by car to a preselected murder site. In some instances, the girls appeared to have been choked into submission prior to the sexual assault. But in others chloroform was discovered in the victims' lungs.'

The inspector paused to moisten his lips. 'Our first two killings took place in Prussia, neither of them far from Berlin. The third occurred in

Bavaria, in the Munich region. Regrettably, the connection between these three murders was not noted at once. As I'm sure you know, Germany has no central organisation like Scotland Yard, which can coordinate enquiries.

'However, with the fourth and fifth murders, which were again in the vicinity of Berlin, it finally became clear that we were looking for a single killer and since then the Prussian and Bavarian authorities have been cooperating closely. And it was the sixth murder, in April this year, also in Bavaria, that provided us at last with a lead of some substance. Though I fear that whatever advantage we gained has turned out to be at your expense.'

Bennett frowned. 'I take it you mean this man has now transferred his activities to England?'

'Yes, to us it seems likely that the enquiries we set in motion may have forced him to seek his victims elsewhere.'

Sinclair stepped in. 'A lead of substance, you said. Tell us about that, Inspector. What happened with the last murder? In Bavaria, was it?'

'Yes, the victim in this case was a farmer's child. Her body was found in woods not far from the main road. The crime came close to being witnessed. A woodcutter's wife was walking through the forest and heard the child's cries, followed by the sound of heavy blows. Guessing that some act of violence was taking place, she was on the point of running back to her house to seek help when she heard someone approaching. Terrified, she hid herself, lying face down, too frightened even to lift her eyes as whoever it was went by. When it was quiet again, she looked up and saw the figure of a man a little way off. He was on his knees, with his back to her, bending over a stream, washing himself. He had taken his shirt off . . .' The inspector hesitated. 'This woman saw that his arms were spattered with blood. She couldn't of course, see his front.'

'Nor his face, either, I imagine?' Sinclair sensed rather than heard, Bennett's faint sigh of relief at that point.

'No, alas! A moment later she ducked her head down again and remained like that until she heard him walking away. Only when she was sure he was gone did she get to her feet and run back to her house.' Probst looked up and caught Sinclair's eye. 'When we received a report of this incident from the Bavarian police, it seemed a golden opportunity to identify our man had gone begging. But in fact the woman saw more than she realised.'

The chief inspector grunted. 'I've known that happen,' he remarked.

'Under repeated questioning this woman was able to add some crucial details. From the start she referred to the man she saw as a "Herr"—a gentleman, if you like—and finally it came out that the reason she thought so was because of his clothes, which were on the ground beside him, and impressed her as being of good quality.

'It wasn't much to go on, but the detectives went to work. Since the murder took place near the main road from Munich to Berlin, they assumed the killer had been travelling on it when he came on his victim. But in which direction? If he was going south, to Munich, there was little chance they could track him down. He would soon be swallowed up in the city. But heading north, the situation was different.' The inspector paused. 'Remember, by this time we knew that the murderer must have spent a good deal of time during the past two years in Berlin. So it was reasonable to assume that if he drove north after killing the girl he was in fact returning to the capital.'

Probst took a handkerchief from his pocket and dabbed his brow.

'One of the Munich detectives had an idea. Since the murder had occurred between ten and eleven in the morning, why not drive north along the Berlin road for two hours and then look for likely places where the killer might have stopped for lunch? Hotels, inns, restaurants. All within a twenty-mile stretch of road were covered and the same question was asked in each place: did anyone remember a well-dressed man eating on his own that day?

'And it didn't stop there. Police notices were placed in newspapers asking any motorist who was on the road that day to come forward. The same thing was done in Berlin. The response was overwhelming. A considerable number came forward not only to report their own presence on the road that day but to inform us of others they had noticed. In this way we were able to form a surprisingly full picture of who was eating in the various establishments and to eliminate most of them by crosschecking. We were left with a handful of men who remained unidentified and who had not come forward of their own accord. Of these, one in particular caught our attention.'

The inspector paused to take a sip of water.

'This man had been noted by several of our voluntary witnesses who had eaten lunch at a roadside hotel near Nuremberg. He was reckoned to be in his forties, and had sat alone at a table in a corner reading a book while he ate. Neither the waitress who served him nor our other witnesses were able to give a satisfactory description of him, and our attempts to obtain some sort of picture of his face, using an artist, failed completely. The impression of all was that there was nothing out of the ordinary about this man's appearance. He ordered, ate quickly, paid and left.

'One thing only about him seemed unusual . . . noteworthy.' Grimacing, Probst nodded to himself. 'It hardly counted as a clue. It was too vague . . . We only returned to it later, after we'd received word from the International Criminal Police Commission about your inquiry. It was something the waitress said in her original deposition.' Probst paused. 'Asked where this man might have come from—whether she'd recognised any regional accent in his voice—she said she had not. "He didn't seem to be from anywhere." That was her exact reply, translated from the German. We asked our Bavarian colleagues to question her again, and this time she was a little more specific. She said that although his German was faultless, at least to her ears, she wondered if he was in fact German at all.'

'She meant he was a *foreigner*?' Sinclair found his tongue before the others. Bennett sat sphinx-like. Holly, beside him, scowled.

'Perhaps, though she didn't say so. Not in so many words.'

Probst removed his pince-nez. He looked at each of them in turn.

'It's our belief the newspaper campaign we launched caused this man to flee Germany. No murders of the kind we've been discussing have been reported for the past six months. In the meantime, however, it would appear he has become active here. Remembering what the waitress in that hotel had to say, and given that he *chose* to come to this country, rather than another, I have to ask myself: Could this man we are seeking be *English*?'

BENNETT LEANED back in his chair. As the afternoon wore on and the gloom of the foggy day outside deepened, the lights in the assistant commissioner's office had grown brighter. He stifled a yawn.

'This has been a long day, and we all have much to reflect on. I suggest we meet again in my office tomorrow morning so that we can lay the groundwork of our future cooperation, before Inspector Probst returns to Berlin.'

Sinclair was relieved to hear Bennett's words. For some time now he'd sat silent, puffing at his pipe, reluctant to take any further part in what he increasingly viewed as a charade. Earlier, there had been a break in the proceedings; the interval had been proposed by Sir Wilfred on the grounds that there were one or two unrelated, urgent matters awaiting his attention that couldn't be delayed, a pretext so transparent, at least to Sinclair's eyes, that he'd wondered whether Probst, too, had seen through it.

But the Berlin inspector had accompanied Sinclair without comment to a nearby waiting room reserved for important visitors and been offered a cup of tea. The chief inspector had then returned swiftly to Bennett's office, where he found the assistant commissioner and Holly sunk in despair. But Sinclair had a bone to pick with the assistant commissioner all the same.

'With respect, sir, why did you tell him we only have *two* murders on our hands? It's virtually certain the Henley case is connected, and the time factor puts a completely different complexion on the matter.'

Bennett's response had been sharp. 'Look, they've already guessed the killer might be a British subject. If we tell Probst there was a linked murder in 1929 by a man who then disappeared for three years, during which time a further *six* killings occurred in Germany, he's quite likely to ask himself what kind of individual would be in a position to lead such an existence. And just as likely to come up with an educated guess that he's a diplomat, or some other accredited person. Until we're sure about Vane, until we've questioned him, I'm not going to allow any hint to surface that the author of these crimes could be a British official.'

On the resumption of the meeting following the break called by Bennett, Sinclair had led his German colleague by stages through the history of the inquiry in Britain. 'We didn't know what we were faced with until the second corpse was uncovered at Bognor Regis. Till then the search had been concentrated on finding this tramp.'

'What made you get in touch with Vienna, if I may ask? Did you have some reason to think this man might have been abroad?'

The question was an obvious one, but since an honest answer would have meant revealing details of the suspected murder at Henley three years before, Sinclair had been forced to take refuge behind a smoke screen.

'No, but it seemed to us this murderer might well have killed before. There was a finished quality to his crimes: the battering of the faces, the fact that he brought a hammer with him to carry out the job. No record of such a criminal existed in this country, so we thought to look elsewhere.' Glancing at Bennett as he produced this farrago of half-truths, the chief inspector was gratified to see that his superior at least had the grace to blush.

At five o'clock, Bennett called a halt, and their visitor addressed them for the last time. 'My superiors have asked me to stress the importance they attach to resolving this case as soon as possible. Quite aside from the human tragedy involved, they believe it contains dangers of which we should all be aware. These are the "special circumstances" to which Herr Nebe referred in his telegram to you, Sir Wilfred. Although we don't yet know the identity of this man we are seeking, it's likely he is either German or English. Which, is not important. What matters, we believe, is that crimes of such brutality committed by a national of one country against the children of another are liable to be seen in the worst light, and given the recent shared history of our two nations there may be those, in both countries, who will seek to make the most of an appalling situation. We on our part are most anxious to avoid any such development and I am authorised to offer Scotland Yard the full cooperation of both the Prussian and Bavarian authorities in bringing this man to justice.'

'That said, I must make it clear that I have no authority to discuss the matter I now wish to raise, so that what I say must be regarded as a personal opinion only. I have already touched on conditions in Germany. No doubt you are aware of how unstable our political scene has been since the end of the war. Neither I nor anyone else can tell you what government my country will have three months from now, except to say that it may well be directed by a party whose leaders are without principle.'

'I take it you mean the Nazis?' Bennett asked.

Probst nodded. 'But I make no biased accusation against them. This is a statement of fact. They boast of it. What others might regard as human decency they see as a weakness to be exploited. I cannot say how a police authority run by such men would deal with a situation of the kind we have been discussing. But one thing is certain: much will change in Germany if they come to power, and I want to stress how urgent I believe it is that this terrible case should be brought to a conclusion before such changes can overtake us.' He looked at each of them in turn.

'Let us do all in our power to identify this man, and to arrest him and bring him to justice,' he pleaded with them. 'And let us do it *soon*.'

PART THREE
7

Madden continued to be gnawed by deep-seated unease that dated from the moment he had come upon the corpse of Alice Bridger. Try as he might he could not shake free of his fears and increasingly he found the quiet rhythms of his life disturbed by unanswered questions, and by the thought of the killer who still walked free.

One autumn morning he returned from the farm to the house for lunch to find Mary, their maid, impatiently awaiting his arrival in the hall.

'Mrs Beck would like to see you, sir.'

'See *me*?' Madden was nonplussed. The household staff were Helen's business. However, Helen had driven up to London that morning on a shopping expedition and would not be back until late afternoon.

'Yes, sir.' Mary Morris's brown eyes bore a suspiciously innocent look. Her smothered smile hinted that there was mischief afoot.

Alerted, Madden made his way to the kitchen where he discovered their cook standing before the back door with folded arms, as though to bar it. She wore a defiant expression.

'There's a person says he wants to see you, sir. He's outside, in the yard.'

'A person, Mrs Beck? Who is he?'

'I didn't take his name, sir.' Cook's voice was heavy with disapproval.

Madden went past her to open the door. One glance at the shabby figure waiting by the kitchen-garden gate, and all was made clear to him. At the insistence of her employers, Mrs Beck had come to accept the occasional presence of tramps in her kitchen. But she drew the line at Gypsies!

'Hello, Joe.' Smiling a greeting, Madden stepped out into the yard, and as he did so, Goram looked up. 'What brings you back to Highfield?'

'*BEEZY, you say*? Are you sure? Is it him?'

'That's the trouble, sir.' Goram rubbed his bristly chin. 'I can't be *sure*.'

They sat facing each other across the kitchen table, the remains of a veal and ham pie and an array of empty cider bottles between them. Two hard days on the road had given an edge to Joe Goram's appetite.

'We're camped in Dorset, sir, t'other side of Blandford. I managed to get one or two lifts on the way, but mostly I've had to walk.' He'd told Madden this while they were still outside, in the yard, and it was plain to see from the leaves and twigs clinging to the Gypsy's twill trousers and the grass stains smearing his grimy, collarless shirt that he'd been sleeping rough. Madden had brought him out a cake of soap and a towel to clean up with.

'We'll go inside in a moment and have something to eat. You look done in.'

It had taken all of the ten minutes Joe had needed to make himself presentable before Cora Beck could be persuaded to lay the kitchen table for two. That done, she had taken leave of the scene, with an injured air, asserting that there was a mountain of ironing awaiting her attention.

Goram had already indicated that he bore news and as Madden seated him at the table he had asked why he hadn't telephoned the information to him.

'Can't say I've ever done that, sir.' Joe had scratched his head. 'Used the telephone, like. Never had cause to. No, I thought I'd better come myself, as I've got a message for Dr Madden from Topper.'

'*Topper?*' Madden's eyebrows rose at the name. 'Have you seen him?'

'Aye, just three nights ago. We were sitting round the fire and he walked in out of the dark.'

'Did he know you were camped there?'

'Must have, sir. It's the same place we stop every year. Anyway, Topper asked if I could get a message to Dr Madden.'

'Dr Madden drove up to London early today, Joe. Can you give *me* the message?'

Goram's face darkened. 'He made me promise I'd keep it a secret,' he muttered. 'But I reckon I can tell you, sir. He said to say there was someone with him who was sick and needed help. *Mortal* sick was how he put it. He said that as soon as Dr Madden came over I was to send one of my boys to Boar's Hill. That's where Topper is now. It's not far from the camp.'

'And you reckon that he could be talking about Beezy?' Madden asked.

'Well, like I say, I can't be *sure* . . . But it could be, couldn't it?'

'I think you're right.' Madden glanced at his watch. 'Blandford's a good three hours' drive. Did Topper tell you what was wrong with his friend?'

Joe shook his head. 'You know what he's like, sir. Two words is all you get from him, if you're lucky. He just said the man was sick and needed help.'

'We may have to get this man into hospital, whoever he is,' Madden remarked, thinking aloud. 'I'm going to drive you back, Joe,' he announced. 'But you'll have to show me the way to Boar's Hill when we get there. Are you game?'

'I reckon so, sir.' Goram's face split into a gap-toothed grin.

'And I want to thank you for what you've done. It was good of you to come all this way to speak to me.'

'I said I would. Anything I heard, you'd hear. I gave you my word.'

'HE SAID to bring the *lady* when she came.' The pale, bearded face was dim in the darkness. 'Didn't say nothing about two *men*.'

'I'm Dr Madden's husband. She wasn't home when Topper's message reached me.' Behind him, Joe Goram clicked his tongue with impatience.

Topper's envoy had been waiting for them, rising silently from a thicket as they approached, and Madden had had a brief glimpse of greasy locks beneath a torn cloth cap before the man ducked away from the light in his face. Looming against the night sky behind him was a dark protuberance of trees and tangled bushes which Joe had already identified as Boar's Hill.

Still short of their ultimate destination, it had taken them many hours to reach the spot, their journey from Highfield having been slowed first by low-lying mist on the road, then by the fading light of late afternoon.

Before leaving home, Madden had scribbled a brief note to Helen, telling her what little he knew and saying he hoped to be back before dawn.

Helen would be collecting Rob from school on her way back from London, and since Lucy was spending the afternoon with Belle Burrows, he had had to do no more than ring May and ask her to take charge of their daughter until relief arrived. His final act before departing had been to collect his policeman's lamp—a souvenir of his days in the force, since appropriated by his son—and to prevail on the long-suffering Mrs Beck to put together a packet of sandwiches and a Thermos of tea for them.

They had left Highfield soon after two o'clock, but it was past six when Madden had finally turned onto the track that led to the Gypsies' camp.

While he'd warmed his hands on the mug of tea that Goram's wife offered him, Joe had sketched out the problems that still faced them.

'It'll take us a good half-hour to walk out there, sir. Can't get no closer with a car. Topper said there'd be someone looking out for us. We'll just have to hope that's so.'

Another potential difficulty had been occupying Madden's mind, meanwhile. 'We may have to carry Beezy, or whoever it is, back with us. Bring a knife with you, Joe, in case we need to cut poles for a stretcher.'

Once they'd set off into the inky blackness beyond the circle of light cast by the fire, Madden lost all sense of direction and had to trust to his guide as he stumbled over rock-strewn slopes and through sharp gullies.

Presently they had glimpsed the darker outline of Boar's Hill ahead of them, and after Madden had flicked his lamp on and off several times, hoping it would be recognised as a signal, Topper's messenger had materialised.

'Been waiting here all day,' he grumbled. 'You'll not be welcome, neither one of you. It's a lady they're expecting.' Turning on his heel, he strode off and they followed him up the hill along a barely marked trail until the canopy of leaves overhead blocked out whatever light might have come from the sky. At last a glimmer of firelight appeared through the trees ahead and the hillside levelled off into a flatter area. The figure in front of them halted.

'Stay here now. Don't move,' he said, and not waiting to see if his order was obeyed, he continued on towards the firelight.

Goram and Madden stood listening as sounds of an altercation broke out ahead of them. Men's voices were raised in angry argument.

'Come on, Joe.' Madden had lost patience. 'Let's get this over with.'

They pushed their way through the bushes into an open space, roughly circular in shape. A fire was burning in the centre of the ring and round it were perhaps a dozen bearded and dishevelled men, all engaged in fierce debate. As Madden stepped into the circle of light, silence fell. Hostile faces were turned in his direction and a low mutter ran through the group.

'I'm here to see Topper,' Madden called out. 'He sent a message to my wife, asking for help—'

'Your wife?'

The voice came from the shadows that lay at the edge of the circle, outside the fire's reach. Madden turned his head and saw a tall man, craggy and stoop-shouldered, move forward into the light. His white hair, uncut, was trapped in the collar of an old army greatcoat that fell below his knees.

'Yes . . . Dr Madden.'

A murmur greeted the name. Several heads turned.

'Ah, well, that's different,' the white-haired man conceded, after a moment's thought. He came closer, offering his hand. 'McBride's the name.' He had a marked Scottish accent.

'John Madden . . .' They shook hands. 'And this is Joe Goram, who showed me the way here.'

McBride glanced at the Gypsy then spoke again to Madden. 'You were wanting to see Topper? Well, he's asleep now.' McBride nodded towards the shadows from which he'd emerged and Madden made out a blanket-wrapped form stretched out on the ground there. 'He's been up and awake these past two nights. You'll not get much sense from him right now.'

'There was someone else I was hoping to talk to,' Madden admitted. 'A friend of his. A man called Beezy. Is he here?'

A hush followed his words. Madden examined the faces round the fire. When he turned his gaze back to McBride he found that his eyes had hardened. 'John Madden . . . I've heard it said you were once a policeman.'

'That's true. But not any more.'

'You wouldn't be doing their job now, would you?'

'It depends what you mean. I'm aware the police are looking for him. But it's my belief they want him only as a witness.'

'Yes, but all this is *police* business, Mr Madden. What's it to *you*?'

Madden hesitated. He looked at the expectant faces round him, then said,

'I happened to be the one who found the body of the child who was murdered at Brookham, and the memory haunts me. I never believed Beezy was the killer, even if others thought differently, but it's possible he saw something that day. Perhaps the murderer's face. I've been trying to find him in my own way, and I'll continue to do so, come what may. I believe Beezy can help me in this.'

His words brought a sigh from the listeners seated round the fire.

'Ah, well, he can't do that, poor man,' McBride said softly. 'The sad fact is he died on this spot not three hours ago.'

MADDEN'S HOPES were dashed by what the Scotsman had said.

'Oh, he had a great deal to say at the end, poor fellow, but most of it was gibberish. Once we'd laid him down over there, he never moved.'

McBride nodded in the direction of the fire, burning low now, where most of the men who'd been sitting earlier were recumbent, some propped on elbows conversing in low voices, others snoring, deeply asleep. Seated among them was Joe Goram. The Gypsy had joined the group some time earlier, offering a bottle of gin like a ticket of admission as he sat down.

McBride took Madden to the edge of the clearing, past where Topper was asleep, and pushed aside the ferns to show him Beezy's body. Madden shone his lamp on the corpse, moving the light slowly up from the cracked boots and canvas trousers, over a torn flannel shirt topped by a buttonless waistcoat, to the old tramp's bearded face. Bending close to examine the features, he noted the missing right ear lobe that had been mentioned in the police circular issued earlier that autumn.

'I'm no doctor, but I'd say he died of bronchitis,' McBride said. 'He coughed and coughed and couldn't clear his chest. In the end he must have suffocated. When it seemed there was no hope of him getting better, Topper had the idea of sending a message to your wife. But by then it was too late.'

They turned away from the body and moved closer to the fire, sitting down close to where Topper was sleeping. 'We'll share out Beezy's clothes and possessions tomorrow,' McBride said. 'It's our way. Then we'll bury him.'

Madden shook his head. 'The police won't be satisfied with that, I can tell you now. They'll want to recover the body.'

'Of course they will.' McBride seemed unconcerned. 'You can tell them he'll be in a shallow grave just over there in the bushes, where he's lying now. We'll have moved on by then. A sip of whisky, Mr Madden?'

The Scotsman had produced a bottle from the pocket of his greatcoat and he offered it to his companion. Madden took a swallow from the neck for hospitality's sake before returning it to its owner's hand.

McBride stretched his cramped muscles. 'I know next to nothing about Beezy. This was the first time we'd met. They turned up a week ago—he and Topper—and even then he was in no fit state to hold a conversation.'

'So he didn't speak of the murder at all?' Madden couldn't hide his disappointment. 'He dropped some of his belongings near the scene of the killing. That made me think he had seen something that caused him to run off.'

'Oh, I dare say you're right about that. He indicated as much to me.'

'Then he *did* talk to you about it?'

McBride shook his head. 'When Topper went off three days ago to seek out your Gypsy friend he asked me to keep an eye on Beezy for him. He talked a good deal, but wasn't making any sense.' The Scotsman paused, frowning. 'I knew about the murder at Brookham, of course. We all did. And I knew the police had been looking for this man. So I guessed what it was he was raving about. He kept speaking of blood . . .'

'Of blood?'

'That was the word he kept repeating. Then there was a man who was trying to wash it off. "I saw him washing off the blood . . ." He said that many times. "I saw him washing off the blood, but it wouldn't wash off . . . no . . ." Then he said something else. "He had the devil's mark on him . . ."'

'The *devil's* mark? What did he mean? Didn't he describe the man at all?'

McBride endeavoured to explain. 'You have to understand, he wasn't speaking rationally, he was wandering. But I will say this: I believe he was trying to tell me *something*, to clear his mind of a burden, if you will.'

'Perhaps he told Topper more?' Madden eyed the sleeping form nearby.

'Apparently not. At least, so Topper says. When Topper arrived here a week ago I took him aside and told him if this friend he had with him was guilty of murdering that child they'd have to leave. We wouldn't have them here. He said Beezy had sworn he was innocent, and he believed him. I took Topper's word for it—and I fancy you'd have done the same.'

'I might.' Madden smiled. 'My wife would have had no hesitation.'

'At any event, they seemed not to have discussed the matter further. Topper was kept well occupied finding food for them both while Beezy stayed hidden. I gather he was terrified of going to the police. He was sure they'd accuse *him* of the crime. He was quite deaf, by the way, poor man, and Topper has less to say than any human being I've ever encountered. I doubt they did much in the way of exchanging confidences. But they were friends. You could tell that. Topper was quite broken up when he died.' McBride shrugged. 'Wake him up if you like, Mr Madden, but you'll get no more from him than I've told you.'

Madden had been considering the question and had made up his mind. He shook his head. 'No, let him sleep.' He rose, stretching. 'Will you tell him something for me? Will you say my wife was away when his message arrived? He'll wonder why she didn't come. And will you tell him she's concerned for him and wants to see him.'

'You may be sure I'll pass that on.' Rising in turn, the Scotsman bowed his head as though to seal the pledge.

'Thank you for your help, Mr McBride. If ever you pass by Highfield you'll find our door is always open.'

The two men shook hands and Madden signalled to Joe, who rose from beside the fire, yawning.

As PROBST reached inside the cab to pull out his suitcase, Sinclair beckoned to one of the porters standing nearby. The chief inspector had insisted on accompanying the German policeman to Victoria station to say goodbye.

'I feel I've hardly arrived, and already I must depart.' Pausing in the concourse, Probst smiled.

'Perhaps you'll come again. If so, and even if your visit's unofficial, please get in touch with me.' Sinclair returned the smile. He'd taken a liking to the younger man, whose pleasant manner hid a mind as sharp as any he'd encountered in his profession. And another quality, too, of which the chief inspector had become increasingly conscious, was one that he would have characterised as moral stature. Observing the Berlin policeman, he'd been reminded of Madden, whose name had come up between them, and who in any case was much in his thoughts that morning.

Even before he'd sat down to breakfast the telephone had rung at his flat in Shepherd's Bush and for the next twenty minutes he'd listened while his old partner revealed what he'd learned at the tramps' gathering.

Prior to the final meeting he'd scheduled with Probst he had paid a call on the assistant commissioner, and passed on Madden's information.

'What's Madden's view of this "devil's mark" then?' Bennett had asked when he'd finished. 'Does he think it's worth pursuing?'

'He wasn't sure until he heard what his wife had to say on the subject. She suggested it might have been a birthmark he'd seen.'

'A birthmark! On the killer's face or body?'

'Yes, but of a particular kind.' Sinclair consulted his notebook. 'The medical term is naevus flammeus. What you and I would call a port wine stain. It's red- or purple-coloured and can be large and disfiguring. Helen Madden believes it's quite possible that the man Beezy saw was washing the blood off himself, but the mark remained. It could well have *looked* like blood . . . blood that wouldn't come off. Madden's of the opinion it's a solid lead. There seems little doubt Beezy witnessed the murder, or at least its aftermath . . .'

Sinclair had gained Bennett's reluctant permission to tell Probst of this discovery, which made his final meeting with the Berlin policeman more agreeable than those that had preceded it, when he'd had to guard against indicating that Scotland Yard had any information about the case it was not prepared to divulge.

'That is most interesting. The connections with our own case are multiplying.' Probst had listened raptly to what Sinclair had had to tell him.

'Connections. What did you have in mind, exactly?' Sinclair asked.

'Our witness's account of the man removing his shirt seems to be borne out here. Perhaps this is also part of his ritual. The battering he gives his victims' faces would be bound to produce a spray of blood. He's fastidious, perhaps. Or just practical.'

'The birthmark—if it's a birthmark—could be on his face.'

'Not if he's the man who was seen eating lunch in that roadside hotel. A mark like that would certainly have been recalled by at least some of the witnesses. No, it suggests a blood-coloured stain on his body to me.' Probst had risen from his chair in front of Sinclair's desk and was pacing up and down. 'He is washing the blood off his arms and chest—that's where most of it would fall. The blood comes off, but the birthmark remains . . .'

'Yes, and then there's the question of the stream . . .'

'Ah, yes . . . the stream.' Probst paused in his pacing. 'He chooses these places with care, it seems, and there's always water nearby.' The inspector brooded. 'Is this a way we can track him down, do you think?'

'By his birthmark, you mean? If he has one.' It had taken Sinclair a moment to catch up with the other's train of thought. 'Difficult, I should say.'

'Yes.' Probst frowned. 'After all, who does a man take his clothes off for? His wife or mistress, certainly. But we doubt this killer has either.'

'His doctor perhaps?' Sinclair asked.

They got no further in their speculations. Glancing at his watch, Sinclair saw that it was time to leave and five minutes later they were climbing into a cab and setting off for the station.

'CHIEF INSPECTOR . . . come in.' Bennett gestured to a chair in front of his desk and Sinclair sat down. Their meeting with Vane had been set for three o'clock and Sinclair had not expected to see his superior until they met to make the short trip to Whitehall together. Instead, he had received a message saying that Bennett wanted to see him before they set out.

'I've something to say to you . . .' Bennett rose. He went from his desk to the windows by the conference table, where he stood, looking out into the grey November day. 'I realise you feel I've been unnecessarily obstructive where Philip Vane is concerned . . . no, there's no need to deny it.' He waved away the instinctive protest that came to the chief inspector's lips.

'Your attitude was quite understandable. But there are issues at stake here of which you're unaware and on which, up to now, I've not felt in a position to enlighten you.' He looked directly at Sinclair. 'However, since we're to speak to Vane together, it's necessary that you should know what I know . . . or at any rate suspect.' He bit his lip. 'As I think I mentioned, I've met Philip Vane on a few occasions. I've also heard his name mentioned in unexpected quarters. Naturally, I was curious, and I asked questions . . .' He shrugged. 'Answers were not forthcoming. But hints were dropped . . .'

Bennett cleared his throat. 'My reluctance to see him dragged into this inquiry doesn't stem only from a desire to avoid any scandal. I can't give you chapter and verse, Chief Inspector. I can only tell you what I strongly suspect: that Vane's job at the Foreign Office is not what it seems. In reality I believe he's a senior intelligence officer.'

8

'Mr Vane will see you now.' The young man rose from behind his desk in the anteroom and opened an inner door, standing back to allow the two Scotland Yard officials to enter the office beyond. Looking onto an inner courtyard, it was modest in size and decorated with a spare elegance that seemed to reflect its occupant, who rose from behind a polished desk, bare of ornament, to receive them.

'Sir Wilfred . . . it's been a while since we last met.' Philip Vane bowed slightly, but made no move to come round his desk to greet them.

'How are you, Vane?' The assistant commissioner kept his tone neutral. 'May I introduce Chief Inspector Sinclair. He's a senior officer in the CID.'

Vane's eyebrows rose a fraction as he gestured towards a matched pair of chairs. He was of medium height and slimly built, and his thin, aristocratic features had been faithfully reproduced in the magazine picture obtained by the Yard; but what the photographic image failed to convey was the poise and confidence of its subject. He seemed in no hurry as he waited for them to settle and if his expression betrayed mild boredom with the occasion, Sinclair assumed it was no more than a cultivated air.

'The CID?' Vane allowed a hint of curiosity to show on his face. 'Not Special Branch? Well, you've got me wondering, Sir Wilfred.' He sat back in his chair, surveying them both. 'What is it you wish to see me about?'

'One of our current investigations.' Bennett's reply came promptly. 'Or rather a series of investigations that are being conducted under the guidance of Scotland Yard. It goes without saying that we wouldn't be here now if the matter were not a grave one, nor if there was any way of resolving it without your personal assistance.' He looked directly at Vane. 'If you're agreeable, I'll now ask Chief Inspector Sinclair to explain in more detail.'

'Chief Inspector?' Vane turned his hooded gaze on the other man facing him. He appeared quite at ease.

Angus Sinclair opened the file that lay on his knee, using it to create an artificial pause while he pretended to sort some papers. He looked up.

'The investigations Sir Wilfred referred to concern a series of brutal murders committed in this country over the past few years. The first took place in 1929. A further two have occurred more recently, during the past summer. The victims were all young girls, children, either just in their teens or younger. They were raped and strangled. A common element in each of these crimes was a post-mortem assault carried out by the killer on his victims' faces. In the two most recent attacks he battered them to pulp.'

The chief inspector was disappointed to see no reaction from his listener.

'It's the first of these killings I want to discuss with you. It took place in July 1929, but because the victim's body was thrown into the Thames and not recovered until recently, it has only just been recognised that a crime occurred. Nevertheless, we've been able to determine with some certainty what happened that day. Briefly, a twelve-year-old girl was picked up by the murderer and taken in his car to the scene of the crime, a nudists' club called Waltham Manor, just outside Henley. We've also been able to identify the make of car the killer used. By good fortune—ours, at any rate—it turns out to have been a foreign-made machine that only went on sale in this country in the spring of that year. The list of those who purchased such a car in that period is short and we've had no trouble tracing them.'

'What make of car are you talking about?' Vane spoke in a dead voice.

'A Mercedes-Benz saloon.'

'You're aware that I own one, of course?' He remained expressionless. Sinclair nodded.

'Purchased in the same period we're discussing, too.' Vane's glance hadn't wavered. 'And on that basis alone, you feel justified in considering me a suspect? In *questioning* me? Please, Sir Wilfred . . .' He held up his hand as Bennett made to speak. 'Let the chief inspector answer.'

'No, Mr Vane. Not on that basis alone. From the moment these crimes came to our attention—I mean both the earlier and the more recent ones— we've been puzzled by the long gap in time separating them. Only lately have we acquired information that might possibly explain this. I emphasise the word *possibly*. Inquiries of this kind are largely a matter of eliminating suspects. That's what we're trying to do here.'

'Forgive me if I express some doubts on that score, Mr Sinclair. I think you came here with quite another object in mind. But you were saying— indicating, at any rate—that you had further reason to regard me with suspicion. Pray tell me what it is?' His manner had become glacial.

'By all means.' Sinclair met the other man's icy gaze without flinching. 'Following enquiries abroad, we have now been informed that a series of murders similar to the ones I've described are currently under investigation by the German police. These crimes fit into a very precise span of time: the first occurred in December 1929, and the sixth and last in April of this year. We are aware that you were posted to the British Embassy in Berlin in October 1929. And returned to England in early summer this year.'

Vane's eyes remained fixed on the chief inspector. But his gaze had turned glassy. Aware that the man had suffered a shock, Sinclair waited for him to speak. Philip Vane was clearly not an individual who would break easily; nevertheless, his response, when it came, proved to be a disappointment.

'And what is it you wish to ask me, Chief Inspector?' he said, calmly.

'Initially, I should like you to account for your movements on two separate days this summer. July the 27th and the 8th of September.'

Vane nodded. 'Those, I take it, would be the days on which the two most recent murders were committed?' He spoke in a toneless voice.

'Yes, sir. The first was near Bognor Regis, the second in Brookham, Surrey.'

Vane reached for a slim book bound in red leather. 'The 27th of July, you say . . .' He riffled through the pages without haste.

'Yes, sir. And September the 8th.'

Vane bent his head. 'The 27th was a Saturday, I see. I stayed in town that weekend, which is unusual. I had some work to do, I recall now. I've no engagements listed. In all likelihood I spent the day at my flat—it's in the Albany, though I dare say you know that—and dined at my club. To antici-pate your question, Chief Inspector, dinner apart, no, I don't believe my movements can be confirmed by anyone.'

There was a pause as Vane flipped through the pages.

'September the 8th was a Sunday. I spent that weekend with friends in Hampshire, this side of Winchester. I can give you their names if you like. Surrey, you said . . . where the other murder was committed . . . not that far away, then. And I left before lunch on the Sunday to drive back to London.' Vane shut the diary and sat down. 'Hardly an alibi, is it?'

He might have seemed unconcerned—he'd continued to speak in a flat voice throughout—were it not for his finger which began to tap on the desk-top in front of him. To the chief inspector it signalled anxiety. Yet he had the curious impression that he and Bennett had become irrelevant to whatever was going on in Vane's mind. Indeed, from the way his eyes strayed to the window just then he appeared to have forgotten their presence.

'The murder you were telling me about earlier—the one that took place near Henley—can you give me a date for that?' He spoke in a drawling voice. But his eyes, when he turned their way again, told a different story, the fixity of his stare reflecting some inner turmoil still under tight control.

'Yes, of course, sir. But I wouldn't ask you here and now to account for your movements so long in the past.'

Vane shook his head impatiently. 'The date, man.'

'The eighth of July,' Sinclair replied, after a pause.

Vane slid his hand beneath the rim of his desk and a bell sounded faintly in the outer office. The door opened behind them.

'Peter, would you find my personal diary for 1929 and bring it in, please.' Not troubling to look up, he sat staring at his desk and they waited in silence until the young man from outside appeared with an identical book bound in red leather and laid it in front of his superior.

'Thank you. That will be all.'

Before the door shut Vane had the book open and the other two watched while he found the page he wanted. He sat staring at it for a long time, then nodded, as though in confirmation of something he had suspected. He flicked backwards and forwards in the diary. Again he nodded. 'The girl was killed on the 8th, you say. The day before that I travelled from Oxford to Birmingham to stay with friends before continuing on to Scotland.' He shut the book. 'Naturally all that can be confirmed.'

Struck speechless by the revelation, Sinclair sat blinking. It was several moments before he could find his voice. 'You were in the Oxford area then?'

'Yes, on holiday. I was a guest of Sir Robert Hancock and his wife at their place near Woodstock. You're welcome to check my story with him.' Vane's tone had altered. To the surprise of the other two, he'd shed his hostile manner. But he showed no sign of relief at having in effect cleared himself. If anything, his anxiety had intensified. His finger had resumed its rapid tattoo on the desk in front of him.

'Did you travel to Birmingham, and to Scotland, in your car, sir?'

For the first time Vane seemed to find difficulty in formulating a reply. 'No, Chief Inspector,' he answered finally. 'I did not. I went by train.'

'You left it garaged in London?'

The question hung in the air between them until it became clear that Vane was not going to respond to it. Again his thoughts seemed to be elsewhere.

Bennett stirred. 'These questions *must* be answered,' he insisted.

Still Vane said nothing, and it was clear to Sinclair that something extra would be needed to shatter the wall of obduracy they were faced by. When Sinclair spoke again, it was in a sharpened tone. 'Sir, this man has killed nine children. Nine that we *know* of. I only ask you to consider what's at stake. If there's anything you can tell us—any small fact—'

'*Chief Inspector! I beg you!*'

Vane's anguished cry caught Sinclair off balance, and he stared back dumbstruck. It was the last thing he'd expected to hear.

'I *see* what's at stake. But the situation's not what you think. I'm not *protecting* anyone. I want to help you, believe me, but I fear we're too late.'

THE FOLDER was marked across one corner with a broad red stripe. Vane had placed the file on his desk a few moments before, having retrieved it from a safe at the back of his office. Some minutes had passed since his outburst, but although he'd regained control of himself, apologising to them both, he was unable to disguise the effects of the strong emotion he'd just experienced. Gone was the air of cold superiority. Anxiety marked his behaviour now and he seemed more human.

'We've only met socially, haven't we, Sir Wilfred?' Vane glanced up. 'I wonder if you're aware of the position I fill here at the Foreign Office?'

'Aware . . . no. At least, not officially.' Bennett allowed himself a slight smile. 'But I admit to having made some enquiries about you. I told Mr Sinclair earlier today that I believed you were engaged in intelligence work.'

'Did you, indeed?' Vane's elegantly raised eyebrow was a mark of his returning poise. 'Well, that clears the air, at any rate.' He looked at them both. 'We're all senior officials accustomed to the need for discretion. But I must stress that much of what I'm about to tell you is for your ears and these walls only, and in the event of it becoming public would almost certainly be denied.'

When the two Scotland Yard officers nodded, Vane continued. 'I'll start by giving you some background,' he said. 'There are various sides to intelligence gathering, but I'm referring now to just one of them: a category of persons whom we use to acquire certain kinds of information and to carry out particular assignments. Agents, in short—or spies, if you prefer. They're engaged mainly to carry out functions of a questionable nature that no diplomat or other government official could afford to be associated with. I regret to have to tell you that the man you're seeking is one of these.'

'An agent employed by this country?' Sinclair wanted to be clear on the point. Vane nodded.

'Would you give me his name?' Seeing the other hesitate, Sinclair said, 'I warn you now you have no right under any law to withhold it.'

'It's not that.' Vane shook his head. 'Of course I'll give you his name. But which? He's gone by so many. To us he's known as Wahl, Emil Wahl. But his real name is Gaston Lang. That's what he was christened.'

'Lang, you say?' Sinclair opened his notebook. As he reached for the pen in his pocket, he saw Vane shake his head.

'Write it down if you wish, Chief Inspector, but of all the names Lang might be using now, I can assure you it's the one he'll never go by again. He'd been working for us for many years by the time I met him—that was in the summer of 1929. But his association with our intelligence services goes back to the war.' Vane eyed his two listeners.

'At that time British intelligence had an outstanding agent working for them, a Swiss called Ernst Hoffmann. He was based in Geneva and through him and his contacts we were able to obtain an extraordinary amount of valuable information from inside Germany. Lang was his secretary.'

Vane frowned. 'We knew little about him. Apparently he grew up in an orphanage. Somehow he'd managed to catch the eye of Ernst Hoffmann and by the time our people got to know him he'd mastered several languages as well as other skills which his employer must have deemed necessary for his education. Hoffmann was an art dealer, by the way: it was a genuine business, and he used it as a cover for his other activities. He was already working for us before the war and during that period he used Lang as a courier and go-between to keep contact with his agents in Germany.

'So he was well placed to help us when war broke out, but in 1917 he died—and Lang was left to take over his work. With gratifying results, at least as far as our people were concerned. Hoffmann's death had thrown them into a panic and they were only too pleased to discover that this young man was able to carry on in his place, and just as effectively.

'However, about a year later, in the spring of 1918, he turned up without warning in France and made his way to the British sector of the front, in the north, where he reported to our intelligence branch. He had a curious tale to tell. He said he'd been identified as a British operative by German counter-intelligence agents in Switzerland who had succeeded in falsely incriminating him with the Swiss police. He'd only narrowly escaped arrest and had managed to slip across the border clandestinely into France.'

'*Incriminating* him?' Sinclair seized on the word. 'As a spy, do you mean?'

Vane shook his head. 'He was being sought for murder. The victim was a young girl.'

'Good Lord!' Bennett couldn't contain his astonishment.

Beside him, the chief inspector's eyes had narrowed. 'And they *believed* him? These so-called intelligence officials?'

Vane shrugged. 'It would have been difficult, if not impossible, to check the truth of his story at that time. The war was still going on, remember. He told them more. He said there'd been an attempt made on his life engineered by these same Germans in conjunction with two Swiss detectives who were in their pay. After a struggle he'd managed to escape, leaving one of the detectives dead. Stabbed. He carries a knife.'

'So now there were *two* murder charges against him.' Sinclair could hardly trust himself to speak.

Vane saw the look on his face. 'Try to understand how the situation must have appeared to our people. The war was being fought as fiercely as ever. Lang had brought a great deal of valuable information with him. He was the only person who knew the details of Hoffmann's network in Germany. The names of *his* agents. He was of immense value to the Allies.'

'So? What happened?'

'Lang disappeared. He was never heard of again. Emil Wahl, a citizen of Belgium, appeared in his place.'

'With all the proper credentials, I suppose?' Sinclair's voice was tight with anger.

Again Vane shrugged. 'I can only repeat, this was a special situation.' With a sigh, he went on. 'At this point I should mention that although Lang had worked for us in a number of European countries, because of this wartime episode he'd never been posted to Germany. However, after a dozen years the danger of exposure was felt to have diminished, and he himself raised no objection to being sent there.

'It was decided to bring him to London for the briefing he would need before setting off for Berlin. Since I didn't want him appearing at the Foreign Office, and since I was about to go on holiday anyway, I arranged for us to meet outside London.'

'Had he been in England long?' Sinclair asked. 'I'd like to get some idea of his movements.'

'I gathered he'd been here for several weeks and had visited different parts of the country. He'd wanted a holiday before taking up his assignment. I can't tell you where he went, but I know he's a birdwatcher—it's in his file.'

'Thank you.' The chief inspector inclined his head. 'You were saying you'd fixed a meeting with him?'

Vane nodded. 'I'd arranged to stay with these friends of mine outside Oxford, and since I was due to travel north myself on the 7th, I'd settled with Lang that we should meet the day before. He took the train up to Oxford and planned to spend a night or two at a hotel there before returning to London. I picked him up at the station and took him to a pub in Woodstock where I gave him a detailed briefing.'

He paused. 'I don't suppose I need tell you that the qualities required for the kind of work Lang did for us are . . . quite special. It's not a profession for the squeamish. But even so, there are limits . . . or ought to be.' Vane tapped the buff folder before him. 'Unfortunately I can't show you this. I'd be in breach of the law. But there are things in it you would find shocking. They certainly were to me. If I were asked to characterise it I would say it was not so much a record of a man without scruple, as one without moral sense. So you'll understand when I say I had considerable misgivings at the thought of working with him. Nor did this meeting of ours offer much in the way of reassurance.'

He mused for a moment, as though in recollection.

'It's not easy to describe the effect he had on me. In many ways he's quite ordinary. Soft-spoken; almost diffident in manner. And the business side of things went without a hitch. I found him quick to grasp what I was telling him, exceptionally so. But it was as though there was a barrier between us. Something real, but transparent, like a pane of glass. And he was on one side of it and I was on the other and there was no connection between us. No human bond. Thinking about it afterwards, I realised this feeling I had sprang from his glance. His eyes. They were quite dead.'

Vane reflected on what he had said. Then he shrugged.

'Later, when we were driving into Oxford, I made some reference to my car. It was new, as you know, but a minor problem had developed with the gears and I must have expressed some irritation over the fact that I couldn't now drive up to Scotland the following day, as I'd intended, but would either have to leave it in a garage in Oxford, or find some way of getting it back to London, so that the necessary repairs could be made while I was away.

'Lang said he planned to spend a day or two in Oxford, but would drive the car to London for me after that. I nearly refused his offer, for no other reason than that I'd taken such a dislike to him. But in the end I let him have it. If only I'd followed my instinct!'

Visibly upset, he stared out of the window where lights could be seen burning in other windows across the courtyard. 'What happened? Did he pick her up on the road?' He spoke without looking round.

'Yes, in Henley. She was running an errand for her mother.'

With a sigh, Vane turned to face them once more. 'The car was delivered to my garage in London, as promised. By the time I returned from Scotland, he was in Germany. I took up my own posting in Berlin in October. It was more than two years before I saw him again.'

'Despite the fact you were there all that time?' Sinclair was incredulous.

'Yes, it was important he should have no contact with our embassy in Berlin. He reported to me in writing.'

'Did his duties take him to Munich, by any chance?' Sinclair asked.

'Most certainly.' Vane hesitated. 'Look, there's no reason I shouldn't tell you what Lang was doing for us in Germany, provided you remain discreet about it. His specific brief was to join the Nazi party and cultivate contacts there. He was sent to Berlin with the assumed character of a representative of an Austrian textile firm. We'd so arranged it that the firm he was supposed to represent had business ties in Munich, and this provided him with an excuse

to go there and hang about the beer halls, make his face known.' He noticed
the glance that passed between his visitors. 'Why? Is that significant?'

'To us, yes.' Sinclair nodded. 'Two of the murders I've spoken of took
place in the Munich region.'

Vane absorbed the information with a frown. He made no comment.
'Well, so much for our plans. Now I'll tell you what occurred. For the first
year or so everything ran like clockwork. Then, midway through the second
year, Lang's work began to fall off. His reports became irregular and showed
signs of diminishing activity on his part. I was beginning to think a face-to-
face meeting between us might be necessary when I received a message from
him asking for just that. He wanted to see me urgently so we met at a small
hotel outside Berlin, where he told me he wanted to cut short his assignment
and leave Germany. He gave as his reason his growing suspicion that he'd
been identified as a British agent. He insisted he was in danger and said he
could no longer carry on with his work.'

'*When* was this?' Sinclair broke in. 'Can you be precise?'

'Early in June of this year. Does that tell you anything?'

'Yes, the last in the chain of murders occurred in April. The Bavarian
authorities got a lead from it and with the Berlin police mounted a newspaper campaign to identify the killer. Lang must have been aware of that.'
Sinclair paused, curious. 'What did *you* make of his behaviour?' he asked.

Vane shrugged. 'As regards his being exposed as one of our agents, I was
far from convinced. After all, his activities weren't directed against the
state. But something was clearly amiss.' He hesitated. 'I won't pretend I had
any sympathy for him. I found him no less alien than before. But I couldn't
discount the possibility that he might be cracking up, and so it was decided
we should withdraw him, temporarily at least. He let it be known he'd been
called back to Vienna on some pretext and left Berlin.'

'But came to England?' The chief inspector was listening closely.

'Yes, we brought him back here discreetly. I took the opportunity to return
to London myself at that time. We wanted to keep him under our eye until it
had been decided what to do next. He was told to take it easy for a few
weeks, and we arranged for him to receive treatment at a clinic in Sussex.'

'For what, precisely?'

'The doctors found he was suffering from nervous exhaustion, which was
no surprise. Other agents have reacted to the pressures of their work in similar ways. But I was more interested in what their psychiatrist had to say, a
man called Bell. In his first report he described Lang as an unusual patient,

one whose personality he found disturbing, but difficult to penetrate.'

'Was that all he had to say?' Sinclair frowned.

'At that stage, yes. Lang was treated simply for strain. He was encouraged to relax. On the advice of the doctors we'd provided him with a car
and I understand he spent time driving about the countryside.'

'Did he, indeed?' The coolness had returned to Sinclair's manner. 'Well,
I dare say he found occasion to pass by Bognor Regis. One of the two murders I mentioned took place near there, as you may recall.'

Vane said nothing. After a moment, he continued. 'In due course we
received a full report from the clinic, in which Bell said he had little doubt
Lang was suffering from some acute psychological disorder and cautioned
us to be wary in our dealings with him.'

'For heaven's sake!' Bennett struck his thigh in impatience. 'Couldn't he
have been more specific?'

'I thought so. So I rang him up to see if I could discover more, but at first
he merely repeated what he'd said earlier: that Lang was someone we'd do
well to keep at arm's length. When I pressed him further, however, he
informed me that various aspects of Lang's behaviour had given him cause
for concern, and one more than any other, which he termed "a lack of ade-
quate emotional response", a condition most psychiatrists regarded as
being inaccessible to treatment. Those who displayed its symptoms frequently felt no guilt or responsibility for their actions, he said, adding it was
one of the classic signs of a psychopath.'

'And what effect did that have on your colleagues?' Sinclair asked.

Vane eyed him. 'Some of us were shocked, certainly. And since I was the
person who'd had to deal with him it fell to me to press the case for dispens-
ing with his services. Using Bell's words as ammunition, I insisted that he
was a man we could no longer trust and that it was time to cut our ties with
him for good.' He laughed harshly. 'My arguments cut no ice at all with those
that mattered. I was reminded that Lang was one of our best agents, with a
long record of achievement. As for his flaws of character, they were no more
than one might expect from one engaged in so dubious a profession.

'It was decided to send him back to Berlin. His claim to have been
unmasked as a British agent had been proven to be groundless, so he was
instructed to return to Germany without delay and resume his assignment.'

'And how did he respond? Did he accept the decision?'

'He seemed to. But then two days later, what amounted to a letter of res-
ignation reached us through the post. He said he'd reviewed his position and

decided he could no longer continue in our employment. He was returning to Brussels—that's where he was based—and would leave the car we'd provided him with at a garage in Dover. Where, incidentally, it was recovered later. Enquiries made at the ferry ticket office revealed that a man answering his description had booked a cross-Channel passage the day before.'

'Was that all? Are you telling me no attempt was made to stop him, or bring him back?' Sinclair was disbelieving.

Vane shrugged. 'We couldn't force him to work for us. Moreover, he knew a good deal about our intelligence activities; the last thing we wanted to do was antagonise him. We decided to let sleeping dogs lie.'

'So you had no further contact with him?'

'None whatsoever. Since then there's been no sign of him in Brussels— or anywhere else we might have expected to catch up with him.'

'Hardly surprising, given that it's clear he remained in England.' The chief inspector made no effort to hide his chagrin. 'This man has made fools of you and your colleagues, Mr Vane. He got you to spirit him out of Germany, leaving no trace behind. That's twice you saved his miserable skin.'

'I'm only too aware of that, Chief Inspector.' Vane held his accuser's gaze without flinching. But his remorse was plain.

'I need some dates from you, sir.' Sinclair sought to keep a rein on his temper. 'When did he enter the clinic, and how long was he there?'

'He arrived towards the end of June and disappeared in mid-August.'

'The Bognor Regis killing occurred in late July, when he was still a patient, then. But the Brookham murder was in September, long after he was supposed to have gone home. Why did he choose to stay in this country? And more important—where do I look for him now? How do I find this man?'

SINCLAIR'S GAZE remained fixed on the photograph Vane had taken from his folder a short while back and handed to them.

An ordinary snapshot, it showed an ordinary man in a black coat and homburg, standing before the wall of a building.

'That's the only one we have of him, I'm afraid.' Vane had been apologetic. 'He's not a man who likes to have his picture taken.'

He had added a description of their quarry, which the chief inspector had noted down. 'He's in his early forties, of average height, lean and fit. Wiry. Stronger than he looks. But his appearance is nondescript: brown hair, brown eyes and with no scars or other identifying marks.'

'What about a birthmark?' Sinclair asked. 'We understand he might have one. He was seen half-naked by a witness to one of his murders.'

'I don't know about that . . .' Vane frowned. 'But wait a minute . . . he must have had a full medical examination at the clinic.'

He opened his file and sorted through the contents.

'Yes, here it is . . .' He picked out a sheet of paper and studied it. 'Well, I never . . . you're quite right. It's on his upper chest. A large naevus flammeus.'

'What else? Any peculiarities he possesses?' Although Sinclair tried to moderate the sharpness of his manner, his anger remained unabated.

'Apart from the fact that he speaks English with an accent, none. He'd be easy to miss in a crowd. Up close, though, it's a different matter. That curious quality I spoke of—a sort of lifelessness—it's unsettling.'

On the crucial question of Lang's whereabouts, Vane could offer only cautious advice. 'It's been three months since he disappeared. What his intentions were is anyone's guess. What I can tell you is that he's probably changed his name. He won't be Emil Wahl any longer. He'll have covered his tracks.'

The chief inspector's response had been to repeat the question he'd put earlier. 'What interests me is why he chose to remain *here*. Why not go?'

It appeared Vane had been pondering the same riddle. 'If you want my opinion, he'd already made up his mind not to return to Europe. Given his situation as he sees it, he'd be bound to look further afield for a place of refuge in the long run. On another continent, perhaps.'

The chief inspector gestured with the snapshot he was holding. 'I'll take this with me, if I may. I want to circulate it, along with a description of Lang.'

'Please do. And I promise to comb through this file for any information that might be of use to you.' Vane watched as the chief inspector tucked the photograph in among his papers. Bennett had already risen to his feet.

'I shall have to inform my colleagues of this meeting.' Vane, too, rose. 'They won't take kindly to what I have to tell them,' he said. 'The thought that Lang might be brought to trial in open court will start all sorts of alarm bells ringing. I do urge you again to tread carefully in this matter.'

He had addressed his last remark to Sinclair, who had not yet got to his feet. Too late he saw his mistake. The chief inspector's face had hardened.

'I'll be frank with you, Mr Vane. I've no sympathy whatever for your colleagues, or their anxieties. It occurs to me, though, that they might feel differently if they were given some idea of what this investigation will involve. Sexual criminals of Lang's type are every policeman's nightmare. They kill at random, you see, and this absence of any link makes them among the hardest to track down. They appear to act from compulsion—a psychologist would certainly tell you so—they can't stop themselves. As time goes by, whatever inhibitions they feel seem to grow weaker, with the result that intervals between attacks tend to shorten.'

Sinclair rose and began to button his coat.

'I'm sure your colleagues will feel concern when you point out to them that more than two months have passed since that child was murdered at Brookham, a long time as these things go, and that wherever Lang is now the chances are he'll be looking for a fresh victim and there's nothing I, or anyone else can do about that. Except pray he hasn't found her already.'

9

After a bite of lunch in Midhurst Sam Watkin drove out to Hobday's Farm, near Rogate, to check that the roof he'd fixed was holding up before calling in at Coyne's Farm.

His plans for making Eddie's life a little brighter had succeeded beyond his best hopes. The day after their encounter he'd picked his old friend up at the roadworks and brought him home to supper, as he'd promised. On the way over he'd given him the good news about the barn at Coyne's Farm and how Mr Cuthbertson had agreed to let him sleep there if he liked.

Eddie's face had lit up and Sam had realised how much he must have hated having to bunk down in that cramped shed with the other men.

Next day he'd collected him again after work and taken him up the path that led over the ridge to the farm. He'd shown him the gap in the hedge that gave onto an orchard and the walled kitchen garden. Beyond lay the farm-yard where the barn stood. Sam had unlocked the double doors.

'Here—you keep this.' He'd tossed Eddie the key to the padlock. 'It's a spare. Be sure and lock the doors each morning when you go to work. I told Mr Cuthbertson you'd keep an eye on the place.'

On his way from Rogate now he paused at the roadworks to tell Eddie he'd leave some stuff that Ada had sent for him at the barn. He hadn't far to drive on. The crew was advancing along the road and now was much closer to the point where it was crossed by Wood Way, and where a space for park-ing had been cleared. In summer, ramblers left their cars there to walk onto the Downs, but today there was only one other vehicle in the car park, and that was half-hidden by the branches of an overhanging oak.

Sam left his van at the edge of the area, near the road, and then walked up Wood Way, over the ridge, with Sal at his heels, carrying Ada's bundle.

Inside the barn he found a number of spots where the roof had leaked, but none at the back over the corner Eddie was occupying.

The first day he had brought him over, the two of them had quickly set the place to rights. They hadn't walked over unburdened, either. Remembering the lamps he'd found, Sam had brought a tin of oil with him, and a small brazier, as well, while Eddie had lugged a bag of coke to build himself a fire.

'Don't worry, Sam. I'll empty the brazier each morning before I leave. I won't burn the place down, I promise.'

He'd been as good as his word, Sam saw now. In fact, Eddie had left few traces of his presence. The mound of hay he used as a mattress was pushed neatly into the corner, but his bedding and the rest of his stuff were nowhere to be seen and must have been stowed away in one of the cupboards.

When they'd done all they needed to at the barn, Sam had suggested that they walk over to Oak Green so that he could show Eddie where he could buy whatever provisions he might need, not knowing what a lucky encounter was awaiting them there.

As they reached the small cluster of houses, the door of the village shop had opened and Nell Ramsay had stepped out into the narrow street. Catching sight of Sally, who was ambling along at their side, the girl had let out a whoop of delight and come running up to greet them.

Sam hadn't noticed she was with anyone until he heard a grown-up's voice behind him. 'I can see we're not going to be introduced, Mr Watkin.' A woman had joined them. She was smiling. 'I'm Nell's mother. I've been hearing for months about you and Sally. I'm so glad we've met at last.'

Dark-haired like her daughter, Mrs Ramsay had offered them her hand, and Sam had seen at once where Nell got her looks from.

Learning that they had walked over from Coyne's Farm, Mrs Ramsay had insisted that they have tea with her and Nell before returning. Sam had accepted without pausing to consider how uncomfortable the prospect might have made Eddie. (He was still in his work clothes, grimy and unshaven.) But as soon as they'd reached the house, a handsome, double-storeyed dwelling, she had shown Eddie to a bathroom, saying, 'You must be longing for a chance to clean up, Mr Noyes. Please don't hurry. We're going to have tea in the kitchen. It's nice and warm there, and Sally can join us.'

During the few minutes they'd had to themselves Sam had explained to her why Eddie was staying at Coyne's Farm, why he looked so down and out.

'He lost his job for no reason, the way people do these days. Bravest bloke I ever knew. They gave him a military medal in the war. Now he has to pick up work wherever he can. It doesn't seem right.'

'I do so agree with you, Mr Watkin,' Mrs Ramsay said.

When Eddie returned—a lot cleaner, but still shy and unsure of himself—she had made a point at once of getting him to talk, asking him where he came from and what his background was. Soon Eddie had been chatting away, telling her about his home near Hove and his mother and sister, the one suffering from angina, the other still mourning the husband she'd lost.

Nor would Mrs Ramsay listen for a moment when he told her he planned to come over to Oak Green from time to time to buy provisions for himself. 'You can't possibly spend all day working and not have a proper meal at night. Even if I'm not here, Bess will have something hot for you.'

'Course I will, Mr Noyes.' The Ramsays' cook had smiled encouragingly. A plump, red-faced woman, she had listened to their conversation with avid interest. 'Just put your head in the kitchen door. I'll be here.'

It had been almost dark by the time they had left to return to Coyne's Farm. Nell had slipped outside earlier—to show Sally the garden, she said—and they had walked with Mrs Ramsay round to the front and watched as the girl raced about in the gathering shadows, with Sal labouring in pursuit.

It was the first time Sam had seen her out of school uniform. Dressed in a plaid skirt and a fair-isle sweater she looked more grown-up. But the high-pitched cries that rang out over the lawn had been those of a child still.

It seemed her mother shared his thoughts. Earlier, Sam had told her about Rosie and Josh, his and Ada's two, and now she glanced at him wistfully.

'They grow up so quickly,' she had said with a sigh.

SMILING IN reminiscence, Sam looked at his watch. It was getting on for four. Nell would be back from school soon. They might meet her on the path. He and Sally had walked up to the ridge behind the farm after locking the barn. Sam had left Ada's bundle on the broken washstand, where Eddie would see it.

Sam's gaze had been fixed on the valley: he'd been running his eye along the length of the stream, checking for signs of life, when his eye was caught by the figure of a man in the farmyard below; he was standing in the middle of the expanse of cobbles, gazing about him. Dressed in tweeds, he had a pair of binoculars in a leather case slung from one shoulder, and the sight of them rang a bell in Sam's memory.

Wasn't this the same bloke he'd seen on the ridge opposite, across the valley, a couple of weeks back? The one he'd taken for a birdwatcher?

His first assumption was that the fellow must have walked up Wood Way, noticed the gap in the hedge and decided to see where it led. It was something that happened with ramblers often enough.

But soon it became clear that the man hadn't got there by accident. Not judging by the interest he was taking in the yard. He went over to a tap that stood against the wall by the back door and turned it on, apparently to check that it was working.

Watching from above, it occurred to Sam that the bloke must have heard the farm was for sale and come to look it over. He was just wondering whether he ought to wander down and offer his assistance, when something happened that drove any notion of a friendly gesture out of his mind.

The man had turned his attention to the barn and finding the doors bolted, he'd begun to fiddle with the padlock. Now, under Sam's disbelieving gaze, he took a penknife from his jacket pocket and began to pick at it.

'*Oi!*' Not sure even if he was within earshot, Sam gave vent to his outrage. 'That's enough of that! Come on, old girl—'

Without waiting for Sal, he marched off down the slope, intending to ask the intruder what he was up to. But once he'd descended from the ridge he lost sight of the tweed-suited figure, and by the time he reached the yard— it had taken him only a few minutes—the cobbled space stood empty.

Sam noticed that the gate to the walled kitchen garden was open. Apparently the man had left the same way he'd come.

Pausing only to check that the padlock was secure, he went after him, hastening through the garden and the orchard beyond, then slipping out through the hedge onto Wood Way.

There he saw that the fellow had already put some distance between them. He was up near the top of the path, approaching the crest of the ridge.

'*Oi! You!*' Sam yelled after him again, but with no more effect than before. Either the bloke hadn't heard him, or he chose not to look round.

'*Go on, then. Hop it!*' Bellowing his frustration, he was distracted by the sight of another figure on the path, ahead of the man, which he recognised. It was Nell. Unmistakable in her white school hat and navy gym-slip, she'd just come over the ridge from the road on the other side, where the bus dropped her. As Sam watched, the two of them passed one another without stopping. A few moments later the man disappeared from sight over the brow of the hill.

Nell, meanwhile, was drawing closer, breaking into a trot as she came to the steeper part of the downslope, waving to them.

'Hello, Mr Watkin . . . hello, Sally.'

Breathless, her cheeks apple-pink, the girl arrived at the spot where they were standing and at once collapsed in a heap on the ground. Sally's whines of welcome were rewarded with a hug. Sam watched them, smiling.

'You look done in,' he remarked.

'I am. I almost missed the bus. I had to chase it for *ages*.'

He waited until she had caught her breath. Then he asked, 'That bloke you passed on the path—'

'The one you were shouting at?' Nell raised her eyes to his.

'Have you seen him before? Around here, I mean?'

'No, I don't think so . . . why?' She brushed the hair from her eyes.

'I caught him poking about in the farmyard, trying to get into the barn.'

'He must have a guilty conscience. You should have seen the look he gave me.' She giggled.

'Look? What look?' The words brought a scowl to Sam's face.

'Oh, you know . . . just a look.' Nell had noticed his reaction. 'It was nothing . . . really.' She began to collect her things. 'It's been so nice having Mr Noyes come over after work.' She looked up. 'Bess absolutely *dotes* on him. I don't know *what* she'll do when he leaves.'

'Eddie's going to miss you all.' Sam helped her to her feet. 'He told me so.'

'Did he? Well, we'll miss him, too. Won't we, Sally?' She bent to bestow her customary kiss on the dog's head. 'Goodbye, Mr Watkin.'

'Goodbye, love.' He watched as she went off, waiting until he had seen her take the fork to Oak Green. Then he turned and, with Sally at his side, started up the path, heading back to the van. 'Gave her a look, did he?' Sam frowned. He didn't like the sound of it. 'Just what was he doing, poking about in the yard, eh, Sal?'

'I'LL BE HONEST with you, John. I doubt we'll ever lay hands on him. Even supposing he's still in England, where do we begin? He has no friends, or family, no occupation we'd recognise as such and no ties to any part of the country. I've just spent the morning telling a group of overworked policemen I've every confidence a well-organised search will uncover his whereabouts, when I think nothing of the sort.'

Angus Sinclair had barely allowed Madden time to greet him and to take his hat before launching into a catalogue of complaints and self-criticism.

The chief inspector had driven to Highfield from Guildford, where a conference of senior detectives had been convened at his request. On the assumption that Lang had been staying in the Surrey/Sussex area prior to the Brookham murder, a search of local hotels and boarding houses was being organised. Sinclair hadn't planned on seeing Madden when he'd set out from London earlier, but as the morning wore on and his dissatisfaction with what he was doing mounted, the temptation to call on his old friend and colleague—the thought of finding at least one sympathetic ear into which to pour his troubles—had become irresistible. A telephone call to the farm had resulted in an invitation to lunch, a proposal Sinclair had been doubly pleased to accept when he'd learned that Helen was taking surgery for a friend in Chiddingfold that day. For the chief inspector had no illusions as to how Madden's wife would react to any fresh attempt on his part to further involve her husband in the inquiry, and he wanted to be able to speak freely and frankly to his friend. What he had to say caused even Madden to express some uneasiness on his behalf.

'Should you be telling me all this, Angus? Doesn't it fall within the Defence of the Realm Act?'

'Damn the Act and damn British intelligence, whoever they may be!'

The chief inspector's mood had already been soured earlier that week on receipt, from Philip Vane, of the information he'd promised to extract from Gaston Lang's confidential file. Rich though it proved to be in details of Lang's movements in Europe, and of the aliases he'd used, it had left Sinclair with the feeling that he'd been handed a bar of soap too slippery to hold on to.

The knowledge that he was being less than frank with his police colleagues had further soured his mood. 'They must have known I wasn't telling them all I knew, John. At the very least they must have wondered how I knew all about Lang's travels abroad.'

Casting all discretion aside, the chief inspector had then embarked on a detailed account of the visit he and Bennett had paid to the Foreign Office. His discourse took them through lunch and coffee and was still not complete when they wandered outside onto the terrace for some air.

'So that's where we stand, John. And I'm damned if I know what to do.'

Madden grunted. 'So that birthmark Beezy spotted was real. Have you been able to make use of the information?'

'Not really.' Sinclair shook his head. 'Since the mark's on his chest, it's hidden by his clothing. Still, I've decided to take a long shot. We're having leaflets sent out to all doctors in Surrey and Sussex asking them if they've treated any man with a large port wine stain recently—not a regular patient, of course—and warning them that he's dangerous.'

They stood in silence while the mist thickened about them. Then a groan issued from Sinclair's lips.

'Damn it, it's not enough. Is there nothing else we can do?'

The silence that was Madden's only response seemed to speak louder than words, and to the chief inspector his dark withdrawn gaze was a confirmation of his own worst fears, to which he now gave expression, his voice harsh with anger at the need he felt to say it.

'Must we wait till he kills again?'

DARKNESS WAS FALLING—it was getting on for five—by the time Eddie Noyes left the site, waving goodbye to the McCarthys, Pat and Jimmy, both from County Mayo, but not related, they said, who'd become special pals of his, and acknowledging the raised hands of some of the others as well. It being a Friday, and the end of their working week, the men had taken longer than usual to gather their tools and put things in order before they departed.

They were a good set of blokes, a dozen men in all, half of them Irish, and their companionship had reminded Eddie of nothing so much as his time in the ranks. It hadn't been easy, fitting in, at first, and as someone not used to manual work he'd had to prove himself in the early days by taking on some of the dirtiest and hardest jobs, before they'd accepted him as one of them.

He had joined the crew some months earlier when they were working on a bit of road near Hove, where he lived. Hearing they were looking for labour, he'd pitched up on the off chance and been taken on. He had lost his salesman's job the previous December and was ready to jump at anything that was offered. The burden of providing for his mother and sister, who shared the small house they lived in, weighed heavily on him.

Continuing along the road, Eddie reached the point where it was crossed by the path that led to Coyne's Farm. Having reached the crest of the ridge, Eddie quickened his pace. The long twilights of summer were a thing of the past and darkness fell swiftly at this time of year. But a new moon had risen in the past few days that would light his way to Oak Green later.

Shy at first of accepting the invitation that had been extended to him, he had come to delight in the hours he spent in the Ramsays' kitchen. He even felt in a strange way that he had become a part of the family, part of the household at least. And he had to admit that what Sam had said jokingly was true—Bess, the Ramsays' cook, did seem to have a soft spot for him.

His presence there was so accepted that when Mrs Ramsay looked in, she would sit down—checking his movement to rise to his feet—and begin talking at once about whatever was in her mind, just as though a conversation they had been having earlier had been interrupted.

What concerned Mrs Ramsay at present was whether she ought to continue to allow her daughter to return home from school on her own.

The shortening hours of daylight were one reason why she was thinking of putting an end to the practice, that plus the fact that now that the autumn was almost over and winter approaching, the path Nell took to Oak Green from the bus stop was increasingly deserted.

'I really think I ought to put a stop to it—at least until the spring—but Nell won't hear of it and she's managed to get her father to take her part. What do you think, Mr Noyes?'

Though Eddie secretly agreed with Mrs Ramsay—most days he didn't see a living soul on the path when he walked back to the barn after work—he was reluctant to say so as he felt it would seem like a betrayal of the child's friendship. And while he recognised that her openness was most likely an unconscious copy of her mother's manner, he found it hard to resist.

Some weeks earlier, when he'd still been shy of accepting the invitation extended to him, she had walked down the road from the bus stop on her way back from school in order to press him again on her mother's behalf to call on them.

Her message delivered, Nell had lingered to watch the men at work— they were tarring a stretch of road when she arrived—questioning them in her unaffected way, taking it for granted they would welcome her curiosity, which they had, to the point where even old Harrigan, the foreman, had shed the beetle-browed scowl with which he had first greeted the sight of her slim figure darting among the busy men and taken it on himself to initiate her into the mysteries of macadamised roads.

Thereafter the men had watched for her every afternoon, looking up from their work when the bus from Midhurst went by to wave to the smiling face in the window. 'Look, there's Nell,' they would call out. 'Hello, Nell!'

Chuckling now at the memory, Eddie quickened his pace still further. He was impatient to get over to Oak Green. Mrs Ramsay had told him that her husband was engaged in auditing a large stationery company's books in Chichester and had made some discreet enquiries about sales vacancies. He hoped to have some news for him tonight.

He slipped through the gap in the hedge and walked through the orchard, and into the weed-filled expanse of old beds that was the kitchen garden. Another gate on the opposite side of the rectangular plot gave access to the yard and there Eddie paused for a moment, his eye caught by the sight of the moon, rising over the looming outline of the barn. He went on and had covered perhaps half the length of the yard when it struck him that the gap between the barn doors was marked by a thin thread of light coming from the inside.

Eddie's first thought was that Sam had dropped in to pay him a visit, but he dismissed the notion at once. Today was a Friday—not one of the days he called at Coyne's Farm, and his van had not been parked by the road.

Then he remembered something else. Only a few days before Sam had told him about the man he'd seen snooping about in the yard.

'I didn't like the look of him, or the way he behaved, so if you see anyone hanging about the place—about my size and dressed like a toff—tell him to shove off,' he'd said.

Eddie strode across the yard, his boot heels ringing on the cobbles. When he reached the barn he saw that the bolt on the doors had been drawn and the padlock, which somehow had been opened, hung loose from it.

He pulled the doors open and looked inside. There was a light burning at the far end of the barn, but he couldn't see where it was coming from.

'Who's there?' he called out loudly.

Silence greeted his words.

'Come on out. I know you're there.'

Again there was no response. Eddie strained his ears, trying to pick up any sound from inside, but heard nothing. The silence was unbroken.

He stepped inside and strode down the broad corridor formed by the hurdles, which were stacked up on either side of him above head height. At the end of this artificial passageway, the rest of the barn's contents— canvas-draped pieces of furniture and odd bits of farm equipment—had been stored haphazardly, turning the area, cloaked in shadow now, into an obstacle course through which he had to pick his way to the back of the building.

There a further surprise awaited him. The source of the light proved to be one of the oil lamps he used himself. It was hanging from a nail in the wood above the corner where he slept, somewhere he would never have placed it himself. He and Sam had agreed that both lamps and brazier should be kept well away from the straw bedding for fear of starting a fire.

Of the intruder himself there was no sign. With the whole of the rear of the barn illuminated, Eddie could see that it was deserted. But if his visitor had made himself scarce, it was plain he had not been idle.

The mound of hay that served him as a mattress had been enlarged to more than double its size and filled the corner. He spied a pitchfork that must have been used for the purpose lying on the floor beside it, the prongs upturned as though it had been dropped in haste.

Eddie scratched his head. At first glance it looked as though whoever had broken in had been seeking a place to spend the night. But that didn't make sense. Or rather, it hardly fitted in with the picture Sam had drawn of the supposed intruder. A toff, he'd called him.

He shrugged. There was no point in racking his brains about it. Clearly the fellow had run off. The riddle would remain unanswered.

Meantime, he thought he'd better check on his own belongings to make sure they were safe. Tidy by nature, he had put his toilet articles in the small cupboard beneath the washstand Sam had provided him with, while his bedroll and spare clothes were stowed away in a tall mahogany wardrobe.

He went to the washstand first, but as he bent to open the cupboard doors he had a flash of intuition that made the hairs on the back of his neck stand up. He whirled round.

The figure of a man had appeared behind him, as if from nowhere. Half hidden in the shadows, he stood at the edge of the circle of light cast by the lamp, in one of the narrow alleys that led into the piles of stored furniture.

'So there you are!' Angry at being given such a fright, Eddie let his feelings show. 'Didn't you hear me call out?'

The man made no reply. Well dressed, he was wearing a tweed coat with a soft hat of the same material pulled down low over his forehead.

'What are you doing here, anyway?'

Eddie scowled. There was something he didn't understand. The fellow had been hiding in the shadows for the past few minutes, not wanting to be discovered. He could easily have slipped away during that time, crept out of the barn and escaped, but instead he had chosen to show himself.

'Don't you know this is private property?' he demanded.

Thus far the man had shown no reaction to the words addressed to him. It was as though he had not been listening. But his eyes, sharp behind gold-rimmed spectacles, were busy. He was studying Eddie closely, examining him from head to toe, and now he spoke: 'Who are you?' he asked. His voice was low and rasping, the accent guttural and foreign-sounding.

'Never mind who I am.' Eddie fairly bristled with anger. The unblinking stare to which he was being subjected had made him conscious of his own appearance: of his torn clothes and unwashed body. It was quite possible the fellow had taken him for a tramp, which would explain his apparent lack of concern at being discovered trespassing. 'You're the one breaking the law. I've a good mind to set the police on you.'

At the word 'police', the man's manner changed. He seemed to stiffen, and as their eyes met Eddie felt a tingle of alarm. The man moved forward, edging to his right and turning so that the lamp was behind him. To Eddie, the manoeuvre seemed hostile: the light was shining in his eyes now.

'Look, I've had just about enough of you, whoever you are,' he declared. 'This is your last warning. Hop it, or you'll get what's coming to you.'

Suiting words to action, he stepped forward, reducing the distance between them, staring the intruder straight in the eye. Although the fellow hadn't offered him any violence—he'd been standing all this time with his hands thrust into his coat pockets—his attitude had implied a challenge.

The man took a step back, raising his right hand in a gesture of surrender. He turned and began to move away towards the doors. Relieved to see the crisis was over, Eddie relaxed. The tension of the last few minutes had kept his muscles taut as bowstrings. Now he let them go loose, shifting his weight back onto his heels, and was helpless to react when the man struck.

Without warning the stranger wheeled round, bringing his left hand into view and swinging it like a boxer's punch into Eddie's unprotected side. So swift was his action that Eddie caught only a glimpse of the knife in his hand before it was buried in his flesh. But the force of the blow made him gasp, and as the blade was withdrawn, then driven in a second time, up beneath his ribs, a pain like nothing he had ever experienced shot through his innards. He sank to his knees.

The floor of the barn was only inches away from his staring eyes and at the periphery of his vision he was aware of a pair of shoes pointing at him. As he watched, one of them drew back, and then came forward, accelerating. His senses, drowned by the flood of pain that was spreading like fire from the centre of his stomach, barely registered the sharp blow to his side.

He heard a grunt from above, followed by words spoken in a foreign language. Just as his consciousness was fading, hands grasped at his clothes and the next thing he knew he was being rolled over onto his back.

Once more he almost lost consciousness: the surging pain inside him seemed to have no limit. But when his wits cleared, he became aware of some activity not far from where he lay, and by turning his head a fraction was able to make out the figure of his assailant, who was clearing a pathway into the heaps of stored furniture, pushing aside strips of trailing canvas.

Just past his own feet he could see the pitchfork lying beside the gathered hay, but it was too far away for him to reach, and in any case all physical effort was beyond him.

Or so he thought until he heard the man returning to where he lay and through half-closed lids watched as he crouched to take hold of his legs, as if to drag his body to some other location. But his first attempt to shift it was thwarted by the boots Eddie was wearing, which prevented him from getting a firm grip on his ankles. Muttering, the man tore open the laces and flung the boots aside, then took a fresh grip and threw his weight back.

It was the moment Eddie had been waiting for. With what remained of his strength, he jerked his right foot free of the grasping fingers and kicked, catching the man on the forehead with his heel and sending him tumbling backwards. His despairing effort was rewarded by a cry of pain as the man rolled free of the upthrust prongs of the pitchfork, plucking at his back.

Eddie could do no more. Emptied now and strangely at peace, he watched as his attacker clambered to his feet and, with the pitchfork clutched in his hands and raised to strike, advanced on him.

He prepared himself for the death blow he knew was coming. As he stared unflinching at the looming form above him, his consciousness faded and the light that had shone so brightly in his eyes went out.

10

'I wish I had better news for you, John. Or any news at all. We've been checking hotels and boarding houses, but there's no trace of him.' Angus Sinclair's clipped tones couldn't disguise the weariness in his voice. At the other end of the telephone line, Madden listened with a heavy heart. More than a week had passed since the chief inspector had unburdened himself at their meeting; they had not spoken since.

'And there's been nothing from abroad?'

'No sightings, if that's what you mean. But the Geneva police have confirmed that Lang's wanted there on a double murder charge. We've also been in touch with the Belgian police. Lang—or Wahl, as he called himself—kept a small flat in Brussels. It's been empty since he went to Germany, but the concierge keeps an eye on it for him.'

'Did they search the flat?'

'They did. No incriminating evidence was found but they discovered a number of works of ornithology in his bookshelves. I've had Styles making enquiries among the birdwatching societies. Nothing's come of it as yet. But hope springs eternal.' The chief inspector's sigh suggested otherwise.

Like his old chief, John Madden had been tormented by one particular anxiety as the weeks passed: that the longer the killer remained at large, the more likely it was he would strike again. But when news of a fresh tragedy reached him later that day, it came from a quarter he had not foreseen.

'IT WAS Molly Henshaw found him, sir. She'd been taking him his meals each day. After his wife left, that is . . .'

'Mrs Bridger left her husband?' Madden was finding it difficult to come to terms with what Will Stackpole was telling him. The Highfield constable, tall in his helmet, stood like a pillar in the misty driveway in front of the house. Drawn up a little way off was an old Morris with its bonnet raised. Billy Styles was leaning on the mudguard, peering down at the motor.

'She hadn't walked out on him. But she said she couldn't go on living in that cottage, not with the child gone, not with the memories. So she went to live with her sister in Liphook. Bridger stayed on. He had his job, I suppose, but even there things weren't going well. He'd started drinking and the farmer he worked for got rid of him not long ago. After that he went to pieces. Poor Molly. To come on a man hanging from his own rafters!'

Lost for words, Madden stared at the ground. He too had only got back a short while before, having fetched Rob from school.

'The Henshaws have got word to his wife. She's coming over.'

Madden shook his head helplessly. In his mind was the memory of the child's body lying beside the stream while thunder crashed above. Catching a look in the constable's eye, he saw that they shared the same thought.

'It's never just the victim, is it?' Stackpole's growl came from deep in his chest. 'It's everything else that comes with it, the pain it spreads . . .'

The sound of footsteps approaching on the gravel made Madden look up. 'How'd you come to be there, Billy?'

'I happened to be at Albury, sir.' The sergeant wiped his oil-smeared fingers on a piece of rag. 'I heard there was some trouble at Brookham, so I drove over . . . and found Will at the Henshaws'.'

The three men stood in silence for a few moments. Then Madden stirred.

'Come inside, both of you. We'll have a drink together.'

'Not for me, thank you, sir. I ought to be getting back.' Stackpole's glance remained grim beneath his helmet. He shook Madden's hand and then clapped his colleague on the shoulder. 'I'll see you soon, Billy.' Wheeling about, he strode off down the drive.

'Albury?' Madden glanced questioningly at Billy.

'I went there to see a birdwatcher, sir.' The sergeant smiled. He'd purposely stood apart while the two older men had spoken together, feeling they might want to share their grief in private.

'Mr Sinclair told me you were handling that line of inquiry. Any luck?'

'Not so far. We've had plenty of reports of strangers spotted here and there, but no one's been able to identify Lang. I've been getting around a good bit, seeing plenty of the countryside.' The sergeant grinned. 'Mind you, I'm not sure I'll be going anywhere in the near future.' He jerked his head in the direction of the Morris. 'The Yard gave me that when I went to Henley. She started playing up this morning. I was lucky to get this far.'

'Stay the night,' Madden said. 'Helen's away, staying with her aunt Maud in London. I'll be glad of your company. So will the children. I'll get someone from the village to look at your car in the morning.'

'Well, if you're sure it's no bother, sir.' The sergeant was pleased to accept the invitation.

'THERE'S NOT MUCH we can do for the moment, Sal. Except wait and see. But if Eddie's got a problem, why hasn't he been in touch?'

Fretting, Sam glanced at his watch again. It was after ten and still there was no sign of the client Mr Cuthbertson had asked him to meet. He and Sal had driven out here to Tillington earlier that morning; to a farm just this side of Petworth, which some prospective buyer was showing an interest in.

It was a side of the business Mr Cuthbertson normally dealt with himself, taking customers around properties. But that morning he'd had a dentist's appointment: one he couldn't postpone, either.

'It's a wisdom tooth, Sam, and it needs to come out pronto,' Cuthbertson had told him, when he'd rung the night before.

Sam had assured his employer it would be no trouble, though in fact going out to Tillington that morning was inconvenient, since he usually spent Tuesdays on the other side of Midhurst, visiting properties to the west of the town, including Coyne's Farm.

But he could see there was no help for it and had already decided to adjust his afternoon's itinerary when a new problem had arisen.

'I do apologise for ringing you so early, Mr Watkin—I found your number in the book—but we're a little worried about your friend Mr Noyes. Do you happen to know where he is?'

If Sam had been surprised to hear Mrs Ramsay's voice on the telephone that morning, what she had to say had left him scratching his head in bafflement. It seemed Eddie had disappeared without a word.

'We were expecting to see him on Friday evening, but he never came, and that was strange because he knew we might have some good news for him. You see, Mr Ramsay has mentioned his name to a company he does business with in Chichester and he heard on Friday that they were interested in meeting Eddie and might be able to offer him a job. We were so puzzled by his not appearing, Nell and I, that we walked up to Coyne's Farm on Saturday. There was no sign of him there, and when Nell came back from school yesterday he wasn't with the other men working on the road, so she spoke to the foreman, a Mr Harrigan, and *he* said Eddie hadn't appeared for work that day.

'The only explanation I can think of is that he went home for the weekend—to Hove, I mean—and the fact that he hasn't come back suggests it might be because of some family emergency. But I want him to know about Chichester. I was hoping you might know how to get in touch with him.'

Sam's thoughts had been moving along similar lines while she was speaking. But first he'd had to explain that he only had an address for Eddie in Hove. The Noyeses didn't have a telephone.

'I'll tell you what, though. I'll send them a telegram. If Eddie's there he'll ring me. If not, then either his mother or sister might be able to help.'

He told her he would look in at Coyne's Farm later—after he'd finished the Tillington job—and would let her know what he'd found out.

'Would you, Mr Watkin? I'd be so grateful. I feel worried about him.'

Mrs Ramsay's call had come just as Sam was leaving, and he'd driven into Petworth in order to send the telegram from the post office there. The more he thought about it, though, the more it seemed likely that Mrs Ramsay was right. Eddie had gone home for some reason and been delayed there. While it was strange that he hadn't let the Ramsays know in advance, particularly in view of this Chichester business, what troubled Sam more was that Eddie hadn't informed Harrigan that he might not be turning up for work on Monday. That didn't sound like him. It was clear he was going to have some explaining to do.

OUT OF TOUCH since the previous day, Billy rang the Yard after breakfast to report his whereabouts only to discover that all calls concerning the Lang case were being referred to Chief Superintendent Holly.

'Mr Sinclair went down to Sussex yesterday to see the chief constable. They have to decide how long it's worth while going on with this search. He was caught by the fog and decided to spend the night in Chichester. You'd better tell me what your movements will be today, Sergeant. He may want to get in touch with you.'

Billy explained that he was not yet sure. 'My car broke down yesterday, sir. Mr Madden was kind enough to put me up for the night. I'm having it fixed now.'

Summoned by telephone, the village mechanic, a man called Pritchard, had appeared at the house soon after dawn and departed shortly thereafter at the wheel of Billy's Morris, lurching down the drive in bottom gear, promising to report back once he knew the extent of the problem.

Word of Fred Bridger's suicide had already reached London and the chief superintendent spoke feelingly of the tragedy. 'Poor fellow. I hope he didn't think we'd failed him. He must have hoped to see justice done.'

He asked Billy for the Maddens' telephone number. 'I'll ring you if anything crops up. Oh, and give my regards to John, would you? Thank him for all his help. I dare say he wants to see this devil caught as much as we do.'

FROM HIS BEDROOM upstairs Billy could hear the phone ringing and he wondered if it was Pritchard calling about his motor car again. He had rung an hour before with the discouraging news that not only was there a fault with the Morris's clutch but there was trouble with the gearbox, too.

'I can't see her being ready before this afternoon at the earliest, sir. And even then I wouldn't go too far, not without a proper overhaul.'

Forcibly immobilised, Billy had spent the morning drafting reports on the series of interviews he had conducted among the birdwatching fraternity. It was a dispiriting exercise. The hunt for Gaston Lang had yielded no dividends to date, and sitting at the window gazing out over the garden his mood of pessimism was mirrored in the drab scene that met his eye outside, where lingering fog hid all trace of the wooded ridge beyond the stream.

Nor had his spirits been raised by an earlier phone call. Helen Madden, ringing to let the staff know her movements, had discovered his presence in the house, and with Madden absent—he was taking the children to school—it had fallen to Billy to break the news of Bridger's suicide to her.

Distressed though she was, Helen's first thought had been for her husband. 'This will upset John terribly. He'll feel he should have done more. You must talk to him, Billy. Make him see it's not his responsibility.'

She had told him she would be back by lunchtime, fog permitting.

The phone had stopped ringing below and presently Billy heard the sound of hurried footsteps in the passage. There was a knock on the door, which opened to reveal the figure of the Maddens' maid, flushed and out of breath.

'You want to watch it, Mary.' The sergeant grinned. 'You'll give yourself a heart attack running up those stairs. Is that call for me?'

'Yes . . .' Panting, she nodded. 'And you're the one who'd better run. It's a Mr Holly ringing from Scotland Yard. He says it won't wait a moment.'

Billy hurried downstairs to the study. As he picked up the receiver he saw through the window that Madden had just returned. 'Styles here, sir.'

'Ah, Sergeant!' Holly's deep voice rang in his ear. 'Lang's been spotted in Midhurst. He was treated by a doctor there yesterday. Some injury to his back. It meant he had to take his shirt off and the nurse saw his birthmark. She rang the police this morning. Mr Sinclair is on his way there now and wants you to join him.'

While Holly was speaking Billy's eye had fallen on a map hanging on the wall beside the desk. It showed Surrey and the adjoining counties. He could see Midhurst marked. It wasn't far, just across the border in Sussex. He became aware that Madden was standing in the doorway, watching him.

'Sir, my car's still out of action. I'll have to go by train.'

'Do whatever's best, Sergeant. But get yourself there.' The line went dead.

'That was Mr Holly, sir,' Billy said to Madden. 'Lang's been seen by a doctor in Midhurst. It was that birthmark. I've got to get down there right away. Do you know if there's a train—' He broke off, silenced by the look on Madden's face.

'*Midhurst*, you say?'

The sergeant nodded. He was transfixed by the other's expression: the intensity of his gaze.

'Damn the train, then.' The growled words made Billy's hair stand on end. 'I'll take you there myself.'

'COME ON, old girl, don't dawdle.' Leaving his van in the otherwise empty parking area by Wood Way, Sam set off along the path. At the crest of the ridge his gaze turned automatically in the direction of Coyne's Farm, visible now in spite of the mist that still clung to the ground.

When he came to the gap in the hedge he paused to let the dog catch up, but Sal was still some distance back up the path, her nose buried in a bank of leaves. Delaying no longer, he slipped through the hedge and crossed the walled garden into the farmyard beyond.

Difficulty with the padlock delayed his entry. For a while it seemed jammed, and it took him several tries, pushing his key in and out and jiggling it about, before the curved arm sprang open.

Even with the double doors pulled wide the interior remained dimly lit—the grey light from outside provided little in the way of illumination. Sam made his way to where Eddie's quarters were, at the back of the barn, and went straight to the tall mahogany wardrobe. When he saw what it contained a sigh of relief issued from his lips.

He'd found what he was looking for: Eddie's bedroll, neatly stowed away, with his spare clothes laid out on the shelf above.

Eddie hadn't walked out on them. The proof was plain to see. Sam could only wait for his return and for the explanation of his sudden departure, which he was sure would follow.

Now that his eyes had grown accustomed to the half-darkness he was able to make out familiar details and he saw at once that Eddie had been making some changes to his living quarters. His bed of hay had grown to more than double the size of the original mattress he had raked together and now it spread in a large triangle across the corner of the barn.

That wasn't all. The mirror had been moved. Formerly it had been propped against the wall behind the washstand so Eddie could use it when shaving. Now it stood in the corner where the bedding was, reflecting the strewn hay in front of it, but little else.

Sam scratched his head. What was the use of putting it *there*?

Then he saw something that brought a scowl to his face. One of the oil lamps was hanging from a nail above the straw bed, and they'd both agreed not to put it there since it only had to slip off the nail and fall onto the straw beneath for everything to go up in flames: hay, hurdles, furniture, barn.

The only thing Sam could think was that it had something to do with the mirror, and where it stood now. Positioned as they both were, the light from the lamp would be reflected more widely, illuminating the area where the hay had been gathered. Though why Eddie should want to do such a thing was beyond him.

Should he leave the lamp where it was, or move it to a safer place? It would be better to leave things as they were. He didn't want Eddie to feel he'd been checking on him. He'd have a quiet word when his chum got back.

He turned to go, but as he did so his toe struck something on the floor and he glanced down and saw it was a workman's boot. Another lay near it. Sam sank to his heels and picked them up. They were old and well-worn and he supposed they must belong to Eddie. The lace of one of them was broken. Had Eddie left in a rush, to catch a bus or a train perhaps?

A feeling of unease was starting to grow in Sam; it was like a cold lump in the pit of his stomach. Something was wrong.

Crouched on his haunches, he scanned the semidarkness around him, bent lower to peer beneath the washstand and as he did so he heard a faint sound behind him and felt a warmth on the back of his neck.

With a start he spun round on his heels.

Sal's moist nose was an inch from his. Her pink tongue touched his cheek.

'Gorblimey! Do you want to give me a heart attack, old girl?' He fondled her head. 'Creeping up on me like that.' Sal wagged her tail, then turned aside to sniff at something on the floor. Sam rose from his crouched position and took a last look round. He noticed Sal was sniffing at something; a long, low object, most likely a chest, covered in canvas like the rest.

He called her name but she paid no attention, remaining stubbornly where she was, running her nose up and down the length of the chest, until in the end he had to go over there and pull her away.

'We can't hang about here, old girl.' He tugged at her collar. 'There's no time to waste. We have to find Eddie.'

11

Sinclair paused at the open door and surveyed the scene before him. Close to a score of detectives were crowded into a room that might comfortably have housed half that number. Most were either standing or sitting on the edges of desks. In the corner a large-scale map of Midhurst was propped on an easel. Silence fell as those nearest the door noticed his appearance and that of the officer beside him, a uniformed inspector by the name of Braddock, who was in command of the Midhurst police station.

'For the benefit of new arrivals,' Braddock began, 'this is Chief Inspector Sinclair from Scotland Yard. He's in charge of the investigation into the girls' murders. According to information received this morning, it now appears likely that this man Lang that we've been looking for has been living here, in Midhurst, or somewhere nearby. From this moment on, you'll take your orders from Mr Sinclair. Sir . . .'

He turned to the chief inspector.

'Thank you, Mr Braddock.' Sinclair walked briskly to the head of the room and took up a position beside the easel. On the wall behind him was a poster that had been sent to all police stations. Taken from the snapshot supplied by Vane, it showed a blown-up image of Gaston Lang's face.

Sinclair faced the assembled detectives. 'While there's every reason to think Lang is in the neighbourhood he may already be preparing to depart, and even if he's not, it won't be long before our search will be common knowledge, and he'll know he's in danger. So time is of the essence.'

While he was speaking the door had opened and more men had entered. The chief inspector waited until the shuffling of feet had subsided. He had arrived from Chichester only an hour earlier himself, his drive across the Downs slowed by the lingering fog. Before leaving he had arranged by telephone with the Sussex chief constable for further reinforcements to be drafted in. Hampered by the same problem that had delayed his journey, they were still arriving in Midhurst in ones and twos.

'Since we've no clue as to Lang's exact whereabouts—and since local hotels and boarding houses have already been checked—it's my intention to search the town itself, to go through it with a fine-tooth comb.'

Again he was interrupted by the door opening. He directed a sharp glance towards the back of the room but his eyes widened in surprise as he saw Madden edge his way in behind Billy Styles. Blinking, he went on.

'The man we believe to be Gaston Lang presented himself at the surgery of a doctor named Driscoll here in Midhurst yesterday needing treatment for an injury to his back. He arrived near the end of morning surgery, explaining that he was a stranger in the region, on a walking tour. His complaint was a small wound on his back, which he'd been unable to deal with himself, since it was too awkwardly placed. In the course of their brief exchange he disclosed that he'd suffered the injury when he'd tripped and fallen onto a pitchfork that happened to be lying behind him.'

The murmur of disbelief that greeted these words was echoed by the chief inspector's own raised eyebrows.

'Yes, I had the same reaction. But curiously, Dr Driscoll says that judging by the appearance of the man's back, it was probably the truth. How he came by this injury is not a mystery I intend to dwell on. Suffice to say the wound required cleaning and dressing. Driscoll himself was in a hurry—he had a round of house calls to make—so after dressing the wound he left the patient in the care of his nurse with instructions that he should return in three days to have the dressing changed.

'Lang had had to take his shirt off to be treated and the doctor had left him in a screened-off area of his office, where he attended to patients, to get dressed, while he himself departed. He'd had no occasion to see Lang from the front since he'd been lying face down for the procedure. But his nurse—a Mrs Hall—caught a glimpse of him while he was putting on his shirt and she noticed that he had a large birthmark on the upper part of his chest.'

The words brought a renewed murmur from his audience.

'As I'm sure all of you know, the man we're after has just such a mark. Notices were sent to all doctors in Surrey and Sussex asking them to be on the lookout for any patients previously not known to them bearing a birthmark. The one addressed to Dr Driscoll only arrived at his surgery this morning. It was opened by Mrs Hall—the doctor had been called out earlier on an emergency—and she remembered what she'd seen. She had the sense to ring the police immediately.' Sinclair turned to Braddock. 'Why don't you go on, Inspector?'

Braddock cleared his throat. He was in his fifties, balding, but with the quick glance and vigorous air of a younger man. 'Detective Sergeant Cole and I went immediately to the surgery, and when we showed the nurse Lang's photograph she said it was him, no question, though he looked different. He was wearing glasses, she said, and his hair was longer, and combed back in a different style.'

'Did he give a name, sir?' The question came from the audience.

'Hendrik De Beer was what he put down on the patient's form he was asked to fill out. To anticipate the next question,' he continued, 'he gave an address, as well, but that was in Amsterdam. He told Mrs Hall he'd been staying in the area temporarily, but didn't say where.'

He exchanged a glance with Sinclair, who nodded. It was the chief inspector who took up the story.

'I've already arranged for the police in Amsterdam to be contacted, but

I'm fairly sure we'll find they haven't heard of him either and that the address he gave there is a false one. He's not Dutch, by the way, he passes for Belgian, but I won't go into his background now, except to remark that he would have been forced to choose a foreign alias while he was here because, although he speaks English fluently, he has an accent. So bear that in mind when you are looking for him.'

'Excuse me, sir.' Another voice came from the crowd. 'How do we know this name he gave the nurse is the one he's using here?'

'Good question. As soon as Mr Braddock reported his discovery to me— I happened to be in Chichester this morning—we agreed that the first place to check was the post office. If Lang had been residing for any length of time locally—and we've reason to believe he's been in England for some months—chances are he's been using the poste restante service to collect any mail that might have been sent to him. It turned out to be a good guess.

'One of the clerks recalled that a man called De Beer had been in to the post office three times a week, regular as clockwork, for the past month asking if there was anything for him. Which there wasn't, not until last Wednesday, when finally a small package arrived for him.

'You'll understand now why we think this man has been residing locally, rather than just passing through. However, as I said earlier, he may be about to leave. Our reason for thinking so springs from something he said to Mrs Hall. When told he would have to come back to have his dressing changed, he said he was returning to Amsterdam and would have to see to it when he got home. Now it's true he might have been lying about his departure, but then there's the matter of this item of post he'd been awaiting. His decision to leave may well be connected to its arrival. At all events, I intend to assume we have very little time in which to lay hands on him.

'What we want, of course, is his address, or, failing that, some indication of his movements in and around Midhurst during the past few months. Since we know Lang hasn't been staying in a hotel or boarding house, local estate agents are being questioned about flats or houses let to single men recently. In the course of the next few hours you'll be visiting shops and offices, showing Lang's photograph and trying out the name De Beer on whoever you meet. It's important that we cover the town systematically, street by street, and you'll be assisted in this by Sergeant Cole, who'll assign each pair of detectives a district to search. No doubt this will cause a stir, but that can't be helped. It's the quickest way to achieve results.

'One final word. If in the course of today you encounter this man, or someone who appears to resemble him—*be on your guard.*' The words issued from the chief inspector's mouth like the crack of a whip. 'Lang isn't just a sexual killer, nor are these poor children his only victims. He's a criminal of a kind none of us has encountered, one who as likely as not will show no surprise if accosted and may even appear to cooperate. Don't be deceived. He carries a knife, and he's used it before, on a detective, too, with fatal consequences. Since arrest for him means a certain death sentence, he'll stop at nothing to escape capture.

'So I say once more, and I urge you to remember it, *be warned.*'

THE TELEPHONE RANG and Braddock picked it up. 'For you, sir.' Putting the receiver down on the desk, he rose, leaving his seat free for Sinclair, and came round to sit beside Madden, who was busy reading the detailed statements made by Dr Driscoll and his nurse. As Sinclair began to speak into the telephone, there was a knock on the door and a constable came in with a tray on which were three steaming cups of tea and a plate of sandwiches. He laid the tray on the desk and went out, shutting the door behind him.

'Thank you, Arthur, that's clear . . . I'll speak to you later.'

Sinclair replaced the receiver. 'That was Chief Superintendent Holly. He says all ports have been warned to look out for Lang. We've told them about the changes to his appearance; they already have copies of the poster.'

'What if he's only moving base?' Braddock offered one of the cups to Madden, who shook his head; he was busy with the statements.

'It's possible, but the odds are he's quitting England for somewhere where he's less noticeable.'

Sinclair began to rise, but Braddock checked him with a gesture.

'You might as well stay there, sir. And help yourself to a sandwich, if you'd like one. It's the only lunch we're likely to get today.' Following his own advice, the Midhurst inspector took one of the cups of tea and slipped a sandwich onto the saucer before resuming his seat beside Madden. 'This piece of mail Lang was expecting . . . what do you reckon it was?'

'Travel documents of some kind, perhaps.' Sinclair shrugged. He glanced at Madden. 'What do you think, John?'

The unexpected appearance of his old partner had caught the chief inspector off guard. No matter what their past connection had been, the presence of a civilian in the midst of a police operation could hardly be squared with standing regulations.

And there was another aspect to be considered, which he'd brought up immediately after greeting his old colleague at the conclusion of the gathering downstairs.

'Does Helen know you're here?'

Discovering from Madden that his wife had been in London overnight and had not yet returned to Highfield when he had departed, and that in consequence he had had to leave her a note explaining his absence, Sinclair had reflected on the near certainty that when the time came for a reckoning, it would be he who would pay the price. Given the degree to which he'd consulted his former partner in the course of the investigation, he could hardly complain of the situation, however, and the chief inspector was honest enough to admit to the comfort he drew from the familiar figure seated opposite him, whose opinion he was seeking once more.

'Travel documents?' Madden glanced up. 'Yes, I should think so, Angus. Papers to support his new identity . . . a passport perhaps. He'd know where to get them forged, wouldn't he? Not here, maybe, but on the Continent?'

'Why do you say that?'

The question came from Braddock, who had realised they were speaking of things to which he was not party. The Midhurst police chief had shown no disposition to question the presence of the former detective, whose reputation he had acknowledged when they were introduced. But Sinclair saw from his frown now that he felt excluded. 'Inspector, I'm going to tell you something I shouldn't. But you must keep it to yourself. Lang's been an agent employed abroad for intelligence purposes. I've underlined how dangerous he is, but there's another side to him we have to consider: his skill at disguising his identity. He's used many aliases in the past, it's something he's accustomed to doing. If he slips through our hands now God knows when we, or anyone else, will catch up with him again.'

'Christ Almighty!' Braddock shook his head ruefully. 'I was starting to wonder . . . and to think, he's been walking around Midhurst for months. I might even have passed him in the street!'

Confirmation of the wanted man's presence in the neighbourhood had not been long in coming following the dispatch of the search teams. Within twenty minutes, word had been sent back to the station that a man answering Lang's description, a foreigner, had purchased cigars in a tobacconist's not far from the post office on several occasions. Soon afterwards, a second message had been received: the proprietor of a stationer's had recognised the features in the poster as belonging to a man to whom he'd sold sketching supplies some three months earlier.

'He remembers the fellow was in again a fortnight ago. They were out of the pads he wanted, but when the owner asked for his name and address so he could let him know when a new supply came in, this man said he was leaving soon to go home to Holland and would get what he needed there.'

The information had been brought upstairs by Billy Styles, who was assisting Sergeant Cole in the CID room. As the lunch hour approached, and shops began closing for the statutory break in the middle of the day, the men had been drifting back to the station. Sinclair noticed Madden still studying the handwritten statements he'd been passed.

'What is it, John? What's the matter?'

Their years together had taught Sinclair to read his old colleague's face. Madden's familiar scowl of preoccupation had been replaced by another expression: a frown, still, but one accompanied by a puzzled look.

'This book Lang had with him . . . it's in the nurse's statement . . .'

'The bird manual? Yes, I saw that. What about it?'

As Madden opened his mouth to reply, they were interrupted by the sound of rapidly approaching footsteps in the passage outside, and then, almost at once, by a hurried knocking on the door, which was flung open.

'Sir!' Billy Styles stood before them, panting.

'What is it, Sergeant?' Sinclair looked up.

'Two of the men just back . . . they talked to a chemist . . .' Billy struggled to catch his breath. 'He said Lang was in his shop only yesterday . . .'

'Yes? What of it?' he snapped. 'We know he's here . . .'

'It's not that, sir . . . it's what he came in for, what he bought . . .'

Billy caught Madden's eye. 'It was a bottle of chloroform.'

THE CID OFFICE, which ten minutes ago had been thronged with plain-clothes men, was deserted. Only Sergeant Cole was there, busy sticking coloured pins into the map of Midhurst, marking out areas of the town already covered by the teams of detectives whose assignments now bore an urgency that needed no underlining.

The news Billy had taken in haste to the office on the floor above had galvanised the chief inspector into action. After canvassing both Braddock and Madden for their opinions, he had telephoned Bennett at Scotland Yard.

'We have to go public, sir. We must see to it that tomorrow's papers carry stories about this investigation, particularly the fact that we're looking for a foreigner, and giving Lang's description. I hate to do it: I think it'll only scare him off. But better that than he kills another child.'

When the call ended a few moments later, Sinclair started drafting a statement to give to the papers. Billy strolled over to inspect Cole's map and see how much progress had been made. So far Billy had found little to do of any use. His position as a Scotland Yard officer set him apart from the others and he'd been forced to stand by while men who knew both the town and each other had gone about their business.

Billy was still inspecting the map when he saw the door open.

Madden entered. 'Ah, Billy! There you are . . .' He was wearing his coat and had his hat in his hand.

'Are you leaving, sir?' Billy asked.

'Yes, I must get back. Helen will be worried. But there's something I want to do first. Perhaps you could give me a hand. Are you busy?'

'Anything but.' Billy grinned ruefully.

'I don't want to bother Mr Sinclair. He's got his hands full. But there's something that ought to be checked . . .' He noticed that Cole had turned from the map and was regarding him with curiosity. 'My name's Madden, Sergeant.' He went over, offering his hand. 'I used to be a policeman.'

'I know, sir,' Cole said. 'The word's gone round the station.' The two shook hands.

'Can I do anything for you, sir?' Cole asked, and Madden nodded.

He gestured to the map. 'Would you show us where your library is?'

ON THE WAY, Madden explained what was in his mind. 'I think Lang might have called in at the library yesterday. Have you read the statement Mrs Hall, the doctor's nurse, gave? The full statement, I mean?'

Billy shook his head. They were striding across the market square, hands plunged into pockets against the freezing fog that had gripped the area. Sergeant Cole had told them the library was only a few minutes' walk.

'She was asked to recall all the details she could about Lang and she mentioned a book he had with him in the waiting room. He took it into the doctor's office when he was called in and later she noticed it lying on the desk and glanced at the title. It had to do with birds, she said, and she thought the author's name might be Howard, though it was probably Coward. T. A. Coward. His books are well known. *Birds of the British Isles.* We've a set of them at home. I wondered what Lang was doing with it.'

Billy scratched his head. 'Well, we know he's a birdwatcher, sir . . .'

'Yes, but I mean what was he doing with it there? At the doctor's rooms?'

'Perhaps he took it along to look at while he was waiting.'

'That's not what the nurse said. She's an observant witness. She said he had it with him. That suggests he'd brought it for some other purpose. But if he was going for a walk in the country later and needed it with him, surely he'd have left it in his car. Driscoll's surgery's not far from here—it's on the Petersfield road. Mrs Hall locked the door when he left—surgery hours were over—and she saw him walking in the direction of North Street. That's the main street. He was heading back to the centre of town.'

'Where he stopped at the chemist's shop,' Billy reminded himself.

Madden scowled. 'Yes, but he still had the book with him, that's the point, and I wondered where he went next, and whether it might have been here.'

They had reached their destination, a timber-framed dwelling with a brass plaque beside the door proclaiming it to be the Midhurst Public Library. When Billy tried the door, he found it locked. It was not yet two o'clock.

'There's no reason he shouldn't have joined the library,' Madden said. 'It's not as though the police have been on his trail. As far as he's concerned, using a false name was only a precaution. If he'd wanted to get his hands on any reference books, this was the obvious place to come. He could have been returning one yesterday. After all, he's on the point of leaving.'

Billy hesitated a moment. 'But would he bother, sir? A man like Lang? Wouldn't he just pocket the book?'

'Oh, no, I don't think so. His aim in life is to avoid attracting attention. If he did borrow the book, he's more likely to return it than not.'

'So if he's a subscriber, they'll have his name. Or rather, De Beer's?'

'More than that. He'd have had to give an address. And while it's possible he might have left a false one, I'm inclined to doubt it. It's the sort of thing that causes questions to be asked. Eyebrows to be raised. If it comes to light, I mean. No, if he joined the library I think he'd have given them his true address.'

BILLY CHECKED the index for a second time, riffling through the cards with his fingers, looking at the Bs now. 'It's no use, sir. He's not here.' He'd already been through the Ds. 'There's no De Beer.'

Madden grunted. He was standing by the desk, watching.

'Could he have used some other name, do you think?' Billy asked.

'Going under one false name is difficult enough; it's something you have to keep in mind constantly. A second would only compound the problem. And as I said before, he's had no reason to feel threatened.'

Although the library had not yet opened—it seemed that a quarter past two was the appointed hour—they'd been admitted, after Billy had knocked on the door, by a harassed-looking woman who told them her name was Miss Kaye, but she was not in charge, merely the assistant to the head librarian.

'Agatha's away, I'm afraid. She's gone to Chichester for the day to see her mother. The poor dear's not well. I've been left to manage as best I can.'

Slight, with red hair in a bun at the back of her neck, and green eyes blinking behind spectacles, she'd ushered them through a raised flap in the counter to a desk on which stood a small wooden cabinet, equipped with drawers. 'That's our index of subscribers. By all means examine it, but you'll have to excuse me. I came in early to tidy up.'

Now Madden glanced at his watch. 'I'm sorry, Billy, I've dragged you over here for nothing. I must be off.'

He saw the librarian approaching with a pile of old newspapers in her arms and he lifted the flap in the counter to let her through. Smiling her thanks, she dropped her burden into a large wicker basket behind the desk.

'Have you had any luck?' she asked.

'I'm afraid not. But thank you all the same.' Madden smiled.

'Just who is this man you're looking for?' she asked, as Billy rose from the desk. She seemed reluctant to let them leave.

'A foreigner called De Beer,' Madden replied. 'We thought he might have joined the library recently. But his name's not in the index.' He paused. 'Sergeant Styles has a photograph of him. May we show it to you?'

'Of course.' Eagerly, she turned to Billy, who'd already taken the poster out of his jacket pocket and was unfolding it on the desktop. But after studying it for a few seconds, she shook her head.

'We think he might have been in yesterday, just before one,' Madden said. 'He was seen with a book that might have been borrowed from a library and it occurred to me he might have come here to return it since we think he's leaving the district. It seems I was wrong. Thank you again.'

He lifted the flap on the counter for Billy, who nodded his own thanks and followed. As they moved towards the door she addressed them again.

'Leaving, did you say?'

'Yes, we think so . . .' Madden paused. Billy was at his shoulder.

'I was working mostly in the stacks yesterday, putting books away, but he might have said something to Agatha.' She spoke hesitantly. 'He might have told her he was going away?'

Madden stared at her. 'I didn't think of that,' he admitted. 'You're quite right—that's exactly what he would have done.' To Billy, he added, 'He'd have wanted his name removed from their list of subscribers.'

'If he was here yesterday, and told Agatha that, she would have taken his card out and torn it up. Deadheading, she calls it.' Miss Kaye smiled.

Madden shook his head in chagrin. 'So we're a day too late.'

'Not necessarily.' Miss Kaye's green eyes sparkled as she pointed at the wicker basket behind her. 'It's only emptied once a week.'

IT WAS BILLY who came on the first piece. Sifting through a stack of old periodicals, holding up each in turn and shaking it, he was rewarded by the sight of a torn shred of lined card slipping out from between the pages of one of them.

'Sir! I've got half of it.'

His eye had fallen on the letters 'eer' penned in a neat hand near the top of the card and right beside the jagged tear. On the line beneath it was the word 'view' and below that the letters 'ane'. At the bottom a single 'd' was visible.

He and Madden were on their knees on either side of a heap of old newspapers and magazines mixed with scrap paper that they had tipped out of the basket onto the floor beside the shelves.

As Billy put the fragment of card to one side, Miss Kaye gave a gasp. She was standing close beside him, bending down. 'There!'

She pointed, and Madden saw a tiny corner of white card showing beneath the edge of a sheet of carbon paper. He drew it out. Picking up the other portion of the card, he fitted the jagged edges together.

'We'll need to use your telephone, Miss Kaye.' Madden spoke calmly.

He handed the joined sections of the card carefully to Billy. Hardly able to believe his eyes, the sergeant read what was written on them:

H. De Beer, 'Downsview', Pit Lane, Near Elsted.

12

Right, Inspector. Let's get this over with.' Sinclair nodded to Braddock, and the Midhurst policeman signalled to Sergeant Cole, who murmured something to the men standing with him at the edge of the trees, and they set off down the slope.

'It doesn't look as though he's spotted us,' Braddock muttered. 'When you hear my whistle, it means we're going in.' He strode off after the men.

Sinclair watched as the men split into two groups, one heading for the front of the cottage, which was enclosed on three sides by a yew hedge the height of a man's head, the other taking up position at the rear, behind a wooden shed. Eight in number, they included five detectives and three uniformed officers. The force had been hurriedly assembled on Sinclair's orders and bundled into a pair of cars. But not before two of the detectives, the most experienced, had been issued with revolvers.

'I've no reason to think Lang carries a gun,' the chief inspector had told his Midhurst colleagues. 'But I'm not taking any chances.'

Remembering his own words now, he glanced at Madden, who was standing beside him, with Billy Styles at his elbow. Before leaving Midhurst he had requested, and received, from his former partner an explicit undertaking not to involve himself in the police operation that was about to get under way.

'You needn't be concerned, Angus.' Madden had been amused. 'It's the last thing I want. Just show me this man in handcuffs. That's all I ask.'

Realising that only a direct order on his part would prevent his old friend from accompanying them, Sinclair had taken the next best option and suggested they go together in Madden's car, taking Braddock and Styles with them. 'You're to stay with Mr Madden at all times,' he'd warned the younger man. 'He's not to put himself at risk. Is that clear?'

Travelling at the tail of the convoy, they had driven west out of the town, following signs to Petersfield, but soon turned south onto a minor road that led down a valley overlooked by a long wooded ridge. The address provided by the library's records had not been difficult to locate. Pit Lane was at the edge of the Downs, no more than a mile from the hamlet of Elsted.

'One of my blokes thinks he knows that cottage.' Braddock had leaned over from the back seat to mutter in Sinclair's ear. 'He's got a girl in Elsted. They walked past it once. She told him it belonged to some old lady who'd had to move into a home and was up for rent. That was six months ago.'

'Why wasn't it on the estate agents' lists?' Sinclair had wondered.

'She might have advertised privately, in a newspaper. What's this now?'

The inspector had frowned as the cars ahead of them drew to a halt; there were roadworks in progress. A group of men wielding picks and shovels were standing aside while one of their number waved the cars through. They had stared at the police uniforms visible through the windows.

A mile further on the cars had slowed once more, this time to turn onto a narrow rutted track. It led over a saddle in the ridge, on the far side of which a cottage could be seen situated a little way down the slope.

The cars had pulled up short of the house, at the edge of the tree line, and Sinclair had climbed out with Braddock to study the situation. At once they had noticed a trickle of smoke coming from the chimney. Sinclair had given orders for the men to get out and gather at the edge of the trees. As they were doing so a light had come on in the kitchen at the back of the cottage and the figure of a man had been glimpsed through the window.

'We'll enter from both sides, front and back.' At a nod from Sinclair, Braddock had issued orders to his men. 'When I blow my whistle, move!'

Watching now as the men below moved silently into place, Sinclair felt a quickening of his pulse. A sideways glance at Madden showed him to be equally tense, gazing down, narrow-eyed.

A few moments later the silence was split by the single piercing blast from a police whistle. Cole reacted like a greyhound loosed from the traps.

'Come on!' he cried, springing forward.

'LESS THAN an hour ago—you're certain of that, are you, Mr Meadows?'

Telephone in hand, Sinclair directed his question towards the rumpled figure on the settee. Receiving a nod in reply, he spoke into the receiver. 'He hasn't had time to get anywhere, Arthur. Not to the Channel ports, certainly.'

The chief inspector paused to listen, peering at Madden, who was standing with folded arms by the fireplace, frowning. Beside him, Billy Styles knelt on the hearth: he was carefully sifting through the ashes in the still-smoking grate. No single piece of physical evidence that could be tied to Gaston Lang had been discovered so far. All they knew for sure was that Lang himself had been there not an hour before. And now he was gone.

'Yes, a Mr Henry Meadows . . .' Sinclair glanced at the man on the settee, who half rose. 'He works for a solicitor in Midhurst who was dealing with the lease for his client. On Friday Lang rang up and announced he was leaving. Although he was paid up to the end of the year, he didn't ask for any money back. Meadows was sent to do an inventory. He was supposed to go through it with Lang, but Lang told him when he got here that he was leaving right away and he'd have to do it on his own. My guess is he heard about the search going on in Midhurst. He's got the luck of the devil, this man.' He shook his head bitterly. 'We must have missed him by half an hour.'

Angry, Sinclair had needed all the self-control he could muster to deal with the hapless Meadows, who, shocked by the sudden eruption of detectives into the cottage, had proved to be a witness of limited value.

'This car he left in—what make was it?' Almost before Meadows had recovered his senses, Sinclair had begun pressing him. 'What model?'

'I'm sorry, sir. I really couldn't say . . .'

Fair-haired, and tending towards plumpness, Meadows had been helped to the settee and given a glass of water, but neither had settled his nerves. Discovered in the sitting room by the detectives who'd burst in at the front, he'd been thrown to the floor and pinned there for several seconds.

'I've never owned a car, you see. I get about on a bike . . . It was black, though . . . the car. Mr De Beer was putting his trunk in it when I arrived.'

'His trunk, you say . . . can you describe it? Size . . . colour . . . anything?'

Meadows's face had turned red. Near tears, he'd stared back at his tormentor. 'It might have been brown, I'm not certain. It was just a trunk . . .'

Sinclair had thanked Meadows for his help and telephoned the information to Chief Superintendent Holly in London, asking that it be passed on to the port authorities, including customs.

With a glance at his watch, he brought their conversation to an end. 'I must ring the solicitor in Midhurst. Bainbridge is his name. He may have other information. I want a forensic team to go through the place. It looks as though Lang's wiped it clean. But we might find a fingerprint somewhere.'

As he put down the phone, Braddock entered. He'd been out to the garage to see if anything had been left there by their quarry. 'There's no need for you to stay, Inspector,' Sinclair said. 'You can take the uniformed officers back if you like. But return the car, if you would. We'll need it later.'

SAM TURNED at the gate and whistled. 'Come along, Sally. Get a move on.' The dog hesitated in the lighted doorway, unwilling to leave the warmth of the kitchen. Behind her he could see Bess's anxious figure. The cook's pink face radiated distress like an alarm beacon.

'You'll let us know what they say, won't you, Sam?' she called out to him.

'Of course I will, love. What's more I'll get them moving. You can tell Mrs Ramsay that, too, when she gets home. Now that's enough of that, Sal. Come on!'

It would be dark in less than an hour and he wanted to get over to the barn again while there was still some light to see by.

Sam couldn't keep his concern from Bess any longer. After speaking to Ada from the Ramsays' sitting room and discovering that Eddie's sister, who had telephoned Ada just half an hour ago, had not heard from Eddie since he sent a card to them a week ago, it occurred to him that Eddie might be hurt in an accident. He asked Bess if he could use the telephone again to see if the Midhurst police had any news of his friend.

'They're all out,' the bloke had said, when he got through, reducing Sam to near apoplexy.

'I'm trying to report a missing person,' he'd roared down the phone. 'Someone who might have been hurt in an accident. Don't you have lists?'

'I'll have to ask someone about this,' the young copper had said, sounding unsure. 'If you could just leave your number, sir . . .'

'Never mind. I'll come in myself.' Sam had slammed down the phone.

Sam's anger had been fuelled partly by fear. In the midst of making the call to the police he'd remembered something from his visit to the barn.

Eddie's work clothes . . . where were they?

He'd found his boots all right, lying on the barn floor, as though they'd been chucked there. As if Eddie had been in haste to depart somewhere.

But where were his dirty clothes? He wouldn't have set out for Hove, or anywhere else, wearing the same soiled garments he wore for work. Sam had seen clean clothes in the wardrobe. But he remembered now that there'd been no sign of his work clothes.

Which didn't mean they weren't there somewhere. Tucked away in a corner, perhaps. But it was something he had to find out. Because if the clothes really were missing, then Eddie couldn't have gone anywhere, which meant something really had happened to him, some accident, and it might have occurred closer at hand than anyone had imagined. In the barn itself, perhaps.

Given that the light was fading, he had to get moving. Sam had hastened back to the kitchen where he'd found Bess, too, was concerned about the gathering dusk, though for a different reason. 'It's time Nell was back,' she said, gazing out across the fields.

'The bus must be late. The days are so short now . . .'

Sam had told her he was leaving, but not why.

'Did you talk to the police?' she had asked. 'Did they tell you anything?'

He'd shaken his head. 'Something's going on at the station—they're at sixes and sevens. I'll have to go there in person. I'll do it on the way home.'

He put his coat on. 'Don't worry about Nell.' He opened the back door and called to Sally. 'I'll keep an eye out for her. I'm going that way.'

He hurried now along the path, drawing his coat closer about him. A bit of a wind had got up in the last hour. He was grateful he'd been able to stop at home on his way back from Tillington earlier and collect his coat. It was the one he'd had all through the war, but better since Ada had sewn a good thick lining of padding.

He could see the top of Wood Way now, where it came through the trees on the ridge, but there was no sign of Nell yet. He was close to the point where the two paths met, and where a small coppice blocked his view for a few moments. Coming out of it he looked up the path and saw her, walking fast, her white school hat bobbing up and down as she approached the spot where the gap in the hedge led to Coyne's Farm.

He waved to her, and she waved back.

Looking round for Sal, he saw she had stopped some distance off to sniff at a bush. Turning again, he started up the path . . . then stopped.

There was no sign of Nell. She'd vanished. Unable to believe his eyes, he stood staring. Then as he peered narrow-eyed through the dusk, he saw a round white object lying on the ground up ahead: Nell's school hat.

The next moment the sound of a scream came to his ears. Though faint, and quickly cut off, the cry shocked him into action.

'Nell!' He roared out her name in response.

The hat lay by the gap in the hedge, and Sam ran flat out towards it, charging up the path, yelling out her name as he went.

THE LIGHT was beginning to fade as John Madden, approaching the top of the ridge, driving carefully over the rutted track, came on the figure of Henry Meadows. The clerk was pushing his bicycle up the slope, which steepened over the last twenty yards or so. Bulky in his coat, and with the added burden of his attaché case, which was strapped to a carrier on the back of his bike, he was making heavy weather of the climb. Hearing the sound of the car behind him, he moved off the road. Madden drew to a halt.

'Would you like a lift, Mr Meadows? I'm going by Midhurst.'

'Oh, goodness, sir . . . thank you.' The doleful look on the clerk's fleshy face was dispelled in an instant. A smile of relief took its place.

'We can put your bike in the back.'

Within minutes they had rejoined the road. 'What an afternoon, sir!' Meadows said. 'I still haven't got over it. What's he done, this Mr De Beer?'

'I can't tell you that, I'm afraid.' Madden glanced at him. 'But you can take it he's a dangerous man.'

Silenced by these words, the clerk swallowed.

'What did you make of him?' Madden switched on his headlamps.

Although it was not yet dark, the light was dull and leaden.

'Nothing, sir. I mean, we hardly spoke. He'd left the keys on the kitchen table and if I'd been ten minutes later he'd have gone. He never said good-bye, he just drove off.'

'He was in a hurry, was he?'

'Oh, yes . . . no doubt of that.' Meadows nodded. 'He looked at his watch twice, I remember, even in the few minutes we were there together. It was as though he had somewhere to go, somewhere else to be.'

'Somewhere else?' Madden repeated the words. But his attention had shifted to the road ahead where a bus had appeared, blocking their progress. He saw a group of men bearing tools on the verge beside the vehicle and realised they had reached the roadworks, where the surface narrowed. The bus was motionless; the driver seemed to be waiting for him to make way.

'There's a parking area just behind us, sir.' Meadows had noted the problem. 'It's for Wood Way. Ramblers going to the Downs use it.'

Twisting about, Madden saw the space he was referring to and reversed the car into the gravelled area, avoiding a small van that was parked there. The bus had already begun moving forward.

'Sir?' Meadows spoke beside him. He'd turned round in his seat while Madden was reversing and he was still looking back.

'Yes?' Madden's eyes were fixed on the bus as it lumbered past.

'That car of Mr De Beer's . . . the one Mr Sinclair was asking me about . . .'

'What about it?' Madden changed gear and they started forward.

'It was just like that one over there.'

Madden put his foot hard on the brake. Turning, he peered through the narrow rear window and saw, on the far side of the parking area, half hidden by the overhanging branch of an oak tree, a black Ford sedan.

'Come on. Let's have a look at it.'

Meadows was on the side nearest and as he opened the door he let out a yelp. 'It's his! It's the same car. Look—there's his trunk! The one I saw.'

Brassbound, and bare of any label, it occupied the rear seat. Swiftly, Madden tried the doors and found them locked.

'Mr Meadows—get your bicycle out!'

The clerk dragged the machine from the back of their car, then turned to find Madden standing on the running board of the other car, peering around.

'I need your help, Mr Meadows.' Madden stepped down from the running board. 'You must ride back to the cottage as quickly as possible and tell Mr Sinclair—the chief inspector—that De Beer's car is here.'

'Yes, sir, of course.' As he bent to fix his bicycle clips he heard a hissing sound and glanced up to see Madden letting the air out of the Ford's tyres.

'You can tell Mr Sinclair he won't be going anywhere.'

'Right, sir.' Meadows mounted the bicycle and moved off, wobbling on the gravel at first, then picking up speed.

MADDEN DROVE his car across the gravelled area and left it parked beside the van. Hastening down the road to where the workmen were assembled, he saw they were knocking off for the day, putting movable signs in place. His own hurried approach had not gone unnoticed, and as he came up, a brawny figure with a thick black moustache came forward, evidently the foreman.

'Madden's my name. I was with that party of police that went by. I dare say you noticed them.' Madden held out his hand.

'Harrigan,' the other responded. He shook Madden's hand. 'Aye, I saw 'em.' He spoke with an Irish accent, his tone wary.

'We're looking for the man who was driving that car.' Madden pointed behind him towards the black Ford. 'Did any of you see where he went?'

He scanned the faces of the men who had gathered around.

'What do they want him for, then, this bloke?' The question came from a man with fair curly hair and stubble coating his cheeks.

'Murder,' Madden replied. He looked the foreman squarely in the eye.

'Jaysus!' Harrigan paled. 'I reckon I saw him. 'Twas about an hour ago. He went up the path there, Wood Way.'

'Where does it go?'

'To the Downs.' He shrugged. 'There's farms there, too.'

'Have you seen anyone else going up the path?'

'A bloke we know called Sam Watkin went over there earlier. It was around two o'clock. That's his van you left your car by.'

'Anyone else?'

Harrigan thought. 'Don't reckon so.' He shrugged again.

With a nod of thanks, Madden turned to leave. As he moved off he heard the men muttering among themselves.

'Except Nell,' a voice said, louder than the rest. It was the same curly-haired man who had spoken earlier. 'She lives over in Oak Green. She was here just a minute ago. We had a word with her.'

'Are you telling me she went up the path?'

The young man paled at the look on his questioner's face. He nodded.

'My God!' Madden stood stunned. 'He's after the girl.'

'What do you say?' It was Harrigan who responded. 'Who's after Nell?'

'That man. He's a killer.' Madden seized his arm. 'Listen to me now. I can't stay . . .' He turned even as he spoke and begun to run down the road, shouting, 'The police are coming. You must wait for them. Tell them Lang's up in the woods. Lang . . . do you hear me? Tell them about the girl. Tell them!'

MADDEN RACED up the hill, peering into the woods on either side of the path, calling out the girl's name as he ran. 'Nell . . . Nell . . .'

He was hoping to disturb her assailant if they were near.

Out of breath by the time he reached the top of the hill, he paused, heart pumping, to take in the wide sweep of country before him. To his left were the lights of a village, which he took to be Oak Green, and to his right, off the path, and separated from it by a hawthorn hedge, a farmhouse with darkened windows.

He set off again, jogging down the hill, looking left and right, but after a few steps he paused, arrested by the sight of an object lying on the path ahead. It was some way off still, but he could just make out its white shape in the dusk. Gripped by a sense of foreboding, he ran flat out down the slope, but even before he reached it he knew his fears had been realised.

Gasping, he picked up the white school hat.

'Nell!' In desperation he shouted out her name again. 'Nell!'

There was no answer. But in a silence broken only by the sound of his own heavy breathing, he heard a faint noise coming from the other side of the hedge and realised after listening hard that it was a dog's whine.

'Who is it? Who's there?' he called out, and was rewarded by a bark.

Madden tore at the hedge, which at first seemed impenetrable, until he discovered a gap. Plunging through it, he found himself in an orchard; beyond was what looked like the wall of a kitchen garden. It had a gate in it.

Again he heard the dog's whine, this time mingled with a man's groan. It was coming from the garden. Madden raced across the orchard and went through the open gate, almost tripping as his foot caught on something. Looking back, he saw a hand reaching up and realised that a man was trying to drag himself out of a compost pit. A dog crouched by the lip, whimpering.

Madden turned to help the man, and as he hauled him from the pit by his arms he saw that his head was wet with blood. But it was his stomach that he clutched as Madden laid him groaning on the ground. Distressed by the scene, the dog, an old labrador bitch, growled and bared her teeth.

'There, now . . .' Madden calmed her, as he pulled open the old army greatcoat the injured man was wearing. Madden discovered a spreading stain on his shirt. 'Lie still,' he urged him.

But the man pushed himself up. 'Not me,' he gasped, struggling to rise, while the dog whined beside him. 'Nell!' He pointed across the garden.

'Where?' Madden looked in the direction indicated. He could see nothing. Tearing off his coat, he tried to lay it on the injured man. 'Keep still.'

But the man wouldn't heed him. 'Not me,' he repeated. 'Nell . . . Nell . . .' His finger continued to point.

'Don't move,' Madden said. 'I'll find her.'

Springing to his feet, he raced across the garden and came to another gate, also open. Beyond it was a large stableyard backed by the farmhouse he'd seen earlier from the crest of the ridge.

Darkness had fallen in the last few minutes, but he was still able to make out a line of stalls to his right, facing the house. Further off, at the end of the yard, a barn was visible, its lofty roof silhouetted against the moon that was rising behind it. There was no sign of life in any of the buildings.

About to run on, he hesitated, disturbed by something he had sensed rather than seen, a change so slight he was not sure at first whether he'd imagined it. As he peered into the blackness he saw what it was: there was the faintest suggestion of illumination coming from inside the barn, a vertical sliver of light at the point where the doors met.

He sprinted across the yard and hauled open the heavy wooden doors. He saw a glow of light coming from the far end of the cavernous structure.

'Gaston Lang!' Madden roared out the name at the top of his lungs. 'Show yourself!' Striding forward between piles of hurdles lining the barn on either side, he called out again. 'Lang! Gaston Lang!'

Wanting only to stop what might be in progress beyond the dark, canvas-covered shapes he could see in front of him, he hurried to the back of the barn where the light was brightest.

He came to a tall shape from which the canvas had been thrown back and saw it was a wardrobe. The lighted area at the back of the barn was just beyond. The illumination, he saw, came from an oil lamp hanging from a nail in one corner above a heap of straw.

Of Lang and his victim there was no sign.

Or so Madden thought, until his glance returned to the lamp and he saw the mirror leaning against the wall beneath it. Reflected in the glass was a sight that brought a cry to his lips.

'Oh God!'

Half hidden in the hay the body of a girl lay sprawled. The skirt of her gym-slip had been pulled up baring her thin white legs.

'No!'

He ran to her side, and, crouching, felt for her pulse. It throbbed faintly against his fingertips. He caught a whiff of anaesthetic on her shallow breath. 'My poor child . . .'

Her face had been turned away from him as she lay and he saw it was undamaged. When he reached to pull down her skirt he found her white pants in place and the sight of them brought tears of relief to his eyes. Covering her legs, he stooped to take her in his arms, glimpsing his own face in the mirror above as he did so—and then behind it the shocking sight of a half-naked figure that sprang out from the open door of the wardrobe with arm upraised and launched itself across the short space that separated them. With a cry, Lang struck.

But Madden had seen the hammer descending, and he flung himself to one side, avoiding the blow by a hair's-breadth, letting the force of it carry his assailant stumbling into the hay where he lost his footing and fell, striking his head against the mirror, cracking the glass. Dazed and bleeding from the forehead, Lang dropped the hammer, and the time it took him to retrieve it from the hay gave Madden the few seconds he needed to scramble to his feet. As his attacker turned to strike again, he caught hold of Lang's wrist with one hand and with the other seized him by the throat, and shook him savagely, like a rat, from side to side.

Lang clawed at Madden's arm, seeking to break the iron grip on his throat, striving to free his hand so that he could strike with the hammer again. But his strength was no match for his adversary's and gradually, choking from lack of breath, he sank to his knees in the straw.

Madden shifted position, bending the wrist he was holding up behind the other's back. The hammer Lang held was now trapped between them, and Madden let go of his throat and caught him once more round the neck in a lock with his free arm. Kneeling behind him, he saw their faces in the mirror, his own flushed and straining, Lang's bloody and twisted with pain.

'Let go.'

Madden's words had no effect. Lang's only response was to jerk his head back savagely, seeking to catch his antagonist unawares.

'Drop it, I say.' He tightened his grip on the other's wrist, twisting it further.

The face in the mirror glared at him, and Madden increased the pressure, bringing a cry from his captive's lips.

'Let go, or I'll break your wrist.' He hoped for some sign of surrender. None came. Their eyes met in the mirror and Lang bared his teeth in a snarl.

With a wrenching jerk, Madden made good his threat. The snap of sinews breaking was echoed by a piercing scream. The hammer dropped from Lang's nerveless fingers and he collapsed face down in the straw.

His thoughts now all for the child who lay unmoving behind him, Madden paused only long enough to hurl the hammer into the shadows behind him. Quickly checking Lang's body for other weapons, he found a small sheath knife in a pocket and threw it after the hammer. Then he stumbled over to the girl and bent to gather her in his arms. But, weakened by the struggle he'd just been through, the task was beyond him.

The sound of movement made him look round and he saw that Lang had rolled over and was lying on his back staring up at the lamp that hung from the wall above him, muttering to himself in a language that Madden could make no sense of. He bent over the girl once more and this time managed to lift her clear of the straw. Summoning his strength, he was on the point of clambering to his feet, when he became aware that something was happening behind him. He glanced round and saw that Lang had got to his knees. His pale brown eyes gleamed yellow in the lamplight.

'Stay where you are.' Unsure what the other intended, Madden made his meaning plain. 'Don't come near us.' He felt no pity for the broken figure. But he shrank from the thought of inflicting further injury on him. 'It's over, Lang. The police will be here any minute. They know who you are and what you've done. It'll go easier with you if you give yourself up.'

His words brought no immediate response. The yellow eyes remained fixed on his, and Madden braced himself for what might follow.

'C'est fini, tu dis?'

Before Madden had properly registered the words, Lang's expression changed. A grin appeared on his face, ghastly as a death's-head.

'Bien, alors . . .'

He unhooked the lamp from the nail where it hung and hurled it against the back wall of the barn near where Madden crouched with the girl in his arms. As the glass shattered, his cry pierced the darkness.

'C'est fini!'

At the same instant the hay burst into flames.

Madden flung himself from the spot, clutching the girl to him. Together they rolled across the barn, away from the roaring inferno which the piled hay had become in seconds. Fuelled by the spilt oil from the lamp, the fire pursued them, carried by the straw strewn on the floor. As Madden staggered to his feet he saw the nearest piece of canvas go up in flames and then all was hidden in a cloud of billowing smoke. With only his sense of direction to guide him he stumbled towards where he knew the doors must lie, running at once into a densely packed mass of objects covered in canvas which formed an obstacle course through which he tried to find a path.

The fire followed close behind them; a piece of burning wood falling from the roof beside them served warning that it would not be long before the whole structure came down on their heads. But the approach of the flames proved a blessing, too, bringing light as well as blistering heat, and with their help he was able to find his way to the broad corridor he remembered and to stumble out into the stableyard.

Reeling, his head spinning, coughing up smoke, Madden staggered away from the burning building, and as he did so the sound of voices came to his ears and he saw a party of men issue from the kitchen garden. Only when he spotted the burden they were bearing and noticed the dog shuffling in their wake did he remember the man he'd helped from the compost pit.

'Is she safe?' The man he recognised as the foreman called out.

They crowded around Madden to peer at the girl, but he could find no words. A great tiredness had come over him, he wanted to lie down and sleep. But he knew he could not do so as long as the child was his to care for, and he was struggling in his mind with this conundrum when his thoughts were interrupted by a sound like the scream of an animal in pain.

'What in God's name . . .?'

Harrigan swung round, the others with him. Looking back towards the burning barn they saw coming through the doors, staggering, spinning, a shape consumed by flames. Blazing like a torch, it came weaving across the yard towards them, hardly human, but still shrieking in agony until all at once the sound ceased and the figure collapsed in a smoking heap.

Shocked into silence, the men stared.

It was Harrigan who found his tongue first. 'Is that him?' he asked.

Madden nodded. He was swaying on his feet now. 'Do something . . . help him if you can.' But he turned from the sight and moved as quickly as his stiffening legs would take him towards the line of stalls. He had felt the girl stir in his arms and knew he must spare her further horror.

The others lingered, trying vainly to bat out the flames that continued to lick at the smouldering corpse, rank with the stench of burning flesh.

But not for long. Having watched their efforts for a minute or so,

Harrigan called a halt. 'Never mind that,' he growled. 'One of you fetch some water. Bring it up to the stalls. It'll be needed.' He cast a last glance at the smoking remains. 'Let the bastard burn.'

IT WAS LATE by the time they reached the village, after nine, and Billy asked two detectives with the Guildford CID to drop him at the gates to the Maddens' house. 'If I don't get to Highfield tonight, my life won't be worth living,' he told them.

He wasn't exaggerating. When the chief inspector had discovered Madden's disappearance from the stableyard, he'd hit the roof.

'Do you mean to say you let him walk out of there? In the condition he was in?' Sinclair had been white with anger.

What Billy had wanted to say was that what with the chaos in the yard caused by the swarm of police and firemen, not to mention casual onlookers, it had been impossible to keep an eye on everything. That there was no way he could have guessed that his former chief would suddenly take it into his head to walk off without a by-your-leave.

But if a dozen years on the force had taught Billy anything, it was that there were times when you bit your tongue, and he'd stayed silent.

'Just pray nothing's happened to him on the way, Sergeant.' The chief inspector had been incandescent. 'Just hope he hasn't had an accident.'

He'd ordered Billy to get himself to Highfield without delay. 'And you might just remind him that leaving the scene of a crime without police permission is an offence punishable by law, and that he ought to know better.'

Not dealt with by the chief inspector had been the question of how he was supposed to get himself back to Midhurst, never mind Highfield, but luck had been on his side and he'd encountered Inspector Braddock in the parking area by the road. The Midhurst commander had just arrived and having no immediate need for his car and driver had told the latter to take Billy back to town.

Whatever doubts Billy might have had regarding his former mentor's surreptitious departure had been removed when he'd spoken to the uniformed sergeant in charge at the car park. He'd had a word with Madden when he'd left in his car some time earlier.

'He asked me to make his excuses to the chief inspector if I saw him. To tell him he felt he had to get home.'

None of which had come as any surprise to Billy when he considered the events of the last few hours. He himself was still shaken by what he'd been through, and could recall the apprehension he'd felt on hearing from the man left behind at the roadworks that Madden had set off in pursuit of Lang alone. Leaving the party of police that was assembling behind him, Billy had sped up the path and on reaching the crest of the ridge had seen the huge fire blazing down in the valley. He'd eventually found a way through to a farmyard, where a sight met his eyes that had turned his blood to ice.

Silhouetted against a blazing barn were two men standing on either side of a smoking shape that lay on the cobbles. Even before he'd reached them Billy had known instinctively that he was looking at the remains of a human being. 'Who is it?' he'd shouted to them, unable to contain his anxiety.

'Some bastard who tried to kill a lass,' one of them had answered.

Moments later, having been directed by the two towards a stall at the side of the yard, his relief had been complete. There he'd found Madden, swollen at the temple and blackened by the fire's ash, and with a burn showing on his hand, cradling a young girl in his arms. Lying close by was another figure, that of a man dressed in an army greatcoat, whose eyes were shut and whose hand rested on the head of an old labrador curled up beside him.

A group of roughly dressed men stood about. Billy had had to push his way through to reach his old chief, whose face had lit up at the sight of him.

'Ah, Billy . . . there you are.'

Pale beneath the caked ash, Madden's features bore the stamp of exhaustion. He was in his shirtsleeves and Billy saw that his tweed jacket was wrapped around the girl, whose head rested on his shoulder.

'She's asleep, poor child.'

Billy had offered to take the girl from him, but Madden had seemed reluctant to let her out of his arms.

'Better not to wake her.' His eyes were bright and staring and it was plain from his dilated pupils that he was suffering from shock.

It was at that point that one of the men standing around had drawn Billy aside. A heavy-browed man by the name of Harrigan, he'd identified himself as the foreman of the road crew.

'I sent a man down to Oak Green to ring for an ambulance. That was after we found Sam Watkin over there.' He'd nodded towards the figure in the greatcoat. 'He'll be all right, though. That coat of his is padded. The knife didn't go in too deep. You'll have to ask your fella what happened.' He gestured towards Madden. 'We've not bothered him with questions. You can see he's done in. One thing I can tell you, though—the lass isn't . . . hurt.' Harrigan had looked away in embarrassment. 'You take my drift. She woke up for a moment and told us she was feeling sick, but that was all. Your bloke said it was from the chloroform that bastard gave her.'

While they were talking the clatter of boots on the cobbles had signalled the arrival of the main police party and Billy had coaxed Madden at last to hand over his burden into the care of a burly sergeant.

Madden had struggled then to rise to his feet.

'I don't know what's come over me. Give me a hand, would you, Billy.'

Helped up, he'd appeared unsteady on his legs and Billy had led him out of the packed stall into the yard where the cold air had revived him. Finding an upturned bucket to hand, he'd persuaded Madden to sit down.

Madden then gave a fragmented account of what had occurred. His audience by now included several of the Midhurst contingent and the chief inspector who had recently arrived, out of breath, after his brisk walk up from the road.

Sinclair had stood before them, wordless. Then, seeing the state his old partner was in, he'd directed him to sit quietly and wait for transport, an order Madden had seemed happy to obey. Taking Billy with him, the chief inspector had then crossed the yard to examine the smoking remains of their quarry.

'I wonder how Lang came to end up here, at this particular spot,' he said.

The answer hadn't been long in coming. Presently Sergeant Cole had approached them. The Sussex detective reported that he'd been speaking to Sam Watkin, who had information he'd wanted to communicate.

'He says he heard the girl scream and ran to help. Lang was waiting for him just inside the garden wall. He hit him with a hammer and then stabbed him. But the point is he'd seen him before hanging around the farm, trying to get into the barn. And when you consider that this same girl, Nell Ramsay, comes home from school every day at the same time . . . and that Lang's been living not more than a mile away . . .'

Cole had gestured wordlessly. 'But there's more. The reason Watkin was over here this afternoon was to look for a pal of his who's gone missing. A bloke called Eddie Noyes. He was part of that road gang. Watkin works for an estate agent in Midhurst. He'd fixed for Noyes to sleep in the barn and he'd asked him only the other day to keep an eye out for any stranger he saw nosing about and to tell him to shove off.'

'So it's possible they ran into each other and Lang disposed of him.' The chief inspector had sighed. 'Tell them to search what's left of the barn carefully. Likely as not they'll find another body in there.'

'AMERICA, SIR. Baltimore, in fact. That's where he was bound. He'd booked passage on a freighter due to sail from Southampton tomorrow. The fellows at Midhurst broke into his car and found his ticket in a briefcase.'

Billy could tell from Madden's expression that he was having trouble following all this. His old chief's eyes were on matchsticks, as the saying went, and his head was nodding towards the kitchen table in exhaustion.

'By freighter, you say . . .' Madden frowned with the effort of trying to keep up. 'Did they find a passport?'

'Yes, they did, sir. French. In the name of Victor Lasalle. There was a file of business correspondence, too, letters and invoices. They made out this Lasalle was an art dealer. Some of the letters were from galleries and the like with fancy letterheads. All forged, most likely, which may explain that package he was expecting. Why it took so long to arrive.'

Billy glanced over his shoulder at the door, wondering when Helen would appear. He himself had arrived ten minutes before and when he'd seen Madden's car in the drive, he'd felt relief for the second time that day.

Seeing the entrance hall dark, Billy had walked round the side of the house to the kitchen, where a light was burning, and found Madden sitting at the table before the remains of a meal, alone and nodding.

'Come in, Billy, come in . . .' Blinking, he had half risen. The sergeant couldn't imagine why he was still up. 'Helen's on the phone . . . she's trying to find out for me about that girl . . . if she's all right. And the man who was stabbed, too. I should have stayed, I know. But I had to get home.'

Billy had been grateful for the chance to reassure him. He described the eventual arrival of the ambulance, which had occurred as he was leaving. 'Someone had gone down to Oak Green to fetch the child's mother. You can imagine the state the poor woman was in. But the girl herself was fine. She'd woken up by then and was more worried about the bloke who was stabbed, Sam Watkin, than anything else. Him and his dog.' Billy had chuckled. 'She's a fine girl, sir, full of spirit. She won't be cast down by what happened to her. You'll see.'

'You'll find Helen's upset,' Madden said, touching the lump on his temple. It was the size of a pigeon's egg now, and tinted with iodine.

They heard the sound of footsteps approaching in the passage outside.

'They went to Petersfield, not Chichester . . .' Helen began speaking even before she had pushed the swing door into the kitchen open. 'She's quite unharmed. A mild case of shock, nothing more . . .'

As she swept into the kitchen her eye fell on Billy. He'd already risen to his feet, but the words of greeting he'd been about to utter died on his lips when he saw the high colour in her cheeks and the anger in her eyes.

'The man's stab wound is quite serious—he's lost a lot of blood—but it wasn't deep enough to damage any vital organs.' Ignoring Billy, Helen went on speaking to Madden. 'He's also got a fracture of the skull. But the doctor said he's fit and strong and should recover well.' She stood by the table looking down at her husband. After a moment she reached out, turning his head a little to one side so she could examine the lump on his temple.

'Do you know, I can't remember how that happened?' Madden spoke to Billy through the crook of Helen's arm.

'*How could you do it?*' Without warning she turned on Billy. '*How could you?* You had no right to put him in danger. He should never have been allowed to get near this man. I thought I could trust you. So how could this have happened?' She demanded an answer, peering into his face, refusing to release him from her gaze. '*You*, Billy . . . I'm asking *you*. How could you—'

'*Stop it, Mummy!*'

Cut short by the cry, Helen turned. She saw her daughter standing by the door in her dressing gown. Lucy's tear-filled eyes had the puffy look of one just roused from sleep. 'Why are you being so horrid to Billy?'

'Lucinda Madden! Go to bed this instant.'

'*No!*' The little girl came forward into the kitchen. She took up a position in front of the sergeant. Pale with the enormity of her rebellion, she faced her mother. 'Not till you promise that you won't be horrid to him any more,' she declared, her voice quavering.

'And why should I do that?'

'Because he's our friend.'

'Because he's our friend?' Helen looked down at the small figure before her, as though in puzzlement. Then a smile came to her lips. 'But of course he is. And thank you for reminding me, my darling. I promise not to be horrid again.' She stooped and kissed the little girl.

As she straightened, Billy saw that tears had begun to stream down her cheeks. Madden had already risen and he came to her side at once. Taking her in his arms, he drew her away from the table and they stood together, not speaking, but holding each other so closely they might have been one.

Wide-eyed, Lucy looked at Billy for an explanation.

The sergeant put a finger to his lips. 'Let's go upstairs,' he whispered in her ear, and hand in hand they tiptoed out together.

EPILOGUE

I t was not until spring of the following year that Angus Sinclair finally closed the file on Gaston Lang, whose shadowy past, like the grainy snapshot supplied to the police by Philip Vane, offered no more than an impression of the man behind the mask, despite weeks of patient digging.

'We've found out all we ever will about him, sir. I think it's time to write *finis* to the case.'

Sinclair had offered his verdict to the assistant commissioner after Bennett had summoned him to his office, along with Chief Superintendent Holly, so he could inform them of the contents of a letter he'd received from Berlin.

'"Many difficulties have arisen in the course of this investigation and the full truth may never be known."' he quoted. 'I think Nebe's warning us not to hold our breath.' Bennett passed the letter to Sinclair.

'*Reichskriminaldirektor.* There's a mouthful for you, Arthur.' The chief inspector handed the letter on to the chief super, who was sitting beside him. 'It seems at least one of our Berlin brethren knows which side his bread is buttered. There's a good reason why they won't pursue this matter. I've received a letter myself on the same subject. I'll get to it in a moment. But first, let me sum up what we've gathered in the way of information.

'The Swiss police have delved a little deeper into Lang's background and come up with some rather chilling details.' Sinclair grimaced. 'He was born a bastard, father unknown. His mother was a domestic servant in a village not far from Geneva. She died soon after he was born and Lang was taken in by the village pastor and his wife, who gave him their name and raised him as a son along with their own baby daughter.'

Bennett sipped at a cup of tea. He'd had a tray sent in. 'But we were told he was raised in an orphanage.'

'Yes, the problem was they'd lost track of the pastor. His wife had died and he'd left the village. More than that: he'd left the ministry.'

'What about his daughter? She must have known something,' Holly said.

The chief inspector grunted. 'That's part of what I have to tell you. It's what the Swiss police learned after they'd tracked down the pastor. He was living in another part of Switzerland, in a village in the mountains. He'd become a recluse, and at first was unwilling to respond to their questions.'

Sinclair shrugged. 'However, by degrees they broke down his resistance and in the end he told them the story.

'It seems that they didn't understand what it was they had burdened themselves with. The pastor and his wife, I mean. As the boy grew older they realised he was not like others: that he had neither the desire nor the capacity to make those connections necessary in human society. But the picture was darker than that. Quite early on they detected a strain of deliberate cruelty in him. He had to be watched when in the company of other small children. In fact his childhood was marked by a growing hostility towards his stepsister. The girl came in time to return the sentiment, and as she grew older made common cause with the other village children, who seem to have been united in their dislike of the boy. He himself, while still quite young, began to pursue a solitary pattern of life, and having developed an interest in birds took to wandering alone in the countryside.

'Pastor Lang was apparently of a disposition to treat whatever trials came his way as an expression of God's will, a test of his faith. However, a point was reached where the situation became untenable. The boy was twelve and increasingly difficult to control. At all events the Langs arranged for him to be taken in by a church-run institution, an orphanage of sorts, in Geneva. He informed the boy accordingly.

'"He looked at me with his pale eyes and said nothing."'

The change in the chief inspector's tone caught his listeners off guard.

'It's a line from the report the Swiss police sent us. I find it sticks in the memory.' Sinclair glanced at them both. 'A few days before he was due to depart his stepsister went missing. A search was organised and her body was found in a gully not far away. It seemed she'd fallen and broken her neck. There was some damage to her face: her nose had been broken and features disfigured.'

Bennett stared at the blotter on his desk. 'Was the boy a suspect?'

'Apparently not. He'd wandered off as he often did and returned to be told the news. Or so he made out. Although the police were called in they concluded it was an accident. There was no evidence of an assault, sexual or otherwise, and no reports of any strangers being seen in the vicinity.'

'But his stepfather, this pastor, thought the boy was responsible?'

'He indicated as much to the police when they tracked him down. Though whether he thought so at the time, I can't say. However, neither he nor his wife ever saw their stepson again. She died a year later and he left the Church. He told the detectives that he'd lost his faith.'

Bennett rose and went to the window. He examined the cloud-covered sky outside. 'What happened to Lang? To the boy, I mean?'

'He was sent to the orphanage, as planned. Interestingly enough, his record there was unexceptional. He gave no trouble and was marked down as intelligent, but unresponsive. Shortly before his sixteenth birthday he absconded. He walked out of the place and was never seen again. Until the murder for which he was sought, there was no record—in Switzerland, at least—of any similar unresolved crimes. All we can say for sure is that there are a number of unsolved sexual crimes in the countries we know he's visited, some of them not dissimilar to the attacks he specialised in.'

The chief inspector placed his cup of tea on the desk. 'It's tempting to believe his fixation with facial assaults harks back to the murder of his stepsister, and I've no doubt a psychologist would make much of it.'

Bennett returned to his desk. 'You said you'd received a letter, Angus. I gather it has some bearing on the German attitude to this investigation?'

'Yes, I have it here.'

Sinclair took an envelope from his pocket and removed several handwritten pages from it. 'It's from Inspector Probst. He wants all the facts about this case to be made known. That's why he's written to me.'

'I see . . .' Bennett's eyes had narrowed. 'But isn't he taking a risk writing to you behind his superior's backs?'

'A risk, I'm sure. But he's not with the police any longer. He resigned as soon as the Nazis took over at the end of January. "As a policeman one cannot serve criminals: it is a contradiction in terms."' Chuckling, Sinclair read from one of the pages. 'But with regard to the Lang investigation, Probst said they'd continued with it up to the time the government changed hands. Enquiring into his background, that is. They discovered his Nazi connections, and it was at this point, Probst says, that the inquiry was brought to a halt.'

Bennett absorbed what he'd been told. 'He joined the party, didn't he? Vane told us that. And the last thing the Nazis would want is for their reputations to be tarred by a case like this only months after they've taken power. So even if they do discover some link to our intelligence service it's unlikely they'd want to air it. Mud sticks, after all.'

'Quite. I think your friends in Whitehall can sleep easy.'

'*My* friends, Chief Inspector?' Bennett favoured him with a stony glance.

'A slip of the tongue, sir.'

'Well, I think it's a damned disgrace,' Holly said bluntly. 'The whole wretched business. What's worse is, no one's going to answer for it. And we've no cause to congratulate ourselves, either. There's only one person who comes out of this with any credit: John Madden. I hope you'll tell him that when you see him next, Angus. And thank him from me.'

'I will, Arthur,' Sinclair promised him. He looked at his colleague with affection. 'I'm going down to Highfield this weekend.'

A SOLITARY FIGURE was standing on the platform when Sinclair's train pulled into Highfield. As he stepped from the compartment, the glint of sunlight on golden hair caught his eye. Helen Madden advanced down the platform to greet him. The pleasure he took in her company had never diminished with the years and he felt a lightening of his step as she linked her arm in his. 'John was planning to meet you himself. But the children insisted on an expedition into the woods. They've been cooped up for days with the rain we've been having.'

The showery weather had begun to clear and the chief inspector's train had passed through sunlit fields bright with spring flowers.

'The house is packed at the moment. Franz was so pleased when he heard you were coming down. He's in London today house-hunting.'

They went out to where her car was parked.

'It seems ages since we last saw you,' Helen continued. 'I'm afraid it took a while to get over that dreadful business.' She glanced at him. 'But I've thought of you often, and particularly the day we went down to Midhurst. That family . . . the Ramsays . . . invited us. Not for the first time, either, poor dears. They wanted to thank John. But I hadn't felt able to face them before. I thought it would be too upsetting. But it turned out to be a lovely day. Mrs Ramsay had organised a picnic for the children on the Downs and they'd also invited the man who was stabbed, Sam Watkin, and his family. It was his friend whose body was found in the burnt-out barn later. Eddie was his name. But they'd all known him, it seems, and they talked of him with such affection.' She mused in silence for a few moments.

'Afterwards we walked up to the farm. The children insisted on seeing it and Nell told them all the grisly details. Poor John couldn't bear to listen. All he could think of was what might have happened.' She brushed a tear from her eye, then turned towards him, smiling, and the chief inspector saw that he had been forgiven. 'That was a month ago, and it was only a few days later that I went to Germany.'

'Yes, I heard about that from John. He rang me.' The chief inspector became animated. 'You brought Dr Weiss and his family back?'

'I went over to help with the move. It seemed sensible, since I'm the one who speaks German, and I worried that Franz might not be able to manage on his own. You know his wife died?'

'John told me.'

'That was soon after Christmas. And something else dreadful had happened. They have two children, a son studying in America, and a daughter called Lotte, who was married to a university lecturer in Berlin, a young man called Josef Stern. He was active in politics, and in the weeks before the Nazis came to power he got involved in a street battle with some Brown Shirt thugs and was terribly beaten. He never recovered consciousness and died in hospital. So thank heavens I went. They were both distraught, Franz and his daughter, quite unable to cope, and I took care of everything.'

She fell silent as they drove through the village, then she continued. 'Franz is looking for a house in Hampstead. He wants to set up in practice. Lotte will live with him. She has a daughter called Hana, who's six. Lucy's taken a great fancy to her. She has such passions for people, my Lucy.'

They'd arrived at the front door. Helen's smile had returned.

SHOWN TO HIS ROOM, Sinclair returned downstairs ten minutes later to find his hostess sitting in a garden chair on the terrace, from which vantage point all the colours of spring were to be seen in the beds bordering the lawn.

Some movement was visible in a shrubbery near the bottom of the garden and presently a man emerged from it pushing a wheelbarrow.

Helen gestured, pointing. 'There they are now.'

Following the direction she indicated, Sinclair caught sight of a pair of darting figures, flitting through the orchard like sprites.

'Those are the two girls,' Helen explained, seeing the chief inspector's furrowed brow. 'Lucy's on the left.'

They watched as the two figures suddenly veered to one side and set off in pursuit of the man with the wheelbarrow, whose movements the chief inspector was following with close attention. His observation was interrupted once again, however, by the appearance of Madden, who came striding out of the orchard in the company of two boys, one of whom was his friends' son.

'Who's the other?' he asked Helen, shading his eyes from the sinking sun.

'Will Stackpole's son, Ted. It means a lot to me that he and Rob are such friends. Will's someone I love. He was the first boy who ever kissed me.'

She smiled. 'I was Lucy's age, six or seven. I love seeing them together now, the boys. But it makes me anxious. They're growing older . . .'

'Why should that bother you?'

'Because there's going to be another war.'

'Oh, surely not.' The chief inspector responded automatically. 'I mean, so many things can happen . . .' She seemed not to have heard him.

'I can't tell you how awful it was in Berlin,' Helen said. 'The flags, the uniforms, the strutting, the never-ending rant. I saw one uniform. It was black. Black from head to toe. The badge on the cap was a death's-head. Can you imagine?' She held her face in her hands. 'I knew then . . .'

He said nothing. Allowing her time to recover, he waved to Madden, who waved back but then gestured towards the side of the house where the kitchen lay.

'They're going to leave their muddy shoes there,' she explained. 'They'll come in the other way.'

The two little girls had emerged from the shrubbery and were running up the lawn, still hand in hand, towards them. As they ascended the steps of the terrace, Helen rose to meet them.

'For you, Mummy,' Lucy declared breathlessly, thrusting a bunch of dripping daffodils into her grasp. Well spattered with mud, the pair seemed in haste to continue on their headlong course, but Helen checked them.

'It's time for your baths.' Helen turned to her daughter. 'Mary's waiting upstairs. Take Hana with you.'

Shrieking as one, the two little girls sprang away and ran across the terrace and into the house.

Leaving his hostess to shake the water from the bouquet she'd been given, Sinclair moved to the edge of the terrace and peered down into the gloaming. The figure he'd noticed earlier was advancing up the lawn now, still pushing the wheelbarrow. 'Who on earth is that?' Sinclair asked. 'And what's he got on his head?'

'Can't you guess?' Helen answered in a teasing tone. 'It's Topper. Surely you remember him.'

'I've not had the pleasure of making his acquaintance. But I recall the name well. Am I not right in thinking he was summoned to give evidence at the inquest in Guildford . . . and never appeared?' Sinclair turned to regard his hostess. 'Harbouring fugitives, are you, Dr Madden?'

Helen smiled. 'He turned up out of the blue at Christmas. Luckily Tom Cooper, our gardener, went down with rheumatism just then. I say luckily, because Topper doesn't like accepting charity beyond the odd meal. So he's a sort of substitute gardener, staying in one of the stalls at the farm.'

She paused. The figure had come to a halt just below the terrace and Sinclair took in the spectacle of the hat with its jaunty pheasant plume.

He watched as Topper removed it and bowed.

'Good night, Topper,' Helen called. 'And thank you for the lovely flowers.'

Replacing his hat, he continued on his way without a word, disappearing round the side of the house.

'John says he'll move on one of these days, but I hope not. He's too old to be wandering around. He needs a home.' She was looking at the daffodils in her hand and he saw her brush something from her cheek. 'My hope is he'll find it hard to leave now. He so loves the children.'

'The children?' Sinclair glanced at the flowers she was holding, then at her face, which was turned away. 'Aye . . . the children.'

'Oh dear . . .' She made no pretence now about wiping away the tears. 'I'm sorry, Angus. I still haven't got over that awful business. I lost my nerve for a while, and I'm not sure I've got it back. I'm afraid of the future. Look what's happened to poor Franz and his family. It's as though some terrible dark night is about to descend on us all and I want to protect the people I love and care for, but I don't know how, or even if I can . . .'

'My dear . . .' Seeing her distress, he put his arm round her to comfort her. 'It's because you're still upset. These wounds take a long time to heal.'

'Yes, of course . . . Dear Angus . . .' She collected herself. 'I must put these in water. Come inside, if you like, or stay and watch the sun go down. But come in soon. I want us all to be together.'

He waited until she had gone inside, then turned to look once more over the deserted garden, his mind full of what she had said. The day was nearly over and only the topmost trees on the hill still glinted in the dying light. The rest of the wooded ridge was already plunged in stygian gloom, and the chief inspector was not disposed to linger. As he stood there a wash of light fell about his feet from the lamps that were being switched on in the drawing room and he heard the high-pitched cries of the children.

Drawn by the thought of the warmth inside and the many dear faces around, he hesitated no longer, turning his back on the end of the day.

And on the dark night that was coming.

RENNIE AIRTH

Born: South Africa, 1935
Former profession: journalism
Place of residence: Italy

The Blood-Dimmed Tide, the second book in a planned trilogy featuring retired police inspector John Madden, skilfully transports the reader to another era—to a time before the Second World War when crime was almost unheard of in rural Britain. In those days, murder of the kind that occurs in the story was almost unknown, and therefore all the more shocking.

Like *River of Darkness*, the first book in the trilogy, *The Blood-Dimmed Tide* is set in the thirties, a decade of great social and political change dominated by the lengthening shadow cast by the rise of Fascism in Germany. 'I wanted to set the novels at a time when attitudes to life in general were in some ways different from those of today, but nevertheless familiar to us all,' Airth explains. 'I researched them by reading books and newspapers from the period. But my parents were of that time and my memories of them also helped when it came to setting the stage for the plots.'

A former Reuters journalist, Airth had long been tempted to try his hand at fiction. 'I wanted to write books with strong plots and I have always been interested in the crime novel and what can be done with the genre,' he says. He sets out to write the sort of book he likes to read: novels where the plot is driven by character rather than circumstance or events.

Airth has now retired, but says that his former career taught him the discipline of writing every day, as well as the important skill of self-editing. When he is in the throes of a book, he applies himself whole-heartedly to the task, working seven days a week. Clearly, the dedication pays off, for *River of Darkness* was short-listed for no less than four crime-fiction awards, including the prestigious Edgar Allan Poe Awards, and went on to win the French Grand Prix de Litterature Policière.

The BBC recently acquired television rights in the John Madden trilogy and will shortly be starting work on an adaptation of the first book.